Additional resources included with your textbook purchase

Each new copy of this text includes a 12-month, prepaid subscription to
The Chemistry Place, Special Edition for Suchocki.

How to activate your prepaid subscription to The Chemistry Place, Special Edition for Suchocki:

1. Point your web browser to **www.chemplace.com/college**.
2. Click on the Suchocki *Conceptual Chemistry* book cover.
3. Click on the "Register Here" button.
4. Enter your pre-assigned access code exactly as it appears below:

WSSU-SCRIM-SOONG-KAPUT-BACCY-SWARD

5. Click on the "Submit" button.
6. Complete the online registration form to create your own personal user ID and password.
7. Once your personal ID and password are confirmed by e-mail, go back to **www.chemplace.com/college** to enter the site with your new ID and password.

Your access code can be used only once to establish your subscription, which is not transferable.

If you have purchased a used copy of this text, this access code may not be valid. However, if your instructor is recommending or requiring use of **The Chemistry Place, Special Edition for Suchocki**, or if you would like to have access to the additional study tools found on this web site, you can find more information about purchasing a subscription directly online at **www.chemplace.com/college**.

The Chemistry Place, Special Edition for Suchocki, contains many tools to help you prepare for exams, including quiz questions for each chapter, interactive tutorials, web links, a glossary, and an interactive periodic table.

Instructors: To access instructor resources on the site, contact your Benjamin/Cummings sales representative. Visit **www.aw.com** and click "Find your rep."

0-8053-3189-1

List of the Elements

Name	Symbol	Atomic Number	Atomic Weight	Name	Symbol	Atomic Number	Atomic Weight
Actinium	Ac	89	227.028	Mercury	Hg	80	200.59
Aluminum	Al	13	26.982	Molybdenum	Mo	42	95.94
Americium	Am	95	243	Neodymium	Nd	60	144.24
Antimony	Sb	51	121.76	Neon	Ne	10	20.180
Argon	Ar	18	39.948	Neptunium	Np	93	237.048
Arsenic	As	33	74.922	Nickel	Ni	28	58.69
Astatine	At	85	210	Niobium	Nb	41	92.906
Barium	Ba	56	137.327	Nitrogen	N	7	14.007
Berkelium	Bk	97	247	Nobelium	No	102	259
Beryllium	Be	4	9.012	Osmium	Os	76	190.23
Bismuth	Bi	83	208.980	Oxygen	O	8	15.999
Bohrium	Bh	107	262	Palladium	Pd	46	106.42
Boron	B	5	10.811	Phosphorus	P	15	30.974
Bromine	Br	35	79.904	Platinum	Pt	78	195.08
Cadmium	Cd	48	112.411	Plutonium	Pu	94	244
Calcium	Ca	20	40.078	Polonium	Po	84	209
Californium	Cf	98	251	Potassium	K	19	39.098
Carbon	C	6	12.011	Praseodymium	Pr	59	140.908
Cerium	Ce	58	140.115	Promethium	Pm	61	145
Cesium	Cs	55	132.905	Protactinium	Pa	91	231.036
Chlorine	Cl	17	35.453	Radium	Ra	88	226.025
Chromium	Cr	24	51.996	Radon	Rn	86	222
Cobalt	Co	27	58.933	Rhenium	Re	75	186.207
Copper	Cu	29	63.546	Rhodium	Rh	45	102.906
Curium	Cm	96	247	Rubidium	Rb	37	85.468
Dubnium	Db	105	262	Ruthenium	Ru	44	101.07
Dysprosium	Dy	66	162.5	Rutherfordium	Rf	104	261
Einsteinium	Es	99	252	Samarium	Sm	62	150.36
Erbium	Er	68	167.26	Scandium	Sc	21	44.956
Europium	Eu	63	151.964	Seaborgium	Sg	106	263
Fermium	Fm	100	257	Selenium	Se	34	78.96
Fluorine	F	9	18.998	Silicon	Si	14	28.086
Francium	Fr	87	223	Silver	Ag	47	107.868
Gadolinium	Gd	64	157.25	Sodium	Na	11	22.990
Gallium	Ga	31	69.723	Strontium	Sr	38	87.62
Germanium	Ge	32	72.61	Sulfur	S	16	32.066
Gold	Au	79	196.967	Tantalum	Ta	73	180.948
Hafnium	Hf	72	178.49	Technetium	Tc	43	98
Hassium	Hs	108	265	Tellurium	Te	52	127.60
Helium	He	2	4.003	Terbium	Tb	65	158.925
Holmium	Ho	67	164.93	Thallium	Tl	81	204.383
Hydrogen	H	1	1.0079	Thorium	Th	90	232.038
Indium	In	49	114.82	Thulium	Tm	69	168.934
Iodine	I	53	126.905	Tin	Sn	50	118.71
Iridium	Ir	77	192.22	Titanium	Ti	22	47.88
Iron	Fe	26	55.845	Tungsten	W	74	183.84
Krypton	Kr	36	83.8	Uranium	U	92	238.029
Lanthanum	La	57	138.906	Vanadium	V	23	50.942
Lawrencium	Lr	103	262	Xenon	Xe	54	131.29
Lead	Pb	82	207.2	Ytterbium	Yb	70	173.04
Lithium	Li	3	6.941	Yttrium	Y	39	88.906
Lutetium	Lu	71	174.967	Zinc	Zn	30	65.39
Magnesium	Mg	12	24.305	Zirconium	Zr	40	91.224
Manganese	Mn	25	54.938	—	Uun	110	269
Meitnerium	Mt	109	266	—	Uuu	111	272
Mendelevium	Md	101	258	—	Uub	112	277

CONCEPTUAL CHEMISTRY
understanding our world of atoms and molecules

John Suchocki

CUSTOM EDITION FOR UNIVERSITY OF COLORADO

Cover Art: "Waterfall," by Angela Sciaraffa.

Taken from:

Conceptual Chemistry: Understanding Our World of Atoms and Molecules, Alternate Edition
By John Suchocki
Copyright © 2001 by John A. Suchocki
Published by Addison Wesley
A Pearson Education Company
San Francisco, California 94111

This special edition published in cooperation with Pearson Custom Publishing

Printed in the United States of America

10 9 8 7 6 5 4 3 2 1

Please visit our web site at www.pearsoncustom.com

ISBN 0–536–63449–1

BA 993256

PEARSON CUSTOM PUBLISHING
75 Arlington Street, Suite 300, Boston, MA 02116
A Pearson Education Company

To
Paul G. Hewitt

loving uncle, mentor, friend,
and vegetable gardener

Detailed Contents

To the Student

Welcome to the world of chemistry—a world where everything around you can be traced to these incredibly tiny particles called atoms. Chemistry is the study of how atoms combine to form materials. By learning chemistry, you gain a unique perspective on what things are made of and why they behave as they do.

Chemistry is a science with a very practical outlook. By understanding and controlling the behavior of atoms, chemists have been able to produce a broad range of new and useful materials—alloys, fertilizers, pharmaceuticals, polymers, computer chips, recombinant DNA, and more. These materials have raised our standards of living to unprecedented levels. Learning chemistry, therefore, is worthwhile simply because of the impact this field has on society. More importantly, with a background in chemistry you can judge for yourself whether or not available technologies are in harmony with the environment and with what you believe to be right.

This book presents chemistry *conceptually*, focusing on the concepts of chemistry with little emphasis on calculations. Though sometimes wildly bizarre, the concepts of chemistry are straightforward and accessible—all it takes is the desire to learn. What you will gain from your efforts, however, may

be more than new knowledge about your environment and your personal relation to it—you may improve your learning skills and become a better thinker! But remember, just like any form of training, you'll only get out as much as you put in.

I enjoy chemistry and I know you can too. So put on your boots and let's go explore this world from the perspective of its fundamental building blocks.

Good chemistry to you!

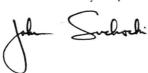

To the Instructor

Living in a small city, I occasionally run into my former liberal arts chemistry students. I find them stocking shelves in grocery stores, managing hair salons, driving delivery trucks, dispensing tickets at movie theaters, singing in bands, canvassing for politicians. These encounters are pleasant and many even heartwarming, but afterward, I often wonder how these people benefitted from successfully completing my course. They may have enjoyed a number of my class sessions, and could perhaps even recall many of the chemistry demonstrations and hands-on activities we did together. But years later, what positive influences, if any, remain?

As instructors, we share a common desire for our teaching efforts to have a long-lasting positive impact on our students. We focus, therefore, on what we think is most important for the student to learn. For students taking liberal arts chemistry courses, certain learning goals are clear. They should become familiar with and, perhaps, even interested in the basic concepts of chemistry, especially the ones that apply to their daily lives. They should understand, for example, how soap works and why ice floats on water. They should be able to distinguish between stratospheric ozone depletion and global warming, and also know what it takes to ensure a safe drinking water supply. Along the way, they should learn how to think about matter from the perspective of atoms and molecules—we sense the smell of a rose, for example, as molecules from its petals journey through the air and into our noses. Furthermore, by studying chemistry, students should come to understand the methods of scientific inquiry and become better equipped to pass this knowledge along to future generations. In short, these students should become citizens of above-average scientific literacy.

These are noble goals and it is crucial that we do our best to achieve them. Judging from my encounters with former liberal arts students in the midst of their daily lives, however, I have come to conclude that this is not what they cherish most from having taken a course in chemistry. Rather, it is the personal development they experienced through the process.

As all science educators know, chemistry—with its many abstract concepts—is fertile ground for the development of higher-thinking skills. Thus, it seems reasonable for us to share this valuable scientific offering—tempered to an appropriate level—with all students. Liberal arts students, like all students, come to college not just to learn about specific subjects, but for personal growth. This growth should include improvements in their analytical and verbal-reasoning skills along with a boost in self-confidence from having successfully met well-placed challenges. The value of our teaching, therefore, rests not only on our ability to help students learn chemistry, but also on our ability to help them learn about themselves.

These are the premises upon which *Conceptual Chemistry* was written. You will find the standard discussions of the applications of chemistry, as shown in the table of contents. True to its title, this textbook also builds a conceptual base from which the nonscience student may view nature more perceptively by helping them visualize the behavior of atoms and molecules and showing how this behavior gives rise to our macroscopic environment. Numerical problem-solving skills and memorization are not stressed. Instead, chemistry concepts are developed in a story-telling fashion with the frequent use of analogies and tightly-integrated illustrations and photographs. Follow-up exercises are designed to challenge the students' understanding of concepts and their ability to synthesize and articulate conclusions. Concurrent to helping students learn chemistry, *Conceptual Chemistry* aims to be a tool by which students can learn how to become better thinkers and reach their personal goals of self-discovery.

Organization

The basic concepts of chemistry are developed within the first twelve chapters of *Conceptual Chemistry*. Threaded into the development, real-life applications facilitate the understanding and appreciation of chemistry concepts. In the remaining seven chapters, students have the opportunity to exercise their understanding of earlier material as they explore numerous chemistry-related topics.

You may choose from the standard text (Chapters 1–19); the Alternate Edition, which includes Chapters 1–12 in print (the concept chapters) with Chapters 13–19 (topical chapters) on CD-ROM; and the Electronic Book version which includes all the chapters of the text in e-book format.

Features

Key features of *Conceptual Chemistry* include the following:

- A conversational and clear writing style aimed at engaging student interest.

- In-text **Concept Checks** pose a question and provide answers immediately following. These questions primarily reinforce ideas just presented before the student moves on to new concepts.

- **Hands-On Chemistry** activities allow students to witness chemistry outside a formal laboratory setting. These can be performed using common household ingredients and equipment. Most chapters have two or three Hands-On features, which lend themselves well to distance learning or to in-class activities.

- **Calculation Corners** appear in selected chapters. They are included so students can practice the quantitative-reasoning skills needed to perform chemical calculations. In each Calculation Corner, an example problem and answer shows students how to perform a specific calculation, then their understanding is tested in a Your-Turn section. None of the calculations involve skills beyond fractions, percentages, or basic algebra.

Extensive end-of-chapter material includes:

- **Key Terms and Matching Definitions** provide a short summary of important terms that appear boldfaced in the text.

- **Review Questions** are a set of simple questions designed to guide the student through the essentials of the chapter. They are grouped by chapter sections to help the student stay focused while reviewing the material.

- **Hands-On Chemistry Insights** are follow-up discussions to the Hands-On Chemistry activities. They are designed to ensure that the student is getting the most out of performing these activities, and also to clear up any misconceptions that may have developed.

- **Exercises** are designed to challenge student understanding of the chapter material and to emphasize critical thinking rather than mere recall. In many cases, they link chemistry concepts to familiar situations. The solutions to all odd-numbered exercises and problems appear in Appendix C. Thus, you can consider assigning even-numbered exercises for group studies, in-class discussions, or exams.

- **Problems** feature concepts that are more clearly understood with numerical values and straightforward calculations. They are based on information presented in the Calculation Corners and therefore appear only within chapters containing this feature.

- **Discussion Topics** appear in the topical chapters (13–19) to prompt students to express their opinions on issues that have no definitive answers. These topics may promote student debate about controversial ideas.

- **Suggested Readings and Web Sites** appear on the last page of every chapter. This feature, however, is particularly important for the topical chapters for which you may be more inclined to assign research papers or poster presentations.

Support Package

The overall *Conceptual Chemistry* instructional package provides complete support materials for both students and faculty.

For the Student

- (**Available Fall 2001**) *Conceptual Chemistry Alive!* is semester-length student tutorial presented by the author through a series of 12 CD-ROMs—one for each of the first 12 chapters. This tutorial features mini-lectures, demonstrations, animations, home chemistry projects, interactive simulations, and explorations of chemistry in the community. Students browse through Quicktime movies in an interactive environment that follows the *Conceptual Chemistry* table of contents. After viewing a segment, the student answers Concept Checks that encourage them to test their understanding of key material before progressing further. A student's answers to these Concept Checks are recorded in an electronic notebook that can be submitted to an instructor for assessment. More than a study supplement, *Conceptual Chemistry Alive!* is a textbook companion suitable for distance learning programs or for instructors seeking to free up class time for student-centered curricula. For a complimentary demo, please contact chem@awl.com.

- The *Chemistry Place* web site (http://www.chemplace.com/college/suchocki) is a unique study tool that offers practice quizzes and collaborative group activities written specifically to accompany the text.

- *Student Laboratory Manual for Conceptual Chemistry* (ISBN 0-8053-3179-4) co-authored with Donna Gibson, Chabot College, features laboratory activities tightly correlated to the chapter content.

For the Instructor

- The *Instructor's Manual* includes a variety of sample syllabi, lecture ideas and topics not treated in the book, teaching tips, and suggested step-by-step lectures and demonstrations. Answers to Matching Key Terms, Review Questions, Exercises, and Problems are available to instructors in a format suitable for photocopying and posting for students to review.

- The *Chemistry Place* web site (http://www.chemplace.com/college/suchocki) contains areas accessible only by the course instructor. These areas provide course management tools, including an on-line syllabus builder, an on-line grade book, and an on-line quiz generator where instructors can create quizzes from pre-existing questions or add their own.

- A set of 250 four-color acetates of figures and tables from the text is available (ISBN 0-8053-3177-8).

- A CD-ROM contains the book's art library for electronic presentation (ISBN 0-8053-3175-1).

- A test bank comes in both printed format (ISBN 0-8053-3169-7) and computerized format [MAC/WIN] (ISBN 0-8053-3183-2).

Acknowledgments

There are numerous individuals I am grateful and indebted to for their assistance in the development of *Conceptual Chemistry*. No one, however, stands out more than my uncle, mentor, and friend, Paul G. Hewitt. He planted the seed for this book in the early 1980s and has lovingly nurtured its growth ever since. Forever encouraging, patient, and inspirational, I thank you, Uncle Paul, for your guidance and more.

As every author knows, no words can express the debt one owes to the members of one's immediate family. My family's tireless support and belief in me have been an invaluable gift. To my wife Tracy, I am grateful for the years of late night conversations and countless paragraph edits that have helped shape the scope and focus of this book. To Ian, Reece, and Maitreya, who have grown knowing only a dad who pours hours over his computer, thank you for reminding me of the important things in life.

I am also blessed with a very capable extended family. Thanks to uncle Paul and cousin Leslie for allowing me to use their material from *Conceptual Physical Science*. Thanks to my pharmacist sister, Joan Lucas, for helping with the early drafts of Chapter 14, and to my chemical engineer brother-in-law, Rick Lucas, for consultations regarding the petroleum industry. To Bill Candler, rock collector and husband to my dear sister Cathy, thank you for supplying various minerals for photographing. I would like to thank my molecular geneticist step-brother, Nicholas Kellar, for assistance in the Chapter 13 laboratory for isolating DNA from plant material. Thanks also to my electron microscopist cousin, George Webster and his wife Lolita, for supplying photos of their SEM.

Special thanks are extended to my mother, Marjorie Hewitt Suchocki, and my father, John M. Suchocki, for their love and for instilling in me a positive attitude about one's life work. Personal thanks are also extended to all my friends and other relatives for their support throughout the years, most notably to my mother-in-law, Sharon Hopwood, for photo research and for being a wonderful grandmother. Personal thanks also go to my past mentors, Professors Everette May and Albert Sneden of Virginia Commonwealth University.

I am particularly grateful for the continued support of the faculty and staff of Leeward Community College, especially during my frequent book-writing sabbatical leaves. I am notably indebted to Michael Reese, Bob Asato, George Shiroma, Patricia Domingo, Manny Cabral, Mike Lee,

Kakkala Mohanan, Irwin Yamamoto, Stacy Thomas, Sharon Narimatsu, and Mark Silliman.

For developing the *Conceptual Chemistry Laboratory Manual*, I am forever grateful to Donna Gibson of Chabot College. It has been a privilege to work with Donna—a remarkable woman and highly skilled instructor. For developing the *Conceptual Chemistry* test bank, I am indebted to Pam Marks of Arizona State University. To Pam's graduate students, Debbie Leedy and Rachel Morgan, I give thanks for creating answers to the matching terms and review questions in the *Instructors Manual.*

The first chapter of this textbook is graced by the research efforts of Professors Jim McClintock of the University of Alabama, Birmingham, and Bill Baker of the Florida Institute of Technology, who were quick to provide not only their permissions but some beautiful photographs of the Antarctic. A big *mahalo* to them both.

There were many individuals in the publishing world who played vital and often pivotal roles in the early development of *Conceptual Chemistry*. These people include Doug Humphrey, Shelly McCarthy, Cathleen Petree, Mary Castellion, John Vondeling, Richard Stratton, Paul Corey, and John Challice—all of them real straight shooters and top-notch at what they do. I thank them for their generous support and sound advice.

For making the publication of *Conceptual Chemistry* possible, I owe special thanks to Ben Roberts, who has been all things to this textbook from acquisitions editor to senior editor. Ben's commitment to providing students with the best possible learning tools is unwavering and runs bone deep. We've been through a lot together and I regard him as a close friend. Thanks, Ben, for your vision and for these opportunities.

Working with me on the nitty-gritty of each paragraph over the course of three very full years was my developmental editor, Hilair Chism, whose brilliant mind was able to keep track of the many details that my own mind was quick to forget. To Hilair I send my deepest appreciation, especially for her focus on integrating the text with the art program. Working with Hilair over the years has been a tremendous learning experience as well as a joy. I will always treasure our kinship.

Working with me on the nitty-gritty of each sentence over the past year was my copyeditor, the very talented Irene Nunes. The text's smooth reading and clear transitions are due to the Herculean efforts of Irene and Hilair.

The level of excellence I experienced working with Ben, Hilair, and Irene is typical of the interactions I had with all the collaborators on this project. These people include Linda Baron Davis and Robin Heyden who I would like to thank for their trust and confidence in me as an author. For overseeing the production of *Conceptual Chemistry*, I send a heartfelt thanks to Joan Marsh. For rendering the art, I send a "Wow, how'd you do that?" thanks to Emi Koike, Blakeley Kim, and the artists at J. B. Woolsey and Associates. Special thanks to Jean Lake and Tony Asaro for managing the ancillary materials and to Margot Otway for providing valuable input throughout the project. Joan Keyes and Jonathan Peck of Dovetail Publishing Services did a superior job of composing pages and keeping track of the work flow. My deep gratitude goes to Stuart Kenter and Rachel Epstein of Stuart Kenter Associates for their remarkable photo research. As for marketing, I am excited to know that *Conceptual Chemistry* is in the very capable hands of

Stacy Treco, Christy Lawrence, and Chalon Bridges. Last, but not least, I send a welcome to Maureen Kennedy, the new chemistry editor at Benjamin Cummings, who will be very instrumental in leading this project into the future. Thanks to you all. An author couldn't possibly ask for more support than this.

The development of *Conceptual Chemistry* relied heavily on the comments and criticisms of numerous reviewers. These people should know that their input was carefully considered and most often incorporated. A tremendous thanks goes to the reviewers listed here in alphabetical order:

Pamela M. Aker, University of Pittsburgh
Edward Alexander, San Diego Mesa College
Sandra Allen, Indiana State University
Susan Bangasser, San Bernardino Valley College
Ronald Baumgarten, University of Illinois, Chicago
Stacey Bent, New York University
Richard Bretz, University of Toledo
Benjamin Bruckner, University of Maryland, Baltimore County
Kerry Bruns, Southwestern University
John Bullock, Central Washington University
Barbara Burke, California State Polytechnical University, Pomona
Robert Byrne, Illinois Valley Community College
Richard Cahill, De Anza College
David Camp, Eastern Oregon University
Jefferson Cavalieri, Dutchess Community College
Ana Ciereszko, Miami Dade Community College
Richard Clarke, Boston University
Cynthia Coleman, SUNY Potsdam
Virgil Cope, University of Michigan-Flint
Kathryn Craighead, University of Wisconsin/River Falls
Jack Cummini, Metropolitan State College of Denver
William Deese, Louisiana Tech University
Jerry A. Driscoll, University of Utah
Melvyn Dutton, California State University, Bakersfield
J.D. Edwards, University of Southwestern Louisiana
Karen Eichstadt, Ohio University
Ana Gaillat, Greenfield Community College
Patrick Garvey, Des Moines Area Community College
Shelley Gaudia, Lane Community College
Donna Gibson, Chabot College
Palmer Graves, Florida International University
Jan Gryko, Jacksonville State University
William Halpern, University of West Florida
Marie Hankins, University of Southern Indiana
Alton Hassell, Baylor University
Barbara Hillery, SUNY Old Westbury
Angela Hoffman, University of Portland
John Hutchinson, Rice University
Mark Jackson, Florida Atlantic University
Kevin Johnson, Pacific University

Stanley Johnson, Orange Coast College
Joe Kirsch, Butler University
Louis Kuo, Lewis and Clark College
Carol Lasko, Humboldt State University
Joseph Lechner, Mount Vernon Nazarene College
Robley Light, Florida State University
Maria Longas, Purdue University
Art Maret, University of Central Florida
Vahe Marganian, Bridgewater State College
Robert Metzger, San Diego State University
Luis Muga, University of Florida
B.I. Naddy, Columbia State Community College
Donald R. Neu, St. Cloud State University
Larry Neubauer, University of Nevada, Las Vegas
Frazier Nyasulu, University of Washington
Frank Palocsay, James Madison University
Robert Pool, Spokane Community College
Brian Ramsey, Rollins College
Kathleen Richardson, University of Central Florida
Ronald Roth, George Mason University
Elizabeth Runquist, San Francisco State University
Maureen Scharberg, San Jose State University
Francis Sheehan, John Jay College of Criminal Justice
Mee Shelley, Miami University
Vincent Sollimo, Burlington County College
Ralph Steinhaus, Western Michigan University
Mike Stekoll, University of Alaska
Dennis Stevens, University of Nevada, Las Vegas
Anthony Tanner, Austin College
Bill Timberlake, Los Angeles Harbor College
Anthony Toste, Southwest Missouri State University
Carl Trindle, University of Virginia
Everett Turner, University of Massachusetts Amherst
George Wahl, North Carolina State University
M. Rachel Wang, Spokane Community College
Karen Weichelman, University of Southwestern Louisiana
Ted Wood, Pierce University
Sheldon York, University of Denver

To the struggling student, thank you for your learning efforts—you are on the road to making this world a better place.

Much effort has gone into keeping this textbook error-free and accurate. It is possible, however, that some errors or inaccuracies may have escaped our notice. Your help in forwarding such errors or inaccuracies to me would be greatly appreciated. Your questions, general comments, and criticisms are also welcome. I look forward to hearing from you.

John Suchocki
ConceptChem@aol.com

Conceptual Chemistry

Understanding Our World of Atoms and Molecules

Alternate Edition

Chapter 1
Chemistry Is a Science

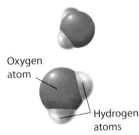

Oxygen atom

Hydrogen atoms

Water molecule, H_2O

Looking at the World of Atoms and Molecules

From afar, a sand dune looks to be made of a smooth, continuous material. Up close, however, the dune reveals itself to be made of tiny particles of sand. In a similar fashion, everything around us—no matter how smooth it may appear—is made of basic units called *atoms*. Atoms are so small, however, that a single grain of sand contains on the order of 125 million trillion of them. There are roughly 250,000 times more atoms in a single grain of sand than there are grains of sand in the dunes of this chapter's opening photograph.

As small as atoms are, there is much we have learned about them. We know, for example, that there are more than 100 different types of atoms, and they are listed in a widely recognized chart known as the *periodic table*. Some atoms link together to form larger but still incredibly small basic units of matter called *molecules*. As shown to the right, for example, two hydrogen atoms and one oxygen atom link together to form a single molecule of water, which you may know as H_2O. Water molecules are so small that an 8 oz glass of water contains about a trillion trillion of them.

Our world can be studied at different levels of magnification. At the *macroscopic* level, matter is large enough to be seen, measured, and handled. A handful of sand and a glass of water are macroscopic samples of matter. At the *microscopic* level, physical structure is so fine that it can be seen only with a microscope. A biological cell is microscopic, as is the detail on a dragonfly's wing. Beyond the microscopic level is the **submicroscopic**—the realm of atoms and molecules and an important focus of chemistry.

1.1 Chemistry Is a Central Science Useful to Our Lives

When you wonder what the Earth, sky, or ocean is made of, you are thinking about chemistry. When you wonder how a rain puddle dries up, how a car gets energy from gasoline, or how your body gets energy from the food you eat, you are again thinking about chemistry. By definition, **chemistry** is the study of matter and the transformations it can undergo. **Matter** is anything that occupies space. It is the stuff that makes up all material things—anything you can touch, taste, smell, see, or hear is matter. The scope of chemistry, therefore, is very broad.

Chemistry is often described as a central science because it touches all the other sciences. It springs from the principles of physics, and it serves as the foundation for the most complex science of all—biology. Indeed, many of the great advances in the life sciences today, such as genetic engineering, are applications of some very exotic chemistry. Chemistry sets the foundation for the Earth sciences—geology, volcanology, oceanography, meteorology— as well as for such related branches as archeology. It is also an important component of space science. Just as we learned about the origin of the moon from the chemical analysis of moon rocks in the early 1970s, we are now learning about the history of Mars and other planets from the chemical information gathered by space probes.

(a) (b) (c) (d) (e)

Figure 1.1
Chemistry is a foundation for many other disciplines. (a) Biochemists preparing samples. (b) Meteorologist relasing weather balloon to study the chemistry of the upper atmosphere. (c) Technicians conducting DNA research. (d) Paleontologists preparing fossilized dinosaur bones for transport to laboratory for chemical analysis. (e) Astronomer studying the composition of asteroids.

Transparent matrix of processed silicon dioxide (Chapter 18)

Chemically disinfected drinking water (Chapter 16)

Caffeine solution (Chapter 14)

Thermoset polymer (Chapter 12)

Prescription medicines stored in refrigerator (Chapter 14)

Chlorofluorocarbon-free refrigerating fluids (Chapter 17)

Electrical energy from a fossil fuel or nuclear power plant (Chapter 19)

Metal alloy (Chapter 18)

Roasting carbohydrates, fats, proteins, and vitamins (Chapter 13)

Natural gas laced with odoriferous sulfur compounds (Chapter 12)

Fertilizer grown vegetables (Chapter 15)

Figure 1.2
Most of the material items in any modern house are shaped by some human-devised chemical process.

Progress in science, including chemistry, is made by scientists as they conduct research, which is any activity aimed at the systematic discovery and interpretation of new knowledge. **Basic research** leads us to a greater understanding of how the natural world operates. Many scientists focus on basic research. The foundation of knowledge laid down by basic research frequently leads to useful applications. Research that focuses on developing these applications is known as **applied research**. The majority of chemists have applied research as their major focus. Applied research in chemistry has provided us with medicine, food, water, shelter, and so many of the material goods that characterize modern life. Just a few of a myriad of examples are shown in Figure 1.2.

Over the course of the 20th century, we excelled at manipulating atoms and molecules to create materials to suit our needs. At the same time, however, mistakes were made when it came to caring for the environment. Waste products were dumped into rivers, buried in the ground, or vented into the air without regard for possible long-term consequences. Many people believed that the Earth was so large that its resources were virtually unlimited and that it could absorb wastes without being significantly harmed.

Most nations now recognize this as a dangerous attitude. As a result, government agencies, industries, and concerned citizens are involved in extensive efforts to clean up toxic-waste sites. Such regulations as the international ban on ozone-destroying chlorofluorocarbons have been enacted to protect the environment. Members of the American Chemistry Council, who as a group produce 90 percent of the chemicals manufactured in the United States, have adopted a program called Responsible Care, in which they have pledged to manufacture without causing environmental damage. The Responsible Care program—its emblem is shown in Figure 1.3—is based on the understanding that just as modern technology can be

Figure 1.3
The Responsible Care symbol of the American Chemistry Council.

Figure 1.4
More than 70 percent of all legislation placed before the Congress of the United States addresses science-related questions and issues, and many of these issues pertain to chemistry. Learning about science is an important endeavor for all citizens, particularly those destined to become leaders.

used to harm the environment, it can also be used to protect the environment. For example, by using chemistry wisely, most waste products can be minimized, recycled, engineered into sellable commodities, or rendered environmentally benign.

Chemistry has influenced our lives in profound ways and will continue to do so in the future. For this reason, it is in everyone's interest to become acquainted with the concepts of chemistry. A knowledge of chemistry gives us a handle on many of the questions and issues we face as a society. Are generic medicines really just as effective as brand-name ones (Chapter 14)? Should food supplements be federally regulated (Chapter 15)? Is genetically modified food safe (Chapter 15)? Should fluoride be added to local water supplies (Chapter 16)? What is happening to stratospheric ozone, and how does this problem differ from the problem of global warming (Chapter 17)? Why is it important to recycle (Chapter 18)? What should be our primary energy resources in the future (Chapter 19)? At some point, either we or the people we elect will be considering questions such as these, as the scene in Figure 1.4 illustrates. The more informed we are, the greater the likelihood that the decisions we make will be good ones.

Concept Check ✓

Chemists have learned how to produce aspirin using petroleum as a starting material. Is this an example of basic or applied research?

Was this your answer? This is an example of applied research because the primary goal was to develop a useful commodity. However, the ability to produce aspirin from petroleum depended on an understanding of atoms and molecules, an understanding that came from many years of basic research.

1.2 Science Is a Way of Understanding the Universe

Although there are many paths scientists can follow in doing science, regardless of which path is taken, a number of key elements traditionally arise: observations, questions, scientific hypotheses, predictions, and tests. A **scientific hypothesis** is a testable assumption, or guess, often used to explain an observed phenomenon. As Figure 1.5 suggests, the results of tests invariably lead to further observations, questions, and scientific hypotheses, meaning that the scientific process can never have any end.

A Study of Sea Butterflies Illustrates the Process of Science

The scientific process is aptly illustrated by the efforts of an Antarctic research team headed by James McClintock, professor of biology at the University of Alabama at Birmingham, and Bill Baker, professor of chemistry at the Florida Institute of Technology, both shown in Figure 1.6. One aspect of their research involved studying the toxic chemicals Antarctic marine organisms secrete to defend themselves against predators. McClintock and Baker observed an unusual relationship between two animal species, a sea butterfly and an amphipod—a relationship that led to a question, a scientific hypothesis, a prediction, and tests about the chemistry involved in the relationship.

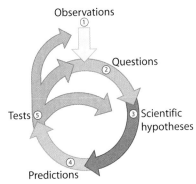

Figure 1.5
The scientific process often—but not always—proceeds in the following order: observations, questions, scientific hypotheses, predictions, tests. Tests lead to more observations, more questions, more scientific hypotheses, and so on. From this cyclic process comes a greater understanding of the universe.

Figure 1.6
The Chemical Ecology of Antarctic Marine Organisms Research Project was initiated in 1988 by James McClintock, shown here (fifth from left) with his team of colleagues and research assistants. In 1992, he was joined by Bill Baker (second from right). Baker is shown in the inset dressing for a dive into the icy Antarctic water. Like many other science projects, this one was interdisciplinary, involving the efforts of scientists from a variety of backgrounds.

1. **Observation.** The sea butterfly *Clione antarctica* is a brightly colored shell-less snail with winglike extensions used in swimming (Figure 1.7a), and the amphipod *Hyperiella dilatata* resembles a small shrimp. McClintock and Baker observed a large percentage of amphipods carrying sea butterflies on their backs, with the sea butterflies held tightly by the hind legs of the amphipods (Figure 1.7b). Any amphipod that lost its sea butterfly would quickly seek another—the amphipods were actively abducting the sea butterflies!

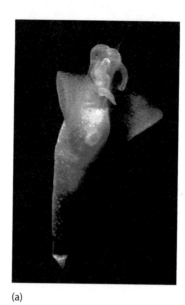

(a)

(b)

Figure 1.7
(a) The graceful Antarctic sea butterfly is a species of snail that does not have a shell. (b) The shrimp-like amphipod attaches a sea butterfly to its back even though doing so limits the amphipod's mobility.

2. **Question.** McClintock and Baker noted that amphipods carrying sea butterflies were slowed considerably, making the amphipods more vulnerable to predators and less adept at capturing prey. Why then did the amphipods abduct the sea butterflies?

3. **Scientific Hypothesis.** Given their experience with the chemical defense systems of various sea organisms, the research team hypothesized that amphipods carry sea butterflies because the sea butterflies produce a chemical that deters a predator of the amphipod.

4. **Prediction.** Based on their hypothesis, they predicted (a) that they would be able to isolate this chemical and (b) that an amphipod predator would be deterred by it.

5. **Tests.** To test their hypothesis and prediction, the researchers captured several predator fish species and conducted the test shown in Figure 1.8. The fish were presented with solitary sea butterflies, which they took into their mouths but promptly spit back out. The fish readily ate uncoupled amphipods but spit out any amphipod coupled with a sea butterfly. These are the results expected if the sea butterfly was secreting some sort of chemical deterrent. The same results would be obtained, however, if a predator fish simply didn't like the feel of the sea butterfly in its mouth. The results of this simple test were therefore ambiguous.

(a) Sea butterfly

(b) Amphipod

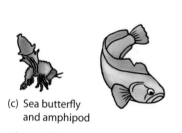

(c) Sea butterfly
    and amphipod

Figure 1.8
In McClintock and Baker's initial experiment, a predatory fish (a) rejected the sea butterfly, (b) ate the free-swimming amphipod, and (c) rejected the amphipod coupled with a sea butterfly.

All scientific tests need to minimize the number of possible conclusions. Often this is done by running an experimental test alongside a **control test**. Ideally, the two tests should differ by only one variable. Any differences in results can then be attributed to how the experimental test differed from the control test.

To confirm that the deterrent was chemical and not physical, the researchers made one set of food pellets containing both fish meal and sea-butterfly extract (the experimental pellets). For their control test, they made a physically identical set containing only fish meal (the control pellets). As shown in Figure 1.9, the predator fish readily ate the control pellets but not the experimental ones. These results strongly supported the chemical-deterrent hypothesis.

Further processing of the sea-butterfly extract yielded five major chemical compounds, only one of which deterred predator fish from eating the pellets. Chemical analysis of this compound revealed it to be the previously unknown molecule shown in Figure 1.10, which they named pteroenone.

As frequently happens in science, McClintock and Baker's results led to new questions. What are the properties of pteroenone? Does this substance have potential for treating human disease? In fact, a majority of the drugs prescribed in the United States were developed by chemists working with naturally occurring materials. As we explore further in Chapter 14, this is an important reason to preserve marine habitats and tropical rainforests, which house countless yet-to-be-discovered substances.

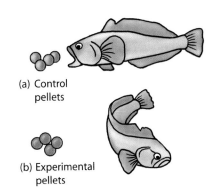

(a) Control
pellets

(b) Experimental
pellets

Figure 1.9
The predator fish (a) ate the control pellets but (b) rejected the experimental pellets, which contained sea-butterfly extract.

Pteroenone

Figure. 1.10
Pteroenone is a molecule produced by sea butterflies as a chemical deterrent against predators. Its name is derived from *ptero-*, which means "winged" (for the sea butterfly), and *-enone*, which describes information about the chemical structure. The black spheres represent carbon atoms, the white hydrogen atoms, and the red oxygen atoms.

Reproducibility and an Attitude of Inquiry Are Essential Components of Science

In addition to running control tests, scientists confirm experimental results by repeated testing. The Antarctic researchers, for example, made many food pellets, both experimental and control, so that each test could be repeated many times. Only after obtaining consistent results can a scientist begin to decide whether the hypothesis in question is supported or not.

If there is an undetected variable or flaw in an experiment, it doesn't matter how many times the tests are repeated. Measuring your weight on a broken scale is a good example of a flawed procedure—no matter how many times you step on the scale, the weight you measure will be wrong every time. Similarly, had the Antarctic researchers not been careful to make sure the fish in the experimental and control tests were equally hungry and of the same species, their results and conclusions would have been unreliable.

Because of the great potential for unseen error in any procedure, the results of a scientific experiment are considered valid only if they can be reproduced by other scientists working in similarly equipped laboratories. This restriction helps to confirm the experimental results and lends more credence to an interpretation. Reproducibility is an essential component of science. Without it, the understandings we gain through science become questionable.

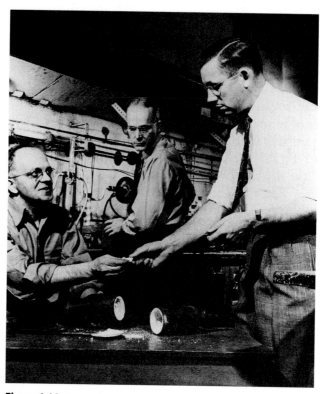

Figure 1.11
Roy Plunkett (right) and his colleagues pose for this reenactment photograph of their discovery of Teflon. Their success was due in great part to their curiosity.

Although the traditional methods of science are powerful, the success of science has more to do with an *attitude* common to scientists rather than to a particular method. This attitude is one of inquiry, experimentation, honesty, and a faith that all natural phenomena can be explained. Accordingly, many scientific discoveries have involved trial and error, experimentation without guessing, or just plain accidental discovery. In the late 1930s, for example, the DuPont researcher Roy Plunkett and his colleagues, shown in Figure 1.11, filled a pressurized cylinder with a gas called tetrafluoroethylene. The next morning they were surprised to discover that the cylinder appeared empty. Not believing that the contents had simply vanished, they hacksawed the cylinder apart and discovered a white solid coating the inner surface. Driven by curiosity, they continued to investigate the material, which eventually came to be known and marketed as the highly useful polymer Teflon.

Concept Check ✔

Why is it important for a scientist to be honest?

Was this your answer? Any discovery made by a scientist is subject to the scrutiny and testing of other scientists. Sooner or later, mistakes or wishful thinking or even outright deceptions are found out. Honesty, so important to the progress of science, thus becomes a matter of self-interest.

A Theory Is a Single Idea That Has Great Explanatory Power

Periodically, science moves to a point where a wide range of observations can be explained by a single comprehensive idea that has stood up to repeated scrutiny. Such an idea is what scientists call a **theory**. Biologists, for instance, speak of the *theory of natural selection* and use it to explain both the unity and the diversity of life. Physicists speak of the *theory of relativity* and use it to explain how we are held to the Earth by gravity. Chemists speak of the *theory of the atom* and use it to explain how one material can transform into another.

Theories are a foundation of science, but they are not fixed. Rather, they evolve as they go through stages of redefinition and refinement. Since it was first proposed 200 years ago, for example, the theory of the atom has been repeatedly refined as new evidence about atomic behavior has been gathered. Those who know little about science may argue that scientific theories have little value because they are always being modified. Those who understand science, however, see it differently—theories grow stronger as they are modified.

Science Has Limitations

Science is a powerful means of gaining knowledge about the natural world, but it is not without limitations. No experiment can ever prove definitively that a scientific hypothesis is correct. What happens instead is that we gain more and more confidence in a hypothesis as it continues to be supported by the results of many different experiments conducted by many different investigators. If any experimental result contradicts the hypothesis, and if this result is reproducible, the hypothesis must be either discarded or revised. Even the most firmly planted theories are subject to this same scrutiny.

Science is a window through which we are able to perceive nature with greater clarity—it is a way of understanding nature. In using *Conceptual Chemistry*, you will certainly learn the ways of science. Your ultimate goal, however, should be to use science to help you gain a richer perspective on the natural environment because you are such an integral part of that environment.

Science deals only with hypotheses that are testable. As such, its domain is restricted to the observable natural world. While scientific methods can be used to debunk various claims, science has no way of verifying testimonies involving the supernatural. The term *supernatural* literally means "above nature." Science works within nature, not above it. Likewise, science is unable to answer such philosophical questions as "What is the purpose of life?" or such religious questions as "What is the nature of the human spirit?" Though these questions are valid and have great importance to us, they rely on subjective personal experience and do not lead to testable hypotheses.

Concept Check ✓

Which statement is a *scientific* hypothesis?
   a. The moon is made of Swiss cheese.
   b. Human consciousness arises from an essence that is undetectable.

Was this your answer? Both statements attempt to explain observed phenomena, and so both are hypotheses. Only statement a is testable however, and therefore only statement a is a *scientific* hypothesis.

While we shall never be able to detect the undetectable, we have traveled to the moon and found that it is not made of Swiss cheese (the last flight to the moon was in 1974). Analyses of moon samples have shown that the moon has a chemical composition very similar to that of the Earth, a finding that led to more questions and scientific hypotheses. For example, why are the moon and the Earth of similar chemical composition? Were they once bound together as a single body that split apart billions of years ago? Continued experiments suggest that the answer to this question is yes!

Science Helps Us Learn the Rules of Nature

Just as you can't enjoy a ball game, computer game, or party game until you know its rules, so it is with nature. Because science helps us learn the rules of nature, it also helps us appreciate nature. You may see beauty in a tree, but you'll see more beauty in that tree when you realize that it was created from substances found not in the ground but primarily in the air—specifically, the carbon dioxide and water put into the air by respiring organisms such as yourself (Figure 1.12).

Learning science builds new perspectives and is not unlike climbing a mountain. Each step builds on the previous step while the view grows ever more astounding.

1.3 Scientists Measure Physical Quantities

Science starts with observations. To get a firm handle on observations, however, scientists take measurements. It's not enough to observe that an object has mass. The scientist will want to measure how much mass. By quantifying observations, the scientist is able to make objective comparisons, share accurate information with other scientists, or look for trends that might reveal some inner workings of nature.

Scientists measure *physical quantities.* Some examples of physical quantities you will be learning about and using in this book are length, time,

Figure. 1.12
The tree Ayano hugs is made primarily from carbon dioxide and water, the very same chemicals Ayano releases through her breath. In return, the tree releases oxygen, which Ayano uses to sustain her life. We are one with our environment down to the level of atoms and molecules.

mass, weight, volume, energy, temperature, heat, and density. Any measurement of a physical quantity must always include a number followed by a *unit* that tells us what was measured. It would be meaningless, for instance, to say that an animal is 3 because the number by itself does not give us enough information. The animal could be 3 meters tall, 3 kilograms in mass, or even 3 seconds old. Meters, kilograms, and seconds are all units that tell us the significance of the physical quantity, and they must be included to complete the description.

There are two major unit systems used in the world today. One is the United States Customary System (USCS, formerly called the British System of Units), used in the United States, primarily for nonscientific purposes.* The other is the Système International (SI), which is used in most other nations. This system is also known as the International System of Units or as the metric system. The orderliness of this system makes it useful for scientific work, and it is used by scientists all over the world, including those in the United States. (And the International System is beginning to be used for nonscientific work in the United States, as Figure 1.13 shows.)

This book uses the SI units given in Table 1.1. On occasion, USCS units are also used to help you make comparisons.

Figure 1.13
The metric system is finally making some headway in the United States, where various commercial goods, such as Reece's favorite soda, are now sold in metric quantities.

Table 1.1

SI Units for Physical Quantities and Their USCS Equivalents

Physical Quantity	SI Unit	Abbreviation	USCS Equivalent
length	kilometer	km	1 km = 0.621 miles (mi)
	meter	m	1 m = 1.094 yards (yd)
	centimeter	cm	1 cm = 0.3937 inches (in.) 1 in. = 2.54 cm
	millimeter	mm	none commonly used
time	second	s	second also used in USCS
mass	kilogram	kg	1 kg = 2.205 pounds (lb)
	gram	g	1 g = 0.03528 ounces (oz) 1 oz = 28.345 g
	milligram	mg	none commonly used
volume	liter	L	1 L = 1.057 quarts (qt)
	milliliter	mL	1 mL = 0.0339 fl oz
	cubic centimeter	cm^3	1 cm^3 = 0.0339 fl oz
energy	kilojoule	kJ	1 kJ = 0.239 kilocalories (kcal)
	joule	J	1 J = 0.239 calories (cal) 1 cal = 4.184 J
temperature	degree Celsius	°C	(°C × 1.8) + 32 = degrees Fahrenheit, °F
	kelvin	K	°C + 273 = K

---

*Two other countries that continue to use the USCS are Liberia and Myanmar.

Calculation Corner: Unit Conversion

Welcome to Calculation Corner! *Conceptual Chemistry* focuses on visual models and qualitative understandings. As with any other science, however, chemistry has its quantitative aspects. In fact, it is only by the interpretation of quantitative data obtained through laboratory experiments that chemical concepts can be reliably deduced. Thus, it is only natural that there are times when your conceptual understanding of chemistry can be nicely reinforced by some simple, straightforward calculations.

Often in chemistry, and especially in a laboratory setting, it is necessary to convert from one unit to another. To do so, you need only multiply the given quantity by the appropriate *conversion factor*. As discussed in more detail in Appendix A, all conversion factors can be written as ratios in which the numerator and denominator represent the equivalent quantity expressed in different units. Because any quantity divided by itself is equal to 1, all conversion factors are equal to 1. For example, the following two conversion factors are both derived from the relationship 100 centimeters = 1 meter:

$$\frac{100 \text{ centimeters}}{1 \text{ meter}} = 1 \qquad \frac{1 \text{ meter}}{100 \text{ centimeters}} = 1$$

Because all conversion factors are equal to 1, multiplying a quantity by a conversion factor does not change the value of the quantity. What does change are the units. Suppose you measured an item to be 60 centimeters in length. You can convert this measurement to meters by multiplying it by the conversion factor that allows you to cancel centimeters.

Example
Convert 60 centimeters to meters.

Answer

$$(60 \text{ centimeters}) \frac{(1 \text{ meter})}{(100 \text{ centimeters})} = 0.6 \text{ meter}$$

↑	↑	↑
quantity in centimeters	conversion factor	quantity in meters

To derive a conversion factor, consult a table that presents unit equalities, such as Table 1.1. Then multiply the given quantity by the conversion factor, and voilà, the units are converted. Always be careful to write down your units. They are your ultimate guide, telling you what numbers go where and whether you are setting up the equation properly.

Your Turn
Multiply each physical quantity by the appropriate conversion factor to find its numerical value in the new unit indicated. You will need paper, pencil, a calculator, and Tables 1.1 and 1.2.

   a. 7320 grams to kilograms.
   b. 235 kilograms to pounds.
   c. 4500 milliliters to liters.
   d. 2.0 liters to quarts.
   e. 100 calories to kilocalories.
   f. 100 calories to joules.

The answers for Calculation Corners appear at the end of each chapter.

One major advantage of the metric system is that it uses a decimal system, which means all units are related to smaller or larger units by a factor of 10. Some of the more commonly used prefixes along with their decimal equivalents are shown in Table 1.2. From this table, you can see that 1 kilometer is equal to 1000 meters, where the prefix *kilo-* indicates

Table 1.2

SI Prefixes

Prefix	Symbol	Decimal Equivalent	Exponential Form	Example
tera-	T	1,000,000,000,000.	10^{12}	1 terameter (Tm) = 1 trillion meters
giga-	G	1,000,000,000.	10^{9}	1 gigameter (Gm) = 1 billion meters
mega-	M	1,000,000.	10^{6}	1 megameter (Mm) = 1 million meters
kilo-	k	1,000.	10^{3}	1 kilometer (km) = 1 thousand meters
hecto-	h	100.	10^{2}	1 hectometer (hm) = 1 hundred meters
deka-	da	10.	10^{1}	1 dekameter (dam) = ten meters
no prefix	—	1.	10^{0}	1 meter (m) = 1 meter
deci-	d	0.1	10^{-1}	1 decimeter (dm) = 1 tenth of a meter
centi-	c	0.01	10^{-2}	1 centimeter (cm) = 1 hundredth of a meter
milli-	m	0.001	10^{-3}	1 millimeter (mm) = 1 thousandth of a meter
micro-	μ	0.000 001	10^{-6}	1 micrometer (μm) = 1 millionth of a meter
nano-	n	0.000 000 001	10^{-9}	1 nanometer (nm) = 1 billionth of a meter
pico-	p	0.000 000 000 001	10^{-12}	1 picometer (pm) = 1 trillionth of a meter

1000. Likewise, 1 millimeter is equal to 0.001 meter, where the prefix *milli-* indicates ¹⁄₁₀₀₀. You need not memorize this table, but you will find it a useful reference when you come across these prefixes in your course of study.

The remaining sections of this chapter introduce some physical quantities important to the study of chemistry. In the spirit of the atomic and molecular theme of *Conceptual Chemistry*, these physical quantities are described from the point of view of atoms and molecules. In addition to physical quantities, the various phases of matter—solid, liquid, gas—are also described from the point of view of atoms and molecules.

1.4 Mass Is How Much and Volume Is How Spacious

To describe a material object, we can quantify any number of properties, but perhaps the most fundamental property is mass. **Mass** is the quantitative measure of how much matter a material object contains. The greater the mass of an object, the greater amount of matter in it. A gold bar that is twice as massive as another gold bar, for example, contains twice as many gold atoms.

Mass is also a measure of an object's *inertia*, which is the resistance the object has to any change in its motion. Tractor trailers, for example, have a lot of mass (inertia), which is why they require powerful engines to get moving and powerful brakes to come to a stop.

The standard unit of mass is the *kilogram*, and a replica of the primary cylinder used to determine exactly what mass "1 kilogram" describes is shown in Figure 1.14. An average-sized human male has a mass of about 70 kilograms (154 pounds). For smaller quantities, we use the *gram*. Table 1.2 tells us that the prefix *kilo-* means "1000," and so we see that 1000 grams are needed to make a single kilogram (1000 grams = 1 kilogram). For even smaller quantities, the *milligram* is used (1000 milligrams = 1 gram).

Figure 1.14

The standard kilogram is defined as the mass of a platinum–iridium cylinder kept at the International Bureau of Weights and Measures in Sevres, France. The cylinder is removed from its very safe location only once a year for comparison with duplicates, such as the one shown here, which is housed at the National Bureau of Standards in Washington, D.C.

Welcome to "Hands-On Chemistry," the interactive corner of your *Conceptual Chemistry* textbook. This feature provides you the opportunity to apply chemistry concepts outside a formal laboratory setting. Each activity is guaranteed to be meaningful, interesting, and, at times, surprising.

At the end of each chapter, you will find follow-up discussions, called Insights, for each Hands-On Chemistry activity. Ideally, you should look over the Insights only after you have attempted the activity. The job of the Insights is to correct any misconceptions you may have about the results of the activity and also to provide food for further thought—sort of a "Minds-On Chemistry." So let's begin!

Hands-On Chemistry: Penny Fingers

Pennies dated 1982 or earlier are nearly pure copper, each having a mass of about 3.5 grams. Pennies dated after 1982 are made of copper-coated zinc, each having a mass of about 2.9 grams. Hold a pre-1982 penny on the tip of your right index finger and a post-1982 penny on the tip of your left index finger. Move your forearms up and down to feel the difference in inertia—the difference of 0.6 grams (600 milligrams) is subtle but not beyond a set of well-tuned senses. If one penny on each finger is below your threshold, try two pre-1982s stacked on one finger and two post-1982s stacked on the other. Share this activity with a friend.

Mass is easy to understand. It is simply a measure of the amount of matter in a sample, which is a function of how many atoms the sample contains. Accordingly, the mass of an object remains the same no matter where it is located. A one kilogram gold bar, for example, has the same mass whether it is on the Earth, on the moon, or floating "weightless" in space. This is because it contains the same number of atoms in each location.

Weight is more complicated. By definition, **weight** is the gravitational force exerted on an object by the nearest most massive body, such as the Earth. The weight of an object, therefore, depends entirely upon its location, as is shown in Figure 1.15. On the moon, a gold bar weighs less than it does on the Earth. This is because the moon is much less massive than the Earth; hence, the gravitational force exerted by the moon on the bar is much less. On Jupiter, the gold bar would weigh more than it does on the Earth because of the greater gravitational force exerted on the bar by this very massive planet.

Because mass is independent of location, it is customary in science to measure matter by its mass rather than its weight. *Conceptual Chemistry* adheres to this convention by presenting matter in units of mass, such as kilograms, grams, and milligrams. Such weight units as pounds and tons (1 ton = 2000 pounds) are occasionally provided as a reference because of their familiarity.

Figure 1.15
(a) A 1-kilogram gold bar resting on the Earth weighs 2.2 pounds. (b) On the moon, this same gold bar would weigh 0.37 pound. (c) Deep in space, free from any planetary surface, the gold bar would weigh 0 pounds but still have a mass of 1 kilogram.

Concept Check ✓

Is there gravity on the moon?

Was this your answer? Yes, absolutely! The moon exerts a downward gravitational pull on any body near its surface, as evidenced by the fact that astronauts were able to land and walk on the moon. This NASA photograph shows an astronaut jumping. Without gravity, this jump would have been his last.

So, since there is gravity, why doesn't the flag droop downward? Look carefully and you'll see that it is held up by a stick across its top edge. There is no wind on the moon (because there is no atmosphere), and so the crew used the support stick to make the wrinkled flag display nicely in photographs.

The amount of space a material object occupies is its **volume**. The SI unit of volume is the liter, which is only slightly larger than the USCS unit of volume, the quart. A liter is the volume of space marked off by a cube measuring 10 centimeters by 10 centimeters by 10 centimeters, which is 1000 cubic centimeters. A smaller unit of volume is the milliliter, which is $\frac{1}{1000}$ of a liter, or 1 cubic centimeter.

A convenient way to measure the volume of an irregular object is shown in Figure 1.16. The volume of water displaced is equal to the volume of the object.

Figure 1.17 gives you a sense of the relative sizes of some familiar objects, some very large ones, and some very small ones.

Figure 1.16
The volume of an object, no matter what its shape, can be measured by the displacement of water. When this rock is immersed in the water, the rise in the water level equals the volume of the rock, which in this example measures about 50 mL.

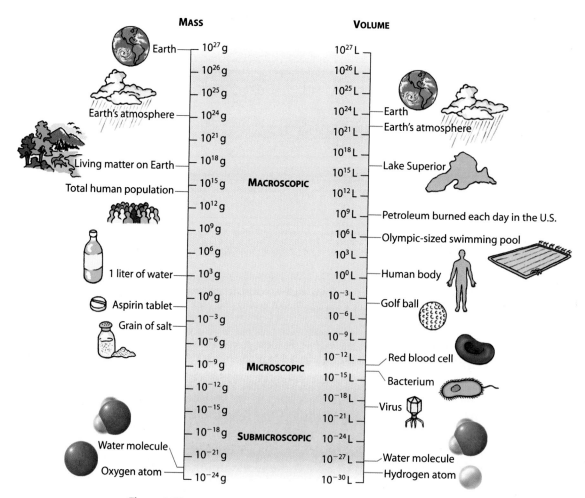

Figure 1.17
Range of masses and volumes in the universe.

Hands-On Chemistry: Decisive Dimensions

This activity challenges any misconceptions you might have about what determines volume as it answers the question "Can one object have a greater mass than another and yet have the same volume?" Try this activity and find out.

What You Need

Tall, narrow glass; masking tape; empty film canister with lid; bunch of pennies

Procedure

① Fill the glass two-thirds full with water and mark the water level with masking tape.

② Fill the canister with pennies. Cap the canister and place it in the water. Note the new water level with a second strip of tape.

③ Remove the canister, being careful not to splash water out of the glass. If the water level after you remove the canister is below the original level, add water until the volume is again at that level.

④ Remove half the pennies from the canister so as to decrease its mass. Cap the canister, predict how much the water level will rise when you submerge the canister, and then submerge it.

Which statement do your results support:

    a. The volume of water an object displaces depends only on the dimensions of the object and not on its mass.

    b. The volume of water an object displaces depends on both the dimensions and the mass of the object.

1.5 Energy Is the Mover of Matter

Matter is substance, and energy is that which can move substance. The concept of energy is abstract and therefore not as easy to define as the concepts of mass and volume. One definition of **energy** is the capacity to do work. If something has energy, it can do work on something else—it can exert a force and move that something else. Accordingly, energy is not something we observe directly. Rather, we only witness its effects.

There are two principal forms of energy: potential and kinetic. **Potential energy** is stored energy. A boulder perched on the edge of a cliff has potential energy due to the force of gravity, just as the poised arrow in Figure 1.18 has potential energy due to the tension of the bow.. The potential energy of an object increases as the distance over which the force is able to act also increases. The higher a boulder is positioned above level ground, the more potential energy it has to do work as it falls downward under the pull of gravity. Similarly, an arrow in a fully drawn bow, for example, has more potential energy than does one in a half-drawn bow.

Figure 1.18
Much of the potential energy in Ian's drawn bow will be converted to the kinetic energy of the arrow upon its release.

Kinetic energy is the energy of motion. Both a falling boulder and a flying arrow have kinetic energy. The faster a body moves, the more kinetic energy it has. Similarly, the faster an arrow flies, the more work it can do to a target, as evidenced by its deeper penetration.

Concept Check ✓

How does a flying arrow have potential energy as well as kinetic energy?

Was this your answer? It has potential energy as long as it remains above the ground. Once it reaches the ground, its potential energy is zero because it no longer has any potential to do work.

Chemical substances possess what is known as *chemical potential energy*, which is the energy that is stored within atoms and molecules. Any material that can burn has chemical potential energy. The firecracker in Figure 1.19, for example, has chemical potential energy. This energy gets released when the firecracker is ignited. During the explosion, some of the chemical potential energy is transformed to the kinetic energy of flying particles. Much of the chemical potential energy is also transformed into light and heat. We explore the relationship between energy and chemical reactions in Chapter 9.

Figure 1.19
A firecracker is a mixture of solids that possess chemical potential energy. When a firecracker explodes, the solids react to form gases that fly outward and so possess a great deal of kinetic energy. Light and heat (both of which are forms of energy) are also formed.

Concept Check ✓

How does a wooden arrow lying on the ground have potential energy?

Was this your answer? The arrow contains chemical potential energy because it can burn.

The SI unit of energy is the *joule*, which is about the amount of energy released from a candle burning for only a moment. In the United States, a common unit of energy is the *calorie*. One calorie is by definition the amount of energy required to raise the temperature of 1 gram of water by 1 degree Celsius. One calorie is 4.184 times larger than 1 joule. Put differently, 4.184 joules of energy is equivalent to 1 calorie (4.184 joules = 1 calorie). So, a joule is about one-fourth of a calorie.

In the United States, the energy content of food is measured by the *Calorie* (note the upper-case C). One Calorie equals 1 kilocalorie, which is 1000 calories (note the lowercase c). The candy bar in Figure 1.20 offers 230 Calories (230 kilocalories), bestowing a total of 230,000 calories to the consumer.

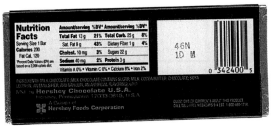

Figure 1.20
The energy content of this candy bar (230 Calories = 230,000 calories), when released through burning, is enough to heat up 230,000 grams (about 507 pounds) of water by 1 degree Celsius.

1.6 Temperature Is a Measure of How Hot—Heat It Is Not

The atoms and molecules that form matter are in constant motion, jiggling to and fro or bouncing from one position to another. By virtue of their motion, these particles possess kinetic energy. Their average kinetic energy is directly related to a property you can sense: how hot something is. Whenever something becomes warmer, the kinetic energy of its submicroscopic particles increases. For example, strike a penny with a hammer and the penny becomes warm because the hammer's blow causes its atoms to jostle faster, increasing their kinetic energy (the hammer becomes warm for the same reason). Put a flame to a liquid and the liquid becomes warmer because the energy of the flame causes the particles of the liquid to move faster, increasing their kinetic energy. For example, the molecules in the hot coffee in Figure 1.21 are moving faster, on average, than those in the cold coffee.

Figure 1.21
The difference between hot coffee and cold coffee is the average speed of the molecules. In the hot coffee, the molecules are moving faster, on average, than they are in the cold coffee. (The longer "motion trails" on the molecules of hot coffee indicate their higher

Figure 1.22
Can we trust our sense of hot and cold? Will both fingers feel the same temperature when they are put in the warm water? Try this yourself, and you will see why we use a thermometer for an objective measurement.

The quantity that tells us how warm or cold an object is relative to some standard is called **temperature**. We express temperature by a number that corresponds to the degree of hotness on some chosen scale. Just touching an object certainly isn't a good way of measuring its temperature, as Figure 1.22 illustrates. To measure temperature, therefore, we take advantage of the fact that nearly all materials expand when their temperature is raised and contract when it is lowered. With increasing temperature, the particles move faster and are on average farther apart—the material expands. With decreasing temperature, the particles move more slowly and are on average closer together—the material contracts. A **thermometer** exploits this characteristic of matter, measuring temperature by means of the expansion and contraction of a liquid, usually mercury or colored alcohol.

Concept Check ✓

You may have noticed telephone wires sagging on a hot day. This happens because the wires are longer in hot weather than in cold. What is happening on the atomic level to cause such changes in wire length?

Was this your answer? On a hot day, the atoms in the wire are moving faster, and as a result the wire expands. On a cold day, those same atoms are moving more slowly, which causes the wire to contract.

The most common thermometer in the world is the Celsius thermometer, named in honor of the Swedish astronomer Anders Celsius (1701–1744), who first suggested the scale of 100 degrees between the freezing point and boiling point of fresh water. In a Celsius thermometer, the number 0 is assigned to the temperature at which pure water freezes and the number 100 is assigned to the temperature at which it boils (at standard atmospheric pressure), with 100 equal parts called *degrees* between these two points.

In the United States, we use a Fahrenheit thermometer, named after its originator, the German scientist G. D. Fahrenheit (1686–1736), who chose to assign 0 to the temperature of a mixture containing equal weights of snow and common salt and 100 to the body temperature of a human. Because these reference points are not dependable, the Fahrenheit scale has since been modified such that the freezing point of pure water is designated 32°F and the boiling point of pure water is designated 212°F. On this recalibrated scale, normal human body temperature is around 98.6°F.

A temperature scale favored by scientists is the Kelvin scale, named after the British physicist Lord Kelvin (1824–1907). This scale is calibrated not in terms of the freezing and boiling points of water but rather in terms of the motion of atoms and molecules. On the Kelvin scale, zero is the temperature at which there is no atomic or molecular motion. This is a theoretical limit called **absolute zero**, which is the temperature at which the particles of a substance have absolutely no kinetic energy to give up. Absolute zero corresponds to −459.7°F on the Fahrenheit scale

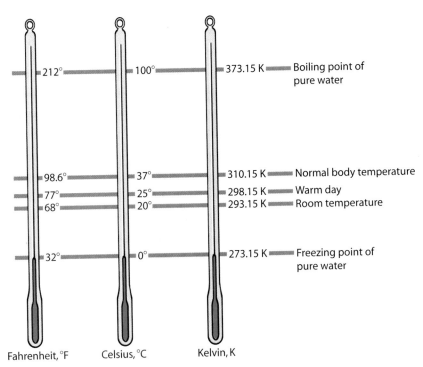

212° — 100° — 373.15 K — Boiling point of pure water

98.6° — 37° — 310.15 K — Normal body temperature
77° — 25° — 298.15 K — Warm day
68° — 20° — 293.15 K — Room temperature

32° — 0° — 273.15 K — Freezing point of pure water

Fahrenheit, °F   Celsius, °C   Kelvin, K

Figure 1.23
Some familiar temperatures measured on the Fahrenheit, Celsius, and Kelvin scales.

and −273.15°C on the Celsius scale. On the Kelvin scale, this temperature is simply 0 K, which is read "zero kelvin" or "zero K." Marks on the Kelvin scale are the same distance apart as those on the Celsius scale, and so the temperature of freezing water is +273 kelvin. (Note that the word *degree* is not used with the Kelvin scale. To say "273 degrees kelvin" is incorrect. To say "273 kelvin" is correct.) The three scales are compared in Figure 1.23.

It is important to understand that temperature is a measure of the *average* amount of energy in a substance, not the *total* amount of energy, as Figure 1.24 shows. The total energy in a swimming pool full of boiling water is much more than the total energy in a cupful of boiling water even though both are at the same temperature. Your utility bill after heating the swimming pool water to 100°C would show this. Whereas the total amount of energy in the pool is much more than in the cup, the *average* molecular motion is the same in both water samples. The water molecules in the swimming pool are moving on average just as fast as the water molecules in the cup. The only difference is that the swimming pool contains more water molecules and hence a greater total amount of energy.

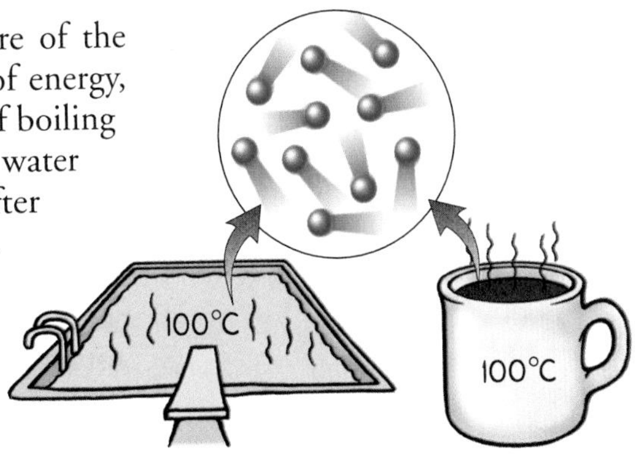

Heat is energy that flows from a higher-temperature object to a lower-temperature object. If you touch a hot stove, heat enters your hand because the stove is at a higher temperature than your hand. When you touch a piece of ice, energy passes out of your hand and into the ice because the ice is at a lower temperature than your hand. From a human

Figure 1.24
Bodies of water at the same temperature have the same average molecular kinetic energies. The *volume* of the water has nothing to do with its temperature.

perspective, if you are receiving heat you experience warmth; if you are giving away heat, you experience cooling. The next time you touch the hot forehead of a sick, feverish friend, ask her or him whether your hand feels hot or cold. Whereas temperature is absolute, hot and cold are relative.

In general, the greater the temperature difference between two bodies in contact with each other, the greater the rate of heat flow. This is why a hot clothes iron can cause much more damage to your skin than a warm clothes iron.

Because heat is a form of energy, its unit is the joule.

Concept Check ✔

When you enter a swimming pool, the water may feel quite cold. After a while, though, your body "gets used to it," and the water no longer feels so cold. Use the concept of heat to explain what is going on.

Was this your answer? Heat flows because of a temperature difference. When you enter the water, your skin temperature is much higher than the water temperature. The result is a significant flow of heat from your body to the water, which you experience as cold. Once you have been in the water awhile, your skin temperature is much closer to the water temperature (due to the cooling effects of the water and your body's ability to conserve heat), and so the flow of heat from your body is less. With less heat flowing from your body, the water no longer feels so cold.

1.7 The Phase of a Material Depends on the Motion of Its Particles

One of the most apparent ways we can describe matter is by its physical form, which may be in one of three phases (also sometimes described as physical states): *solid, liquid,* or *gas.* A **solid** material, such as a rock, occupies a constant amount of space and does not readily deform upon the application of pressure. In other words, a solid has both definite volume and definite shape. A **liquid** also occupies a constant amount of space (it has a definite volume), but its form changes readily (it has an indefinite shape). A liter of milk, for example, may take the shape of its carton or the shape of a puddle, but its volume is the same in both cases. A **gas** is diffuse, having neither definite volume nor definite shape. Any sample of gas assumes both the shape and the volume of the container it occupies. A given amount of air, for example, may assume the volume and shape of a toy balloon or the volume and shape of a bicycle tire. Released from its container, a gas diffuses into the atmosphere, which is a collection of various gases held to our planet only by the force of gravity.

On the submicroscopic level, the solid, liquid, and gaseous phases are distinguished by how well the submicroscopic particles hold together. This is illustrated in Figure 1.25. In solid matter, the attractions between particles are strong enough to hold all the particles together in some fixed three-dimensional arrangement. The particles are able to vibrate about fixed positions, but they cannot move past one another. Adding heat causes these vibrations to increase until, at a certain temperature, the vibrations are rapid enough to disrupt the fixed arrangement. The particles can then slip past one another and tumble around much like a bunch of marbles in a bag. This is the liquid phase of matter, and it is the mobility of the submicroscopic particles that gives rise to the liquid's fluid character—its ability to flow and take on the shape of its container.

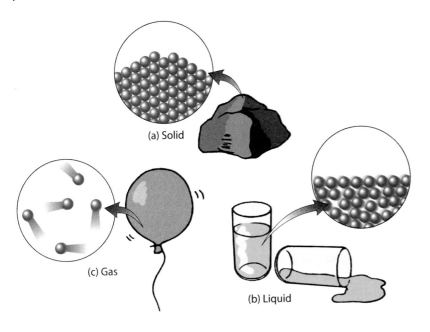

(a) Solid

(c) Gas

(b) Liquid

Figure 1.25
The familiar bulk properties of a solid, liquid, and gas. (a) The submicroscopic particles of the solid phase vibrate about fixed positions. (b) The submicroscopic particles of the liquid phase slip past one another. (c) The fast-moving submicroscopic particles of the gaseous phase are separated by large average distances.

Further heating causes the submicroscopic particles in the liquid to move so fast that the attractions they have for one another are unable to hold them together. They then separate from one another, forming a gas. Moving at an average speed of 500 meters per second (1,100 miles per hour), the particles of a gas are widely separated from one another. Matter in the gaseous phase therefore occupies much more volume than it does in the solid or liquid phase, as Figure 1.26 shows. Applying pressure to a gas squeezes the gas particles closer together, which makes for a smaller volume.

(a)

(b)

(c)

Figure 1.26
The gaseous phase of any material occupies significantly more volume than either its solid or liquid phase. (a) Solid carbon dioxide (Dry Ice) is broken up into powder form. (b) The powder is funneled into a balloon. (c) The balloon expands as the contained carbon dioxide becomes a gas as the powder warms up.

Figure 1.27
In traveling from point A to point B, the typical gas particle travels a circuitous path because of numerous collisions with other gas particles—about eight billion collisions every second! The changes in direction shown here represent only a few of these collisions. Although the particle travels at very high speeds, it takes a relatively long time to cross between two distant points because of these numerous collisions.

Enough air for an underwater diver to breathe for many minutes, for example, can be squeezed (compressed) into a tank small enough to be carried on the diver's back.

Although gas particles move at high speeds, the speed at which they can travel from one side of a room to the other is relatively slow. This is because the gas particles are continually hitting one another, and the path they end up taking is circuitous. At home, you get a sense of how long it takes for gas particles to migrate each time someone opens the oven door after baking, as Figure 1.27 shows. A shot of aromatic gas particles escapes the oven, but there is a notable delay before the aroma reaches the nose of someone sitting in the next room.

Concept Check ✓

Why are gases so much easier to compress into smaller volumes than are solids and liquids?

Was this your answer? Because there is a lot of space between gas particles. The particles of a solid or liquid, on the other hand, are already close to one another, meaning there is little room left for a further decrease in volume.

Familiar Terms Are Used to Describe Changing Phases

Figure 1.28 illustrates that you must either add heat to a substance or remove heat from it if you want to change its phase. The process of a solid transforming to a liquid is called **melting**. To visualize what happens when heat begins to melt a solid, imagine you are holding hands with a group of people and each of you start jumping around randomly. The more violently you jump, the more difficult it is to hold onto one another. If everyone jumps violently enough, keeping hold is impossible. Something like this happens to the submicroscopic particles of a solid when it is heated. As heat is added to the solid, the particles vibrate more and more violently. If enough heat is added, the attractive forces between the particles are no longer able to hold them together. The solid melts.

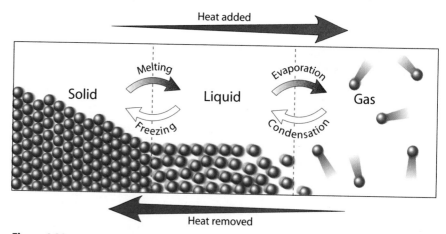

Figure 1.28
Melting and evaporation involve the addition of heat; condensation and freezing involve the removal of heat.

A liquid can be changed to a solid by the removal of heat. This process is called **freezing**, and it is the reverse of melting. As heat is withdrawn from the liquid, particle motion diminishes until the particles, on average, are moving slowly enough for attractive forces between them to take permanent hold. The only motion the particles are capable of then is vibration about fixed positions, which means the liquid has solidified, or frozen.

A liquid can be heated so that it becomes a gas—a process called **evaporation**. As heat is added, the particles of the liquid acquire more kinetic energy and move faster. Particles at the liquid surface eventually gain enough energy to jump out of the liquid and enter the air. In other words, they enter the gaseous phase. As more and more particles absorb the heat being added, they too acquire enough energy to escape from the liquid surface and become gas particles. Because a gas results from evaporation, this phase is also sometimes referred to as *vapor*. Water in the gaseous phase, for example, may be referred to as water vapor.

The rate at which a liquid evaporates increases with temperature. A puddle of water, for example, evaporates from a hot pavement more quickly than it does from your cool kitchen floor. When the temperature is hot enough, evaporation occurs beneath the surface of the liquid. As a result, bubbles form and are buoyed up to the surface. We say that the liquid is **boiling**. A substance is often characterized by its *boiling point*, which is the temperature at which it boils. At sea level, water's boiling point is 100°C.

The transformation from gas to liquid—the reverse of evaporation—is called **condensation**. This process can occur when the temperature of a gas decreases. The water vapor held in the warm daylight air, for example, may condense to form a wet dew in the cool of the night.

Hands-On Chemistry: Hot-Water Balloon

See for yourself that a material in its gaseous phase occupies much more space than it does in its liquid phase.

What You Need

2 teaspoons of water, 9-inch rubber balloon, microwave oven, oven mitt

Procedure

① Pour the water into the balloon. Squeeze out as much air as you can and knot the balloon.

② Put the balloon in the microwave oven and cook at full power for however many seconds it takes for boiling to begin, which is indicated by a rapid growth in the size of the balloon. It may take only about 10 seconds for the balloon to reach full size once it starts expanding. (The balloon will pop if you add too much water or if you cook it for too long.)

③ Remove the heated balloon with the oven mitt, shake the balloon around, and listen for the return of the liquid phase. You should be able to hear it raining inside the balloon.

What happens if you submerge the inflated balloon in a pot of ice-cold water?

1.8 Density Is the Ratio of Mass to Volume

The relationship between an object's mass and the amount of space it occupies is the object's density. Density is a measure of compactness, of how tightly mass is squeezed into a given volume. A block of lead has much more mass squeezed into its volume than does a same-sized block of aluminum. The lead is therefore more dense. We think of density as the "lightness" or "heaviness" of objects of the same size, as Figure 1.29 shows.

Figure 1.29
The amount of mass in a block of lead far exceeds the amount of mass in a block of aluminum of the same size. Hence, the lead weighs much more and is more difficult to lift.

Density is the amount of mass contained in a sample divided by the volume of the sample:

$$\text{density} = \frac{\text{mass}}{\text{volume}}$$

An object having a mass of 1 gram and a volume of 1 milliliter, for example, has a density of

$$\text{density} = \frac{1 \text{ g}}{1 \text{ mL}} = 1\frac{\text{g}}{\text{mL}}, \text{ which reads "one gram per milliliter"}$$

An object having a mass of 2 grams and a volume of 1 milliliter is denser; its density is

$$\text{density} = \frac{2 \text{ g}}{1 \text{ mL}} = 2\frac{\text{g}}{\text{mL}}, \text{ which reads "two grams per milliliter"}$$

Other units of mass and volume besides gram and milliliters may be used in calculating density. The densities of gases, for example, because they are so low, are often given in grams per liter. In all cases, however, the units are a unit of mass divided by a unit of volume.

Concept Check ✓

Which occupies a greater volume: 1 kilogram of lead or 1 kilogram of aluminum?

Was this your answer? The aluminum. Think of it this way. Because lead is so dense, you need only a little bit in order to have 1 kilogram. Aluminum, by contrast, is far less dense, and so 1 kilogram of aluminum occupies much more volume than the same mass of lead.

Calculation Corner: Manipulating an Algebraic Equation

With a little algebraic manipulation, it is easy to change the equation for density around so that it solves either for mass or for volume. The first step is to multiply both sides of the density equation by volume. Then canceling the volumes that appear in the numerator and denominator results in the equation for the mass of an object:

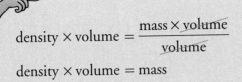

$$\text{density} \times \text{volume} = \frac{\text{mass} \times \cancel{\text{volume}}}{\cancel{\text{volume}}}$$

$$\text{density} \times \text{volume} = \text{mass}$$

Example
A pre-1982 penny has a density of 8.92 grams per milliliter and a volume of 0.392 milliliters. What is its mass?

Answer

$$D \times V = M = 8.92 \frac{g}{\cancel{mL}} \times 0.392 \ \cancel{mL} = 3.50 \ g$$

To solve for the volume of an object, divide both sides of the equation for the mass by the density. Canceling the densities results in the equation for volume:

$$\frac{\cancel{\text{density}} \times \text{volume}}{\cancel{\text{density}}} = \frac{\text{mass}}{\text{density}}$$

$$\text{volume} = \frac{\text{mass}}{\text{density}}$$

Example
A post-1982 penny has a density of 7.40 grams per milliliter and a mass of 2.90 grams. What is its volume?

Answer

$$V = \frac{M}{D} = \frac{2.90 \ \cancel{g}}{7.40 \ \frac{\cancel{g}}{mL}} = 0.392 \ mL$$

In summary, the three equations expressing the relationship among density, mass, and volume are

Density	Mass	Volume
$D = \dfrac{M}{V}$	$M = D \times V$	$V = \dfrac{M}{D}$

Your Turn

1. What is the average density of a loaf of bread that has a mass of 500 grams and a volume of 1000 milliliters?

2. The loaf of bread in the previous problem loses all its moisture after being left out for several days. Its volume remains at 1 liter, but its density has been reduced to 0.45 grams per milliliter. What is its new mass?

3. A sack of groceries accidently set on a 500 gram loaf of bread increases the average density of the loaf to 2 grams per milliliter. What is its new volume?

Table 1.3

Densities of Some Solids, Liquids, and Gases

Substance	Density (g/mL)	Density (g/L)
Solids		
osmium	22.5	22,500
gold	19.3	19,300
lead	11.3	11,300
copper	8.92	8,920
iron	7.86	7,860
zinc	7.14	7,140
aluminum	2.70	2,700
ice	0.92	920
Liquids		
mercury	13.6	13,600
sea water	1.03	1,030
water at 4°C	1.00	1,000
ethyl alcohol	0.81	810
*Gases**		
dry air		
0°C	0.00129	1.29
20°C	0.00121	1.21
helium at 0°C	0.000178	0.178
oxygen at 0°C	0.00143	1.43

*All values at sea-level atmospheric pressure.

The densities of some substances are given in Table 1.3. Which would be more difficult to pick up: a liter of water or a liter of mercury?

Gas densities are much more affected by pressure and temperature than are the densities of solids and liquids. With an increase in pressure, gas molecules are squeezed closer together. This makes for volume and therefore greater density. The density of the air inside a diver's breathing tank, for example, is much greater than the density of air at normal atmospheric pressure. With an increase in temperature, gas molecules are moving faster and thus have a tendency to push outward, thereby occupying a greater volume. Thus, hot air is less dense than cold air, which is why hot air rises and the balloon in Figure 1.30 can take its passengers for a breathtaking ride.

Concept Check ✓

1. Which has a greater density: 1 gram of water or 10 grams of water?
2. Which has a greater density: 1 gram of lead or 10 grams of aluminum?

Was this your answer?

1. The density is the same for any amount of water. Whereas 1 gram of water occupies a volume of 1 milliliter, 10 grams occupies a volume of 10 milliliters. The ratio 1 gram/1 milliliter is the same as the ratio 10 grams/10 milliliters.
2. The lead. Density is mass per volume, and this ratio is greater for any amount of lead than for any amount of aluminum.

Figure 1.30
The hot air inside this hot-air balloon is less dense than the surrounding colder air, which is why the balloon rises.

A Word About Chapter Endmatter from the Author

Each chapter in this book concludes with a list of Key Terms and Matching Definitions, Review Questions, Hands-On Chemistry Insights, Exercises, and in some chapters, a few mathematical Problems.

Key Terms are listed alphabetically and followed by **Matching Definitions** listed in order of appearance in the chapter. For a guided review of the Key Terms, find the term that matches each definition. To get the most out of this format, match as many definitions as you can before checking back in the chapter. The more familiar you are with these terms, the easier it will be for you to apply the concepts.

The **Review Questions** help you fix ideas more firmly in your mind and catch the essentials of the chapter material. Like the Key Terms and Matching Definitions, they are not meant to be difficult. You can find the answers to the Review Questions in the chapter. If you study only the Key Terms and Review Questions and nothing else, you are minimizing your chance for success in this class.

The **Hands-On Chemistry Insights** are follow-up discussions designed to make sure you are getting the most out of performing these activities and also to clear up any misconceptions that may develop. Ideally, you should read these follow-ups after performing the activities.

In contrast to the Review Questions, the **Exercises** are designed to challenge your understanding of the chapter material. They emphasize thinking rather than mere recall and should be attempted only after you are well acquainted with the chapter through the Matching Definitions and Review Questions. In many cases, the intention of a particular Exercise is to help you to apply the ideas of chemistry to familiar situations. Your answers should be in complete sentences, with an explanation or sketch when applicable. Exercises are a favorite among instructors for exam material. If you do well with the Exercises, you can expect to do well on your exams. To help keep you on track, the answers to all odd-numbered exercises and problems are provided in Appendix C.

Problems feature concepts that are more clearly understood with numerical values and straightforward calculations. Most are based on information given in the chapter's *Calculation Corners*. Be sure to include units in your answers. The Problems are relatively few in number to avoid an emphasis on problem-solving that could obscure the primary goal of *Conceptual Chemistry*—a focus on the concepts of chemistry and how they relate to everyday living.

Key Terms and Matching Definitions

_____ absolute zero
_____ applied research
_____ basic research
_____ boiling
_____ chemistry
_____ condensation
_____ control test
_____ density
_____ energy
_____ evaporation
_____ freezing
_____ gas
_____ heat
_____ kinetic energy
_____ liquid
_____ mass
_____ matter
_____ melting
_____ potential energy
_____ scientific hypothesis
_____ solid
_____ submicroscopic
_____ temperature
_____ theory
_____ thermometer
_____ volume
_____ weight

1. The realm of atoms and molecules, where objects are smaller than can be detected by optical microscopes.
2. The study of matter and the transformations it can undergo.
3. Anything that occupies space.
4. Research dedicated to the discovery of the fundamental workings of nature.
5. Research dedicated to the development of useful products and processes.
6. A testable assumption often used to explain an observed phenomenon.
7. A test performed by scientists to increase the conclusiveness of an experimental test.
8. A comprehensive idea that can be used to explain a broad range of phenomena.
9. The quantitative measure of how much matter an object contains.

10. The gravitational force of attraction between two bodies (where one body is usually the Earth).
11. The quantity of space an object occupies.
12. The capacity to do work.
13. Stored energy.
14. Energy due to motion.
15. How warm or cold an object is relative to some standard. Also, a measure of the average kinetic energy per molecule of a substance, measured in degrees Celsius, degrees Fahrenheit, or kelvins.
16. An instrument used to measure temperature.
17. The lowest possible temperature any substance can have; the temperature at which the atoms of a substance have no kinetic energy: $0 \text{ K} = -273.15°\text{C} = -459.7°\text{F}$.
18. The energy that flows from one object to another because of a temperature difference between the two.
19. Matter that has a definite volume and a definite shape.
20. Matter that has a definite volume but no definite shape, assuming the shape of its container.
21. Matter that has neither a definite volume nor a definite shape, always filling any space available to it.
22. A transformation from a solid to a liquid.
23. A transformation from a liquid to a solid.
24. A transformation from a liquid to a gas.
25. Evaporation in which bubbles form beneath the liquid surface.
26. A transformation from a gas to a liquid.
27. The ratio of an object's mass to its volume.

Review Questions

Chemistry Is a Central Science Useful to Our Lives

1. Are atoms made of molecules, or are molecules made of atoms?

2. What is the difference between basic research and applied research?

3. Why is chemistry often called the central science?

4. What do members of the Chemical Manufacturers Association pledge in the Responsible Care program?

Science Is a Way of Understanding the Universe

5. Why were McClintock and Baker exploring the oceans off Antarctica?

6. What evidence supported McClintock and Baker's hypothesis that amphipods abducted sea butterflies for chemical defense against predators?

7. What is the purpose of a control test?

8. Why is reproducibility such a vital component of science?

9. Does a thory become stronger or weaker the more it is modified to account for experimental evidence?

10. What kind of questions is science unable to answer?

Scientists Measure Physical Quantities

11. Why are the units of a measurement just as important as the number?

12. What are the two major systems of measurement used in the world today?

13. Why are prefixes used in the metric system?

14. Which is greater: a micrometer or a decimeter?

15. A kilogram is equal to how many grams?

16. A milligram is equal to how many grams?

Mass Is How Much and Volume Is How Spacious

17. What is inertia, and how is it related to mass?

18. Which is the more complicated concept: mass or weight?

19. Which can change from one location to another: mass or weight?

20. What is volume?

21. What is the difference between an object's mass and its volume?

Energy Is the Mover of Matter

22. Why is energy hard to define?

23. What do we call the energy an object has because of its position?

24. What do we call the energy an object has because of its motion?

25. Which represents more energy: a joule or a calorie?

26. Which represents more energy: a calorie or a Calorie?

Temperature Is a Measure of How Hot—Heat It Is Not

27. In which is the average speed of the molecules less: in cold coffee or in hot coffee?

28. What happens to the volume of most materials when they are heated?

29. Which temperature scale has its zero point as the point of zero atomic and molecular motion?

30. Which has more total energy: a cup of boiling water at 100°C or a swimming pool of boiling water at 100°C?

31. Is it natural for heat to travel from a cold object to a hotter object?

32. What determines the direction of heat flow?

The Phase of a Material Depends on the Motion of Its Particles

33. How are the particles in a solid arranged differently from those in a liquid?

34. How does the arrangement of particles in a gas differ from the arrangements in liquids and solids?

35. Which occupies the greatest volume: 1 gram of ice, 1 gram of liquid water, or 1 gram of water vapor?

36. Gas particles travel at speeds of up to 500 meters per second. Why, then, does it take so long for gas molecules to travel the length of a room?

37. As liquid water evaporates, what is happening to the molecules?

38. Which requires the extraction of energy: melting or freezing?

39. Which requires the input of energy: evaporation or condensation?

40. What is it called when evaporation takes place beneath the surface of a liquid?

Density Is the Ratio of Mass to Volume

41. Is a more massive object necessarily more dense than a less massive object?

42. Is a denser object necessarily more massive than a less dense object?

43. The units of density are a ratio of what two quantities?

44. What happens to the density of a gas as it is compressed into a smaller volume?

Hands-On Chemistry Insights

Penny Fingers

You have to be moving the pennies up and down in order to optimize your threshold of detection. What you are sensing here is the *difference* in inertia. Recall that inertia is an object's resistance to any change in its motion. If you minimize the motion, you minimize your ability to detect any difference in inertia the two coins may have. Switch pennies between your left and right index fingers (with your eyes closed) to confirm your ability to detect a difference.

With or without the motion, the pennies exert a downward pressure that your nerve endings sense. To feel this pressure, repeat the experiment with the pre-1982s on one index finger and the post-1982s on the other index finger, but this time keep your hands still. How many do you need to stack before you can sense a difference in pressure? If you did this pressure experiment on the moon, would you need to stack more or fewer? Why?

Decisive Dimensions

Don't feel bad if your prediction was wrong—you are in good company. But now you understand that the volume of water displaced by an object is equal to the object's volume, not its mass or its weight.

Hot-Water Balloon

A marble hitting your hand pushes against your hand. In a similar fashion, a gaseous water molecule hitting the inside of the balloon pushes against the balloon. The force of a single water molecule is not that great, but the combined forces of the billions and billions of them in this activity is sufficient to inflate the balloon as the liquid water evaporates to the gaseous phase. Thus, you saw how the gaseous phase occupies much more volume than the liquid phase. If you observed the balloon carefully, you noticed it continues to inflate (although not so rapidly) after all the water has been converted to water vapor. This occurs because the microwaves continue to heat the gaseous water molecules, making them move faster and faster, pushing harder and harder against the balloon's inner surface.

After you take the balloon out of the microwave, the balloon is in contact with air molecules, which, being cooler, move more slowly than the water molecules. Gaseous water molecules colliding with the inner surface of the balloon pass their kinetic energy to the slower air molecules, and the air molecules get warmer because their kinetic energy increases. (This is similar to how the kinetic energy of a hammer pounding a nail into a flimsy wall can be transferred to a picture frame hanging on the opposite side of the wall.) You can feel this warming by holding your hand close to the balloon.

As the gaseous water molecules lose kinetic energy, they begin to condense into the liquid phase, a noisy process amplified by the balloon (listen carefully).

From a molecular point of view, why does the balloon shrink more quickly in ice water? How is this activity similar to the demonstration depicted in Figure 1.26?

Exercises

1. Why is it important to work through the Review Questions before attempting the Exercises?

2. In what sense is a color computer monitor or television screen similar to our view of matter? Place a drop (and only a drop) of water on your computer monitor or television screen for a closer look.

3. Of the three sciences physics, chemistry, and biology, which is the most complex?

4. Is chemistry the study of the submicroscopic, the microscopic, the macroscopic, or all three? Defend your answer.

5. Some politicians take pride in maintaining a particular point of view. They think a change of mind would be seen as a sign of weakness. How is a change of mind viewed differently in science?

6. Why is the process of science not restricted to any one particular method?

7. Distinguish between a scientific hypothesis and a theory.

8. How might the demand for reproducibility in science have the long-run effect of compelling honesty?

9. McClintock and Baker worked together on scientific research projects involving marine organisms of the Antarctic seas, yet they have different scientific backgrounds—McClintock in biology and Baker in chemistry. Is this unusual? Explain.

10. Which of the following are scientific hypotheses?
    a. Stars are made of the lost teeth of children.
    b. Albert Einstein was the greatest scientist ever to have lived.
    c. The planet Mars is reddish because it is coated with cotton candy.
    d. Aliens from outer space have transplanted themselves into the minds of government workers.
    e. Tides are caused by the moon.
    f. You were Abraham Lincoln in a past life.
    g. You remain self-aware while sleeping.
    h. You remain self-aware after death.

11. In answer to the question "When a plant grows, where does the material come from?", the ancient Greek philosopher Aristotle (384–322 B.C.) hypothesized that all material came from the soil. Do you consider his hypothesis to be correct, incorrect, or partially correct? What experimental tests do you propose to support your choice?

12. The great philosopher and mathematician Bertrand Russell (1872–1970) wrote, "I think we must retain the belief that scientific knowledge is one of the glories of man. I will not maintain that knowledge can never do harm. I think such general propositions can almost always be refuted by well-chosen examples. What I will maintain—and maintain vigorously—is that knowledge is very much more often useful than harmful and that fear of knowledge is very much more often harmful than useful." Think of examples to support this statement.

13. Name two physical quantities discussed in this chapter that change when a junked car is neatly crushed into a compact cube.

14. Which would you rather have: a decigram of gold or a kilogram of gold?

15. Can an object have mass without having weight? Can it have weight without having mass?

16. Why do we use different units for mass and weight?

17. Gravity on the moon is only one-sixth as strong as gravity on the Earth. What is the mass of a 6-kilogram object on the moon and what is its mass on the Earth?

18. Does a 2-kilogram iron brick have twice as much mass as a 1-kilogram iron brick? Twice as much weight? Twice as much volume?

19. Does a 2-kilogram iron brick have twice as much mass as a 1-kilogram block of wood? Twice as much volume? Explain.

20. Which is more evident: potential or kinetic energy? Explain.

21. Will your body possess energy after you die? If so, what kind?

22. What is temperature a measure of?

23. An old remedy for separating two nested drinking glasses stuck together is to run water at one temperature into the inner glass and then run water at a different temperature over the surface of the outer glass. Which water should be hot and which cold?

24. A Concorde supersonic airplane heats up considerably when traveling through the air at speeds greater than the speed of sound. As a result, the Concorde in flight is about 20 centimeters longer than when it is on the ground. Offer an explanation for this length change from a submicroscopic perspective.

25. Which has more total energy: a cup of boiling water at 100°C or a swimming pool of slightly cooler water at 90°C?

26. If you drop a hot rock into a pail of water, the temperature of the rock and that of the water both change until the two are equal. The rock cools and the water warms. Does this hold true if the hot rock is dropped into the Atlantic Ocean?

27. Which has stronger attractions among its submicroscopic particles: a solid at 25°C or a gas at 25°C? Explain.

28. The diagram at the left shows the moving particles of a gaseous material within a rigid container. Which of the three boxes on the right (a, b, or c) best represents this material upon the addition of heat.

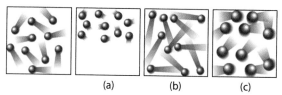

(a)   (b)   (c)

29. The diagram at the left shows two phases of a single substance. In the middle box, draw what these particles would look like if heat were taken away. In the box on the right, show what they would look like if heat were added. If each particle represents a water molecule, what is the temperature in the box on the left?

30. Humidity is a measure of the amount of water vapor in the atmosphere. Why is humidity always very low inside your kitchen freezer?

31. What happens to the density of a gas as the gas is compressed into a smaller volume?

32. A post-1982 penny is made with zinc, but its density is greater than that of zinc. Why?

33. The following three boxes represent the number of submicroscopic particles in a given volume of a particular substance at different temperatures. Which box represents the highest density? Which box represents the highest

temperature? Why would this be a most unusual substance if box a represented the liquid phase and box b represented the solid phase?

  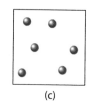

(a)   (b)   (c)

Problems

1. What is the mass in kilograms of a 130-pound human standing on the Earth?

2. What is the mass in kilograms of a 130-pound human standing on the moon?

3. How many joules are there in a candy bar containing 230,000 calories?

4. How many milliliters of dirt are there in a hole measuring 5 liters? How many milliliters of air?

5. Someone wants to sell you a piece of gold and says it is nearly pure. Before buying the piece, you measure its mass to be 52.3 grams and find that it displaces 4.16 milliliters of water. Calculate its density and consult Table 1.3 to assess its purity.

6. What volume of water will a 52.3-gram sample of pure gold displace?

Answers to Calculation Corners

Unit Conversion

a. 7.32 kilograms
b. 518 pounds
c. 4.5 liters
d. 2.1 quarts
e. 0.1 kilocalories
f. 400 J

Perhaps you are wondering about how many digits to include in your answers. Were you perplexed, for example, that the answer to f is 400 J and not 418.4 J? There are specific procedures to follow in figuring which digits from your calculator to write down. The digits you are supposed to write down are called *significant figures*. Because there are few calculations in the chapter portions of *Conceptual Chemistry*, however, a full discussion of significant figures is left to Appendix B. It is there for those of you looking for a little more quantitative depth, which is certainly often needed when performing experiments in the laboratory.

Manipulating an Algebraic Equation

1. 0.5 grams per milliliter
2. 0.45 grams
3. 0.25 milliliters

Suggested Readings and Web Sites

Ronald Breslow, *Chemistry Today and Tomorrow: The Central, Useful, and Creative Science.* Sudbury, MA: Jones and Bartlett, 1997.
Written by a past president of the American Chemical Society, this paperback analyzes the role chemistry has played in the development of our modern society and how chemistry is sure to play an increasing role in our future.

Roald Hoffmann, *The Same and Not the Same.* New York: Columbia University Press, 1995.
Written by a noted Nobel Prize winner, researcher, and teacher, this book seeks to explain the workings of chemistry to the general public, with an emphasis on the beauty of molecular design.

John Allen Paulos, *Innumeracy: Mathematical Illiteracy and Its Consequences.* New York: Vintage Books, 1990.
A delightful account of the statistical misunderstandings of the common citizen. What *illiteracy* is to reading, *innumeracy* is to mathematics.

Royston Roberts, *Serendipity: Accidental Discoveries in Science.* New York: John Wiley & Sons, 1989.
Fascinating stories illustrating how many scientific advances are made by chance discovery when an investigator is keen enough to recognize the significance of the discovery.

Carl Sagan, *The Demon-Haunted World: Science as a Candle in the Dark.* New York: Random House, 1995.
An eloquent account of the present status of society's attitudes toward science and the dangers we face when reason gives way to the myths of pseudoscience, New Age thinking, and fundamentalism.

http://www.chemcenter.org
Maintained by the American Chemical Society, this site is an excellent starting point for searching out such chemistry-related information as current events or the status of a particular avenue of research.

http://www.csicop.org/
Home page for the Committee for the Scientific Investigation of Claims of the Paranormal. This organization of Nobel laureates and other respected scientists takes on the claims of pseudoscience with all the rigor required of any scientific claim.

http://www.rsc.org/lap/rsccom/wcc/wccindex.htm
Home page for the Women Chemists Committee of The Royal Society of Chemistry (UK). This organization promotes the entry and re-entry of women to the profession of chemistry and collects and disseminates information about women in chemistry.

http://www.sciencenews.org/sn_arch
Archives of *ScienceNews*, a widely read weekly magazine covering current developments in science.

Chapter 2
Elements of Chemistry

Understanding Chemistry Through Its Language

As you progress through this chemistry course, you will note an accumulating list of terms. Chapter 1 introduced 27 key terms, and in this chapter you'll find another 32! Why all these new terms? In the laboratory, chemists perform experiments, make many observations, and then draw conclusions. Over time, the result is a growing body of new knowledge that inevitably exceeds the capacity of everyday language. For example, in the language of chemistry we say that there are more than 100 kinds of *atoms* and that any material consisting of a single kind of atom is an *element*. (Some examples of elements are shown in this chapter's opening photograph.) Atoms can link together to form a *molecule*, and a molecule consisting of atoms from different elements is a *compound*. And on and on, one term building on another as we attempt to describe the nature of matter beyond its casual appearance.

Rather than memorizing all the chemistry-related terms in this text, however, you will serve yourself far better by focusing on the underlying concept each term represents. Based on what you learned in Chapter 1, for example, why is it that hot coffee can burn your tongue? One answer might be that hot coffee contains a large amount of molecular kinetic energy. While true, this answer assumes an understanding of the term *kinetic energy* (Section 1.5). A term is only a label, however. It is possible to know the term without understanding the chemistry—just as it is possible to understand the chemistry without knowing the term. If you truly understand the chemistry but forget the term, you may find yourself comparing the energy of molecular motion to that of a speeding bullet. The faster the bullet—in other words, the greater its kinetic energy—the greater its capacity to cause harm. Similarly, the faster the speed of the molecules in the coffee, the greater their capacity to harm your tongue. So, while *kinetic energy* and other chemistry-related terms are useful for communication, they do not guarantee conceptual understanding. If you focus first on the concepts, the language used to describe them will come to you much more easily.

Because this chapter focuses on how chemists describe and classify matter, it lays the foundation for all future chapters. Take special note of the **boldfaced** terms, and be sure to practice articulating and paraphrasing the concepts they represent. Do this by describing these concepts aloud to yourself (or to a friend) without looking at the book. When you are able to express these concepts in your own words, you will have the insight to do well in this course and beyond.

We begin by looking at how chemists describe matter by its physical and chemical properties.

2.1 Matter Has Physical and Chemical Properties

Properties that describe the look or feel of a substance, such as color, hardness, density, texture, and phase, are called **physical properties**. Every substance has its own set of characteristic physical properties that we can use to identify that substance. As Figure 2.1 shows, for example, gold is an opaque, yellowish substance that is a solid at room temperature (25°C) and has a density of 19.3 grams per milliliter; diamond is a transparent substance that is a solid at room temperature and has a density of 3.5 grams per milliliter; and water is a transparent substance that is a liquid at room temperature and has a density of 1.0 gram per milliliter.

Gold
Opacity: opaque
Color: yellowish
Phase at 25°C: solid
Density: 19.3 g/mL

Diamond
Opacity: transparent
Color: colorless
Phase at 25°C: solid
Density: 3.5 g/mL

Water
Opacity: transparent
Color: colorless
Phase at 25°C: liquid
Density: 1.0 g/mL

Figure 2.1
Gold, diamond, and water can be identified by their physical properties. If a substance has all the physical properties listed under gold, for example, it must be gold.

The physical properties of a substance can change when conditions change, but that does not mean a different substance is created. Cooling liquid water to below 0°C causes the water to transform to solid ice, but the substance is still water because it is still H_2O no matter which phase it is in. The only difference is how the H_2O molecules are oriented relative to one another. In the liquid, the water molecules tumble around one another, whereas in the ice they vibrate about fixed positions. The freezing of water is an example of what chemists call a **physical change**. During a physical change, a substance changes its phase or some other physical property but *not* its chemical composition, as Figure 2.2 shows.

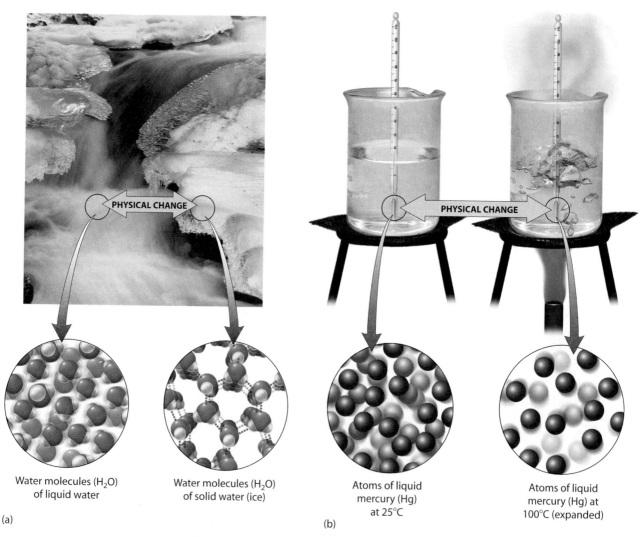

PHYSICAL CHANGE

PHYSICAL CHANGE

Water molecules (H_2O) of liquid water

Water molecules (H_2O) of solid water (ice)

Atoms of liquid mercury (Hg) at 25°C

Atoms of liquid mercury (Hg) at 100°C (expanded)

(a)

(b)

Figure 2.2
Two physical changes. (a) Liquid water and ice might look like different substances, but at the submicroscopic level, it is evident that both consist of water molecules. (b) At 25°C, the atoms in a sample of mercury are a certain distance apart, yielding a density of 13.53 grams per milliliter. At 100°C, the atoms are farther apart, meaning that each milliliter now contains fewer atoms than at 25°C, and the density is now 13.35 grams per milliliter. The physical property we call density has changed with the temperature, but the identity of the substance remains unchanged: mercury is mercury.

Concept Check ✔

The melting of gold is a physical change. Why?

Was this your answer? During a physical change, a substance changes only one or more of its *physical* properties; its *identity* does not change. Because melted gold is still gold but in a different form, this change is a physical change.

Methane
Reacts with oxygen to form carbon dioxide and water, giving off lots of heat during the reaction.

Baking soda
Reacts with vinegar to form carbon dioxide and water, absorbing heat during the reaction.

Copper
Reacts with carbon dioxide and water to form the greenish-blue substance called patina.

Figure 2.3
The chemical properties of substances allow them to transform to new substances. Natural gas and baking soda transform to carbon dioxide, water, and heat. Copper transforms to patina.

Chemical properties are those that characterize the ability of a substance to react with other substances or to transform from one substance to another. Figure 2.3 shows three examples. The methane of natural gas has the chemical property of reacting with oxygen to produce carbon dioxide and water, along with lots of heat energy. Similarly, it is a chemical property of baking soda to react with vinegar to produce carbon dioxide and water while absorbing a small amount of heat energy. Copper has the chemical property of reacting with carbon dioxide and water to form a greenish-blue solid known as patina. Copper statues exposed to the carbon dioxide and water in the air become coated with patina. The patina is not copper, it is not carbon dioxide, and it is not water. It is a new substance formed by the reaction of these chemicals with one another.

All three of these transformations involve a change in the way the atoms in the molecules are *chemically bonded* to one another. (A *chemical bond* is the attraction between two atoms that holds them together in a molecule.) A methane molecule, for example, is made of a single carbon atom bonded to four hydrogen atoms, and an oxygen molecule is made of two oxygen atoms bonded to each other. Figure 2.4 shows the chemical change in which the atoms in a methane molecule and those in two oxygen molecules first pull apart and then form new bonds with different partners, resulting in the formation of molecules of carbon dioxide and water.

Figure 2.4
The chemical change in which molecules of methane and oxygen transform to molecules of carbon dioxide and water as atoms break old bonds and form new ones. The actual mechanism of this transformation is more complicated than depicted here; however, the idea that new materials are formed by the rearrangement of atoms is accurate.

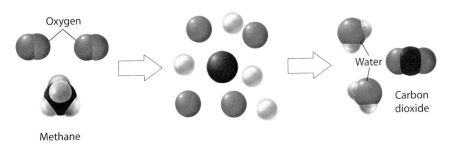

Oxygen

Water

Carbon dioxide

Methane

Any change in a substance that involves a rearrangement of the way atoms are bonded is called a **chemical change**. Thus the transformation of methane to carbon dioxide and water is a chemical change, as are the other two transformations shown in Figure 2.3.

The chemical change shown in Figure 2.5 occurs when an electric current is passed through water. The energy of the current causes the water molecules to split into atoms that then form new chemical bonds to create molecules of hydrogen and oxygen, two substances that are very different from water. The hydrogen and oxygen are both gases at room temperature, and they can be seen as bubbles rising to the surface.

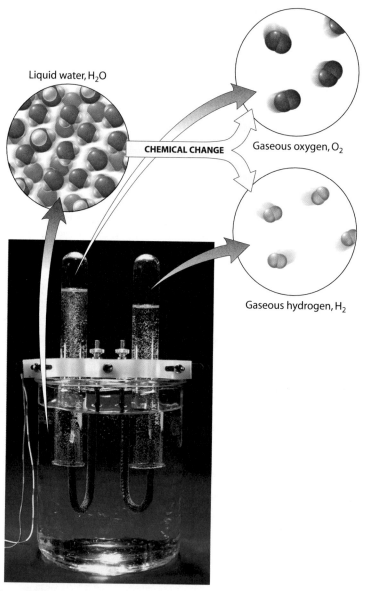

Liquid water, H_2O

CHEMICAL CHANGE

Gaseous oxygen, O_2

Gaseous hydrogen, H_2

Figure 2.5
Water can be transformed to hydrogen gas and oxygen gas by the energy of an electric current. This is a chemical change because new materials (the two gases) are formed as the atoms originally in the water molecules are rearranged.

In the language of chemistry, materials undergoing a chemical change are said to be *reacting*. Methane *reacts* with oxygen to form carbon dioxide and water, and water *reacts* upon exposure to electricity to form hydrogen gas and oxygen gas. Synonymous with the term *chemical change*, therefore, is the term *chemical reaction*. During a **chemical reaction**, new materials are formed by a change in the way atoms are bonded together. We shall explore chemical bonds and the reactions in which they are formed and broken in subsequent chapters.

Concept Check ✓

Each sphere in the following diagrams represents an atom. Joined spheres represent molecules. One set of diagrams shows a physical change, and the other shows a chemical change. Which is which?

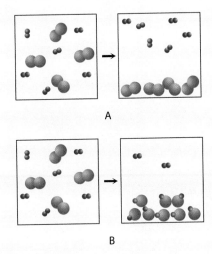

Was this your answer? Remember that a chemical change (also known as a chemical reaction) involves molecules breaking apart so that the atoms are free to form new bonds with new partners. You must be careful to distinguish this breaking apart from a mere change in the relative positions of a group of molecules. In set A, the molecules before and after the change are the same. They differ only in their positions relative to one another. Set A therefore represents a physical change. In set B, new molecules consisting of bonded red and blue spheres appear after the change. These molecules represent a new material, and so B is a chemical change.

Hands-On Chemistry: Fire Water

This activity is for those of you with access to a gas stove. Place a large pot of cool water on top of the stove, and set the burner on high. What product from the combustion of the natural gas do you see condensing on the outside of the pot? Where did it come from? Would more or less of this product form if the pot contained ice water? Where does this product go as the pot gets warmer? What physical and chemical changes can you identify?

Determining Whether a Change Is Physical or Chemical Can Be Difficult

Deciding whether an observed change is physical or chemical can be tricky because in both cases there are changes in physical appearance. Water, for example, looks quite different after it freezes, just as a car looks quite different after it rusts (Figure 2.6). The freezing of water results from a change in how water molecules are oriented relative to one another. This is a physical change because liquid water and frozen water are both forms of water. The rusting of a car, by contrast, is the result of the transformation of iron to rust. This is a chemical change because iron and rust are two different materials, each consisting of a different arrangement of atoms. As we shall see in the next two sections, iron is an *element* and rust is a *compound* consisting of iron and oxygen atoms.

Figure 2.6
The transformation of water to ice and the transformation of iron to rust both involve a change in physical appearance. The formation of ice is a physical change, and the formation of rust is a chemical change.

By studying this chapter, you can expect to learn the difference between a physical change and a chemical change. However, you cannot expect to have a firm handle on how to categorize an observed change as physical or chemical because doing so requires a knowledge of the chemical identity of the materials involved as well as an understanding of how their atoms and molecules behave. This sort of insight builds over many years of study and laboratory experience.

There are, however, two powerful guidelines that can assist you in assessing physical and chemical changes. First, in a physical change, a change in appearance is the result of a new set of conditions imposed on the *same* material. Restoring the original conditions restores the original appearance: frozen water melts upon warming. Second, in a chemical change, a change in appearance is the result of the formation of a *new* material that has its own unique set of physical properties. The more evidence you have suggesting that a different material has been formed, the greater the likelihood that the change is a chemical change. Iron is a material that can be used to build cars. Rust is not. This suggests that the rusting of iron is a chemical change.

Figure 2.7 shows potassium chromate, a material whose color depends on temperature. At room temperature, potassium chromate is a bright canary yellow. At higher temperatures, it is a deep reddish orange. Upon cooling, the canary color returns, suggesting that the change is physical. With a chemical change, reverting to original conditions does not restore the original appearance. Ammonium dichromate, shown in Figure 2.8, is an orange material that when heated explodes into ammonia, water vapor, and green chromium(III) oxide. When the test tube is returned to the original temperature, there is no trace of orange ammonium dichromate. In its place are new substances having completely different physical properties.

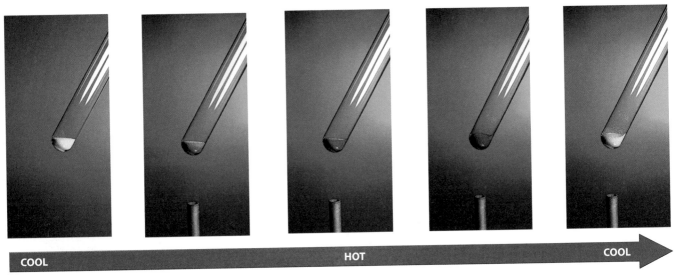

Figure 2.7
Potassium chromate changes color as its temperature changes. This change in color is a physical change. A return to the original temperature restores the original bright yellow color.

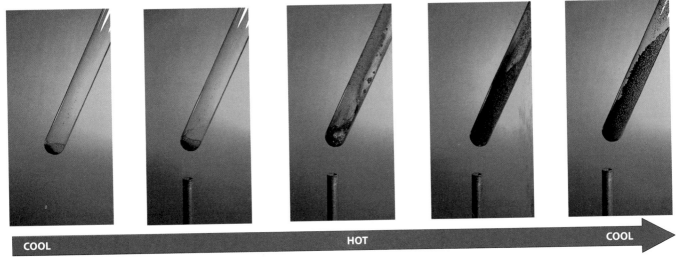

Figure 2.8
When heated, orange ammonium dichromate undergoes a chemical change to ammonia, water vapor, and chromium(III) oxide. A return to the original temperature does not restore the orange color because the ammonium dichromate is no longer there.

Concept Check ✓

Michaela has grown an inch in height over the past year. Is this best described as a physical or a chemical change?

Was this your answer? Are new materials being formed as Michaela grows? Absolutely—created out of the food she eats. Her body is very different from, say, the peanut butter sandwich she ate yesterday. Yet through some very advanced chemistry, her body is able to take the atoms of that peanut butter sandwich and rearrange them into new materials. Biological growth, therefore, is best described as a chemical change.

Atomic symbol
for gold

Au

A gold atom

The element gold

Atomic symbol
for nitrogen

N

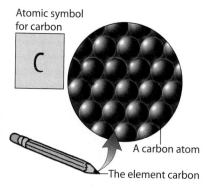

A nitrogen atom in
a nitrogen molecule

The element nitrogen

Atomic symbol
for carbon

C

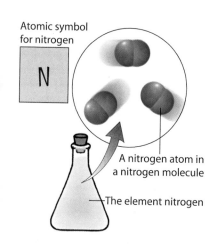

A carbon atom

The element carbon

Figure 2.9
Any element consists of only one kind of atom. Gold consists of only gold atoms, a flask of gaseous nitrogen consists of only nitrogen atoms, and the carbon of a graphite pencil consists of only carbon atoms.

2.2 Atoms Are the Fundamental Components of Elements

You might think that an enormous number of different kinds of atoms must exist to account for the rich variety of substances in the universe, but the number of different atoms is surprisingly small. The great variety of substances results not from a great variety of atoms but from the many ways a few kinds of atoms can be combined. Just as the three colors red, green, and blue can be combined to form any color on a television screen, only a relatively few kinds of atoms combine in different ways to produce all substances. To date, we know of more than 100 distinct types of atoms. Of these, about 90 can be found in nature; the remainder have been created in the laboratory.

Any material consisting of only one type of atom is classified as an **element**, with a few examples shown in Figure 2.9. Pure gold, for instance, is an element because it consists of only gold atoms. Similarly, the element called nitrogen consists solely of nitrogen atoms, and the element carbon solely of carbon atoms. Because we know of more than 100 different types of atoms, we also know of more than 100 different types of elements. All of these elements are listed in an organizing scheme called the **periodic table**, which is shown in Figure 2.10.

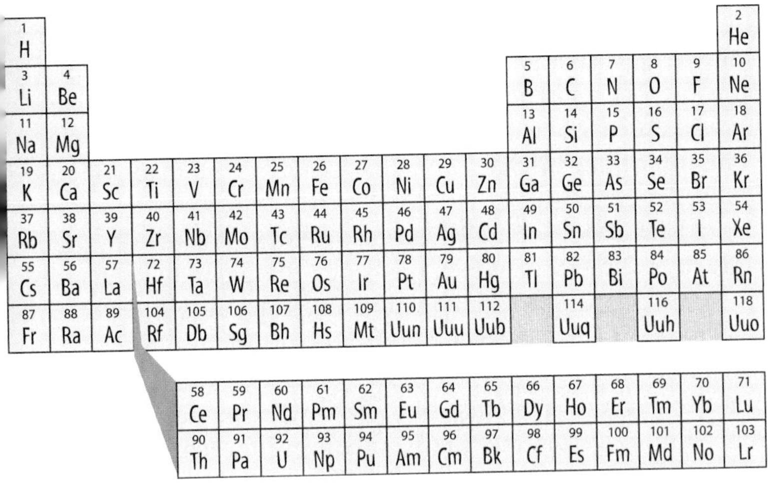

1 H																	2 He
3 Li	4 Be											5 B	6 C	7 N	8 O	9 F	10 Ne
11 Na	12 Mg											13 Al	14 Si	15 P	16 S	17 Cl	18 Ar
19 K	20 Ca	21 Sc	22 Ti	23 V	24 Cr	25 Mn	26 Fe	27 Co	28 Ni	29 Cu	30 Zn	31 Ga	32 Ge	33 As	34 Se	35 Br	36 Kr
37 Rb	38 Sr	39 Y	40 Zr	41 Nb	42 Mo	43 Tc	44 Ru	45 Rh	46 Pd	47 Ag	48 Cd	49 In	50 Sn	51 Sb	52 Te	53 I	54 Xe
55 Cs	56 Ba	57 La	72 Hf	73 Ta	74 W	75 Re	76 Os	77 Ir	78 Pt	79 Au	80 Hg	81 Tl	82 Pb	83 Bi	84 Po	85 At	86 Rn
87 Fr	88 Ra	89 Ac	104 Rf	105 Db	106 Sg	107 Bh	108 Hs	109 Mt	110 Uun	111 Uuu	112 Uub		114 Uuq		116 Uuh		118 Uuo

58 Ce	59 Pr	60 Nd	61 Pm	62 Sm	63 Eu	64 Gd	65 Tb	66 Dy	67 Ho	68 Er	69 Tm	70 Yb	71 Lu
90 Th	91 Pa	92 U	93 Np	94 Pu	95 Am	96 Cm	97 Bk	98 Cf	99 Es	100 Fm	101 Md	102 No	103 Lr

Figure 2.10
The periodic table lists all the known elements.

As you can see in Figure 2.10, each element is designated by its **atomic symbol**, which comes from the letters of the element's name. For example, the atomic symbol for carbon is C, and that for chlorine is Cl. In many cases, the atomic symbol is derived from the element's Latin name. Gold has the atomic symbol Au after its Latin name, *aurum*. Lead has the atomic symbol Pb after its Latin name, *plumbum* (Figure 2.11). Elements having symbols derived from Latin names are usually those discovered earliest.

Note that only the first letter of an atomic symbol is capitalized. The symbol for the element cobalt, for instance, is Co, while CO is a combination of two elements: carbon, C, and oxygen, O.

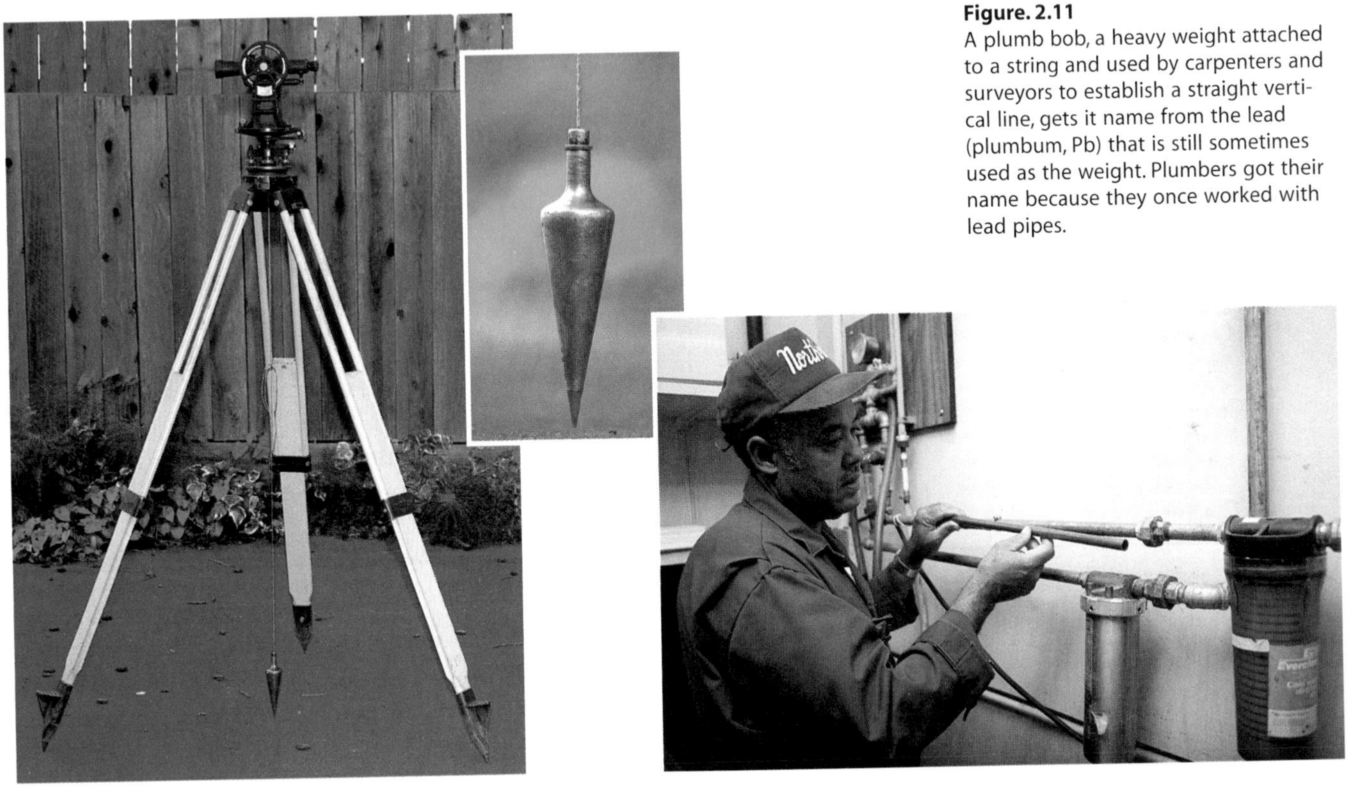

Figure. 2.11
A plumb bob, a heavy weight attached to a string and used by carpenters and surveyors to establish a straight vertical line, gets it name from the lead (plumbum, Pb) that is still sometimes used as the weight. Plumbers got their name because they once worked with lead pipes.

The terms *element* and *atom* are often used in a similar context. You might hear, for example, that gold is an element made of gold atoms. Generally, *element* is used in reference to an entire macroscopic or microscopic sample, and *atom* is used when speaking of the submicroscopic particles in the sample. The important distinction is that elements are made of atoms and not the other way around.

How many atoms are bound together in an element is shown by an **elemental formula**. For elements in which the basic units are individual atoms, the elemental formula is simply the chemical symbol: Au is the elemental formula for gold, and Li is the elemental formula for lithium, to name just two examples. For elements in which the basic units are two or more atoms bonded into molecules, the elemental formula is the chemical symbol followed by a subscript indicating the number of atoms in each molecule. For example, elemental nitrogen, as was shown in Figure 2.9, commonly consists of molecules containing two nitrogen atoms per molecule. Thus N_2 is the usual elemental formula given for nitrogen. Similarly, O_2 is the elemental formula for oxygen, and S_8 is the elemental formula for sulfur.

Concept Check ✓

The oxygen we breathe, O_2, is converted to ozone, O_3, in the presence of an electric spark. Is this a physical or chemical change?

Was this your answer? When atoms regroup, the result is an entirely new substance, and that is what happens here. The oxygen we breathe, O_2, is odorless and life-giving. Ozone, O_3, can be toxic and has a pungent smell commonly associated with electric motors. The conversion of O_2 to O_3 is therefore a chemical change. However, both O_2 and O_3 are elemental forms of oxygen.

Sodium atom
Chlorine atom

Sodium chloride, NaCl

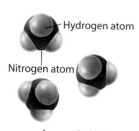

Hydrogen atom

Nitrogen atom

Ammonia, NH_3

Figure 2.12
The compounds sodium chloride and ammonia are represented by their chemical formulas, NaCl and NH_3. A chemical formula shows the ratio of atoms used to make the compound.

2.3 Elements Can Combine to Form Compounds

When atoms of *different* elements bond to one another, they make a **compound**. Sodium atoms and chlorine atoms, for example, bond to make the compound sodium chloride, commonly known as table salt. Nitrogen atoms and hydrogen atoms join to make the compound ammonia, a common household cleaner.

A compound is represented by its **chemical formula**, in which the symbols for the elements are written together. The chemical formula for sodium chloride is NaCl, and that for ammonia is NH_3. Numerical subscripts indicate the ratio in which the atoms combine. By convention, the subscript 1 is understood and omitted. So the chemical formula NaCl tells us that in the compound sodium chloride there is one sodium for every one chlorine, and the chemical formula NH_3 tells us that in the compound ammonia there is one nitrogen atom for every three hydrogen atoms, as Figure 2.12 shows.

Compounds have physical and chemical properties that are different from the properties of their elemental components. The sodium chloride,

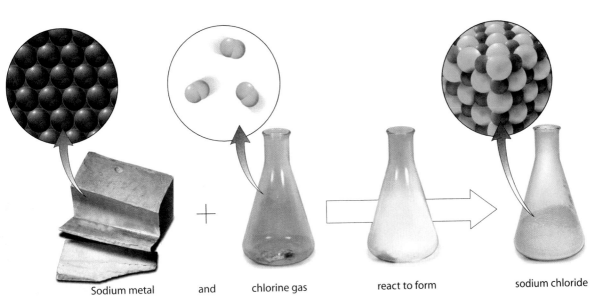

Figure 2.13
The chemical property of sodium metal and chlorine gas react together to form sodium chloride. Although the compound sodium chloride is composed of sodium and chlorine, the physical and chemical properties of sodium chloride are very different from the physical and chemical properties of either sodium metal or chlorine gas.

NaCl, shown in Figure 2.13 is very different from the elemental sodium and elemental chlorine used to form it. Elemental sodium, Na, consists of nothing but sodium atoms, which form a soft, silvery metal that can be cut easily with a knife. Its melting point is 97.5°C, and it reacts violently with water. Elemental chlorine, Cl_2, consists of chlorine molecules. This material, a yellow-green gas at room temperature, is very toxic and was used as a chemical warfare agent during World War I. Its boiling point is -34°C. The compound sodium chloride, NaCl, is a translucent, brittle, colorless crystal having a melting point of 800°C. Sodium chloride does not chemically react with water the way sodium does, and not only is it not toxic to humans the way chlorine is, but the very opposite is true: it is an essential component of all living organisms. Sodium chloride is not sodium, nor is it chlorine; it is uniquely sodium chloride, a tasty chemical when sprinkled lightly over popcorn.

Concept Check ✓

Hydrogen sulfide, H_2S, is one of the smelliest compounds. Rotten eggs get their characteristic bad smell from the hydrogen sulfide they release. Can you infer from this information that elemental sulfur, S_8, is just as smelly?

Was this your answer? No, you cannot. In fact, the odor of elemental sulfur is negligible compared with that of hydrogen sulfide. Compounds are truly different from the elements from which they are formed. Hydrogen sulfide, H_2S, is as different from elemental sulfur, S_8, as water, H_2O, is from elemental oxygen, O_2.

Hands-On Chemistry: Oxygen Bubble Bursts

Compounds can be broken down to their component elements. For example, when you pour a solution of the compound hydrogen peroxide, H_2O_2, over a cut, an enzyme in your blood decomposes it to produce oxygen gas, O_2, as evidenced by the bubbling that takes place. It is this oxygen at high concentrations at the site of injury that kills off microorganisms. A similar enzyme is found in baker's yeast.

What You Need

Packet of baker's yeast; 3% hydrogen peroxide solution; short, wide drinking glass; tweezers; matches

Safety Note

Wear safety glasses, and remove all combustibles, such as paper towels, from the area. Keep your fingers well away from the flame because it will glow brighter as it is exposed to the oxygen.

Procedure

① Pour the yeast into the glass. Add a couple of capfuls of the hydrogen peroxide and watch the oxygen bubbles form.

② Test for the presence of oxygen by holding a lighted match with the tweezers and putting the flame near the bubbles. Look for the flame to glow brighter as the escaping oxygen passes over it.

Describe oxygen's physical and chemical properties.

Compounds Are Named According to the Elements They Contain

A system for naming the countless number of possible compounds has been developed by the International Union for Pure and Applied Chemistry (IUPAC). This system is designed so that a compound's name reflects the elements it contains and how those elements are put together. Anyone familiar with the system, therefore, can deduce the chemical identity of a compound from its *systematic name*.

As you might imagine, this system is very intricate. However, you need not learn all its rules. At this point, there are only three guidelines you should be familiar with. These guidelines alone will not enable you to name every compound, however, they will acquaint you with how the system works for many simple compounds consisting of only two elements.

Guideline 1 The name of the element farther to the left in the periodic table is followed by the name of the element farther to the right, with the suffix *-ide* added to the name of the latter:

NaCl	Sodium chloride	HCl	Hydrogen chloride
Li_2O	Lithium oxide	MgO	Magnesium oxide
CaF_2	Calcium fluoride	Sr_3P_2	Strontium phosphide

Guideline 2 When two or more non-metal compounds have different numbers of the same elements, prefixes are added to remove the ambiguity. The first four prefixes are *mono-* ("one"), *di-* ("two"), *tri-* ("three"), and *tetra-* ("four"). The prefix *mono-*, however, is commonly omitted from the beginning of the first word of the name:

Carbon and oxygen

CO Carbon monoxide
CO_2 Carbon dioxide

Nitrogen and oxygen

NO_2 Nitrogen dioxide
N_2O_4 Dinitrogen tetroxide

Sulfur and oxygen

SO_2 Sulfur dioxide
SO_3 Sulfur trioxide

Guideline 3 Many compounds are not usually referred to by their systematic names. Instead, they are assigned *common names* that are more convenient or have been used traditionally for many years. Some common names we use in *Conceptual Chemistry* are *water* for H_2O, *ammonia* for NH_3, and *methane* for CH_4. Pteroenone, the name of the compound extracted from the sea butterfly referred to in Chapter 1, is a common name. The systematic name for this compound, though more descriptive of the elements it contains, is much longer: 5(S)-methyl-6(R)-hydroxy-7,9-dimethyl-7,9-diene-4-undecanone.

Concept Check ✓

What is the systematic name for NaF?

Was this your answer? This compound is the a cavity-fighting substance added to some toothpastes—sodium fluoride.

2.4 Most Materials Are Mixtures

A **mixture** is a combination of two or more substances in which each substance retains its properties. Most materials we encounter are mixtures: mixtures of elements, mixtures of compounds, or mixtures of elements and compounds. Stainless steel, for example, is a mixture of the elements iron, chromium, nickel, and carbon. Seltzer water is a mixture of the liquid compound water and the gaseous compound carbon dioxide. Our atmosphere, as Figure 2.14 illustrates, is a mixture of the elements nitrogen, oxygen, and argon plus small amounts of such compounds as carbon dioxide and water vapor.

Figure 2.14
The Earth's atmosphere is a mixture of gaseous elements and compounds. Some of them are shown here.

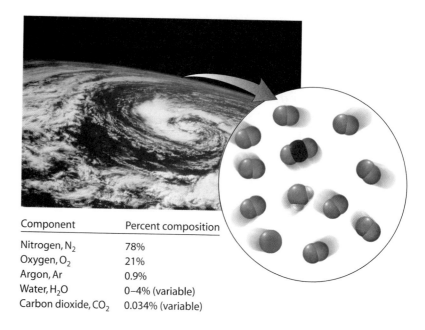

Component	Percent composition
Nitrogen, N_2	78%
Oxygen, O_2	21%
Argon, Ar	0.9%
Water, H_2O	0–4% (variable)
Carbon dioxide, CO_2	0.034% (variable)

Figure 2.15
Tap water provides us with water as well as a large number of other compounds, many of which are flavorful and healthful. Bottoms up!

Tap water is a mixture containing mostly water but also many other compounds. Depending on your location, your water may include compounds of calcium, magnesium, fluorine, iron, and potassium; chlorine disinfectants; trace amounts of compounds of lead, mercury, and cadmium; organic compounds; and dissolved oxygen, nitrogen, and carbon dioxide. While it is surely important to minimize any toxic components in your drinking water, it is unnecessary, undesirable, and impossible to remove all other substances from it. Some of the dissolved solids and gases give water its characteristic taste, and many of them promote human health: fluoride compounds protect teeth, chlorine destroys harmful bacteria, and as much as 10 percent of our daily requirement for iron, potassium, calcium, and magnesium is obtained from drinking water (Figures 2.15 and 2.16).

Figure 2.16
Most of the oxygen in the air bubbles produced by an aquarium aerator escapes into the atmosphere. Some of the oxygen, however, mixes with the water. It is this oxygen the fish depend on to survive. Without this dissolved oxygen, which they extract with their gills, the fish would promptly drown. So fish don't "breathe" water. They breathe the oxygen, O_2, dissolved in the water.

Concept Check ✓

So far, you have learned about three kinds of matter: elements, compounds, and mixtures. Which box below contains only an element? Which contains only a compound? Which contains a mixture?

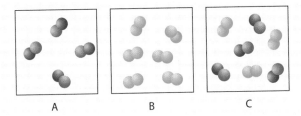

A   B   C

Was this your answer? The molecules in box A each contain two different types of atoms and so are representative of a compound. The molecules in box B each consist of the same atoms and so are representative of an element. Box C is a mixture of the compound and the element.

Note how the molecules of the compound and those of the element remain intact in the mixture. That is, upon the formation of the mixture, there is no exchange of atoms between the components.

There is a difference between the way substances—either elements or compounds—combine to form mixtures and the way elements combine to form compounds. Each substance in a mixture retains its chemical identity. The sugar molecules in the teaspoon of sugar in Figure 2.17, for example, are identical to the sugar molecules already in the tea. The only difference is that the sugar molecules in the tea are mixed with other substances, mostly water. The formation of a mixture, therefore, is a physical change. As was discussed in Section 2.3, when elements join to form compounds, there is a change in chemical identity. Sodium chloride is not a mixture of sodium and chlorine atoms. Instead, sodium chloride is a compound, which means it is entirely different from the elements used to make it. The formation of a compound is therefore a chemical change.

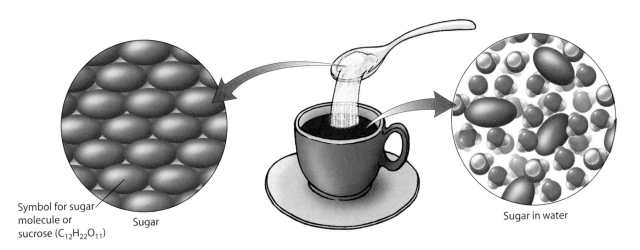

Symbol for sugar molecule or sucrose ($C_{12}H_{22}O_{11}$)   Sugar   Sugar in water

Figure 2.17
Table sugar is a compound consisting of only sugar molecules. Once these molecules are mixed into hot tea, they become interspersed among the water and tea molecules and form a sugar–tea–water mixture. No new compounds are formed, and so this is an example of a physical change.

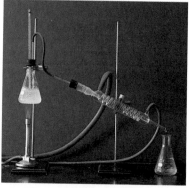

(a)

(b)

Figure 2.18
(a) A simple distillation setup used to separate one component—water— from the mixture we call seawater. The seawater is boiled in the flask on the left. The rising water vapor is channeled into a downward-slanting tube kept cool by cold water flowing across its outer surface. The water vapor inside the cool tube condenses and collects in the flask on the right. (b) A whiskey still works on the same principle. A mixture containing alcohol is heated to the point where the alcohol, some flavoring molecules, and some water are vaporized. These vapors travel through the copper coils, where they condense to a liquid ready for collection.

Mixtures Can Be Separated by Physical Means

The components of mixtures can be separated from one another by taking advantage of differences in the components' physical properties. A mixture of solids and liquids, for example, can be separated using filter paper through which the liquids pass but the solids do not. This is how coffee is often made: the caffeine and flavor molecules in the hot water pass through the filter and into the coffee pot while the solid coffee grinds remain behind. This method of separating a solid–liquid mixture is called *filtration* and is a common technique used by chemists.

Mixtures can also be separated by taking advantage of a difference in boiling or melting points. Seawater is a mixture of water and a variety of compounds, mostly sodium chloride. Whereas pure water boils at 100°C, sodium chloride doesn't even *melt* until 800°C. One way to separate pure water from the mixture we call seawater therefore, is to heat the seawater to about 100°C. At this temperature, the liquid water readily transforms to water vapor but the sodium chloride stays behind dissolved in the remaining water. As the water vapor rises, it can be channeled into a cooler container, where it condenses to a liquid without the dissolved solids. This process of collecting a vaporized substance, called *distillation*, is illustrated in Figure 2.18. After all the water has been distilled from seawater, what remains are dry solids. These solids, also a mixture of compounds, contain a variety of valuable materials, including sodium chloride, potassium bromide, and a small amount of gold! (For details on why this gold is not recoverable, see Section 19.3.) Further separation of the components of this mixture is of significant commercial interest (Figure 2.19).

Figure 2.19
At the southern end of San Francisco Bay are areas where the seawater has been partitioned off. These are evaporation ponds where the water is allowed to evaporate, leaving behind the solids that were dissolved in the seawater. These solids are further refined for commercial sale. The remarkable color of the ponds results from suspended particles of iron oxide and other minerals, which are easily removed during refining.

Hands-On Chemistry: Bottoms Up and Bubbles Out

What's in a glass of water? Separate the components of your tap water to find out.

What You Need

Tap water, sparkling clean cooking pot, stove, knife

Safety Note

Wear safety glasses for step 1 because some splattering may occur.

Procedure

① Put on your safety glasses and add the tap water to the cooking pot. Boil the water to dryness. (Turn off the burner before the water is all gone. The heat from the pot will finish the evaporation.)

② Examine the resulting residue by scraping it with the knife. These are the solids you ingest with every glass of water you drink.

③ To see the gases dissolved in your water, fill a clean cooking pot with water and let it stand at room temperature for several hours. Note the bubbles that adhere to the inner sides of the pot.

Where did the bubbles of step 3 come from? What do you suppose they contain?

2.5 Chemists Classify Matter as Pure or Impure

If a material is **pure**, it consists of only a single element or a single compound. In pure gold, for example, there is nothing but the element gold. In pure table salt, there is nothing but the compound sodium chloride. If a material is **impure**, it is a mixture and contains two or more elements or compounds. This classification scheme is shown in Figure 2.20.

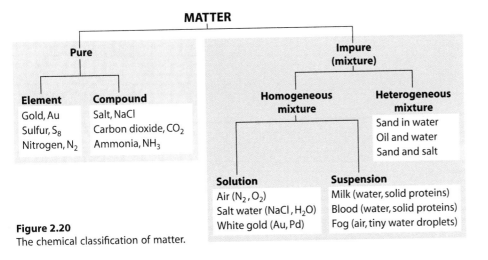

Figure 2.20
The chemical classification of matter.

The smallness of atoms and molecules makes it impractical to prepare a sample that is truly pure—that is, truly 100 percent of a single material. For example, if just one atom or molecule out of a trillion trillion were different, then the 100 percent pure status would be lost. Samples can be "purified" by various methods, however, such as distillations and *pure* is understood to be a relative term. Comparing the purity of two samples, the purer one contains fewer impurities. A sample of water that is 99.9 percent pure has a greater proportion of impurities than does a sample of water that is 99.9999 percent pure.

Sometimes naturally occurring mixtures are labeled as being pure, as in "pure orange juice." Such a statement merely means that nothing artificial has been added. According to a chemist's definition, however, orange juice is anything but pure, as it contains a wide variety of materials, including water, pulp, flavorings, vitamins, and sugars.

Mixtures may be heterogeneous or homogeneous. In a **heterogeneous mixture**, the different components can be seen as individual substances, such as pulp in orange juice, sand in water, or oil globules dispersed in vinegar. The different components are visible. **Homogeneous mixtures** have the same composition throughout. Any one region of the mixture has the same ratio of substances as does any other region, and the components cannot be seen as individual identifiable entities. The distinction is shown in Figure 2.21.

Granite   "Snow" in snow globe   Pizza

(a) Heterogeneous mixtures

Air   Clear seawater   White gold

(b) Homogeneous mixtures

Figure 2.21
(a) In heterogeneous mixtures, the different components can be seen with the naked eye.
(b) In homogeneous mixtures, the different components are mixed at a much finer level and so are not readily distinguished.

A homogeneous mixture may be either a solution or a suspension. In a **solution**, all components are in the same phase. The atmosphere we breathe is a gaseous solution consisting of the gaseous elements nitrogen and oxygen as well as minor amounts of other gaseous materials. Salt water is a liquid solution because both the water and the dissolved sodium chloride are found in a single liquid phase. An example of a solid solution is white gold, which is a homogeneous mixture of the elements gold and palladium. We shall be discussing solutions in more detail in Chapter 7.

A **suspension** is a homogeneous mixture in which the different components are in different phases, such as solids in liquids or liquids in gases. In a suspension, the mixing is so thorough that the different phases cannot be readily distinguished. Milk is a suspension because it is a homogeneous mixture of proteins and fats finely dispersed in water. Blood is a suspension composed of finely dispersed blood cells in water. Another example of a suspension is clouds, which are homogeneous mixtures of tiny water droplets suspended in air. Shining a light through a suspension, as is done in Figure 2.22, results in a visible cone as the light is reflected by the suspended components.

The easiest way to distinguish a suspension from a solution in the laboratory is to spin a sample in a centrifuge. This device, spinning at thousands of revolutions per minute, separates the components of suspensions but not those of solutions, as Figure 2.23 shows.

Figure 2.22
The path of light becomes visible when the light passes through a suspension.

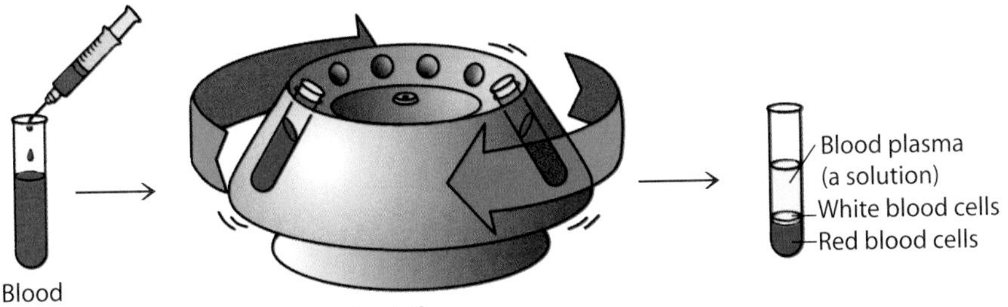

Blood
(a suspension)   Centrifuge

Blood plasma
(a solution)
White blood cells
Red blood cells

Figure 2.23
Blood, because it is a suspension, can be centrifuged into its components, which include the blood plasma (a yellowish solution) and white and red blood cells. The components of the plasma cannot be separated from one another here because a centrifuge has no affect on solutions.

Concept Check ✔

Impure water can be purified by
- a. removing the impure water molecules.
- b. removing everything that is not water.
- c. breaking down the water to its simplest components.
- d. adding some disinfectant such as chlorine.

Was this your answer? Water, H_2O, is a compound made of the elements hydrogen and oxygen in a 2-to-1 ratio. Every H_2O molecule is exactly the same as every other, and there's no such thing as an impure H_2O molecule. Just about anything, including you, beach balls, rubber ducks, dust particles, and bacteria, can be found in water. When something other than water is found in water, we say that the water is impure. It is important to see that the impurities are *in* the water and not part *of* the water, which means that it is possible to remove them by a variety of physical means, such as filtration or distillation. The answer to this Concept Check is b.

Please put to rest any fear you may have about needing to memorize the periodic table, or even parts of it—better to focus on the many great concepts behind its organization.

2.6 Elements Are Organized in the Periodic Table by Their Properties

As was mentioned in Section 2.2, the periodic table is a listing of all the known elements. There is so much more to this table, however. Most notably, the elements are organized in the table based on their physical and chemical properties. One of the most apparent examples is how the elements are grouped as metals, nonmetals, and metalloids.

As shown in Figure 2.24, most of the known elements are **metals**, which are defined as those elements that are shiny, opaque, and good conductors of electricity and heat. Metals are *malleable*, which means they can be hammered into different shapes or bent without breaking. They are also *ductile*, which means they can be drawn into wires. All but a few metals are solid at room temperature. The exceptions include mercury, Hg; gallium, Ga; cesium, Cs; and francium, Fr; which are all liquids at a warm room temperature of 30°C (86°F). Another interesting exception is hydrogen, H,

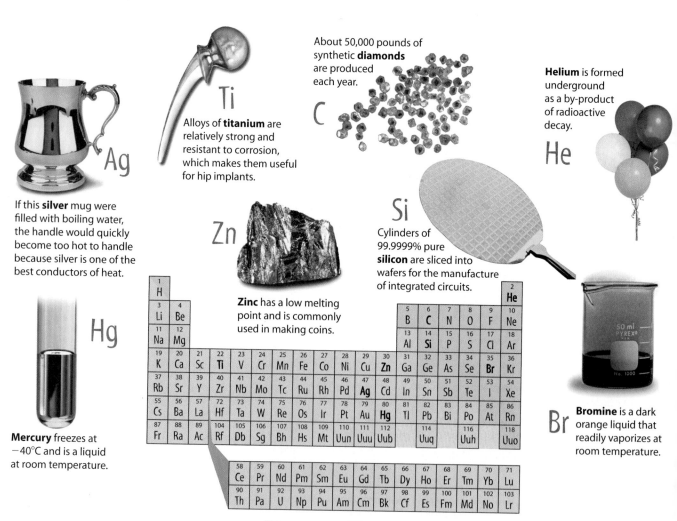

About 50,000 pounds of synthetic **diamonds** are produced each year.

Ti
Alloys of **titanium** are relatively strong and resistant to corrosion, which makes them useful for hip implants.

Helium is formed underground as a by-product of radioactive decay.

He

Ag
If this **silver** mug were filled with boiling water, the handle would quickly become too hot to handle because silver is one of the best conductors of heat.

Zn
Zinc has a low melting point and is commonly used in making coins.

Si
Cylinders of 99.9999% pure **silicon** are sliced into wafers for the manufacture of integrated circuits.

Hg

Mercury freezes at −40°C and is a liquid at room temperature.

Br **Bromine** is a dark orange liquid that readily vaporizes at room temperature.

Metal   Metalloid   Nonmetal

Figure 2.24
The periodic table color-coded to show metals, nonmetals, and metalloids.

Figure 2.25
Geoplanetary models suggest that hydrogen exists as a liquid metal deep beneath the surfaces of Jupiter (shown here) and Saturn. These planets are composed mostly of hydrogen. Inside them, the pressure exceeds 3 million times the Earth's atmospheric pressure. At this tremendously high pressure, hydrogen is pressed to a liquid-metal phase. Back here on the Earth at our relatively low atmospheric pressure, hydrogen exists as a nonmetallic gas of hydrogen molecules, H_2.

which takes on the properties of a liquid metal only at very high pressures (Figure 2.25). Under normal conditions, hydrogen atoms combine to form hydrogen molecules, H_2, which behave as a nonmetallic gas.

The nonmetallic elements, with the exception of hydrogen, are on the right of the periodic table. **Nonmetals** are very poor conductors of electricity and heat, and may also be transparent. Solid nonmetals are neither malleable nor ductile. Rather, they are brittle and shatter when hammered. At 30°C (86°F), some nonmetals are solid (carbon, C), others are liquid (bromine, Br), and still others are gaseous (helium, He).

Six elements are classified as **metalloids**: boron, B; silicon, Si; germanium, Ge; arsenic, As; tin, Sn; and antimony, Sb. Situated between the metals and the nonmetals in the periodic table, the metalloids have both metallic and nonmetallic characteristics. For example, these elements are weak conductors of electricity, which makes them useful as semiconductors in the integrated circuits of computers. Note from the periodic table how germanium, Ge (number 32), is closer to the metals than to the nonmetals. Because of this positioning, we can deduce that germanium has more metallic properties than silicon, Si (number 14), and is a slightly better conductor of electricity. So we find that integrated circuits fabricated with germanium operate faster than those fabricated with silicon. Because silicon is much more abundant and less expensive to obtain, however, silicon computer chips remain the industry standard.

A Period Is a Horizontal Row, a Group a Vertical Column

Two other important ways in which the elements are organized in the periodic table are by horizontal rows and vertical columns. Each horizontal row is called a **period**, and each vertical column is called a **group**

Figure 2.26
The 7 periods (horizontal rows) and 18 groups (vertical columns) of the periodic table. Note that not all periods contain the same number of elements. Also note that, for reasons explained later, the sixth and seventh periods each include a subset of elements, which are listed apart from the main body.

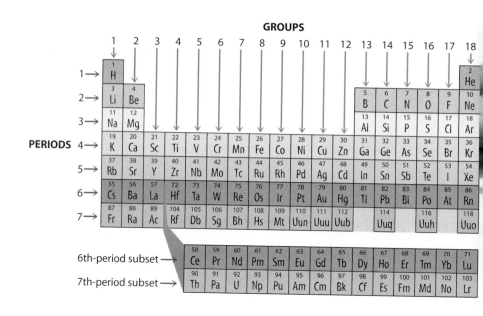

Figure 2.27
The size of atoms gradually decreases in moving from left to right across any period. Atomic size is a periodic (repeating) property.

(or sometimes a *family*). As shown in Figure 2.26, there are 7 periods and 18 groups.

Across any period, the properties of elements gradually change. This gradual change is called a **periodic trend**. As is shown in Figure 2.27, one periodic trend is that atomic size tends to decrease as you move from left to right across any period. Note that the trend repeats from one horizontal row to the next. This phenomenon of repeating trends is called *periodicity*, a term used to indicate that the trends recur in cycles. Each horizontal row is called a *period* because it corresponds to one full cycle of a trend. As we explore in further detail in Section 5.8, there are many other properties of elements that change gradually in moving from left to right across the periodic table.

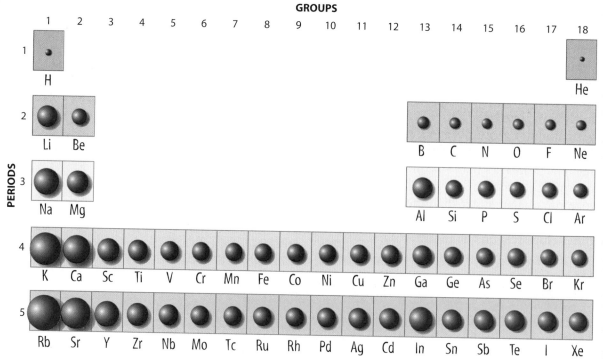

Concept Check ✓

Which are larger: atoms of cesium, Cs (number 55), or atoms of radon, Rn (number 86)?

Was this your answer? Perhaps you tried looking to Figure 2.27 to answer this question and quickly became frustrated because the 6th period elements are not shown. Well, relax. Look at the trends and you'll see that all atoms to the left are larger than those to the right. Accordingly, cesium is positioned at the far left of period 6, and so you can reasonably predict that its atoms are larger than those of radon, which is positioned at the far right of period 6. The periodic table is a road map to understanding the elements.

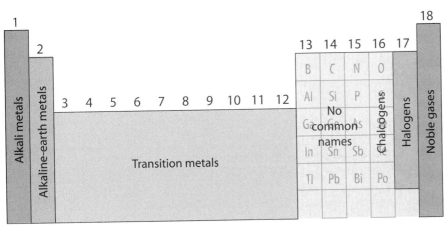

Figure 2.28
The common names for various groups of elements.

Down any group (vertical column), the properties of elements tend to be remarkably similar, which is why these elements are said to be "grouped" or "in a family." As Figure 2.28 shows, several groups have traditional names that describe the properties of their elements. Early in human history, people discovered that ashes mixed with water produce a slippery solution useful for removing grease. By the Middle Ages, such mixtures were described as being *alkaline*, a term derived from the Arabic word for ashes, *al-qali*. Alkaline mixtures found many uses, particularly in the preparation of soaps (Figure 2.29). We now know that alkaline ashes contain compounds of group 1 elements, most notably potassium carbonate, also known as *potash*. Because of this history, group 1 elements, which are metals, are called the **alkali metals**.

Elements of group 2 also form alkaline solutions when mixed with water. Furthermore, medieval alchemists noted that certain minerals (which we now know are made up of group 2 elements) do not melt or change when put in fire. These fire-resistant substances were known to the alchemists as "earth." As a holdover from these ancient times, group 2 elements are known as the **alkaline-earth metals**.

Over toward the right side of the periodic table elements of group 16 are known as the *chalcogens* ("ore-forming" in Greek) because the top two elements of this group, oxygen and sulfur, are so commonly found in ores. Elements of group 17 are known as the **halogens** ("salt-forming" in Greek) because of their tendency to form various salts. Interestingly, a small

Figure 2.29
Ashes and water make a slippery alkaline solution once used to clean hands.

amount of the halogen's iodine or bromine inside a lamp allows the tungsten filament of the lamp to glow brighter without burning out so quickly. Such lamps are commonly referred to as halogen lamps. Group 18 elements are all unreactive gases that tend not to combine with other elements. For this reason, they are called the **noble gases**, presumably because the nobility of earlier times were above interacting with common folk.

The elements of groups 3 through 12 are all metals that do not form alkaline solutions with water. These metals tend to be harder than the alkali metals and less reactive with water; hence they are used for structural purposes. Collectively they are known as the **transition metals**, a name that denotes their central position in the periodic table. The transition metals include some of the most familiar and important elements. They are iron, Fe; copper, Cu; nickel, Ni; chromium, Cr; silver, Ag; and gold, Au. They also include many lesser-known elements that are nonetheless important in modern technology. Persons with hip implants appreciate the transition metals titanium, Ti; molybdenum, Mo; and manganese, Mn, because these noncorrosive metals are used in implant devices.

Concept Check ✓

The elements copper, Cu; silver, Ag; and gold, Au, are three of the few metals that can be found naturally in their elemental state. These three metals have found great use as currency and jewelry for a number of reasons, including their resistance to corrosion and their remarkable colors. How is the fact that these metals have similar properties reflected in the periodic table?

Was this your answer? Copper (number 29), silver (number 47), and gold (number 79) are all in the same group in the periodic table (group 11), which suggests they should have similar—though not identical—physical and chemical properties.

In the sixth period is a subset of 14 metallic elements (numbers 58 to 71) that are quite unlike any of the other transition metals. A similar subset (numbers 90 to 103) is found in the seventh period. These two subsets are the **inner transition metals**. Inserting the inner transition metals into the main body of the periodic table as in Figure 2.30 results in a long and cumbersome table. So that the table can fit nicely on a standard paper size, these elements are commonly placed below the main body of the table, as shown in Figure 2.31.

Figure 2.30
Inserting the inner transition metals between atomic groups 3 and 4 results in a periodic table that is not easy to fit on a standard sheet of paper.

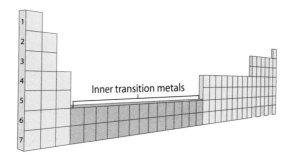

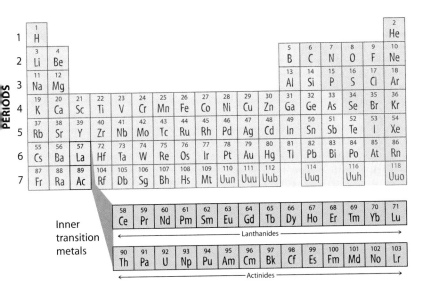

Figure 2.31
The typical display of the inner transition metals. The count of elements in the sixth period goes from lanthanum (La, 57) to cerium (Ce, 58) on through to lutetium (Lu, 71) and then back to hafnium (Hf, 72). A similar jump is made in the seventh period.

The sixth-period inner transition metals are called the **lanthanides** because they fall after lanthanum, La. Because of their similar physical and chemical properties, they tend to occur mixed together in the same locations in the Earth. Also because of their similarities, lanthanides are unusually difficult to purify. Recently, the commercial use of lanthanides has increased. Several lanthanide elements, for example, are used in the fabrication of the light-emitting diodes (LEDs) of laptop computer monitors.

The seventh-period inner transition metals are called the **actinides** because they fall after actinium, Ac. They, too, all have similar properties and hence are not easily purified. The nuclear power industry faces this obstacle because it requires purified samples of two of the most publicized actinides: uranium, U, and plutonium, Pu. Actinides heavier than uranium are not found in nature but are synthesized in the laboratory.

In this chapter we explored many of the rudiments of chemistry, including how matter is described by its physical and chemical properties and denoted by elemental and chemical formulas. We saw how compounds are different from the elements from which they are formed and how mixtures can be separated by taking advantage of differences in the physical properties of the components. Also addressed was what a chemist means by "pure" and how matter can be classified as element, compound, or mixture. Lastly, we saw how elements are organized in the periodic table by their physical and chemical properties. Along the way, you were introduced to some of the most important key terms of chemistry. With an understanding of these fundamental concepts and of the language used to describe them, you are well equipped to continue your study of nature's submicroscopic realm.

Key Terms and Matching Definitions

_____ actinide
_____ alkali metal
_____ alkaline-earth metal
_____ atomic symbol
_____ chemical change
_____ chemical formula
_____ chemical property
_____ chemical reaction
_____ compound
_____ element
_____ elemental formula
_____ group
_____ halogen
_____ heterogeneous mixture
_____ homogeneous mixture
_____ impure
_____ inner transition metal
_____ lanthanide
_____ metal
_____ metalloid
_____ mixture
_____ noble gas
_____ nonmetal
_____ period
_____ periodic table
_____ periodic trend
_____ physical change
_____ physical property
_____ pure
_____ solution
_____ suspension
_____ transition metal

1. Any physical attribute of a substance, such as color, density, or hardness.
2. A change in which a substance changes its physical properties without changing its chemical identity.
3. A type of property that characterizes the ability of a substance to change its chemical identity.
4. During this kind of change, atoms in a substance are rearranged to give a new substance having a new chemical identity.
5. Synonymous with chemical change.
6. A fundamental material consisting of only one type of atom.

7. A chart in which all known elements are organized by physical and chemical properties.
8. An abbreviation for an element or atom.
9. A notation that uses the atomic symbol and (sometimes) a numerical subscript to denote how atoms are bonded in an element.
10. A material in which atoms of different elements are bonded to one another.
11. A notation used to indicate the composition of a compound, consisting of the atomic symbols for the different elements of the compound and numerical subscripts indicating the ratio in which the atoms combine.
12. A combination of two or more substances in which each substance retains its properties.
13. The state of a material that consists of a single element or compound.
14. The state of a material that is a mixture of more than one element or compound.
15. A mixture in which the various components can be seen as individual substances.
16. A mixture in which the components are so finely mixed that the composition is the same throughout.
17. A homogeneous mixture in which all components are in the same phase.
18. A homogeneous mixture in which the various components are in different phases.
19. An element that is shiny, opaque, and able to conduct electricity and heat.
20. An element located toward the upper right of the periodic table and is neither a metal nor a metalloid.
21. An element that exhibits some properties of metals and some properties of nonmetals.
22. A horizontal row in the periodic table.
23. A vertical column in the periodic table, also known as a family of elements.
24. The gradual change of any property in the elements across a period.
25. Any group 1 element.
26. Any group 2 element.
27. Any "salt-forming" element.
28. Any unreactive element.
29. Any element of groups 3 through 12.
30. Any element in the two subgroups of the transition metals.
31. Any sixth-period inner transition metal.
32. Any seventh-period inner transition metal.

Review Questions

Matter Has Physical and Chemical Properties

1. What is a physical property?

2. What is a chemical property?

3. What doesn't change during a physical change?

4. Why is it sometimes difficult to decide whether an observed change is physical or chemical?

5. What are some of the clues that help us determine whether an observed change is physical or chemical?

Atoms Are the Fundamental Components of Elements

6. How many types of atoms can you expect to find in a sample of any element?

7. Distinguish between an atom and an element.

8. How many atoms are in a sulfur molecule that has the elemental formula S_8?

Elements Can Combine to Form Compounds

9. What is the difference between an element and a compound?

10. How many atoms are there in one molecule of H_3PO_4? How many atoms of each element are there in one molecule of H_3PO_4?

11. Are the physical and chemical properties of a compound necessarily similar to those of the elements from which it is composed?

12. What is the IUPAC systematic name for the compound KF?

13. What is the chemical formula for the compound titanium dioxide?

14. Why are common names often used for chemical compounds instead of systematic names?

Most Materials Are Mixtures

15. What defines a material as being a mixture?

16. How can the components of a mixture be separated from one another?

17. How does distillation separate the components of a mixture?

18. What is the phase of oxygen, O_2, at 80 K ($-193°C$)? What is the phase of nitrogen, N_2, at this temperature?

Chemists Classify Matter as Pure or Impure

19. Why is it not practical to have a macroscopic sample that is 100 percent pure?

20. Classify the following as (a) homogeneous mixture, (b) heterogeneous mixture, (c) element, or (d) compound:

    milk _____   steel _____

    ocean water _____   blood _____

    sodium _____   planet Earth _____

21. How is a solution different from a suspension?

22. How can a solution be distinguished from a suspension?

Elements Are Organized in the Periodic Table by Their Properties

23. How is the periodic table more than just a listing of the known elements?

24. Are most elements metallic or nonmetallic?

25. Why is hydrogen, H, most often considered a nonmetallic element?

26. How do the physical properties of nonmetals differ from the physical properties of metals?

27. Where are metalloids located in the periodic table?

28. How many periods are there in the periodic table? How many groups?

29. What happens to the properties of elements across any period of the periodic table?

30. Why are group 1 elements called alkali metals?

31. Why are group 17 elements called halogens?

32. Which group of elements are all gases at room temperature?

33. Why are the inner transition metals not listed in the main body of the periodic table?

34. Why is it difficult to purify an inner transition metal?

Hands-On Chemistry Insights

Fire Water

As you can see in Figure 2.4, the two primary products when natural gas burns are carbon dioxide and water. Because of the heat generated by the burning, the water is released as water vapor. When it comes into contact with the relatively cool sides of the pot, this water vapor condenses to the liquid phase and is seen as "sweat." If the pot contained ice water, more vapor would condense, enough to form drops that roll off the bottom edge. As the pot gets warmer, this liquid water is heated and returns to the gaseous phase.

The only chemical change is the conversion of natural gas to carbon dioxide and water vapor. There are two physical changes—condensation of the water vapor created in the methane combustion and evaporation of this water once the pot gets sufficiently hot. (Of course, the evaporation of the water in the pot is another physical change.)

Oxygen Bubble Bursts

Hydrogen peroxide, H_2O_2, is a relatively unstable compound. In solution with water, it slowly decomposes, producing oxygen gas. In describing oxygen's physical properties, you should have noted that it is an invisible gas having no odor detectable over that of the yeast. Oxygen is light enough to rise out of the glass once it is released from the bubbles. What is your evidence of this? A chemical property of oxygen is that it intensifies burning.

Bottoms Up and Bubbles Out

It would be humorous to scrape the residue from your boiled-down drinking water into sealable containers labeled as drinking water from your particular region, such as "Rocky Mountain Drinking Water." Think of the potential market. You could ship these containers to customers around the world, and because the containers are not weighted down with water, shipping costs would be very low. Of course, each bottle would have to come with the instruction: "Just add distilled water." Would you or would you

not want to push it by adding the word *Pure* to your label? With your classmates, discuss the science and ethics of such a venture.

As we explore in Chapter 7, gases do not dissolve well in hot liquids. Air that is dissolved in room-temperature water, for example, will bubble out when the water is heated. Thus you can speed up step 3 by using warm water.

For further experimentation, perform step 3 in two pots side by side. In one pot, use warm water from the kitchen faucet. In the second pot, use boiled water that has cooled down to the same temperature. You'll find that boiling *deaerates* the water, that is, removes the atmospheric gases. Chemists sometimes need to use deaerated water, which is made by allowing boiled water to cool in a sealed container. Why don't fish live very long in deaerated water?

Exercises

1. Each night you measure your height just before going to bed. When you arise each morning, you measure your height again and consistently find that you are 1 inch taller than you were the night before but only as tall as you were 24 hours ago! Is what happens to your body in this instance best described as a physical change or a chemical change? Be sure to try this activity if you haven't already.

2. Classify the following changes as physical or chemical. Even if you are incorrect in your assessment, you should be able to defend why you chose as you did.
   a. grape juice turns to wine   _____
   b. wood burns to ashes   _____
   c. water begins to boil   _____
   d. a broken leg mends itself   _____
   e. grass grows   _____
   f. an infant gains 10 pounds   _____
   g. a rock is crushed to powder   _____

3. Is the following transformation representative of a physical change or a chemical change?

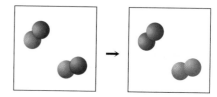

4. Each sphere in the diagrams below represents an atom. Joined circles represent molecules. Which box represents the lower temperature?

A   B

5. Based on the information given in the following diagrams, which substance has the higher boiling point,  or  ?

A   B

6. What physical and chemical changes occur when a wax candle burns?

7. Which elements are some of the oldest known? What is your evidence?

8. Oxygen atoms are used to make water molecules. Does this mean that oxygen, O_2, and water, H_2O, have similar properties? Why do we drown when we breathe in water despite all the oxygen atoms present in this material?

9. A sample of water that is 99.9999 percent pure contains 0.0001 percent impurities. Consider from Chapter 1 that a glass of water contains on the order of a trillion trillion (1×10^{24}) molecules. If 0.0001 percent of these molecules were the molecules of some impurity, about how many impurity molecules would this be?
   a. 1,000 (one thousand: 1×10^3)
   b. 1,000,000 (one million: 1×10^6)
   c. 1,000,000,000 (one billion: 1×10^9)
   d. 1,000,000,000,000,000,000 (one million trillion: 1×10^{18})

   How does your answer make you feel about drinking water that is 99.9999 percent free of some poison, such as a pesticide? (See Appendix C for a discussion of scientific notation.)

10. Read carefully: Twice as much as one million trillion is two million trillion. One thousand times as much is 1,000 million trillion. One million times as much is 1,000,000 million trillion, which is the same as one trillion trillion. Thus, one trillion trillion is one million times greater than a million trillion. Got that? So how many more water molecules than impurity molecules are there in a glass of water that is 99.9999 percent pure?

11. Someone argues that he or she doesn't drink tap water because it contains thousands of molecules of some impurity in each glass. How would you respond in defense of the water's purity, if it indeed does contain thousands of molecules of some impurity per glass?

12. Explain what chicken noodle soup and garden soil have in common without using the phrase *heterogeneous mixture*.

13. Classify the following as element, compound, or mixture, and justify your classifications: salt, stainless steel, tap water, sugar, vanilla extract, butter, maple syrup, aluminum, ice, milk, cherry-flavored cough drops.

14. If you eat metallic sodium or inhale chlorine gas, you stand a strong chance of dying. Let these two elements react with each other, however, and you can safely sprinkle the compound on your popcorn for better taste. What is going on?

15. Which of the following boxes contains an elemental material? A compound? A mixture? How many different types of molecules are shown altogether in all three boxes?

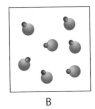  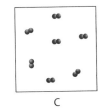

A   B   C

16. Common names of chemical compounds are generally much shorter than the corresponding systematic names. The systematic names for water, ammonia, and methane, for example, are dihydrogen monoxide, H_2O; trihydrogen nitride, NH_3; and tetrahydrogen carbide, CH_4.

For these compounds, which would you rather use: common names or systematic names? Which do you find more descriptive?

17. What is the difference between a compound and a mixture?

18. How might you separate a mixture of sand and salt? How about a mixture of iron and sand?

19. Mixtures can be separated into their components by taking advantage of differences in the chemical properties of the components. Why might this separation method be less convenient than taking advantage of differences in the physical properties of the components?

20. Why can't the elements of a compound be separated from one another by physical means?

21. Germanium, Ge (number 32), computer chips operate faster than silicon, Si (number 14), computer chips. So how might a gallium, Ga (number 31), chip compare with a germanium chip?

22. Is the air in your house a homogeneous or heterogeneous mixture? What evidence have you seen?

23. Helium, He, is a nonmetallic gas and the second element in the periodic table. Rather than being placed adjacent to hydrogen, H, however, helium is placed on the far right of the table. Why?

24. Name ten elemental materials you have access to macroscopic samples of as a consumer here on the Earth.

25. Strontium, Sr (number 38), is especially dangerous to humans because it tends to accumulate in calcium-dependent bone marrow tissues (calcium, Ca, number 20). How does this fact relate to what you know about the organization of the periodic table?

26. With the periodic table as your guide, describe the element selenium, Se (number 34), using as many of this chapter's key terms as you can.

27. Many dry cereals are fortified with iron, which is added to the cereal in the form of small iron particles. How might these particles be separated from the cereal?

28. Why is half-frozen fruit punch always sweeter than the same fruit punch completely melted?

Suggested Reading and Web Sites

The CRC Handbook of Chemistry and Physics. Boca Raton, FL: CRC Press, 1996.

Toward the front of this classic reference book, you'll find a section on the history and general properties of each element.

http://www.chemsoc.org

Chemistry news updates, an on-line chemistry magazine, and much more at this site run by the Royal Society of Chemistry.

http://clri6c.gsi.de/~demo/wunderland/englisch/Inhalt.html

Web site for the heavy-ion research facility in Darmstadt, Germany, where many of the heaviest but shortest-lived elements are being created.

http://www.csc.fi/lul/chem/graphics.html

A virtual art gallery of molecular animations and other cool things, maintained by Finland's Center for Scientific Computing.

http://www.shef.ac.uk/~chem/web-elements/

There are a large number of periodic tables posted on the Web, and this is one of the most popular ones.

Chapter 3
Discovering the Atom and Subatomic Particles

Where We've Been and What We Know Now

The origin of most atoms goes back to the birth of the universe. Hydrogen, H, the lightest atom, was probably the original atom, and hydrogen atoms make up more than 90 percent of the atoms in the known universe. Heavier atoms are produced in stars, which are massive collections of hydrogen atoms pulled together by gravitational forces. The great pressures deep in a star's interior cause hydrogen atoms to fuse to heavier atoms. With the exception of hydrogen, therefore, all the atoms that occur naturally on the Earth—including those in your body—are the products of stars. A tiny fraction of these atoms came from our own star, the sun, but most are from stars that ran their course long before our solar system came into being. You are made of stardust, as is everything that surrounds you.

So most atoms are ancient. They have existed through imponderable ages, recycling through the universe in innumerable forms, both nonliving and living. In this sense, you don't "own" the atoms that make up your body—you are simply their present caretaker. There will be many caretakers to follow.

Atoms are so small that there are more than 10 billion trillion of them in each breath you exhale. This is more than the number of breaths in the Earth's atmosphere. Within a few years, the atoms of your breath are uniformly mixed throughout the atmosphere. What this means is that anyone anywhere on the Earth inhaling a breath of air takes in numerous atoms that were once part of you. And, of course, the reverse is true: you inhale atoms that were once part of everyone who has ever lived. We are literally breathing one another.

In this chapter, we trace the history of the discovery of the atom, which is perhaps the most important discovery humans have ever made. We also look at how researchers discovered that atoms are made of even smaller units of matter known as subatomic particles. Along the way, you will see how progress in science depends not only on keen observations and interpretations but also on an open-mindedness so frequently found in each new generation of investigators.

3.1 Chemistry Developed Out of Our Interest in Materials

We humans have long tinkered with the materials around us and used them to our advantage. Once we learned how to control fire, we were able to create many new substances. Moldable wet clay, for example, was found to harden to ceramic when heated by fire. By 5000 B.C., pottery fire pits gave way to furnaces hot enough to convert copper ores to metallic copper. By 1200 B.C., even hotter furnaces were converting iron ores to iron. This technology allowed for the mass production of metal tools and weapons and made possible the many achievements of ancient Chinese, Egyptian, and Greek civilizations.

In the fourth century B.C., the influential Greek philosopher Aristotle (384–322 B.C.) described the composition and behavior of matter in terms of the four qualities shown in Figure 3.1: hot, cold, moist, and dry. Although we know today that Aristotle's model is wrong, it was nonetheless a remarkable achievement for its day, and people using it in Aristotle's time found it made sense. When pottery was made, for example, wet clay was converted to ceramic because the heat of the fire drove out the moist quality of the wet clay and replaced it with the dry quality of the ceramic. Likewise, warm air caused ice to melt by replacing the dry quality characteristic of ice with the moist quality characteristic of water.

Aristotle's views on the nature of matter made so much sense to people that less obvious views were difficult to accept. One alternative view was the forerunner to our present-day model: Matter is composed of a finite number of incredibly small but discrete units we call atoms. This model was advanced by several Greek philosophers, including Democritus (460–370 B.C.), who coined the term *atom* from the Greek phrase *a tomos*, which means "not cut" or "that which is indivisible." According to the atomic model of Democritus, the texture, mass, and color of a material were a function of the texture, mass, and color of its atoms, as illustrated in Figure 3.2. So compelling was Aristotle's reputation, however, that the atomic model would not reappear for 2000 years.

According to Aristotle, it was theoretically possible to transform any substance to another substance simply by altering the relative proportions of the four basic qualities. This meant that, under the proper conditions, a metal like lead could be transformed to gold. This concept laid the foundation of **alchemy**, a field of study concerned primarily with finding potions that would produce gold or confer immortality. Alchemists from the time of Aristotle to as late as the 1600s tried in vain to convert various metals to gold.

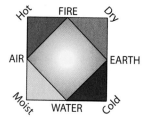

Figure 3.1
Aristotle thought that all materials were made of various proportions of four fundamental qualities: hot, dry, cold, and moist. Various combinations of these qualities gave rise to the four basic *elements*: hot and dry gave fire, moist and cold gave water, hot and moist gave air, and dry and cold gave earth. A hard substance like rock contained mostly the dry quality, for example, and a soft substance like clay contained mostly the moist quality.

Figure 3.2
In his atomic model, Democritus imagined that atoms of iron were shaped like coils, making iron rigid, strong, and malleable, and that atoms of fire were sharp, lightweight, and yellow.

Despite the futility of their efforts, the alchemists learned much about the behavior of many chemicals, and many useful laboratory techniques were developed.

3.2 Lavoisier Laid the Foundation of Modern Chemistry

In the 1400s, the printing press was invented in Europe, and an explosion of information, including scientific information, followed. Evidence against Aristotle's model of matter began to accumulate. In 1661, a well-known English experimentalist, Robert Boyle (1627–1691), departed from Aristotelian thought by proposing that a substance was not an element if it was made of two or more components. He published these and related thoughts in a text entitled *The Skeptical Chymist*, which had a significant impact on future generations of chemical thinkers.

About a century after Boyle, huge steps toward our present understanding of elements and compounds were taken by the French chemist Antoine Lavoisier (1743–1794). Embracing Boyle's views, Lavoisier accepted the idea of an *element* as any material made of only one component. Taking this model a step further, as shown in Figure 3.3, he identified a *compound* as any material composed of two or more elements. As you may recall from Chapter 2, these definitions are in line with our present understanding. Hydrogen, for example, is an element because it is made of only hydrogen atoms, and water is a compound because it is made of atoms of the elements hydrogen and oxygen.

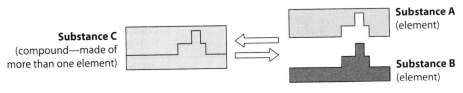

Substance C
(compound—made of more than one element)

Substance A
(element)

Substance B
(element)

Figure 3.3
A representation of Lavoisier's notion of elements and compounds. Substances A and B cannot be broken down to smaller components and so are classified as elements. These two elements can react together to form the more complex substance C, which is classified as a compound because it is made of more than one element.

Antoine Lavoisier, shown here with his wife, Marie-Anne, who assisted him in many of his experiments, was a concerned citizen as well as a first-rate scientist. He established free schools, advocated the use of fire hydrants, and designed street lamps to make travel through urban neighborhoods safer at night. To help finance his scientific projects, Lavoisier took part-time employment as a tax collector. Because of this employment, he was beheaded in 1794 during the French Revolution. Soon after his execution, however, the French government was erecting statues in his honor.

The significance of Lavoisier's definitions is that they required experimentation. This was counter to the old ways of the Greek philosophers, who formulated their ideas based on logic and reason. Because he focused on the results of laboratory research, Lavoisier was a key player in the development of modern chemistry. To many, he is known as the "father of modern chemistry."

Mass Is Conserved in a Chemical Reaction

In the important experiment illustrated in Figure 3.4, Lavoisier carefully measured the mass of a sealed glass vessel that contained tin. When he heated the vessel, a chemical reaction occurred and the tin turned to a white powder. Lavoisier again measured the vessel's mass and found it had not changed. From the results of his experiments and the results of similar experiments performed by other investigators, Lavoisier hypothesized that mass is always conserved during a chemical reaction, where *conserved* in this context means that the amount of the mass does not change—the number of grams of mass present after the reaction is the same as the number of grams present before the reaction. This hypothesis is now considered to be a **scientific law**, which is any scientific hypothesis that has been tested over and over again and has not been contradicted. (A scientific law is sometimes referred to as a *scientific principle*.) Formally, the **law of mass conservation** states the following:

> There is no detectable change in the total mass of materials when they react chemically to form new materials.

The law of mass conservation remains one of the most important laws in chemistry today. It is easy to see, however, why it took earlier investigators so long to formulate this law. After all, when wood burns, the mass of the ashes is always less than the mass of the original wood. Also, it was known that some substances, such as hardening cement, tend to gain mass as they undergo chemical change. What early investigators failed to recognize, however, is the role gases play in many chemical reactions. When

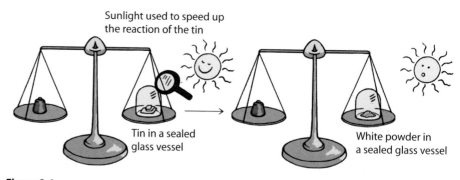

Sunlight used to speed up the reaction of the tin

Tin in a sealed glass vessel

White powder in a sealed glass vessel

Figure 3.4
Lavoisier measured the mass of a sealed glass vessel containing tin and the mass of the same vessel containing a white powder left after the tin underwent a chemical reaction. He found the mass to be the same before and after the reaction.

wood burns, gaseous carbon dioxide and water vapor are released. The ashes have less mass because they are only one of the products of the reaction. Cement gains mass as it absorbs atmospheric carbon dioxide.

Lavoisier was exceedingly careful in attending to details. In recognizing the role that gases might play, he knew the importance of sealing his apparatus before performing a chemical reaction.

Concept Check ✓

Had Lavoisier been a follower of ancient Greek philosophy, what might have prevented him from discovering the law of mass conservation?

Was this your answer? Using only logic and reason, it is difficult to conclude that mass is conserved in a chemical reaction. In most reactions, the total amount of mass appears to change because some of the products of the reaction are invisible atmospheric gases. Thus the law of mass conservation would have likely escaped Lavoisier's notice had he relied on the "common sense" logic and reason used by Greek philosophers rather than on precise measurements and experimentation.

When Lavoisier opened the sealed vessel in which the white powder had formed, he observed that air rushed in. He hypothesized that, as it formed the white powder, the tin absorbed either the air inside the vessel or perhaps only some component of the air. To find out what percentage of the air had reacted with the tin, he performed the same experiment using the arrangement shown in Figure 3.5. When the tin was done reacting, the water level in the jar had risen to about one-fifth of the total volume of the jar. Lavoisier realized that the only possible explanation was that air originally in the jar (which kept water out before the reaction began) had somehow been consumed in the chemical reaction with the tin. Because water replaced about 20 percent of the original volume of air, he reasoned that air is a mixture of at least two gaseous materials. One gas, making up about 20 percent of the air, disappeared from its gaseous phase by combining with the tin. The second gas, making up the other 80 percent, must have remained in the gaseous phase because it did not combine with the metal.

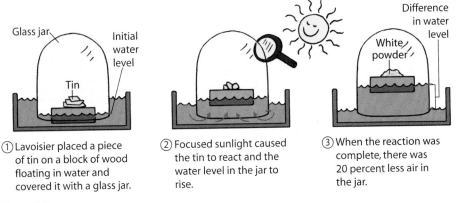

① Lavoisier placed a piece of tin on a block of wood floating in water and covered it with a glass jar.

② Focused sunlight caused the tin to react and the water level in the jar to rise.

③ When the reaction was complete, there was 20 percent less air in the jar.

Figure 3.5
Lavoisier directed sunlight at tin floating on a block of wood in a glass jar inverted over water. As the tin reacted to form a powder, the water level in the jar rose, indicating that some of the air originally in the jar had taken part in the reaction.

Hands-On Chemistry: Air Out

You can witness the involvement of a gas in a reaction by performing an experiment similar to the ones Lavoisier performed with tin.

What You Need

Nonsoapy steel-wool pad; narrow, straight-sided jar, such as an olive jar; shallow cooking pot; water

Procedure

① Follow the setup shown in the photograph. Stuff the steel-wool pad into the bottom of the jar. A pad that doesn't fit through the jar opening can be cut into strips with scissors. Pour water into the pot to a depth of about 2 inches. Then invert the jar into the water.

② Note the water level inside the jar.

③ Leave the setup alone until the steel wool, which is primarily iron, begins to look rusty (a couple of hours should do it).

What has happened to the water level in the inverted jar? Why?

Joseph Priestley was a self-trained scientist. He was the first to recognize the nature of carbonated beverages and began the study of photosynthesis with his discovery that plants absorb carbon dioxide when exposed to sunlight. A radical in many of his political views, Priestley was regarded with much suspicion, especially after he publicly sympathized with the French Revolution. After he was harassed and a mob had burned his home and library, he took the advice of his good friend Benjamin Franklin and moved to America, where he spent the last few years of his life in self-imposed exile.

Soon after Lavoisier completed these experiments, he learned that an English chemist, Joseph Priestley (1733–1804), had prepared and isolated a gas that had remarkable properties. This gas caused candles to burn brighter and charcoal to burn hotter. Lavoisier found that this gas couldn't be broken down to simpler substances and so recognized it to be an element. Because the gas produced acidic solutions when bubbled through water, Lavoisier gave it the name *oxygen*, which means "acid former." He found that oxygen was the reacting component of the air in his tin experiments.

See Figure 3.6 for a description of how Priestley first prepared and isolated oxygen.

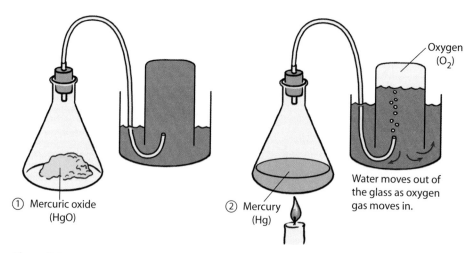

① Mercuric oxide (HgO)

② Mercury (Hg)

Oxygen (O_2)

Water moves out of the glass as oxygen gas moves in.

Figure 3.6
Priestley collected oxygen gas by heating the highly toxic metallic compound known today as mercuric oxide, HgO. When heated, mercuric oxide decomposes to liquid mercury and oxygen gas. Priestley collected the oxygen gas in an apparatus similar to the one illustrated here. As the gas is formed, it displaces water in the submerged inverted glass.

Hands-On Chemistry: Collecting Bubbles

A common method of collecting a gas produced in a chemical reaction is by the displacement of water. In this activity, you will collect the carbon dioxide produced from the reaction between baking soda and vinegar.

What You Need

Large pot (or sink), water, small plastic soda bottle (the 20-ounce size works nicely), film canister with lid, sharp knife, baking soda, vinegar, long wooden match, assistant

Safety Note

Wear safety glasses while using the knife and while the chemical reaction is taking place.

Procedure

① Cut a hole no wider than a pencil in the lid of the film canister. Add a teaspoon of baking soda to the canister and leave it uncapped.

② Fill the large pot (or the sink) three-fourths full with water. Fill the soda bottle with water, and with your hand over the opening, invert it into the water in the pot. Have your assistant hold the soda bottle upright in the pot with the mouth of the bottle not touching the pot bottom.

③ Pour a capful of vinegar into the film canister. As the bubbles begin to form, quickly cap the canister, placing your thumb over the hole in the lid to hold in as much gas as possible. Immediately submerge the canister right side up directly below the mouth of the soda bottle. Release your thumb, and bubbles of carbon dioxide will rise and be captured in the bottle.

④ To collect more carbon dioxide, drain the water from the film canister and repeat the procedure while your assistant continues to hold the inverted bottle.

⑤ To examine the properties of the gas generated in the baking soda–vinegar reaction, seal your hand over the mouth of the inverted soda bottle, carefully place the bottle upright on a table, and then uncover the mouth. There may still be some water in the bottle, but the gas above the water is carbon dioxide, which stays in the bottle because it is heavier than air. Light the match and place the flame into the carbon dioxide. Because there is no oxygen (there is only carbon dioxide), the flame is quickly extinguished because carbon dioxide does not support burning the way oxygen does.

Proust Proposed the Law of Definite Proportions

In 1766, the English chemist Henry Cavendish (1731–1810) isolated a gas that could be ignited in air to produce water and heat. Lavoisier was the first to recognize this gas as an element, which he named hydrogen—a Greek word that means "water former." Lavoisier was also the first to recognize that in forming water, the hydrogen was reacting with atmospheric oxygen. Thus, water must be a compound (not an element as Aristotle professed) made of the two elements hydrogen and oxygen.

By the 1790s, the French chemist Joseph Proust (1754–1826) had noted that, in forming water, hydrogen and oxygen always react in a particular mass ratio. He found, for example, that 8 grams of oxygen reacts with 1 gram of hydrogen (no more and no less) to produce 9 grams of water. Equivalently, 32 grams of oxygen reacts with 4 grams of hydrogen (no more and no less) to produce 36 grams of water. In all cases, the ratio of oxygen mass to hydrogen mass is 8:1. Even if oxygen and hydrogen are not mixed in an 8:1 ratio, they react as though they were. If 10 grams of oxygen, for example, is mixed with 1 gram of hydrogen, only 8 grams of oxygen reacts, leaving 2 grams of oxygen untouched. The result is still 9 grams of water, as Figure 3.7 shows.

These and similar results with other chemical reactions, especially those involving metallic compounds, led Proust to propose the **law of definite proportions:**

Elements combine in definite mass ratios to form compounds.

Another example of the law of definite proportions involves nitrogen and hydrogen, which react in a 14:3 mass ratio to form ammonia. This means that 14 grams of nitrogen reacts with 3 grams of hydrogen to produce 17 grams of ammonia. Accordingly, mixing 14 grams of nitrogen with 14 grams of hydrogen also produces 17 grams of ammonia, not 28 grams. Somehow the 14 grams of ammonia "knows" to react with only 3 grams of hydrogen, despite the presence of 14 grams of hydrogen. How elements "knew" to react in particular mass ratios was a great mystery. The law of definite proportions, however, turned out to be one of the greatest clues to the discovery of the atom.

	Oxygen	+ Hydrogen ⟶	Water	+ Oxygen	+ Hydrogen
(a)	8 g	1 g	9 g		
(b)	10 g	1 g	9 g	2 g	
(c)	8 g	2 g	9 g		1 g

Leftover unreacted chemicals

Figure 3.7

(a) In forming water, oxygen and hydrogen always react in an 8:1 mass ratio. (b) When an excess of oxygen is present, the reaction still occurs in an 8:1 ratio, with the excess oxygen—2 grams in this case—remaining unreacted. (c) When an excess of hydrogen is present, the reaction still occurs in an 8:1 ratio, with the excess hydrogen remaining unreacted.

Concept Check ✔

How many grams of water can be produced when 16 grams of oxygen is mixed with 2 grams of hydrogen?

Was this your answer? Oxygen and hydrogen react in an 8:1 mass ratio to form water, but that doesn't mean you have to have exactly 8 grams of oxygen and exactly 1 gram of hydrogen in the reaction vessel. What this ratio means is that the mass of oxygen taking part in the reaction is always exactly eight times the mass of hydrogen taking part. Because here the oxygen mass—16 grams—is eight times the hydrogen mass—2 grams—the 16 grams of oxygen reacts fully with the 2 grams of hydrogen to produce 18 grams of water. Note that a 16:2 ratio is mathematically the same as an 8:1 ratio.

Calculation Corner: Finding Out How Much of a Chemical Reacts

When the definite proportions for a given reaction are known, unit conversion (see the Calculation Corner on page 12) can help you determine the amount of a chemical that takes part in the reaction. For instance, we can express the law of definite proportions for the formation of water as:

8 g oxygen : 1 g hydrogen

From this relationship, we can derive two conversion factors:

$$\frac{8 \text{ g oxygen}}{1 \text{ g hydrogen}} \quad \text{and} \quad \frac{1 \text{ g hydrogen}}{8 \text{ g oxygen}}$$

If you are given a certain amount of one element and want to know how much of the other element is needed for a complete reaction, you need only multiply by the appropriate conversion factor to find the answer.

Example
How much hydrogen is needed in order for 64 grams of oxygen to react completely in the formation of water?

Answer

$$64 \text{ g oxygen} \times \frac{1 \text{ g hydrogen}}{8 \text{ g oxygen}} = 8 \text{ g hydrogen}$$

↑ Quantity of oxygen in grams
↑ Conversion factor
↑ Quantity of hydrogen in grams

Knowing how much of each element must be present for complete reaction then allows you to determine how much product forms. If 64 grams of oxygen reacts with 8 grams of hydrogen, then a total of 64 grams + 8 grams = 72 grams of water is formed.

Your Turn

1. Nitrogen and hydrogen react in a 14:3 mass ratio to form ammonia. How much hydrogen is needed in order for 7.0 grams of nitrogen to react completely?

2. How much ammonia forms in the reaction between 7.0 grams of nitrogen and 7.0 grams of hydrogen?

3.3 Dalton Deduced That Matter Is Made of Atoms

The observations of Lavoisier, Proust, and others led John Dalton (1766–1844), a self-educated English schoolteacher, to reintroduce the atomic ideas of Democritus. In 1803 Dalton wrote a series of postulates—claims he assumed to be true based on experimental evidence—that can be summarized as follows:

1. Each element consists of indivisible, minute particles called atoms.

2. Atoms can be neither created nor destroyed in chemical reactions.

3. All atoms of a given element are identical.

4. Atoms chemically combine in definite whole-number ratios to form compounds.

5. Atoms of different elements have different masses.

John Dalton was born into a very poor family. Although his formal schooling ended at age 11, he continued to learn on his own and even began teaching others when he was only 12. His primary research interest was weather, which led him to conduct many experiments with gases. Soon after publishing his conclusions on the atomic nature of matter, his reputation as a first-rate scientist increased rapidly. In 1810, he was elected into Britain's premiere scientific organization, the Royal Society.

Even though Dalton was not correct about atoms being indivisible or about all atoms of a given element being identical (we'll see why later in the chapter), his postulates answered many questions about the nature of elements and compounds. Postulate 2, for example, which described the *indestructible* nature of atoms, accounted for Lavoisier's mass-conservation principle. During a chemical reaction, atoms may be exchanged, but never are they created out of nothing nor do they simply vanish. Postulate 4 explained compounds as the combination of the atoms of different elements. Oxygen and hydrogen atoms, for example, combine to form water.

Dalton concluded that because 8 grams of oxygen always combines with 1 gram of hydrogen, the oxygen atom must be eight times more massive than the hydrogen atom. In drawing this conclusion, he assumed that a single oxygen atom joins with a single hydrogen atom. According to Dalton, therefore, the most fundamental unit of water was HO rather than the familiar H_2O we know today.

Dalton Defended His Atomic Hypothesis Against Experimental Evidence

In 1808, the French chemist Joseph Gay-Lussac (1778–1850) reported that when gases react, their volumes—in a manner similar to Proust's law of definite proportions—are in the ratio of small whole numbers. Gay-Lussac's experiments showed, for example, that 2 liters of hydrogen completely reacts with 1 liter of oxygen (no more and no less) to form 2 liters of water vapor:

2 liters hydrogen gas + **1** liter oxygen gas ⟶ **2** liters water vapor

Dalton, however, was highly critical of Gay-Lussac's experiments. Dalton had already firmly established in his own mind that the formula for water was HO. If water contained twice as much hydrogen as oxygen, the formula would have to be H_2O. In addition, Dalton could not understand how 2 liters of water formed and not just 1 liter. Assuming that hydrogen gas and oxygen gas consisted of individual atoms, and assuming that equal volumes of two gases contain equal numbers of particles, as shown in Figure 3.8, 2 liters of hydrogen should react with 1 liter of oxygen to produce 1 liter of water vapor, as shown in Figure 3.8a.

Gay-Lussac's results, illustrated in Figure 3.8b, showed that *2* liters of water vapor formed. So where did the atoms needed to create the additional liter of water vapor come from? Did each hydrogen atom and each oxygen atom split in half? This would effectively double the number of atoms, allowing for a second volume of water. The notion of an atom splitting in half, however, was counter to Dalton's already-well-received atomic hypothesis.

In 1811, the Italian physicist and lawyer Amadeo Avogadro (1776–1856) gave an accurate explanation for Gay-Lussac's experimental results. Avogadro hypothesized that the fundamental particles of hydrogen and oxygen were not atoms but rather diatomic molecules, where the term *diatomic* indicates two atoms per molecule. Thus, the formula for hydro-

In addition to exploring the chemical identity of gases and the nature of chemical reactions, Joseph Gay-Lussac was one of the first balloonists. In one of his balloon flights to test hypotheses on the composition of air and the extent of the Earth's magnetic field, Gay-Lussac reached an altitude of 7000 meters (23,000 feet). This record remained unbroken for the next 50 years.

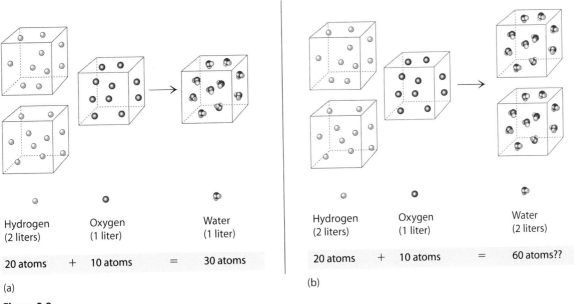

Hydrogen (2 liters)   Oxygen (1 liter)   Water (1 liter)

20 atoms   +   10 atoms   =   30 atoms

(a)

Hydrogen (2 liters)   Oxygen (1 liter)   Water (2 liters)

20 atoms   +   10 atoms   =   60 atoms??

(b)

Figure 3.8
(a) Dalton pointed out that if water had the formula H_2O, then 2 liters of hydrogen (shown here as 20 atoms) and 1 liter of oxygen (shown here as 10 atoms) should yield 1 liter of water vapor (shown here as 10 molecules containing a total of 30 atoms). (b) Gay-Lussac's experiments showed that 2 liters of water vapor formed. Where did the atoms for this second liter of water vapor come from? Questions such as these led Dalton to distrust Gay-Lussac's experimental results.

gen is H_2 and the formula for oxygen is O_2. Diatomic particles of hydrogen and oxygen would have double the number of atoms in a given volume, thus allowing for the formation of a second volume of water, as Figure 3.9 shows.

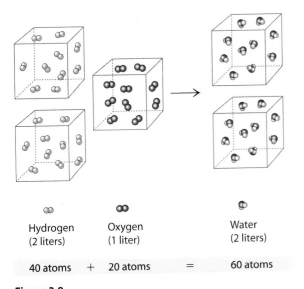

Hydrogen (2 liters)   Oxygen (1 liter)   Water (2 liters)

40 atoms   +   20 atoms   =   60 atoms

Figure 3.9
Because each particle of gaseous hydrogen and gaseous oxygen is diatomic, 2 liters of hydrogen and 1 liter of oxygen form 2 liters of water vapor. In this way, molecules of hydrogen, H_2, and oxygen, O_2, are split rather than *atoms* of hydrogen, H, and oxygen, O, and Dalton's atomic theory is not violated.

Amadeo Avogadro received a doctor of law degree when he was 20 years old. He enjoyed practicing law but was more interested in science, which eventually became his life's occupation. As a professor of physics and mathematics in Italy, he was geographically and intellectually isolated from the chemical community developing on the other side of the Alps in northern France and in England. This isolation made it difficult for him to defend his views on the nature of atoms. In addition, he valued his privacy and preferred focusing his energies on family

Concept Check ✓

How many molecules of hydrogen chloride, HCl, form when ten molecules of diatomic hydrogen, H_2, react with ten molecules of diatomic chlorine, Cl_2? If ten molecules represent one volume, how many volumes of hydrogen chloride form?

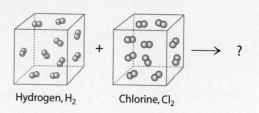

Hydrogen, H_2 Chlorine, Cl_2 ⟶   ?

Were these your answers? In this reaction, 20 hydrogen chloride molecules are formed. One volume of hydrogen plus one volume of chlorine react to form two volumes of hydrogen chloride.

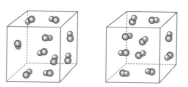

◌⊙ Hydrogen chloride

Stanislao Cannizzaro's main research interests were in the chemistry of carbon compounds found in living organisms. Cannizzaro did much to dispel the then widely held belief that the laws governing those chemicals were different from those governing chemicals not found in living organisms.

Dalton understood Avogadro's creative argument but found it unacceptable because it failed to explain how two atoms of the same element could bond to each other. Based on his own research, Dalton had come to the erroneous conclusion that atoms of the same kind always have a natural repulsion for one another. Because of Dalton's authority in the scientific community, Avogadro's hypothesis was discarded and did not reappear for another half-century.

In 1860, an international conference of chemists convened to discuss how the masses of atoms of different elements could be measured and compared with one another. (As we explore in Section 11.5, knowing the relative masses of atoms helps chemists understand and control chemical reactions.) At the time, there was little agreement because different chemists using different experimental procedures and assuming different theories came up with different results. Progress in chemistry was stymied by this problem.

At this conference, a pamphlet written by the Italian chemist Stanislao Cannizzaro (1826–1910) was presented. In this pamphlet, which he had used with his students for several years, Cannizzaro explained and justified Avogadro's hypothesis and showed how correct atomic masses and formulas could be obtained through easy calculations. The concept was simple: Provided equal volumes of gases contain equal numbers of atoms or molecules, the relative masses of these particles can be obtained by weighing equal volumes of gases that are at the same temperature and pressure. As shown in Figure 3.10, for example, 1 liter of oxygen is 16 times heavier (more massive) than 1 liter of hydrogen, suggesting that, assuming the same number of atoms per molecule, an oxygen molecule is 16 times heavier (more massive) than a hydrogen molecule. Analysis of equal volumes of

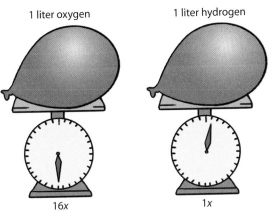

1 liter oxygen   1 liter hydrogen

16x   1x

Figure 3.10
One liter of oxygen is 16 times more massive than the same volume of hydrogen. Assuming 1 liter of oxygen and 1 liter of hydrogen contain the same number of particles, the mass of an oxygen particle must be 16 times greater than the mass of a hydrogen particle.

gases for many other elements resulted in the first tables of accurate relative atomic masses, and from these tables grew the all-important periodic table.

Despite the critical attacks by Dalton, the contributions of Gay-Lussac and Avogadro turned out to be most important to the development of atomic theory. Their efforts, however, were not widely recognized until after their deaths. Gay-Lussac died 10 years prior to the 1860 conference, and Avogadro died 4 years prior.

Mendeleev Used Known Relative Atomic Masses to Create the Periodic Table

By the 1860s, many scientists working independently had noted that when they listed elements in order of relative masses, a number of interesting patterns arose. Many physical and chemical properties, for example, tended to change gradually in moving from one element to the next. At regular intervals, however, an element had properties that were vastly different from those of the preceding element and more like those of a much lighter element. In other words, the properties of elements tended to recur in *cycles*, exhibiting the *periodicity* we looked at in Section 2.6.

In 1869, a Russian chemistry professor, Dmitri Mendeleev (1834–1907), produced a chart summarizing the properties of known elements for his students. Mendeleev's chart was unique in that it resembled a calendar. Across each horizontal row, he placed all the elements that appeared in one interval of repeating properties. Down each vertical column he placed elements of similar properties. He found, however, that in order to align elements properly in a column, he had to shift elements left or right occasionally. This left gaps—blank spaces that could not be filled by any known element (Figure 3.11). Instead of looking on these gaps as defects, Mendeleev boldly predicted the existence of elements that had not yet been discovered. Furthermore, his predictions about the properties of some of those missing elements led to their discovery.

Dmitri Mendeleev was a devoted and highly effective teacher. Students adored him and would fill lecture halls to hear him speak about chemistry. Much of his work on the periodic table occurred in his spare time following his lectures. Mendeleev taught not only in the university classrooms but anywhere he traveled. During his journeys by train, he would travel third class with peasants to share his findings about agriculture.

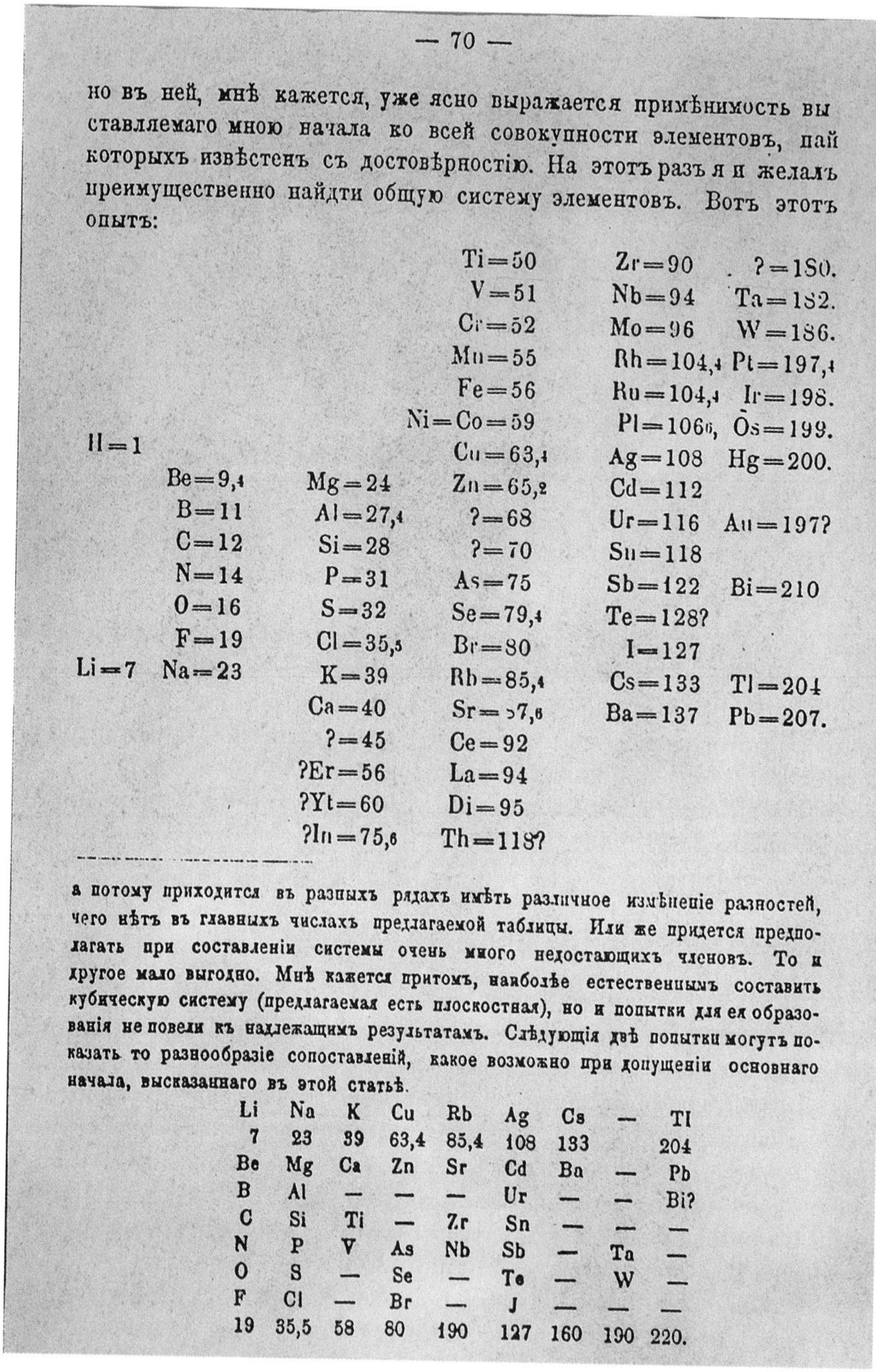

— 70 —

но въ ней, мнѣ кажется, уже ясно выражается примѣнимость вы ставляемаго мною начала ко всей совокупности элементовъ, пай которыхъ извѣстенъ съ достовѣрностію. На этотъ разъ я и желалъ преимущественно найдти общую систему элементовъ. Вотъ этотъ опытъ:

			Ti=50	Zr=90	?=180.
			V=51	Nb=94	Ta=182.
			Cr=52	Mo=96	W=186.
			Mn=55	Rh=104,4	Pt=197,4
			Fe=56	Ru=104,4	Ir=198.
		Ni=Co=59		Pl=106,6	Os=199.
H=1			Cu=63,4	Ag=108	Hg=200.
Be=9,4	Mg=24	Zn=65,2	Cd=112		
B=11	Al=27,4	?=68	Ur=116	Au=197?	
C=12	Si=28	?=70	Sn=118		
N=14	P=31	As=75	Sb=122	Bi=210	
O=16	S=32	Se=79,4	Te=128?		
F=19	Cl=35,5	Br=80	I=127		
Li=7 Na=23	K=39	Rb=85,4	Cs=133	Tl=204	
	Ca=40	Sr=57,6	Ba=137	Pb=207.	
	?=45	Ce=92			
	?Er=56	La=94			
	?Yt=60	Di=95			
	?In=75,6	Th=118?			

а потому приходится въ разныхъ рядахъ имѣть различное измѣненіе разностей, чего нѣтъ въ главныхъ числахъ предлагаемой таблицы. Или же придется предпо лагать при составленіи системы очень много недостающихъ членовъ. То и другое мало выгодно. Мнѣ кажется притомъ, наиболѣе естественнымъ составить кубическую систему (предлагаемая есть плоскостная), но и попытки для ея образо ванія не повели къ надлежащимъ результатамъ. Слѣдующія двѣ попытки могутъ по казать то разнообразіе сопоставленій, какое возможно при допущеніи основнаго начала, высказаннаго въ этой статьѣ.

Li	Na	K	Cu	Rb	Ag	Cs	—	Tl
7	23	39	63,4	85,4	108	133		204
Be	Mg	Ca	Zn	Sr	Cd	Ba	—	Pb
B	Al	—	—	—	Ur	—	—	Bi?
C	Si	Ti	—	Zr	Sn	—	—	—
N	P	V	As	Nb	Sb	—	Ta	—
O	S	—	Se	—	Te	—	W	—
F	Cl	—	Br	—	J	—	—	—
19	35,5	58	80	190	127	160	190	220.

Figure 3.11
An early draft of Mendeleev's periodic table.

That Mendeleev was able to predict the properties of new elements helped convince many scientists of the accuracy of Dalton's atomic hypothesis. This in turn helped promote Dalton's proposed atomic nature of matter from a hypothesis to a more widely accepted theory. Mendeleev's chart, which ultimately led to our modern periodic table with its horizontal periods and vertical groups, also helped lay the groundwork for our understanding of atomic behavior and is recognized as one of the most important achievements of modern science.

Concept Check ✓

The following statements summarize the scientific discoveries presented in Sections 3.2 and 3.3. Place them in chronological order.

a. Elements are made of atoms.
b. Chemicals react in definite whole-number ratios.
c. Relative masses of atoms can be measured.
d. Hydrogen gas and oxygen gas consist of diatomic molecules.
e. The periodic table can be used to predict the properties of elements.
f. Mass is conserved during a chemical reaction.

Was this your answer? Lavoisier discovered that *mass is conserved during a chemical reaction*, which led Proust to discover that *chemicals react in definite whole-number ratios*. Based on this information, Dalton proposed that *elements are made of atoms*. This was followed by Gay-Lussac's experiments, which suggested to Avogadro that *hydrogen gas and oxygen gas consist of diatomic molecules*. Using this as a premise, Cannizzaro was able to show how Avogadro's hypothesis could be used to *measure the relative masses of atoms*. Knowing relative masses allowed Mendeleev to *devise the periodic table and use it to predict the properties of elements* yet to be discovered. The correct sequence is therefore f, b, a, d, c, e.

Today, the results of many scientific experiments confirm the atomic nature of matter. Contrary to Dalton's notion of the indivisible atom, however, an accumulation of evidence tells us that atoms are in fact divisible and that they are made of smaller particles called *electrons, protons*, and *neutrons*. For the remainder of this chapter, we explore these *subatomic particles* in detail, continuing with our historical perspective.

3.4 The Electron Was the First Subatomic Particle Discovered

In 1752, Benjamin Franklin (1706–1790) learned from experiments with thunderstorms that lightning is a flow of electrical energy through the atmosphere. This discovery prompted other scientists to explore whether or not electrical energy could travel through gases other than the atmosphere. To find out, they applied a voltage across glass tubes in which they had sealed various gases. To apply a voltage means to connect each end of a tube to a wire and then connect the free ends of the two wires to a battery. Electricity is the flow of particles carrying either a positive (+) electric charge or a negative (−) electric charge. As electricity from the battery moves through the wires, positively charged particles accumulate at one end of the glass tube and negatively charged particles accumulate at the other end. The end where the positively charged particles accumulate is called the *anode*, and the end where the negatively charged particles accumulate is called the *cathode*.

In every case, the result was a brightly glowing ray (Figure 3.12a). This meant that electrical energy was able to travel through different types of gases. To the surprise of these early investigators, a ray was also produced when the voltage was applied across a glass tube that had been evacuated and was thus empty of any gas (Figure 3.12b). This implied that the ray was not a consequence of the gas but rather an entity in and of itself.

(a)

(b)

Figure 3.12

(a) Electrical energy passing through a neon gas-filled glass tube (of any design) generates a bright red glowing ray. (b) The ray passing through an evacuated glass tube is not usually visible. In the tube shown here, the ray is highlighted by a fluorescent backing that glows green as the ray passes over it.

Experiments showed that the ray in the evacuated tube was blocked from reaching the anode when an object was placed in its path. It was thus reasoned that the ray emerged from the cathode. For this reason, the apparatus, shown in Figure 3.13a, was named a **cathode ray tube**. Magnetic fields caused the ray to deflect, as did electrically charged particles. When electrically charged particles were used, the ray was always deflected toward the positively charged particles and away from the negatively charged par-

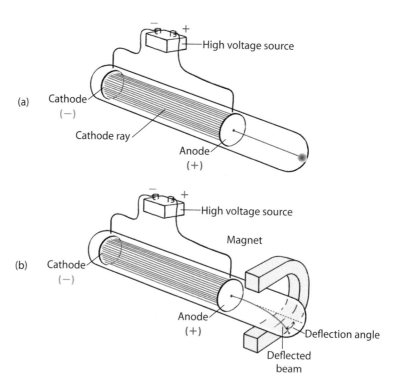

Figure 3.13

(a) A simple cathode ray tube. The small hole in the anode permits the passage of a narrow beam that strikes the end of the evacuated tube, producing a glowing dot as the beam interacts with the glass. (b) Moving charged particles, such as those in a cathode ray, are deflected by a magnetic field.

ticles. Because like-signed particles repel each other, this meant the ray was negatively charged. The speed of the ray was found to be considerably less than the speed of light. Because of these characteristics, it appeared that the ray behaved more like a beam of particles than a beam of light.

In 1897, J. J. Thomson (1856–1940) measured the deflection angles of cathode ray particles in a magnetic field, using a magnet positioned as shown in Figure 3.13b. He reasoned that the deflection of the particles depended on their mass and electric charge. The greater a particle's mass, the greater its resistance to a change in motion and therefore the *smaller* the deflection. The greater a particle's charge, the stronger the magnetic interactions and therefore the *larger* the deflection. The angle of deflection, he concluded, was equal to the ratio of the particle's charge to its mass:

$$\text{angle of deflection} = \frac{\text{charge}}{\text{mass}}$$

Knowing only the angle of deflection, however, Thomson was unable to calculate either the charge or the mass of each particle. In order to calculate the mass, he needed to know the charge, but in order to calculate the charge, he needed to know the mass.

In 1909, the American physicist Robert Millikan (1868–1953) calculated the numerical value of a single increment of electric charge on the basis of the innovative experiment shown in Figure 3.14. Millikan sprayed tiny oil droplets into a specially designed chamber in which droplets could be suspended in air by the application of an electric field. (This is similar to the way a person's hair can be made to stand straight up away from the head by placing a statically charged balloon near the hair.) When the field was strong on Millikan's apparatus, some of the droplets moved upward, indicating they had a very slight negative charge and so were attracted to the upper, positively charged plate. Millikan adjusted the field so that some of the droplets would hover motionless. He knew that the downward force of gravity on these motionless droplets was exactly balanced by the upward electric force. By altering the field strength, he could make other droplets,

Joseph John Thomson, known to his colleagues as J. J., was one of the first directors of the famous Cavendish Laboratory of Cambridge University in England, where almost all the discoveries concerning subatomic particles and their behavior were made. Seven of Thomson's students went on to receive Nobel prizes for their scientific work. Thomson himself won a Nobel prize in 1906 for his work with the cathode ray tube.

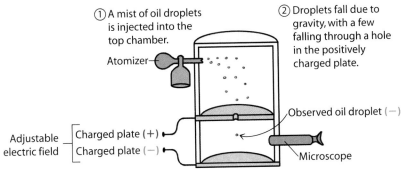

① A mist of oil droplets is injected into the top chamber.

② Droplets fall due to gravity, with a few falling through a hole in the positively charged plate.

Atomizer

Adjustable electric field

Charged plate (+)

Charged plate (−)

Observed oil droplet (−)

Microscope

③ The electric field is adjusted until a droplet hovers. The upward electric force exerted on the droplet by the positively charged plate is exactly balanced by the downward force of gravity exerted on the droplet.

Figure 3.14
Millikan determined the charge of an electron with this oil-drop experiment.

The European science community of the 1800s viewed most American scientists as inventors—clever, but not profound in their thinking or discoveries. This attitude began to change at the turn of the 20th century, principally because of the work of the American scientist Robert Millikan, who excelled in his experimental designs and conclusions. In addition to research, he also spent much time preparing textbooks so that his students did not have to rely so much on lectures. He won a Nobel prize in 1923 and served as the president of Caltech from 1921 to 1945.

of different masses, hover motionless. Repeated measurements showed that the electric charge on any droplet was always some multiple of a single very small value, 1.60×10^{-19} coulomb, which Millikan proposed to be the fundamental increment of all electric charge. (The *coulomb* is a unit of electric charge.) Using this value and the charge-to-mass ratio discovered by Thomson, Millikan calculated the mass of a cathode ray particle to be considerably less than that of the smallest known atom, hydrogen. This was remarkable because it provided strong evidence that the atom was not the smallest particle of matter.

Concept Check ✔

What do the numbers 45, 30, 60, 75, 105, 35, 80, 55, 90, 20, 65 have in common?

Was this your answer? They are all multiples of 5. In a similar fashion, Millikan noted that all the readings from his electronic equipment were multiples of a very small number, which he calculated to be 1.60×10^{-19} coulomb.

The cathode ray particle is known today as the **electron**, a name that comes from the Greek word for amber (*electrik*), which is a material the early Greeks used to study the effects of static electricity. The electron is a fundamental component of all atoms. All electrons are identical, each having a negative electric charge and an incredibly small mass of 9.1×10^{-31} kilograms. Electrons determine many of a material's properties, including chemical reactivity and such physical attributes as taste, texture, appearance, and color.

The cathode ray—a stream of electrons—has found a great number of applications. Most notably, a traditional television set (not the superthin ones that can hang on a wall) is a cathode ray tube with one end widened out into a phosphor-coated screen. Signals from the television station cause electrically charged plates in the tube to control the direction of the ray such that images are traced onto the screen.

Hands-On Chemistry: Bending Electrons

Stare at a television set or computer monitor, and you stare down the barrel of a cathode ray tube. You can find evidence for this by holding a magnet up to the screen. Note the distortion. *Important: Use only a small magnet and hold it up to the screen only briefly; otherwise the distortion may become permanent.*

3.5 The Mass of an Atom Is Concentrated in Its Nucleus

It was reasoned that if atoms contained negatively charged particles, some balancing positively charged matter must also exist. From this, Thomson put forth what he called a *plum-pudding model* of the atom, shown in Figure 3.15. Further experimentation, however, soon proved this model to be wrong.

Around 1910, a more accurate picture of the atom came to one of Thomson's former students, the New Zealand physicist Ernest Rutherford (1871–1937). Rutherford oversaw the now-famous gold-foil experiment, which was the first experiment to show that the atom is mostly empty space and that most of its mass is concentrated in a tiny central core called the **atomic nucleus.**

In Rutherford's experiment, shown in Figure 3.16, a beam of positively charged particles, called alpha particles, was directed through an ultrathin sheet of gold foil. Since alpha particles were known to be thousands of times more massive than electrons, it was expected that the alpha-particle stream would not be impeded as it passed through the "atomic pudding" of gold foil. This was indeed observed to be the case—for the most part. Nearly all alpha particles passed through the gold foil undeflected and produced spots of light when they hit a fluorescent screen positioned around the gold foil. However, some particles were deflected from their straight-line path as they passed through the foil. A few of them were widely deflected, and a very few were even deflected straight back toward the source! These alpha particles must have hit something relatively massive, but what? Rutherford reasoned that undeflected particles traveled through regions of the gold foil that were empty space, as Figure 3.17 shows, and the deflected ones were repelled from extremely dense positively charged centers. Each atom, he concluded, must contain one of these centers, which he named the *atomic nucleus.*

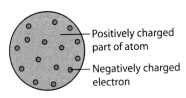

Figure 3.15
Thomson's plum-pudding model of the atom. Thomson proposed that the atom might be made of thousands of tiny, negatively charged particles swarming within a cloud of positive charge, much like plums and raisins in an old-fashioned Christmas plum pudding.

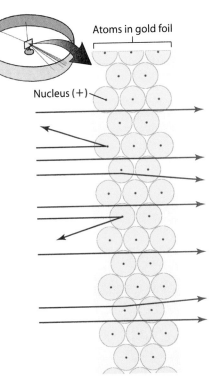

Figure 3.17
Rutherford's interpretation of the results from his gold-foil experiment. Most alpha particles passed through the empty space of the gold atoms undeflected, but a few were deflected by an atomic nucleus.

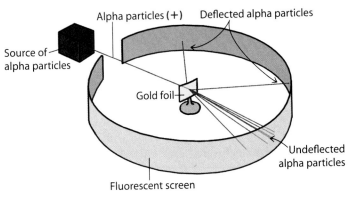

Figure 3.16
Rutherford's gold-foil experiment. A beam of positively charged alpha particles was directed at a piece of gold foil. Most of the particles passed through the foil undeflected, but some were deflected. This result implied that each gold atom was mostly empty space with a concentration of mass at its center—the atomic nucleus.

When Ernst Rutherford was 24, he placed second in a New Zealand scholarship competition to attend Cambridge University in England, but the scholarship was awarded to Rutherford after the winner decided to stay home and get married. In addition to discovering the atomic nucleus, Rutherford was also first to characterize and name many of the nuclear phenomena discussed in the following chapter. He won a Nobel prize in 1908 for showing how elements such as uranium can become different elements through the process of radioactive decay. At the time, the idea of one element transforming to another was shocking and met with great skepticism because it seemed reminiscent of alchemy.

Rutherford guessed that the atomic nucleus must have a positive electric charge to balance the negative charge of the electrons in the atom. He also guessed that the electrons were not part of this nucleus and so must be outside it but still somewhere in the atom. Today we know that, as Figure 3.18 illustrates, the electrons do indeed exist outside the nucleus, swirling around it at ultrahigh speeds. Figure 3.18 also shows that an atom is mostly empty space, with the diameter of the whole atom being about 10,000 times greater than the diameter of its nucleus. If a nucleus were the size of the period at the end of this sentence, the outer edges of the atom would be located 3.3 meters (11 feet) away. Also, because the nucleus is so dense, the mass of such a period-sized nucleus would be on the order of 2500 kilograms—the mass of a large pick-up truck.

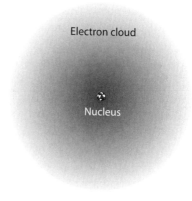

Electron cloud

Nucleus

Figure 3.18
Electrons whiz around the atomic nucleus, forming what can be best described as a cloud. If this illustration were drawn to scale, the atomic nucleus would be too small to be seen. An atom is mostly empty space.

Figure 3.19
As close as Tracy and Ian are in this photograph, none of their atoms meet. The closeness between us is in our hearts.

We and all materials around us are mostly empty space because the atoms we are made of are mostly empty space. So why don't atoms simply pass through one another? How is it that we are supported by the floor despite the empty nature of its atoms? Although subatomic particles are much smaller than the volume of the atom, the range of their electric field is several times larger than that volume. In the outer regions of any atom are electrons, which repel the electrons of neighboring atoms. Two atoms therefore can get only so close to each other before they start repelling (provided they don't join in a chemical bond, as is discussed in Chapter 6).

When the atoms of your hand push against the atoms of a wall, electrical repulsions between electrons in your hand and electrons in the wall prevent your hand from passing through the wall. These same electrical repulsions prevent us from falling through the solid floor. They also allow us the sense of touch. Interestingly, when you touch someone, your atoms and those of the other person do not meet. Instead, atoms from the two of you get close enough so that you sense an electrical repulsion. There is still a tiny, though imperceptible, gap between the two of you (Figure 3.19).

3.6 The Atomic Nucleus Is Made of Protons and Neutrons

The positive charge of any atomic nucleus was found to be equal in magnitude to the combined negative charge of all the electrons in the atom. It was thus reasoned, and then experimentally confirmed, that positively charged subatomic particles make up the nucleus. Today we call these positively charged particles **protons**. The proton is nearly 2000 times more massive than the electron. The electric charge on the proton is numerically equal to the electric charge on the electron, but, as just mentioned, the charge on the proton is positive. Thus each electron has an electric charge of -1.60×10^{-19} coulomb, and each proton has an electric charge of $+1.60 \times 10^{-19}$ coulomb. The number of protons in the nucleus of any atom is equal to the number of electrons whirling about the nucleus, and so the positive charge and negative charge cancel each other, which means the atom is electrically balanced. For example, an electrically balanced oxygen atom has eight electrons and eight protons.

Scientists have agreed to identify elements by **atomic number**, which is the number of protons each atom of a given element contains. The modern periodic table lists the elements in order of increasing atomic number. Hydrogen, with one proton per atom, has atomic number 1; helium, with two protons per atom, has atomic number 2; and so on.

Concept Check ✔

How many protons are there in an iron atom, Fe (atomic number 26)?

Was this your answer? The atomic number of an atom and its number of protons are the same. Thus, there are 26 protons in an iron atom. Another way to put this is that all atoms that contain 26 protons are, by definition, iron atoms.

If we compare the electric charges and masses of different atoms, we see that the atomic nucleus must be made up of more than just protons. Helium, for example, has twice the electric charge of hydrogen but *four* times the mass. The added mass is due to another subatomic particle found in the nucleus, the **neutron**, which was first detected in 1932 by the British physicist James Chadwick (1891–1974). The neutron has about the same mass as the proton, but it has no electric charge. Any object that has no net electric charge is said to be *electrically neutral,* and that is where the neutron got its name. We discuss the important role that neutrons play in holding the atomic nucleus together in the following chapter.

Both protons and neutrons are called **nucleons**, a term that denotes their location in the atomic nucleus.

A neutron goes into a restaurant and asks the waiter, "How much for a drink?" The waiter replies, "For you, no charge."

Table 3.1 summarizes the basic facts about our three subatomic particles.

Table 3.1

Subatomic Particles

	Particle	Charge	Relative Mass	Actual Mass* (kg)
	Electron	-1	1	9.11×10^{-31} **
Nucleons {	Proton	$+1$	1836	1.673×10^{-27}
	Neutron	0	1841	1.675×10^{-27}

* Not measured directly but calculated from experimental data.

** 9.11×10^{-31} kg = 0.00000000000000000000000000000911 kg (see Appendix A).

For any element, there is no set number of neutrons in the nucleus. For example, most hydrogen atoms (atomic number 1) have no neutrons. A small percentage, however, have one neutron, and a smaller percentage have two neutrons. Similarly, most iron atoms (atomic number 26) have 30 neutrons, but a small percentage have 29 neutrons. Atoms of the same element that contain different numbers of neutrons are **isotopes**.

We identify isotopes by their **mass number**, which is the total number of protons and neutrons (in other words, the number of nucleons) in the nucleus. As Figure 3.20 shows, a hydrogen isotope with only one proton is called hydrogen-1, where 1 is the mass number. A hydrogen isotope with one proton and one neutron is therefore hydrogen-2, and a hydrogen isotope with one proton and two neutrons is hydrogen-3. Similarly, an iron isotope with 26 protons and 30 neutrons is called iron-56, and one with only 29 neutrons is iron-55.

Figure 3.20
Isotopes of an element have the same number of protons but different numbers of neutrons and hence different mass numbers. The three hydrogen isotopes have special names: protium for hydrogen-1, deuterium for hydrogen-2, and tritium for hydrogen-3. Of these three isotopes, hydrogen-1 is most common. For most elements, such as iron, the isotopes have no special names and are indicated merely by mass number.

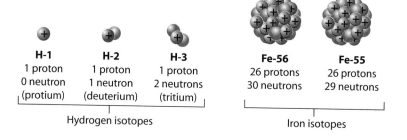

H-1	**H-2**	**H-3**	**Fe-56**	**Fe-55**
1 proton	1 proton	1 proton	26 protons	26 protons
0 neutron	1 neutron	2 neutrons	30 neutrons	29 neutrons
(protium)	(deuterium)	(tritium)		

Hydrogen isotopes   Iron isotopes

An alternative method of indicating isotopes is to write the mass number as a superscript and the atomic number as a subscript to the left of the atomic symbol. For example, an iron isotope with a mass number of 56 and atomic number of 26 is written

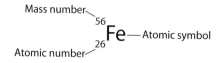

Mass number $\searrow$
$^{56}_{26}\text{Fe}$ — Atomic symbol
Atomic number $\nearrow$

The total number of neutrons in an isotope can be calculated by subtracting its atomic number from its mass number:

$$
\begin{array}{r}
\text{mass number} \\
- \text{ atomic number} \\
\hline
\text{number of neutrons}
\end{array}
$$

For example, uranium-238 has 238 nucleons. The atomic number of uranium is 92, which tells us that 92 of these 238 nucleons are protons. The remaining 146 nucleons must be neutrons:

Nucleons — $^{238}_{92}\text{U}$ — Protons

$$
\begin{array}{r}
238 \text{ protons and neutrons} \\
- \quad 92 \text{ protons} \\
\hline
146 \text{ neutrons}
\end{array}
$$

Atoms interact with one another electrically. Therefore the way any atom behaves in the presence of other atoms is largely determined by the charged particles it contains, especially its electrons. Isotopes of an element differ only by mass, not by electric charge. For this reason, isotopes of an element share many characteristics—in fact, as chemicals they cannot be distinguished from one another. For example, the way sugars containing carbon atoms with seven neutrons are digested is no different from the way sugars containing carbon atoms with six neutrons are digested. In fact, about 1 percent of the carbon we eat is the carbon-13 isotope containing seven neutrons per nucleus. The remaining 99 percent of the carbon in our diet is the more common carbon-12 isotope containing six neutrons per nucleus.

The total mass of an atom is called its **atomic mass**. This is the sum of the masses of all the atom's components (electrons, protons, and neutrons). Because electrons are so much less massive than protons and neutrons, their contribution to atomic mass is negligible. As we explore further in Section 9.5, a special unit has been developed for atomic masses. This is the *atomic mass unit*, amu, where 1 atomic mass unit is equal to 1.661×10^{-24} gram, which is slightly less than the mass of a single proton. As shown in Figure 3.21, the atomic masses listed in the periodic table are in atomic mass units. As is explored in the Calculation Corner on page 91, the atomic mass of an element as presented in the periodic table is actually the average atomic mass of its various isotopes.

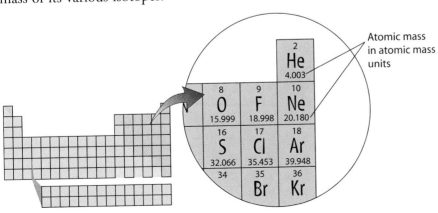

Atomic mass in atomic mass units

Figure 3.21
Helium, He, has an atomic mass of 4.003 atomic mass units, and neon, Ne, has an atomic mass of 20.17 atomic mass units.

Concept Check ✓

Distinguish between mass number and atomic mass.

Was this your answer? Both terms include the word *mass* and so are easily confused. Focus your attention on the second word of each term, however, and you'll get it right every time. Mass *number* is a count of the number of nucleons in an isotope. An atom's mass number requires no units because it is simply a count. Atomic *mass* is a measure of the total mass of an atom, which is given in atomic mass units. If necessary, atomic mass units can be converted to grams using the relationship 1 atomic mass unit $= 1.661 \times 10^{-24}$ grams.

You may recognize that the atomic masses given in the periodic table are the relative masses attendees at the 1860 chemistry conference were so avidly working toward. From the atomic masses, for example, we can easily calculate that neon atoms are $20.18/4.003 = 5.041$ times more massive than helium atoms. In this and many other regards, the periodic table is the culmination of the efforts of many talented individuals, only some of whom were discussed in this chapter. Table 3.2 summarizes all the atomic history we have covered.

When the initial discoveries about atoms were being made, scientists based their conclusions on experimental evidence, and such evidence is always open to critical review. Investigators were thus able to look beyond the biases of the past to conceive new and more accurate models of nature.

Table 3.2

Aristotle (384–322 B.C.)		Proposed that matter is continuous
Democritus (460–370 B.C.)		Proposed an atomic model for matter
Boyle (1627–1691)	1661	Identified an element as that which cannot be broken down to simpler parts
Franklin (1706–1790)	1752	Investigated the nature of electricity
Cavendish (1731–1810)	1766	Discovered hydrogen
Lavoisier (1743–1794)	1774	Developed the law of mass conservation
Priestley (1733–1804)	1774	Discovered oxygen but did not identify it
Proust (1754–1826)	1797	Proposed the law of definite proportions
Dalton (1766–1844)	1803	Developed five postulates describing the atomic model of matter
Gay-Lussac (1778–1850)	1808	Showed that gases react in definite volume ratios
Avogadro (1776–1856)	1811	Explained Gay-Lussac's observations by proposing that the particles of a gas exist as diatomic molecules
Cannizzaro (1826–1910)	1860	Reintroduced the work of Gay-Lussac and Avogadro as a reliable means of measuring relative atomic masses
Mendeleev (1834–1907)	1869	Developed a chart—forerunner to our modern periodic table—that organized the elements by properties
Thomson (1856–1940)	1897	Measured the charge-to-mass ratio for a beam of electrons
Millikan (1868–1953)	1909	Calculated the mass of an electron and found it to be smaller than the mass of the smallest known atom
Rutherford (1871–1937)	1910	Discovered the atomic nucleus
Chadwick (1891–1974)	1932	Discovered the neutron

Calculation Corner: Calculating Atomic Mass

Most elements have a variety of isotopes, each with its own atomic mass. For this reason, the atomic mass listed in the periodic table for any given element is the average of the masses of all the element's isotopes based on their relative abundance.

About 99 percent of all carbon atoms, for example, are the isotope carbon-12, and most of the remaining 1 percent are the heavier isotope carbon-13. This small amount of carbon-13 raises the *average* mass of carbon from 12.000 atomic mass units to the slightly greater value 12.011 atomic mass units.

To arrive at the atomic mass presented in the periodic table, you first multiply the mass of each naturally occurring isotope of an element by the fraction of its abundance and then add up all the fractions.

Example

Carbon-12 has a mass of 12.0000 atomic mass units and makes up 98.89 percent of naturally occurring carbon. Carbon-13 has a mass of 13.0034 atomic mass units and makes up 1.11 percent of naturally occurring carbon. Use this information to show that the atom mass of carbon shown in the periodic table, 12.011 atomic mass units, is correct.

Answer

Recognize that 98.89 percent and 1.11 percent expressed as fractions are 0.9889 and 0.0111, respectively.

	Contributing Mass of C^{12}	Contributing Mass of C^{13}
Fraction of Abundance	0.9889	0.0111
Mass (amu)	$\times$ 12.0000	$\times$ 13.0034
	11.867	0.144

step 1

step 2

atomic mass =
11.867 + 0.144 = 12.011

Your Turn

Chlorine-35 has a mass of 34.97 atomic mass units, and chlorine-37 has a mass of 36.95 atomic mass units. Determine the atomic mass of chlorine, Cl (atomic number 17), if 75.53 percent of all chlorine atoms are the chlorine-35 isotope and 24.47 percent are the chlorine-37 isotope.

Key Terms and Matching Definitions

_____ alchemy
_____ atomic mass
_____ atomic nucleus
_____ atomic number
_____ cathode ray tube
_____ electron
_____ isotope
_____ law of definite proportions
_____ law of mass conservation
_____ mass number
_____ neutron
_____ nucleon
_____ proton
_____ scientific law

1. A medieval endeavor concerned with turning other metals to gold.
2. Any scientific hypothesis that has been tested over and over again and has not been contradicted. Also known as a scientific principle.
3. A law stating that matter is neither created nor destroyed in a chemical reaction.
4. A law stating that elements combine in definite mass ratios to form compounds.
5. A device that emits a beam of electrons.
6. An extremely small, negatively charged subatomic particle found outside the atomic nucleus.
7. The dense, positively charged center of every atom.
8. A positively charged subatomic particle of the atomic nucleus.
9. A count of the number of protons in the atomic nucleus.
10. An electrically neutral subatomic particle of the atomic nucleus.
11. Any subatomic particle found in the atomic nucleus. Another name for either proton or neutron.
12. Atoms of the same element whose nuclei contain the same number of protons but different numbers of neutrons.
13. The number of nucleons (protons and neutrons) in the atomic nucleus. Used primarily to identify isotopes.
14. The mass of an element's atoms listed in the periodic table as an *average* value based on the relative abundance of the element's isotopes.

Review Questions

Chemistry Developed Out of Our Interest in Materials

1. In what ways was Aristotle's erroneous model of matter a remarkable achievement?
2. According to Aristotle's model, how is clay converted to ceramic?
3. How did chemistry benefit from alchemy?

Lavoisier Laid the Foundation of Modern Chemistry

4. How did Lavoisier define an element and a chemical compound?
5. Why did Lavoisier's mass-conservation law escape earlier investigators?
6. Who named the element oxygen?
7. What is the meaning of the word *hydrogen*?
8. How many grams of water can be formed from the reaction between 10 grams of oxygen and 1 gram of hydrogen?

Dalton Deduced That Matter Is Made of Atoms

9. How did Dalton define an element?
10. How did Dalton explain the fact that elements combine in whole-number ratios to form chemical compounds?
11. Which of Dalton's five postulates accounts for Lavoisier's mass-conservation principle?
12. According to Dalton, how do the atoms of different elements differ from one another?
13. What was Dalton's proposed formula for water?
14. In what volume ratio do hydrogen gas and oxygen gas react to form water?
15. How did Avogadro account for the formation of two volumes of water from two volumes of hydrogen and one volume of oxygen?
16. When was Avogadro's hypothesis finally accepted by the scientific community?
17. What observation led Mendeleev to develop his early version of the periodic table?

The Electron Was the First Subatomic Particle Discovered

18. What is a cathode ray?

19. Why is a cathode ray deflected by a nearby electric charge or magnet?

20. What did Thomson discover about the electron?

21. Why couldn't Thomson calculate the mass of the electron?

22. What did Millikan discover about the electron?

The Mass of an Atom Is Concentrated in Its Nucleus

23. What did Rutherford discover about the atom?

24. What was the fate of the vast majority of alpha particles in Rutherford's gold-foil experiment?

25. To Rutherford's surprise, what was the fate of a tiny fraction of alpha particles in the gold-foil experiment?

26. What kind of force prevents atoms from squishing into one another?

The Atomic Nucleus Is Made of Protons and Neutrons

27. A proton is how much more massive than an electron?

28. Compare the electric charge on the proton with the electric charge on the electron.

29. What is the definition of atomic number?

30. What role does atomic number play in the periodic table?

31. What effect do isotopes of a given element have on the atomic mass calculated for that element?

32. Name two nucleons.

33. Distinguish between atomic number and mass number.

34. Distinguish between mass number and atomic mass.

Hands-On Chemistry Insights

Air Out

As the iron rusts, it absorbs oxygen molecules from the air in the jar. This allows the water to rise into the jar. How far the water rises is a function of the amount of oxygen removed. You can find out how much oxygen was removed by rubber-banding a ruler to the jar such that the zero mark on the ruler is at the initial water level inside the jar. When the water stops rising, divide the water height inside the jar by the height of the air that was initially inside the jar. The fraction you obtain gives a rough estimate of the percentage of air removed from the jar, which corresponds to the percentage of oxygen in the atmosphere. How close do you come to the accepted value of 21 percent?

You might also make a graph plotting the water height in the inverted jar at successive 10-minute intervals. Why does the graph gradually level off? What effect does the volume of the steel wool have on your data?

Collecting Bubbles

Don't restrict yourself to the setup given in this hands-on activity. Improvise with available household items, and you may well devise a more successful way of collecting the carbon dioxide. Consider, for example, using either rubber tubing or a drinking straw to connect the CO_2 source to the inverted bottle. You can shape one end of the tubing into a J shape by inserting a straightened paper clip into the tubing and then bending the clip until the tubing end remains curved. Then slip the curved end into the inverted bottle.

In this activity, always be wary of the pressure that builds up when baking soda and vinegar are mixed in a closed container.

You can pour the carbon dioxide over the flame of a birthday candle. As the carbon dioxide flows out of the bottle, it falls onto the candle and extinguishes the flame. (Don't tilt the bottle too far or some water will pour out.) At times, you may see the motion of the carbon dioxide by the streaming of the smoke from the extinguished candle. This is all evidence that carbon dioxide is heavier than air.

Bending Electrons

If you can find one, a black-and-white television or computer monitor shows this effect most vividly. On a color screen, you'll see color changes in addition to the distortions. Most televisions and monitors today are equipped with automatic "degaussers" that alleviate distortion from the magnets in a nearby audio speaker or even from the Earth's magnetic field.

Are the distortions you see the same for both ends of the magnet?

Exercises

1. A cat strolls across your backyard. An hour later, a dog with its nose to the ground follows the trail of the cat. Explain what is going on from a molecular point of view.

2. If all the molecules of a body remained part of that body, would the body have any odor?

3. Which are older, the atoms in the body of an elderly person or those in the body of a baby?

4. Where did the atoms that make up a newborn baby originate?

5. In what sense can you truthfully say that you are a part of every person around you?

6. Considering how small atoms are, what are the chances that at least one of the atoms exhaled in your first breath will be in your last breath?

7. Describe how Lavoisier used the scientific approach (observation, questions, hypothesis, predictions, tests) in his development of the principle of mass conservation.

8. Lavoisier heated a piece of tin on a floating block of wood covered by a glass jar. As the tin decomposed, the water level inside the jar rose. How did Lavoisier explain this result?

9. According to Proust, why are only 9 grams of water formed when 10 grams of oxygen reacts with 1 gram of hydrogen?

10. Substances A and B combine to make substance C. Substances C and B combine to make substances A and D. Place the letter of each substance next to the symbol that best describes its atomic or molecular structure:

11. Proust noted that oxygen and hydrogen react in an 8:1 ratio, whereas Gay-Lussac noted that they react in a 1:2 ratio. Who was right? Defend your answer.

12. Two of the substances in Exercise 10 are elements and two are compounds. Which are which?

13. A sample of iron weighs more after it rusts. Why?

14. The following diagram depicts the reaction between gaseous oxygen, O_2, and gaseous hydrogen, H_2, to form water vapor, H_2O. What symbols and how many of them should be drawn in the empty box? How many grams of water are formed under these conditions? How many grams of what chemical remain unreacted?

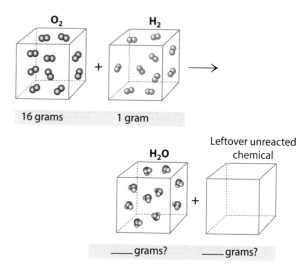

15. How did Avogadro account for Dalton's observation that a given volume of oxygen gas weighs more than an equal volume of water vapor?

16. If all atoms had the same mass, and 8 grams of oxygen still reacted with 1 gram of hydrogen, what would be the formula for water?

17. The following diagrams depict the reaction between gaseous chlorine, Cl_2, and gaseous hydrogen, H_2, to form gaseous hydrogen chloride, HCl. What should be drawn in the empty boxes? Specify the quantities beneath each box.

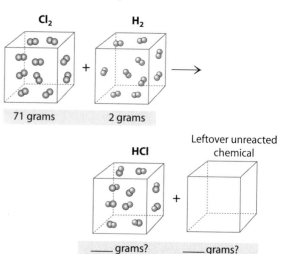

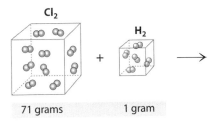

Cl₂   H₂

71 grams   1 gram

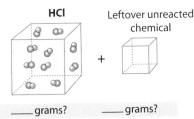

HCl   Leftover unreacted chemical

_____ grams?   _____ grams?

18. Gas A is composed of diatomic molecules (two atoms per molecule) of a pure element. Gas B is composed of triatomic molecules (three atoms per molecule) of another pure element. A volume of gas B is found to be three times heavier than an equal volume of gas A. How does the mass of an atom of gas B compare with the mass of an atom of gas A?

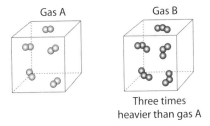

Gas A   Gas B

Three times heavier than gas A

19. Max Planck, a famous physicist of the early 20th century, is quoted as saying, "A new scientific truth does not triumph by convincing its opponents and making them see the light, but rather because its opponents eventually die and a new generation grows up." Cite a case where this statement applies to the development of modern chemistry.

20. How might Planck's statement apply to politics or religion?

21. Of all the investigators presented in this chapter, who was the youngest at the time of his discovery besides Democritus and Aristotle? (See Table 3.2.)

22. Why is it important for a chemist to know the relative masses of atoms? Why do we refer to relative masses rather than absolute masses?

23. If the particles of a cathode ray had a greater electric charge, would the ray be bent more or less in a magnetic field?

24. Why did Rutherford assume that the atomic nucleus was positively charged?

25. Why does the ray of light in a neon sign bend when a magnet is held up to it?

26. How does Rutherford's model of the atom explain why some of the alpha particles directed at the gold foil were deflected straight back toward the source?

27. Which of the following diagrams best represents the size of the atomic nucleus relative to the size of the atom:

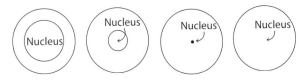

28. If two protons and two neutrons are removed from the nucleus of an oxygen atom, what nucleus remains?

29. You could swallow a capsule of germanium, Ge (atomic number 32), without ill effects. If a proton were added to each germanium nucleus, however, you would not want to swallow the capsule. Why? (Consult a periodic table of the elements.)

30. If an atom has 43 electrons, 56 neutrons, and 43 protons, what is its approximate atomic mass? What is the name of this element?

31. The nucleus of an electrically neutral iron atom contains 26 protons. How many electrons does this iron atom have?

32. Evidence for the existence of neutrons did not come until many years after the discoveries of the electron and the proton. Give a possible explanation.

33. Which has more atoms: a 1-gram sample of carbon-12 or a 1-gram sample of carbon-13? Explain.

34. Why are the atomic masses listed in the periodic table not whole numbers?

Problems

1. How many grams of water can be produced by the combination of 8 grams of oxygen and 8 grams of hydrogen?

2. How many grams of water can be produced from the combination of 25 grams of hydrogen and 225 grams of oxygen? How much of which element will be left over?

3. The isotope lithium-7 has a mass of 7.0160 atomic mass units, and the isotope lithium-6 has a mass of 6.0151 atomic mass units. Given the information that 92.58 percent of all lithium atoms found in nature are lithium-7 and 7.42 percent are lithium-6, calculate the atomic mass of lithium, Li (atomic number 3).

4. The element bromine, Br (atomic number 35), has two major isotopes of similar abundance, both around 50 percent. The atomic mass of bromine is reported in the periodic table as 79.904 atomic mass units. Choose the most likely set of mass numbers for these two bromine isotopes: (a) ^{80}Br, ^{81}Br; (b) ^{79}Br, ^{80}Br; (c) ^{79}Br, ^{81}Br.

Answers to Calculation Corner

Finding Out How Much of a Chemical Reacts

1. The fact that 14 grams nitrogen reacts fully with 3 grams of hydrogen gives you two conversion factors:

$$\frac{14 \text{ g nitrogen}}{3 \text{ g hydrogen}} \quad \text{and} \quad \frac{3 \text{ g hydrogen}}{14 \text{ g nitrogen}}$$

Use the second conversion factor to convert the 7.0 grams of nitrogen to grams of hydrogen:

$$7.0 \text{ g nitrogen} \times \frac{3.0 \text{ g hydrogen}}{14 \text{ g nitrogen}} = 1.5 \text{ g hydrogen}$$

(See Appendix B for why 3.0 g is used rather than 3 g.)

2. From the preceding answer, you know that 7.0 grams of nitrogen reacts with 1.5 grams of hydrogen to form 7.0 grams + 1.5 grams = 8.5 grams of ammonia. If 6.0 grams of hydrogen is mixed with 7.0 grams of nitrogen, only 1.5 grams of that 6.0 grams reacts, so still only 8.5 grams of ammonia is formed. A total of 6.0 grams − 1.5 grams = 4.5 grams of hydrogen remains unreacted.

Calculating Atomic Mass

	Contributing Mass of ^{35}C	Contributing Mass of ^{37}C
Fraction of Abundance	0.7553	0.2447
Mass (amu)	× 34.97	× 36.95
	26.41	9.04

atomic mass = 26.41 + 9.04
= 35.45

Suggested Readings and Web Sites

Jean-Pierre Poirer (translated by Rebecca Balinski), *Lavoisier: Chemist, Biologist, Economist.* Philadelphia: University of Pennsylvania Press, 1997.
   An authoritative and detailed look at the life and times of the father of modern chemistry. With an intriguing account of the dynamics leading to his execution, this book explores Lavoisier's life not only as a chemist but as an accountant, administrator, educator, and tax collector.

Hugh Salzburg, *From Caveman to Chemist: Circumstances and Achievements.* Washington, DC: American Chemical Society, 1991.
   An easy to read, informative, absorbing account of the history of chemistry.

http://www.aip.org/history/electron/jjthomson.htm
   An in-depth presentation of the discovery of the electron by J. J. Thomson.

http://www.woodrow.org/teachers/ci/1992/
   A series of insightful biographies of historical figures in chemistry, written by participants at the 1992 Institute on the History of Chemistry and sponsored by the Woodrow Wilson National Fellowship Foundation.

Chapter 4
The Atomic Nucleus

Nuclear fission

Uranium-235 nucleus

Neutron

Know Nukes

Nuclear power plants generate electricity in much the same way fossil-fuel power plants do. Water is heated to create steam that, in expanding, can be used to turn electricity-generating turbines. The fundamental difference between these two types of power plants is the fuel used to heat the water. A fossil-fuel plant burns fossil fuel, such as coal or petroleum, but a nuclear plant, such as the one shown in this chapter's opening photograph, uses the heat created by nuclear fission to heat the water.

The burning of fossil fuel is a chemical reaction, which, as you recall from Section 2.1, is a reaction that involves changes in the way atoms are bonded and results in the formation of new materials. For fossil fuels, these new materials are mostly carbon dioxide and water vapor. As we explore in future chapters, the ability of atoms to form new materials in a chemical reaction has only to do with their ability to share or exchange *electrons*—the atomic nucleus is not directly involved. The chemistry of an atom is therefore more a function of its electrons than of its nucleus. Nuclear fission, by contrast, involves *nuclear reactions*, which, as shown in the chapter opening photograph, involve the atomic nucleus. In this sense, the study of the atomic nucleus is not a primary focus of chemistry.

Nuclear processes, however, have certainly impacted society, raising many issues regarding our health, energy sources, and national security. At the same time, the atomic nucleus is one of the most misunderstood areas of science. Public fears about anything *nuclear* are much like the fears people had about electricity a century ago. Since that time, however, society has determined that the benefits of electricity outweigh the risks. Today, we are making similar decisions about the risks and benefits of nuclear technology. In order that we make the best possible decisions, everyone should have an adequate understanding of the atomic nucleus and its processes. So, as part of our study of the atom, we briefly turn to the atomic nucleus and the related concept of radioactivity. We shall then be set to revisit the nucleus in Chapter 19 when we study energy sources.

4.1 The Cathode Ray Led to the Discovery of Radioactivity

In 1896, the German physicist Wilhelm Roentgen (1845–1923) discovered a "new kind of ray" emanating from a point where cathode rays hit the glass surface of a high-voltage cathode ray tube. (Recall from Chapter 3 that a cathode ray is a beam of electrons.) Unlike cathode rays, these new rays were not deflected by either an electric field or a magnetic field. Furthermore, they could pass through opaque materials.

Roentgen discovered this latter property when he let the rays fall on a photographic plate wrapped in a black paper thick enough to keep all visible light from falling on the plate. A photographic plate is coated with light-sensitive chemicals, and when light falls on the chemicals, the plate is said to have been *exposed* to the light. Light is one form of radiation, as we shall learn in Chapter 5, and Roentgen's rays are another form of radiation. Because the rays were able to pass through the lightproof paper in which Roentgen's plate was wrapped, the rays exposed the plate, as Figure 4.1 shows. Not able to deduce the nature of these rays, Roentgen called them X rays.

Figure 4.1
X rays can pass through solid materials. The denser a material, however, the greater its ability to block X rays. Bones, for example, are more effective at blocking X rays than is soft tissue. For this reason, the region of the plate lying below the bone parts of the hand are less exposed than are the regions lying below the tissue parts. As a result, the shadow of bones shows up clearly on the plate.

X rays

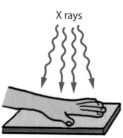

Photographic film enclosed in lightproof holder

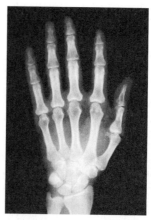

Exposed and developed photographic film

A few months after Roentgen announced his discovery of X rays, the French physicist Antoine Henri Becquerel (1852–1908) experimented to see if they were emitted by phosphorescent substances—those that glow in the dark after being exposed to bright light. One substance that appeared to confirm the idea that phosphorescence resulted in X rays was uranium. When placed in the sunlight and on top of a photographic plate wrapped in dark paper, uranium exposed the photographic plate much the way X rays from the cathode ray tube did. When cloudy weather forced Becquerel to suspend his research, he stored the uranium and a photographic plate together in a closed drawer. Several days later on a whim, he thought to develop the plate, and to his amazement, he saw something like what is shown in Figure 4.2—the plate had been exposed to some sort of rays without sunlight or any other source of energy. The rays must have originated from the uranium! Subsequent experiments revealed that these rays emanating from the uranium had nothing to do with X rays or phosphorescence.

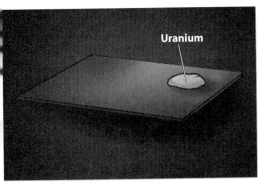

Photographic film enclosed in lightproof paper and stored in total darkness

Developed photographic film

Figure 4.2
Becquerel noted that a piece of uranium left on a photographic plate wrapped in opaque black paper exposed the plate even in the absence of light. From this he deduced that the uranium was giving off some sort of radiation.

A couple of years later, one of Becquerel's students, Marie Sklodowska Curie (1867–1934), shown in Figure 4.3, became keenly interested in this strange form of radiation. She showed that the radiation was also emitted by several other elements known at the time and suggested that it should be possible to isolate yet undiscovered elements by studying any radiation they might be emitting. Using chemical techniques, she and her husband, Pierre Curie (1859–1906), laboriously divided an 8-ton pile of uranium ore

Figure 4.3
For their work on radioactivity, (a) Becquerel and (b) the Curies shared the 1903 Nobel Prize in Physics.

(a)

(b)

into fractions, keeping those fractions giving off high levels of radiation and discarding the rest. The Curies used the term **radioactivity** to describe the tendency of these elements to emit radiation. Ultimately, they succeeded in isolating purified samples of two new radioactive elements. Marie named the first element *polonium* after her native Poland and the second *radium* because of its intense radioactivity.

The Three Major Products of Radioactivity Are Alpha, Beta, and Gamma Rays

At about the time the Curies were isolating new radioactive elements, Ernest Rutherford discovered that there are at least two major forms of radioactivity, which he identified as alpha rays and beta rays. Alpha rays, he found, consist of positively charged particles he called alpha particles. As discussed in Section 3.5, these are the particles he used in his discovery of the atomic nucleus. An **alpha particle** is a combination of two protons and two neutrons (in other words, it is the nucleus of a helium atom, atomic number 2). Beta rays he found to be identical to cathode rays. A **beta particle** therefore is simply another name for an electron ejected from a nucleus.

Shortly after Rutherford had identified alpha and beta rays, a third major form of radioactivity, gamma rays, was discovered by other investigators. Unlike alpha and beta rays, **gamma rays** carry no electric charge and have no mass. Instead, they are an extremely energetic form of nonvisible light.

As is shown in Figure 4.4, the three major types of radiation given off by radioactive materials can be separated by putting a magnetic field across their paths.

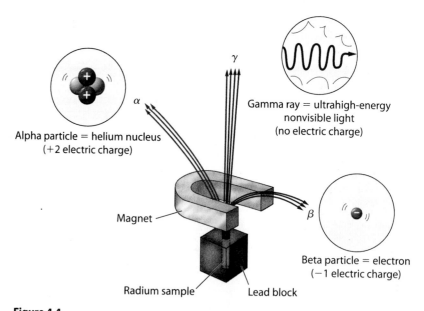

Figure 4.4
The three most common forms of radiation coming from a radioactive substance are called by the first three letters of the Greek alphabet, α, β, γ—alpha, beta, and gamma. In a magnetic field, alpha rays bend one way, beta rays bend the other way, and gamma rays do not bend at all. Note that the alpha rays bend less than do the beta rays. This happens because the alpha particles have more inertia (because they have more mass) than the beta particles. The source of all three radiations is a radioactive material placed at the bottom of a hole drilled in a lead block.

Alpha particles do not easily penetrate solid material because of their relatively large size and their double positive charge (+2). Because of their great kinetic energies, however, alpha particles can cause significant damage to the surface of a material, especially living tissue. As they travel through air, even through distances as short as a few centimeters, alpha particles pick up electrons, slow down, and become harmless helium. Almost all the Earth's helium atoms, including those in a helium balloon, were once energetic alpha particles ejected from radioactive elements.

Beta particles are normally faster than alpha particles and not as easy to stop. For this reason, they are able to penetrate light materials such as paper and clothing. They can penetrate fairly deeply into skin, where they have the potential for harming or killing cells. They are not able to penetrate deeply into denser materials, however, such as aluminum. Beta particles, once stopped, become part of the material they are in, like any other electron.

Like visible light, a gamma ray is pure energy. The amount of energy in a gamma ray is much greater than the amount of energy in visible light. Because they have no mass or electric charge and because of their high energies, gamma rays are able to penetrate through most materials. However, they cannot penetrate unusually dense materials such as lead, which absorbs them. Delicate molecules in cells throughout our bodies that are exposed to gamma rays suffer structural damage. Hence, gamma rays are generally more harmful to us than alpha or beta rays.

Figure 4.5 shows the relative penetrating power of the three types of radiation, and Figure 4.6 shows an interesting practical use for gamma radiation.

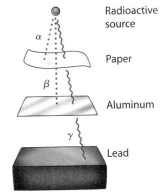

Figure 4.5
Alpha particles are the least penetrating form of radiation and can be stopped by a sheet of paper. Beta particles readily pass through paper but not through a sheet of aluminum. Gamma rays penetrate several centimeters into solid lead.

Figure 4.6
The shelf life of fresh strawberries and other perishables is markedly increased when the food is subjected to gamma rays from a radioactive source. The strawberries on the right were treated with gamma radiation, which kills the microorganisms that normally lead to spoilage. The food is only a receiver of radiation and is in no way transformed to an emitter of radiation as can be confirmed with a radiation detector.

Concept Check ✔

> Pretend you are given three radioactive rocks—one an alpha emitter, one a beta emitter, and one a gamma emitter. You can throw one away, but of the remaining two, you must hold one in your hand and place the other in your pocket. What can you do to minimize your exposure to radiation?

Was this your answer? Ideally you should get as far from all the rocks as possible. If you must hold one and put one in your pocket, however, hold the alpha emitter because the skin on your hand will shield you. Put the beta emitter in your pocket because its rays might be stopped by the combined thickness of clothing and skin. Throw away the gamma emitter because its rays would penetrate deep into your body from either of these places.

4.2 Radioactivity Is a Natural Phenomenon

A common misconception is that radioactivity is new in the environment, but it has been around far longer than the human race. It is as much a part of our environment as the sun and the rain. It has always occurred in the soil we walk on and in the air we breathe, and it warms the interior of the Earth and makes it molten. The energy released by radioactive substances in the Earth's interior heats the water that spurts from a geyser and the water that wells up from a natural hot spring.

As Figure 4.7 shows, most of the radiation we encounter is natural background radiation that originates in the Earth and in space and was present long before we humans got here. Even the cleanest air we breathe is somewhat radioactive as a result of bombardment by cosmic rays. At sea level, the protective blanket of the atmosphere reduces background radiation, but at higher altitudes radiation is more intense. In Denver, the "Mile-High City," a person receives more than twice as much radiation from cosmic rays as at sea level. A couple of round-trip flights between New York and San Francisco exposes us to as much radiation as we receive in a chest X ray at the doctor's office. The air time of airline personnel is limited because of this extra radiation.

Cells are able to repair most kinds of molecular damage caused by radiation if the damage is not too severe. A cell can survive an otherwise lethal dose of radiation if the dose is spread over a long period of time to allow intervals for healing. When radiation is sufficient to kill cells, the dead cells can be replaced by new ones. Sometimes radiation alters the genetic information of a cell by damaging its DNA molecules (see Section 13.5). New cells arising from the damaged cell retain the altered genetic information, which is called a *mutation*. Usually the effects of a mutation are insignificant, but occasionally the mutation results in cells that do not function as well as unaffected ones, sometimes leading to a cancer. If the damaged DNA is in an individual's reproductive cells, the genetic code of the individual's offspring may retain the mutation.

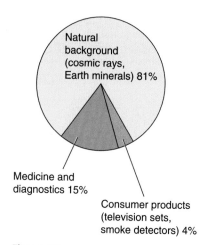

Medicine and diagnostics 15%

Consumer products (television sets, smoke detectors) 4%

Figure 4.7
Origins of radiation exposure for an average individual in the United States.

Rads and Rems Are Units of Radiation

Radiation dosage is often measured in rads (*r*adiation *a*bsorbed *d*ose), a unit of absorbed energy. One **rad** is equal to 0.01 joule of radiant energy absorbed per kilogram of tissue.

The capacity for nuclear radiation to cause damage is not a function just of the energy of the radiation, however. There are different forms of radiation, some more harmful than others. Suppose you have two arrows, one with a pointed tip and one with a suction cup at its tip. Shoot the two of them at an apple at the same speed and they have the same amount of kinetic energy. The one with the pointed tip, however, will invariably do more damage to the apple than the one with the suction cup. Similarly, some forms of radiation cause greater harm than other forms even when we receive the same number of rads from both forms.

We measure the ability of radiation to cause harm in rems (*r*oentgen *e*quivalent *m*an). In calculating dosage in **rems**, we multiply the number of rads by a factor that accounts for the different health effects of different types of radiation and is determined by clinical studies. For example, 1 rad of alpha particles has the same biological effect as 10 rads of beta particles, and so the multiplying factor for alpha particles is 10. We call both of these dosages 10 rems:

Particle	Radiation dosage		Factor		Health effect
Alpha	1 rad	×	10	=	10 rems
Beta	10 rads	×	1	=	10 rems

Concept Check ✓

Would you rather be exposed to 1 rad of alpha particles or 1 rad of beta particles?

Was this your answer? Multiply these quantities by the appropriate factor to get the dosages in rems. Alpha: 1 rad × 10 = 10 rems; beta: 1 rad × 1 = 1 rem. The factors show us that, physiologically speaking, alpha particles are ten times more damaging than beta particles.

Lethal doses of radiation begin at 500 rems. A person has about a 50 percent chance of surviving a dose of this magnitude received over a short period of time. During radiation therapy, a patient may receive localized doses in excess of 200 rems each day for a period of weeks (Figure 4.8).

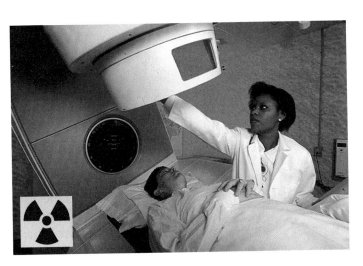

Figure 4.8
Nuclear radiation is focused on harmful tissue, such as a cancerous tumor, to selectively kill or shrink the tissue in a technique known as *radiation therapy*. This application of nuclear radiation has saved millions of lives—a clear-cut example of the benefits of nuclear technology. The inset shows the international symbol indicating an area where radioactive material is being handled or produced.

All the radiation we receive from natural sources and medical procedures is only a fraction of 1 rem. For convenience, the smaller unit *millirem* is used, where 1 millirem (mrem) is 1/1000 of a rem.

The average person in the United States is exposed to about 360 millirems a year, as Table 4.1 indicates. About 80 percent of this radiation comes from natural sources, such as cosmic rays (radiation from our sun as well as other stars) and the Earth. A typical diagnostic X ray exposes a person to between 5 and 30 millirems (0.005 and 0.030 rem), less than 1/10,000 of the lethal dose. Interestingly, the human body is a significant source of natural radiation, primarily from the potassium we ingest. Our bodies contain about 200 grams of potassium. Of this quantity, about 20 milligrams is the radioactive isotope potassium-40, a gamma-ray emitter. In a human body, about 5000 potassium-40 atoms emit pulses of radioactivity in the time it takes the heart to beat once.

Table 4.1

Annual Radiation Exposure

Source	Typical Amount Received in One Year
Natural Origin	
Cosmic radiation	26
Ground	33
Air (radon-222)	198
Human tissues (potassium-40; radium-226)	35
Human Origin	
Medical procedures	
Diagnostic X rays	40
Nuclear medicine	15
Television tubes, other consumer products	11
Weapons-test fallout	1

The leading source of naturally occurring radiation, however, is radon-222, an inert gas arising from uranium deposits. Radon is heavier than air and therefore tends to accumulate in basements after it seeps up through cracks in the floor. Levels of radon vary from region to region, depending on local geology. You can check the radon level in your home with a radon detection kit like the one shown in Figure 4.9. If levels are abnormally high, corrective measures, such as sealing the basement floor and walls and maintaining adequate ventilation, are recommended. The U.S. Environmental Protection Agency projects that anywhere from 7000 to 30,000 cases of lung cancer each year are attributed to radon exposure. Smokers who inhale the radon that occurs naturally in tobacco smoke are at particularly high risk.

About one-fifth of our annual exposure to radiation comes from non-natural sources, primarily medical procedures. Television sets, fallout from nuclear testing, and the coal and nuclear power industries are minor but significant non-natural sources. Interestingly, the coal industry far outranks the nuclear power industry as a source of radiation. The global combustion of coal annually releases into the atmosphere about 13,000 tons of radioactive thorium and uranium. Worldwide, the nuclear power industries generate about 10,000 tons of radioactive waste each year. Most of this waste is

Figure 4.9
A commercially available radon test kit for the home.

contained, however, and is *not* released into the environment. As we explore n Chapter 19, where to bury this contained radioactive waste is a heated ssue yet to be resolved.

Hands-On Chemistry: Personal Radiation

We all live with radiation. It was in our environment well before the discovery of the atom and even before the first human civilization. Recent technologies, however, have increased our exposure. Use the following worksheet to estimate your annual exposure.

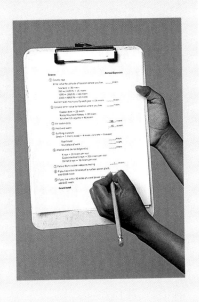

Source	Annual Exposure
1. Cosmic rays	
Enter value for altitude of location where you live:	_____mrem
Sea level = 30 mrem	
500 m (1650 ft) = 35 mrem	
1000 m (3300 ft) = 40 mrem	
2000 m (6600 ft) = 60 mrem	
Airline travel: Hours you fly each year × 0.6 mrem	_____mrem
2. Ground: enter value for location where you live:	_____mrem
Coastal state = 23 mrem	
Rocky Mountain Plateau = 90 mrem	
All other U.S. regions = 46 mrem	
3. Air (radon-222):	__198__ mrem
4. Food and water:	__40__ mrem
5. Building materials	
(brick = 7 mrem; wood = 4 mrem; concrete = 8 mrem)	
Your house	_____mrem
Your place of work	_____mrem
6. Medical and dental diagnostics	_____mrem
X rays = 20 mrem per visit	
Gastrointestinal X rays = 200 mrem per visit	
Dental X rays = 10 mrem per visit	
Radiation therapy (ask your radiologist)	
7. Fallout from nuclear weapons testing	__1__ mrem
8. If you live within 50 miles of a nuclear power plant, add 0.009 mrem	_____mrem
9. If you live within 50 miles of a coal power plant, add 0.03 mrem	_____mrem
Grand total	_____**mrem**

Data from the U.S. Environmental Protection Agency and the National Council for Radiation Protection. See the Web page http://www.epa.gov/rpdweb00/students/calculate.html for a more detailed calculation.

4.3 Radioactive Isotopes Are Useful as Tracers and for Medical Imaging

Radioactive isotopes can be incorporated into molecules whose location can be traced by the radiation they emit. When used in this way, radioactive isotopes are called *tracers*, and Figure 4.10 shows one use. To check the action of a fertilizer, researchers incorporate radioactive isotopes into the molecules of the fertilizer and then apply the fertilizer to plants. The amount taken up by the plants can be measured with radiation detectors. From such measurements, scientists can tell farmers how much fertilizer to use because fertilizer uptake is a physical and chemical process that is not affected by the radioactivity of the materials involved.

Fertilizer with radioactive isotope applied to crop   Radioactivity detected in plant

Figure 4.10
Tracking fertilizer uptake with a radioactive isotope.

Tracers are also used in industry. Motor oil manufacturers can quantify the lubricating qualities of their products by running oil in engines containing small but measurable amounts of radioactive isotopes. As the engine runs and the pistons rub against the inner chambers, some of the metal from the engine invariably makes its way into the motor oil, and this metal carries with it the embedded radioactive isotopes. The better the lubricating qualities of a motor oil, the fewer radioactive isotopes it will contain after running in the engine for a given length of time.

In a technique known as *medical imaging*, tracers are used in medicine for the diagnosis of internal disorders. Small amounts of a radioactive material, such as sodium iodide, NaI, containing the radioactive isotope iodine-131, are administered to a patient and traced through the body with a radiation detector. The result, shown in Figure 4.11, is an image that shows how the material is distributed in the body. This technique works because the path the tracer material takes is influenced only by its physical and chemical properties, not by its radioactivity. The tracer may be introduced alone or along with some other chemical, known as a *carrier compound*, that helps target the isotope to a particular type of tissue in the body.

Table 4.2 lists the uses of a number of radioactive isotopes.

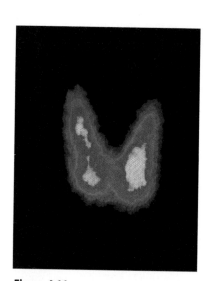

Figure 4.11
The thyroid gland, located in the neck, absorbs much of the iodine that enters the body in food and drink. This image of the gland was obtained by giving a patient the radioactive isotope iodine-131. Such images are useful in diagnosing metabolic disorders.

Table 4.2

Uses for various radioactive isotopes

Isotope	Usage
Calcium-47	Used in the study of bone formation in mammals
Californium-252	Used to inspect airline luggage for explosives
Hydrogen-3 (tritium)	Used for life science and drug metabolism studies to ensure safety of potential new drugs
Iodine-131	Used to diagnose and treat thyroid disorders
Iridium-192	Used to test integrity of pipeline welds, boilers, and aircraft parts
Thallium-201	Used in cardiology and for tumor detection
Xenon-133	Used in lung ventilation studies and blood flow studies

Source: Nuclear Regulatory Council

4.4 Radioactivity Results from an Imbalance of Forces in the Nucleus

We know that electric charges of like sign repel one another. So how is it possible that all the positively charged protons of the nucleus can stay clumped together? This question led to the discovery of an attractive force that is called the **strong nuclear force**, which acts between all nucleons. This force is very strong but only over extremely short distances (about 10^{-15} meter, the diameter of a typical atomic nucleus). Repulsive electrical interactions, on the other hand, are relatively long-ranged. Figure 4.12 compares the strength of these two forces over distance. For protons that are close together, as in a small atomic nucleus, the attractive strong nuclear force easily overcomes the repulsive electric force. For protons that are far apart, like those on opposite edges of a large nucleus, the attractive strong nuclear force may be smaller than the repulsive electric force.

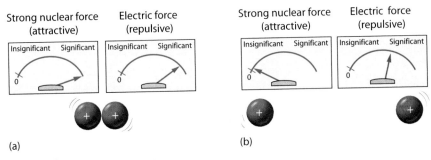

Figure 4.12
(a) Two protons near each other experience both an attractive strong nuclear force and a repulsive electric force. At this tiny separation distance, the strong nuclear force overcomes the electric force, and as a result the protons stay close together. (b) When the two protons are relatively far from each other, the electric force is more significant than the strong nuclear force, and as a result the protons repulse each other. It is this proton–proton repulsion in large atomic nuclei that causes radioactivity.

Because the strong nuclear force decreases over distance, a large nucleus is not as stable as a small one, as shown in Figure 14.13. In other words, a large atomic nucleus is more susceptible to falling apart and emitting high-energy particles or gamma rays. This process is radioactivity which, because it involves the decay of the atomic nucleus, is sometimes also called *radioactive decay.*

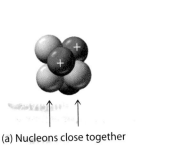

(a) Nucleons close together

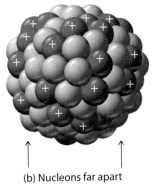

(b) Nucleons far apart

Figure 4.13
(a) All nucleons in a small atomic nucleus are close to one another; hence, they experience an attractive strong nuclear force. (b) Nucleons on opposite sides of a large nucleus are not as close to one another, and so the attractive strong nuclear forces holding them together are much weaker. The result is that the large nucleus is less stable.

Neutrons serve as "nuclear cement" holding the atomic nucleus together. Protons attract both other protons and neutrons by the strong nuclear force, but they also repel other protons by the electric force. Neutrons, on the other hand, have no electric charge and so only attract protons and other neutrons by the strong nuclear force. The presence of neutrons therefore adds to the attraction among nucleons and helps hold the nucleus together, as illustrated in Figure 4.14.

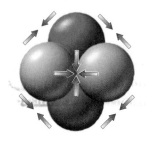

All nucleons, both protons and neutrons, attract one another by the strong nuclear force.

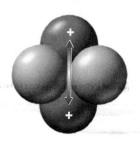

Only protons repel one another by the electric force.

Figure 4.14
The presence of neutrons helps hold the atomic nucleus together by increasing the effect of the attractive strong nuclear force, represented by the single-headed arrows.

The more protons there are in a nucleus, the more neutrons are needed to help balance the repulsive electric forces. For light elements, it is sufficient to have about as many neutrons as protons. The most common isotope of carbon, carbon-12, for instance, has six protons and six neutrons. For large nuclei, more neutrons than protons are required. Remember that the strong nuclear force diminishes rapidly with increasing distance between nucleons. Nucleons must be practically touching in order for the strong nuclear force to be effective. Nucleons on opposite sides of a large atomic nucleus are not as attracted to one another. The electric force, however, does not diminish by much across the diameter of a large nucleus and so begins to win out over the strong nuclear force. To compensate for the weakening of the strong nuclear force across the diameter of the nucleus, large nuclei have more neutrons than protons. Lead, for example, has about one and a half times as many neutrons as protons.

Concept Check ✔

Two protons in an atomic nucleus repel each other, but they are also attracted to each other. Explain.

Was this your answer? Two protons repel each other by the electric force, true, but they also attract each other by the strong nuclear force. Both forces act simultaneously. So long as the attractive strong nuclear force is more influential than the repulsive electric force, the protons remain together. Under conditions where the electric force overcomes the strong nuclear force, the protons fly apart.

Neutrons are stabilizing and large nuclei require an abundance of them. Neutrons, however, are not always successful in keeping a nucleus intact, for two reasons. First, neutrons are not stable when they are by themselves. A lone neutron will spontaneously transform to a proton and an electron, as shown in Figure 4.15a. A neutron seems to need protons around to keep

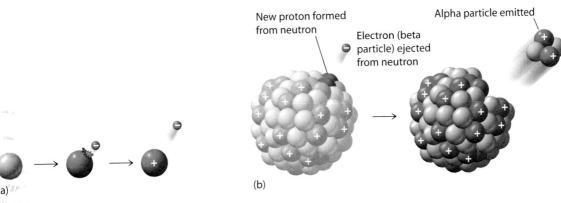

New proton formed
from neutron

Electron (beta
particle) ejected
from neutron

Alpha particle emitted

(a)

(b)

Figure 4.15
(a) A neutron near a proton is stable, but a neutron by itself is unstable and decays to a proton
by emitting an electron. (b) Destabilized by an increase in the number of protons, the nucleus
begins to shed fragments, such as alpha particles.

this from happening. After the size of a nucleus reaches a certain point,
there are so many more neutrons than protons that there are not enough
protons in the mix to prevent the neutrons from turning into protons. As
neutrons in a nucleus change to protons, the stability of the nucleus
decreases because the repulsive electric force becomes more and more significant. The result is that pieces of the nucleus fragment away in the form
of radiation, as Figure 4.15b shows.

The second reason the stabilizing effect of neutrons is limited is that any
proton in the nucleus is attracted by the strong nuclear force only to adjacent
protons but is electrically repelled by all other protons in the nucleus. As
more and more protons are squeezed into the nucleus, the repulsive electric
forces increase substantially. For example, each of the two protons in a helium
nucleus feels the repulsive effect of the other. Each proton in a nucleus containing 84 protons, however, feels the repulsive effects of 83 protons! The
attractive nuclear force exerted by each neutron, however, extends only to its
immediate neighbors. The size of the atomic nucleus is therefore limited.
This in turn limits the number of possible elements in the periodic table. It
is for this reason that all nuclei having more than 83 protons are radioactive.
Also, the nuclei of the heaviest elements produced in the laboratory are so
unstable (radioactive) that they exist for only fractions of a second.

Concept Check ✓

Which is more sensitive to distance: the strong nuclear force or the electric
force?

Was this your answer? The strong nuclear force weakens rapidly over relatively short distances,
but the electric force remains powerful over such distances.

Small nuclei also have the potential for being radioactive. This generally
occurs when a nucleus contains more neutrons than protons. The nucleus of
carbon-14, for example, contains eight neutrons but only six protons. With
not enough protons to go around, one of the neutrons inevitably transforms
to a proton, releasing an electron (beta radiation) in the process.

4.5 A Radioactive Element Can Transmute to a Different Element

When a radioactive nucleus emits an alpha or beta particle, the identity of the nucleus is changed because there is a change in atomic number. The changing of one element to another is called **transmutation**. Consider a uranium-238 nucleus, which contains 92 protons and 146 neutrons. When an alpha particle is ejected, the nucleus loses two protons and two neutrons. Because an element is defined by the number of protons in its nucleus, the 90 protons and 144 neutrons left behind are no longer identified as being uranium. What we have now is a nucleus of a different element—thorium. This transmutation can be written as a nuclear equation:

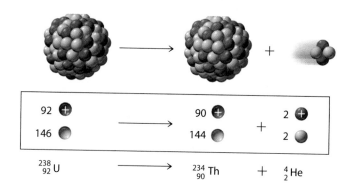

$$^{238}_{92}\text{U} \longrightarrow ^{234}_{90}\text{Th} + ^{4}_{2}\text{He}$$

This equation shows that $^{238}_{92}\text{U}$ transmutes to the two elements written to the right of the arrow. When this transmutation happens, energy is released, partly in the form of gamma radiation and partly in the form of kinetic energy in the alpha particle ($^{4}_{2}\text{He}$) and the thorium atom. In this and all other nuclear equations, the mass numbers balance ($238 = 234 + 4$) and the atomic numbers also balance ($92 = 90 + 2$).

Thorium-234 is also radioactive. When it decays, it emits a beta particle. Recall that a beta particle is an electron emitted by a neutron as the neutron transforms to a proton. So with thorium, which has 90 protons, beta emission leaves the nucleus with one fewer neutron and one more proton. The new nucleus has 91 protons and is no longer thorium; now it is the element protactinium. Although the atomic number has increased by 1 in this process, the mass number (protons + neutrons) remains the same. The nuclear equation is

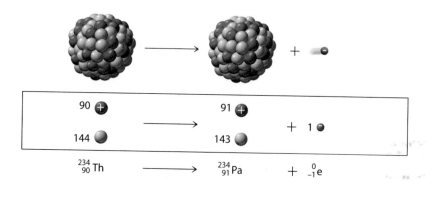

$$^{234}_{90}\text{Th} \longrightarrow ^{234}_{91}\text{Pa} + ^{0}_{-1}\text{e}$$

We write an electron as $_{-1}^{0}e$. The superscript 0 indicates that the electron's mass is insignificant relative to that of protons and neutrons. The subscript −1 is the electric charge of the electron.

So we see that when an element ejects an alpha particle from its nucleus, the mass number of the remaining atom is decreased by 4 and its atomic number is decreased by 2. The resulting atom is an atom of the element two spaces back in the periodic table because this atom has two fewer protons. When an element ejects a beta particle from its nucleus, the mass of the atom is practically unaffected, meaning there is no change in mass number, but its atomic number increases by 1. The resulting atom is an atom of the element one place forward in the periodic table because it has one more proton.

The decay of $_{92}^{238}U$ to $_{82}^{206}Pb$, an isotope of lead, is shown in Figure 4.16. Each green arrow shows an alpha decay, and each red arrow shows a beta decay.

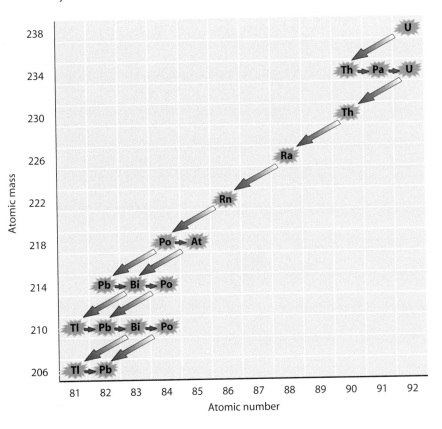

Figure 4.16
Uranium-238 decays to lead-206 through a series of alpha (blue) and beta (red) decays.

Concept Check ✓

1. Complete the nuclear reactions (a) $_{84}^{218}Ra \longrightarrow {}_{?}^{?}? + {}_{-1}^{0}e$ and
   (b) $_{84}^{210}Po \longrightarrow {}_{82}^{206}Pb + {}_{?}^{?}?$.
2. What finally becomes of all the uranium that undergoes radioactive decay?

Were these your answers?
1. (a) $_{84}^{218}Ra \longrightarrow {}_{85}^{218}At + {}_{-1}^{0}e$; and (b) $_{84}^{210}Po \longrightarrow {}_{82}^{206}Pb + {}_{2}^{4}He$.
2. All uranium ultimately becomes lead. On the way, it exists as the elements shown in Figure 4.16.

4.6 The Shorter the Half-Life, the Greater the Radioactivity

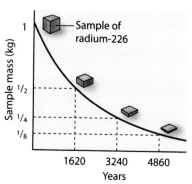

Figure 4.17
Radium-226 has a half-life of 1620 years, meaning that every 1620 years the amount of radium decreases by half as it transmutes to other elements.

The rate of decay of a radioactive isotope is measured in terms of a characteristic time called the **half-life**. This is the time it takes for half of the material in a radioactive sample to decay. For example, Figure 4.17 shows that radium-226 has a half-life of 1620 years. This means that half of a sample of radium has decayed to other elements by the end of 1620 years. In the next 1620 years, half of the remaining radium decays, leaving only one-fourth the original amount.

Half-lives are remarkably constant and not affected by external conditions. Some radioactive isotopes have half-lives that are less than a millionth of a second, while others have half-lives of more than a billion years. For example, uranium-238 has a half-life of 4.5 billion years, which means that in 4.5 billion years, half the uranium in the Earth today will be lead.

It is not necessary to wait through the duration of a half-life in order to measure it. The half-life of an element can be accurately estimated by measuring the rate of decay of a known quantity of the element. This is easily done using a radiation detector. In general, the shorter the half-life of a substance, the faster it disintegrates and the more radioactivity per minute is detected. Figure 4.18 shows a Geiger counter being used by environmental workers.

Figure 4.18
A Geiger counter detects incoming radiation by the way the radiation affects a gas enclosed in the tube that the technician is holding in his right hand.

Hands-On Chemistry: Radioactive Paper Clips

You can simulate radioactive decay with a bunch of paper clips representing atoms of a radioactive element. The "atoms" are thrown onto a flat surface. The ones that land in a certain orientation are imagined to have decayed and so are now atoms of a different element. Decayed atoms are removed from the pile and not used for successive throws. This process is continued until all the atoms have decayed.

What You Need

At least 20 metal paper clips, paper, pencil

Procedure

① Unfold the two loops of each clip by 90 degrees so that the loops are at right angles to each other. Pull the end of the larger loop outwards by 90 degrees to form a structure that looks like the drawing at right.

   The orientation drawn on the top we'll call the leg-up orientation. Tip the upwards pointing "leg" over on its side, and you'll have the orientation drawn on the bottom, which we'll call the head-up orientation. You will be investigating the half-life of two pretend elements. The first, "legonium," decays when it lands in the leg-up orientation. The second, "headonium,"decays when it lands in the head-up orientation.

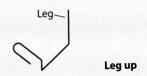

Leg up

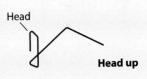

Head up

② You'll do two simulations similar to the one at right, one for legonium and one for headonium, and each simulation will involve five trials. For each trial, create a data table consisting of two columns, the first labeled "Throw" and the second labeled "Number of atoms remaining." In the row numbered zero, write the number of paper clips you start with (at least 20) in the column labeled "Number of atoms remaining."

③ Pretending each paper clip is a legonium atom, toss all of them onto a flat surface. Remove all the atoms in the leg-up orientation and write down the number remaining in row 1 of the data table for trial 1. Continue until all the legonium atoms have been removed. This completes one trial, and so you need to run four more because there will be a lot of statistical variation. Count the number of throws required to remove all atoms in each trial and calculate an average.

④ Repeat the procedure, now pretending the paper clips are headonium atoms. The paper clips removed will be the ones that fall in the head-up orientation.

   Compare the legonium trials with the headonium trials. Half-life is given in units of time, but for this simulation the units are different. What are they? Estimate the half-life of legonium and headonium. Which element is more radioactive?

   If you were an atom in a sample of a radioactive element that has a half-life of 5 minutes, would you necessarily be decayed to another type of atom after 5 minutes?

LEGONIUM TRIAL 1	
Throw	Number of Atoms Remaining
0	20
1	——
2	——
.	.
.	.
.	.

Concept Check ✓

1. If you have a sample of a radioactive isotope that has a half-life of one day, how much of the original sample is left at the end of the second day? The third day?
2. What becomes of the atoms of the sample that decay?
3. With equal quantities of material, which gives a higher counting rate on a radiation detector, radioactive material that has a short half-life or radioactive material that has a long half-life?

Were these your answers?

1. At the end of two days, one-fourth of the original sample is left—one-half disappears by the end of the first day, and one-half of that one-half ($1/2 \times 1/2 = 1/4$) disappears by the end of the second day. At the end of three days, one-eighth of the original sample is left.
2. The atoms that decay are now atoms of a different element.
3. The material with the shorter half-life is more active and so gives a higher counting rate.

4.7 Isotopic Dating Measures the Age of a Material

The Earth's atmosphere is continuously bombarded by cosmic rays, and this bombardment causes many atoms in the upper atmosphere to transmute. These transmutations result in many protons and neutrons being "sprayed out" into the environment. Most of the protons are stopped as they collide with the atoms of the upper atmosphere, stripping electrons from these atoms to become hydrogen atoms. The neutrons, however, keep going for longer distances because they have no electric charge and therefore do not interact electrically with matter. Eventually, many of them collide with atomic nuclei in the lower atmosphere. A nitrogen that captures a neutron, for instance, becomes an isotope of carbon by emitting a proton:

$$^{1}_{0}n + ^{14}_{7}N \longrightarrow ^{14}_{6}C + ^{1}_{1}H$$

This carbon-14 isotope, which makes up less than one-millionth of 1 percent of the carbon in the atmosphere, is radioactive and has eight neutrons. (The most common isotope, carbon-12, has six neutrons and is not radioactive.). Because both carbon-12 and carbon-14 are forms of carbon, they have the same chemical properties. Both of these isotopes, for example, chemically react with oxygen to form carbon dioxide, which is taken in by plants. This means that all plants contain a tiny bit of radioactive carbon-14. All animals eat either plants or plant-eating animals, and therefore all animals have a little carbon-14 in them. In short, all living things on the Earth contain some carbon-14.

Carbon-14 is a beta emitter and decays back to nitrogen:

$$^{14}_{6}C \longrightarrow \ ^{14}_{7}N \ + \ ^{0}_{-1}e$$

Because plants take in carbon dioxide as long as they live, any carbon-14 lost to decay is immediately replenished with fresh carbon-14 from the atmosphere. In this way, a radioactive equilibrium is reached where there is a constant ratio of about one carbon-14 atom to every 100 billion carbon-12 atoms. When a plant dies, replenishment of carbon-14 stops. Then the percentage of carbon-14 decreases at a constant rate given by its half-life, but the amount of carbon-12 does not change because this isotope does not undergo radioactive decay. The longer a plant or other organism is dead, therefore, the less carbon-14 it contains relative to the constant amount of carbon-12.

The half-life of carbon-14 is about 5730 years. This means that half of the carbon-14 atoms now present in a plant or animal that dies today will decay in the next 5730 years. Half of the remaining carbon-14 atoms will then decay in the following 5730 years, and so on.

With this knowledge, scientists are able to calculate the age of carbon-containing artifacts, such as wooden tools or the skeleton shown in Figure 4.19, by measuring their current level of radioactivity. This process, known as **carbon-14 dating**, enables us to probe as much as 50,000 years into the past. Beyond this time span, there is too little carbon-14 remaining to permit an accurate analysis. (Understanding the local geology is another important tool used by archeologists in the dating of ancient relics.)

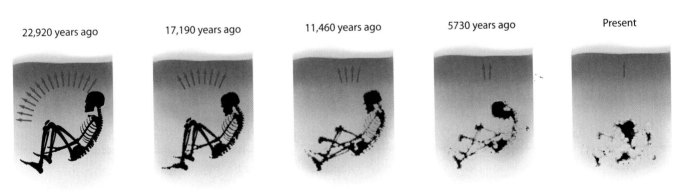

| 22,920 years ago | 17,190 years ago | 11,460 years ago | 5730 years ago | Present |

Figure 4.19
The amount of radioactive carbon-14 in the skeleton diminish by one-half every 5730 years, with the result that today the skeleton contains only a fraction of the carbon-14 it originally had. The red arrows symbolize relative amounts of carbon-14.

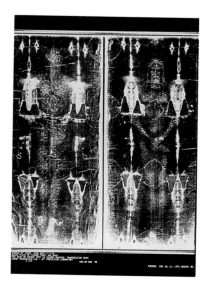

Figure 4.20
The Shroud of Turin was carbon-14 dated to the 13th or 14th century A.D.

Carbon-14 dating would be an extremely simple and accurate dating method if the amount of radioactive carbon in the atmosphere had been constant over the ages, but it hasn't been. Fluctuations in the magnetic field of the sun and in that of the Earth cause fluctuations in cosmic-ray intensity in the Earth's atmosphere. These ups and downs in cosmic-ray intensity in turn produce fluctuations in the amount of carbon-14 in the atmosphere at any given time. In addition, changes in the Earth's climate affect the amount of carbon dioxide in the atmosphere. As we explore in Chapter 18, the oceans are great reservoirs of carbon dioxide. When the oceans are cold, they release less carbon dioxide into the atmosphere than when they are warm. Because of all these fluctuations in the carbon-14 production rate through the centuries, carbon-14 dating has an uncertainty of about 15 percent. This means, for example, that the straw of an old adobe brick dated to be 500 years old may really be only 425 years old on the low side or 575 years old on the high side. For many purposes, this is an acceptable level of uncertainty.

The famous Shroud of Turin, shown in Figure 4.20, holds an image of an average-sized adult male who was apparently crucified. For many years, this was believed to have been the burial shroud (large cloth used to wrap a body) of Jesus Christ. Carbon-14 dating indicates that the flax from which the cloth was made was grown between 1260 and 1390 A.D., however. This is strong evidence against the possibility that the image on the shroud was produced by the human body of Jesus, who is recognized as having lived and died more than 1000 years earlier than this.

Concept Check ✓

> Suppose an archeologist extracts 1.0 g of carbon from an ancient ax handle and finds that carbon to be one-fourth as radioactive as 1.0 g of carbon extracted from a freshly cut tree branch. About how old is the ax handle?

Was this your answer? The ax handle is two half-lives of ^{14}C; that's 2 × 5730 years ≈ 11,000 years old.

Scientists use radioactive minerals to date very old nonliving things. The naturally occurring mineral isotopes uranium-238 and uranium-235 decay very slowly and ultimately become lead—but not the common isotope lead-208. Instead, as was shown in Figure 14.16, uranium-238 decays to lead-206. Uranium-235, on the other hand, decays to lead-207. Thus the lead-206 and lead-207 that now exist in a uranium-bearing rock were at one time uranium. The older the rock, the higher the percentage of these remnant isotopes.

If you know the half-lives of uranium isotopes and the percentage of lead isotopes in some uranium-bearing rock, you can calculate the date the rock was formed. Rocks dated in this way have been found to be as much as 3.7 *billion* years old. Samples from the moon have been dated at 4.2 billion years, which is close to the estimated age of our solar system: 4.6 billion years.

4.8 Nuclear Fission Is the Splitting of the Atomic Nucleus

In 1938, two German scientists, Otto Hahn (1879–1968) and Fritz Strassmann (1902–1980), made a discovery that was to change the world. While bombarding a sample of uranium with neutrons in the hopes of creating heavier elements, they were astonished to find chemical evidence for the production of barium, an element having about half the mass of uranium. Hahn wrote of this news to his former colleague Lise Meitner (1878–1968), who had fled from Nazi Germany to Sweden because of her Jewish ancestry. From Hahn's evidence, Meitner concluded that the uranium nucleus, activated by neutron bombardment, had split in half. Soon thereafter, Meitner, working with her nephew Otto Frisch (1904–1979), published a paper in which the term *nuclear fission* was coined.

In the nucleus of every atom, there exists a delicate balance between attractive strong nuclear forces between nucleons and repulsive electric forces between protons. In all known nuclei, the strong nuclear forces dominate. In many of the heavier nuclei, however, this domination is tenuous and, as discussed earlier, radioactive decay may occur. For a select number of isotopes, however, another possibility exists. For example, a uranium-235 nucleus hit with a fast-moving neutron elongates as shown in Figure 4.21. In a nucleus stretched into this elongated shape, the strong nuclear force weakens substantially because of the increased distance between opposite ends. The repulsive electric forces between protons remain powerful, however, and these forces may elongate the nucleus even more. If the elongation passes a certain point, the electric forces overwhelm the distance-sensitive strong nuclear forces and the nucleus splits into *fragments*—typically two large fragments accompanied by several smaller ones, such as fast-flying nucleons. This splitting of a nucleus into fragments is **nuclear fission**.

The energy released by the fission of one uranium-235 atom is enormous—about seven million times the energy released by the explosion of one TNT molecule. This energy is mainly in the form of kinetic energy of the fission fragments, which fly apart from one another. A much smaller amount of energy is released as gamma radiation.

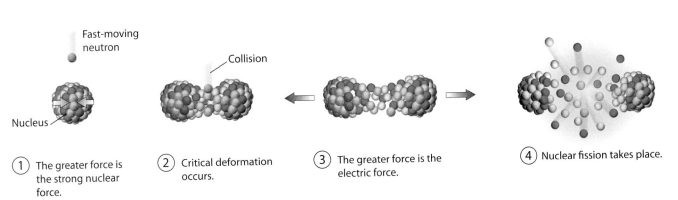

Fast-moving neutron

Collision

Nucleus

① The greater force is the strong nuclear force.

② Critical deformation occurs.

③ The greater force is the electric force.

④ Nuclear fission takes place.

Figure 4.21
Nuclear deformation may result in repulsive electric forces overcoming attractive strong nuclear forces, in which case fission occurs.

Here is the equation for a typical uranium fission reaction:

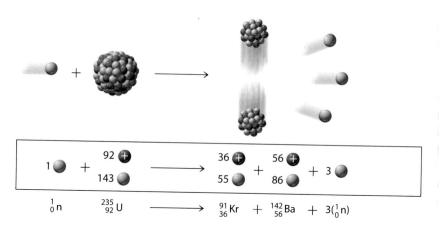

$$\underset{0}{\overset{1}{}}n \; + \; \underset{92}{\overset{235}{}}U \; \longrightarrow \; \underset{36}{\overset{91}{}}Kr \; + \; \underset{56}{\overset{142}{}}Ba \; + \; 3(\underset{0}{\overset{1}{}}n)$$

Note in this reaction that one neutron starts the fission of the uranium nucleus and that the fission produces three neutrons. (It is also possible for a given fission event to produce either fewer than three neutrons or more than three. In fact, the *average* number of neutrons per fission is about 2.7.) These product neutrons can cause the fissioning of three other uranium atoms, releasing nine more neutrons. If each of these 9 neutrons succeeds in splitting a uranium atom, the next step in the reaction produces 27 neutrons, and so on. Such a sequence, illustrated in Figure 4.22, is called a **chain reaction**—a self-sustaining reaction in which the products of one reaction event stimulate further reaction events.

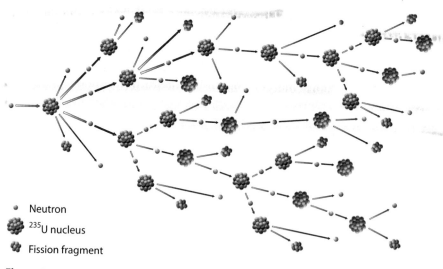

• Neutron

^{235}U nucleus

Fission fragment

Figure 4.22
A chain reaction.

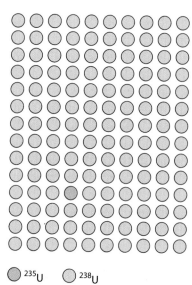

◯ ^{235}U   ◯ ^{238}U

Figure 4.23
Only 1 part in 140 of naturally occurring uranium is uranium-235.

Chain reactions do not occur to any great extent in naturally occurring uranium ore because not all uranium atoms fission so easily. Fission occurs mainly in the rare isotope uranium-235, which makes up only 0.7 percent of the uranium in pure uranium metal (Figure 4.23). When the prevalent isotope uranium-238 absorbs neutrons created by fission of a uranium-235 atom, the uranium-238 typically does not undergo fission. So any chain reaction getting set up in the uranium-235 atoms in an ore sample is snuffed out by the neutron-absorbing uranium-238, as well as by other neutron-absorbing elements in the rock in which the ore is imbedded.

If a chain reaction occurred in a baseball-sized chunk of pure uranium-235, an enormous explosion would result. If the chain reaction were started in a smaller chunk of pure uranium-235, however, no explosion would occur. This is because of geometry: The ratio of surface area to mass is larger in a small piece than in a large piece. Just as there is more skin on six small potatoes having a combined mass of 1 kilogram than there is on a single 1-kilogram potato, there is more surface area on a bunch of smaller pieces of uranium-235 than on a large piece. In a small piece of uranium-235, therefore, neutrons have a greater chance of reaching the surface and escaping before they cause additional fission events, as Figure 4.24 illustrates. In a bigger piece, the chain reaction builds up to enormous energies before the neutrons get to the surface and escape. For masses greater than a certain amount, called the **critical mass**, an explosion of enormous magnitude may take place.

Consider a large quantity of uranium-235 divided into two pieces, each having a mass smaller than critical. The units are *subcritical.* Neutrons in either piece readily reach the surface and escape before a sizable chain reaction builds up. If the pieces are suddenly pushed together, however, the total surface area decreases. If the timing is right and the combined mass is greater than critical, a violent explosion takes place. This is what happens in a nuclear fission bomb, as Figure 4.25 shows.

Constructing a fission bomb is a formidable task. The difficulty is in separating enough uranium-235 from the more abundant uranium-238. Scientists took more than two years to extract enough of the 235 isotope from uranium ore to make the bomb detonated at Hiroshima in 1945. To this day, uranium isotope separation remains a difficult process.

Neutrons escape surface

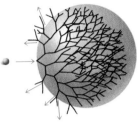

Neutrons trigger more reactions

Figure 4.24
This exaggerated view shows that a chain reaction in a small piece of pure uranium-235 runs its course before it can cause a large explosion because neutrons leak from the surface too soon. The surface area of the small piece is large relative to the mass. In a larger piece, more uranium and less surface are presented to the neutrons.

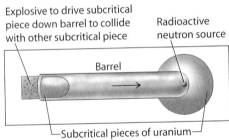

Explosive to drive subcritical piece down barrel to collide with other subcritical piece

Radioactive neutron source

Barrel

Subcritical pieces of uranium

Figure 4.25
Simplified diagram of a uranium fission bomb.

Concept Check ✔

A 1-kilogram ball of uranium-235 has critical mass, but the same ball broken up into small chunks does not. Explain.

Was this your answer? The small chunks have more combined surface area than the ball from which they came. Neutrons escape via the surface of each small chunk before a sustained chain reaction can build up.

Nuclear Fission Reactors Convert Nuclear Energy to Electrical Energy

The awesome energy of nuclear fission was introduced to the world in the form of nuclear bombs, and this violent image still colors our thinking about nuclear power, making it difficult for many people to recognize its potential usefulness. Currently, about 20 percent of electrical energy in the United States is generated by *nuclear fission reactors*, which are simply nuclear boilers, as Figure 4.26 shows. Like fossil-fuel furnaces, reactors do nothing more elegant than boil water to produce steam for a turbine. The

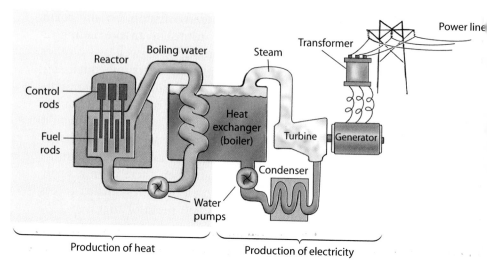

Figure 4.26

Diagram of a nuclear fission power plant. Note that the water in contact with the fuel rods is completely contained, and radioactive materials are not involved directly in the generation of electricity. The details of the production of electricity are covered in Chapter 20.

Figure 4.27

A nuclear reactor is housed within a dome-shaped containment building designed to prevent the release of radioactive isotopes in the event of an accident.

greatest practical difference is the amount of fuel involved: A mere 1 kilogram of uranium fuel yields more energy than 30 freightcar loads of coal.

A fission reactor contains three components: nuclear fuel, control rods, and a liquid (usually water) to transfer the heat created by fission from the reactor to the turbine. The nuclear fuel is primarily uranium-238 plus about 3 percent uranium-235. Because the uranium-235 atoms are so highly diluted with uranium-238 atoms, an explosion like that of a nuclear bomb is not possible. The reaction rate, which depends on the number of neutrons available to initiate fission of uranium-235 nuclei, is controlled by rods inserted into the reactor. The control rods are made of a neutron-absorbing material, usually cadmium or boron.

Water surrounding the nuclear fuel is kept under high pressure to keep it at a high temperature without boiling. Heated by fission, this water transfers heat to a second, lower-pressure water system, which operates a turbine and an electric generator. Two separate water systems are used so that no radioactivity reaches the turbine, and the entire setup resides inside a building like the one shown in Figure 4.27, designed to keep any radioactive material from ever being released into the environment.

One disadvantage of fission power is the generation of waste products that are radioactive. Smaller atomic nuclei are most stable when composed of equal numbers of protons and neutrons, as we learned earlier, and it is mainly heavy nuclei that need more neutrons than protons for stability. For example, there are 143 neutrons but only 92 protons in uranium-235. When this uranium fissions into two medium-sized elements, the extra neutrons in their nuclei make them unstable. These fragments are therefore radioactive. Most of them have very short half-lives, but some of them have half-lives of thousands of years. Safely disposing of these waste products as well as materials made radioactive in the production of nuclear fuels requires special storage casks and procedures. Although fission power goes back nearly a half-century, the technology of radioactive waste disposal is still in the developmental stage. You can read further details on the subject in Section 19.3.

4.9 Nuclear Energy Comes from Nuclear Mass and Vice Versa

In the early 1900s, Albert Einstein (1879–1955) discovered that mass is actually "congealed" energy. He realized that mass and energy are two sides of the same coin, as stated in his celebrated equation $E = mc^2$. In this equation, E stands for the energy that any mass at rest has, m stands for mass, and c is the speed of light. This relationship between energy and mass is the key to understanding why and how energy is released in nuclear reactions. Any time a nucleus fissions to two smaller nuclei, the combined mass of all nucleons in the smaller nuclei is less than the combined mass of all nucleons in the original nucleus. The mass "missing" after the fission event is converted to energy and given off to the surroundings. Let's see how.

From physics we know that energy is the capacity to do work (Section 1.5) and that work is equal to the product of force times distance:

work = force × distance

Think of the enormous external force required to pull a nucleon out of the nucleus through a distance sufficient to overcome the attractive strong nuclear force, comically represented in Figure 4.28. As per the word equation for work just given, enormous *force* exerted through a *distance* means that enormous work is required. This work is energy that has been added to the nucleon.

According to Einstein's equation, this newly acquired energy reveals itself as an increase in the nucleon's mass—the mass of a nucleon outside a nucleus is greater than the mass of the same nucleon locked inside a nucleus. For example, a carbon-12 atom—the nucleus of which is made up of six protons and six neutrons—has a mass of exactly 12.00000 atomic mass units. Therefore, each proton and each neutron contributes a mass of 1 atomic mass unit. However, outside the nucleus, a proton has a mass of 1.00728 atomic mass units and a neutron has a mass of 1.00867 atomic mass units. Thus we see that the combined mass of six free protons and six free neutrons—(6 × 1.00728) + (6 × 1.00867) = 12.09570—is greater than the mass of one carbon-12 nucleus. The greater mass reflects the energy that was required to pull the nucleons apart from one another. Thus, what mass a nucleon has depends on where the nucleon is.

The graph shown in Figure 4.29 results when we plot average mass *per nucleon* for the elements hydrogen through uranium. This graph is the key to understanding the energy released in nuclear processes. To obtain the average mass per nucleon, you divide the total mass of a nucleus by the number of nucleons in the nucleus. (Similarly, if you divide the total mass of a roomful of people by the number of people in the room, you get the average mass per person.)

Figure 4.28
Much work is required to pull a nucleon from an atomic nucleus.

Figure 4.29
This graph shows that the average mass of a nucleon depends on which nucleus it is in. Individual nucleons have the most mass in the lightest nuclei, the least mass in iron, and intermediate mass in the heaviest nuclei.

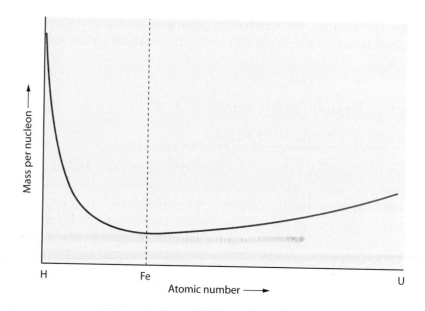

From Figure 4.29 we can see how energy is released when a uranium nucleus splits into two nuclei of lower atomic number. Uranium, being at the right of the graph, has a relatively large amount of mass per nucleon. When a uranium nucleus splits, however, smaller nuclei of lower atomic numbers are formed. As shown in Figure 4.30, these nuclei are lower on the graph than uranium, which means they have a smaller amount of mass per nucleon. Thus, nucleons lose mass as they go from being in a uranium nucleus to being in one of its fragments. All the mass lost by the nucleons as they change from being nucleons of uranium to being nucleons of atoms such as barium and krypton is converted to energy, and this energy is what we harness and use as "nuclear power." If you wanted to calculate exactly how much energy is released in each fission event, you'd use Einstein's equation: multiply the decrease in mass by the speed of light squared (c^2 in the equation), and the product is the amount of energy yielded by each uranium nucleus as it undergoes fission.

Figure 4.30
The mass of each nucleon in a uranium nucleus is greater than the mass of each nucleon in any one of its fission fragments. This lost mass has been converted to energy, which is why nuclear fission is an energy-releasing process.

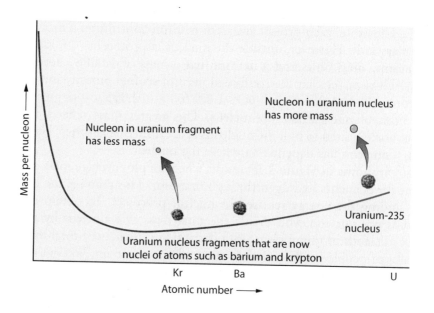

Interestingly, Einstein's mass/energy relationship applies to chemical reactions as well as to nuclear reactions. For nuclear reactions, the energies involved are so great that the change in mass is measureable, corresponding to about 1 part in a 1000. In chemical reactions, the energy involved is so small that the change in mass, about 1 part in 1,000,000,000, is not detectable. This is why the mass conservation law (Section 3.2) states that there is no *detectable* change in the total mass of materials as they chemically react to form new materials. In truth, there are changes in the mass of atoms during a chemical reaction. These changes are too small to be of any concern to the working chemist, however.

Concept Check ✔

Correct this statement: When a heavy element undergoes fission, there are fewer nucleons after the reaction than before.

Was this your answer? When a heavy element undergoes fission, there aren't fewer nucleons after the reaction. Instead, there's *less mass* in the same number of nucleons.

We can think of the mass-per-nucleon graph shown in Figure 4.29 as an energy valley that starts at hydrogen (the highest point) and slopes steeply to the lowest point (iron), then slopes gradually up to uranium. Iron is at the bottom of the energy valley and is therefore the most stable nucleus. It is also the most tightly bound nucleus; more energy per nucleon is required to separate nucleons from an iron nucleus than from any other nucleus.

4.10 Nuclear Fusion Is the Combining of Atomic Nuclei

As mentioned earlier, a drawback to nuclear fission is the production of radioactive waste products. A more promising long-range source of nuclear energy is to be found with the lightest elements. In a nutshell, energy is produced as small nuclei *fuse* (which means they combine). This process is **nuclear fusion**—the opposite of nuclear fission. We see from Figure 4.29 that, as we move along the elements from hydrogen to iron (the steepest part of the energy valley), the average mass per nucleon decreases. Thus if two small nuclei were to fuse, such as two nuclei of hydrogen-2, the mass of the fused nucleus, helium-4, would be less than the mass of the two hydrogen-2 nuclei, as Figure 4.31 on page 124 shows. As with fission, the mass lost by the nucleons is converted to energy we can use.

If a fusion reaction is to occur, the nuclei must be traveling at extremely high speeds when they collide in order to overcome their mutual electrical repulsion. The required speeds correspond to the extremely high temperatures found in the sun and other stars. Fusion brought about by high temperatures is called **thermonuclear fusion**. In the high temperatures of the sun, approximately 657 million tons of hydrogen is fused to 653 million tons of helium *each second*. The 4 million tons of nucleon mass lost is discharged as radiant energy.

Figure 4.31
The mass of each nucleon in a hydrogen-2 nucleus is greater than the mass of each nucleon in a helium-4, which results from the fusion of two hydrogen-2 nuclei. This lost mass has been converted to energy, which is why nuclear fusion is an energy-releasing process.

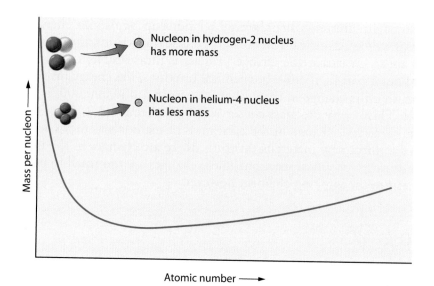

Concept Check ✓

To get energy from the element iron, should iron be fissioned or fused?

Was this your answer? Neither, because iron is at the very bottom of the energy-valley curve of Figure 4.29. If you fuse two iron nuclei, the product lies somewhere to the right of iron on the curve, which means the product has a higher mass per nucleon. If you split an iron nucleus, the products lie to the left of iron on the curve, which again means a higher mass per nucleon. Because no mass decrease occurs in either reaction, no mass is available to be converted to energy, and as a result no energy is released.

Prior to the development of the atomic bomb, the temperatures required to initiate nuclear fusion on the Earth were unattainable. When researchers found that the temperature inside an exploding atomic bomb is four to five times the temperature at the center of the sun, the thermonuclear bomb was but a step away. This first thermonuclear bomb, a hydrogen bomb, was detonated in 1952. Whereas the critical mass of fissionable material limits the size of a fission bomb (atomic bomb), no such limit is imposed on a fusion bomb (thermonuclear or hydrogen bomb). A typical thermonuclear bomb stockpiled by the United States today, for example, is about 1000 times more destructive than the atomic bomb detonated over Hiroshima, Japan, at the end of World War II.

The hydrogen bomb is another example of a discovery used for destructive rather than constructive purposes. The potential constructive possibility is the controlled release of vast amounts of clean energy.

The Holy Grail of Nuclear Research Today Is Controlled Fusion

Carrying out fusion reactions under controlled conditions requires temperatures of millions of degrees. As you can imagine, a big problem is that any reaction vessel being used would melt and vaporize long before these temperatures were reached. The solution to this problem is to confine the reaction in a *nonmaterial container*.

One type of nonmaterial container is a magnetic field—an example is shown in Figure 4.32—which can exist at any temperature and can exert powerful forces on charged particles in motion. "Magnetic walls" provide a kind of magnetic straitjacket for hot gases called *plasmas*, which are a fourth phase of matter, created when matter is heated so much (beyond the gaseous phase) that electrons are stripped away from nuclei and a hot gaslike fluid of charged particles is formed. The sun is a plasma, as is the inside of a fluorescent lamp when the lamp is operating.

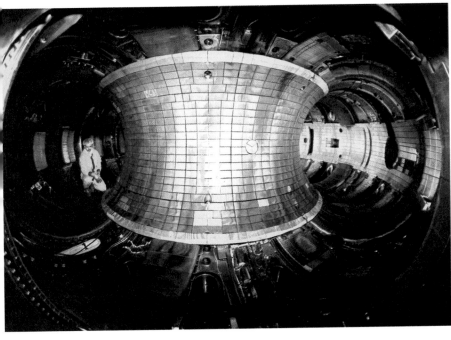

Figure 4.32
An interior view of the Tokamak Fusion Test Reactor at the Princeton Plasma Physics Laboratory. Magnetic fields confine a fast-moving plasma to a circular path. At a high enough temperature, the atomic nuclei in the confined plasma fuse to produce energy.

Once a plasma is produced and placed in its magnetic nonmaterial container, magnetic compression further heats the plasmas to fusion temperatures. At about 1 million degrees, some nuclei are moving fast enough to overcome repulsive electric forces, and these nuclei slam together and fuse. The energy released by this fusion, however, is less than the energy used to heat the plasma. Even at 100 million degrees, more energy must be put into the plasma than is given off by fusion. It is not until about 350 million degrees that the fusion reactions produce enough energy to be self-sustaining. At this ignition temperature, all that is needed to produce continuous power is a steady feed of nuclei.

Although several fusion devices are now capable of releasing more energy than they consume, instabilities in the plasma have thus far prevented a sustained reaction. A big problem has been devising a magnetic field system that can hold the plasma steady long enough to allow a sufficient number of nuclei to fuse. A variety of magnetic confinement devices are the subject of much present-day research.

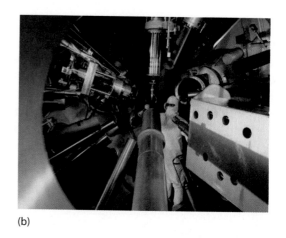

(a)   (b)

Figure 4.33
(a) Fusion with multiple laser beams. Pellets of hydrogen isotopes are rhythmically dropped into synchronized laser crossfire in this planned device. The resulting heat is carried off by molten lithium to produce steam. (b) The pellet chamber at Lawrence Livermore Laboratory. The laser source is Nova, the most powerful laser in the world, which directs ten beams into the target region.

Another approach uses high-energy lasers. One proposed technique is to aim an array of laser beams at a common point and drop solid pellets of hydrogen isotopes through the synchronous crossfire, as Figure 4.33 shows. The energy of the multiple beams should crush the pellets to densities 20 times that of lead. Such a fusion could produce several hundred times more energy than the amount delivered by the laser beams. Like the succession of fuel/air explosions in an automobile engine's cylinders that convert to a smooth flow of mechanical power, the successive ignition of pellets in a laser fusion device may similarly produce a steady stream of electric power. A plant equipped with the device could produce 1000 million watts of electric power, enough to supply a city of 600,000 people. High-power lasers that work reliably, however, have yet to be developed.

Other fusion schemes, some of which are explored in Chapter 19, are also under development.

Concept Check ✓

Fission and fusion are opposite processes, yet each releases energy. Isn't this contradictory?

Was this your answer? No, no, no! As Figure 4.29 shows, only the fusion of light elements and the fission of heavy elements result in a decrease in nucleon mass and therefore a release of energy.

If people are one day to dart about the universe the way we jet about the Earth today, their supply of fuel is assured. The fuel for fusion—hydrogen—is found in every part of the universe, not only in the stars but also in the space between them. About 91 percent of the atoms in the universe are estimated to be hydrogen. For people of the future, the supply of raw materials is also assured because all the elements known to exist result from the fusing of more and more hydrogen nuclei. Simply put, if you fuse 8 hydrogen-2 nuclei, you have oxygen; 26, you have iron; and so forth. Future humans might synthesize their own elements and produce energy in the process, just as the stars have always done.

Key Terms and Matching Definitions

_____ alpha particle
_____ beta particle
_____ carbon-14 dating
_____ chain reaction
_____ critical mass
_____ gamma ray
_____ half-life
_____ nuclear fission
_____ nuclear fusion
_____ rad
_____ radioactivity
_____ rem
_____ strong nuclear force
_____ thermonuclear fusion
_____ transmutation

1. The tendency of some elements, such as uranium, to emit radiation as a result of changes in the atomic nucleus.
2. A helium atom nucleus, which consists of two neutrons and two protons and is ejected by certain radioactive elements.
3. An electron ejected from an atomic nucleus during the radioactive decay of certain nuclei.
4. High-energy radiation emitted by the nuclei of radioactive atoms.
5. A unit for measuring radiation dosage, equal to 0.01 joule of radiant energy absorbed per kilogram of tissue.
6. A unit for measuring radiation dosage, obtained by multiplying the number of rads by a factor that allows for the different health effects of different types of radiation.
7. The force of interaction between all nucleons, effective only at very, very, very close distances.
8. The conversion of an atomic nucleus of one element to an atomic nucleus of another element through a loss or gain of protons.
9. The time required for half the atoms in a sample of a radioactive isotope to decay.

10. The process of estimating the age of once-living material by measuring the amount of a radioactive isotope of carbon present in the material.
11. The splitting of a heavy nucleus into two lighter nuclei, accompanied by the release of much energy.
12. A self-sustaining reaction in which the products of one fission event stimulate further events.
13. The minimum mass of fissionable material needed in a reactor or nuclear bomb that will sustain a chain reaction.
14. The joining together of light nuclei to form a heavier nucleus, accompanied by the release of much energy.
15. Nuclear fusion produced by high temperature.

Review Questions

The Cathode Ray Led to the Discovery of Radioactivity

1. What did Wilhelm Roentgen discover in 1896?
2. How did Henri Becquerel determine that phosphorescence was not responsible for the emission of X rays by uranium?
3. Who coined the term *radioactivity*?
4. How do the electric charges of alpha, beta, and gamma rays differ from one another?
5. Which of the three rays has the greatest penetrating power?

Radioactivity Is a Natural Phenomenon

6. What is the origin of most of the radiation you encounter?
7. Which is worse: having cells in your body damaged by radiation or killed by radiation?
8. Is radioactivity on the Earth something relatively new? Defend your answer.

9. Rads and rems are both units of radiation. Which is a unit of radiation energy? Which is a unit of the harm radiation can cause to living tissue?

Radioactive Isotopes Are Useful as Tracers and for Medical Imaging

10. What is a radioactive tracer?

11. How are radioactive isotopes used in medical imaging?

Radioactivity Results from an Imbalance of Forces in the Nucleus

12. How are the strong nuclear force and the electric force different from each other?

13. What role do neutrons play in the atomic nucleus?

14. Why is there a limit to the number of neutrons a nucleus can contain?

A Radioactive Element Can Transmute to a Different Element

15. When thorium, atomic number 90, decays by emitting an alpha particle, what is the atomic number of the resulting nucleus?

16. When thorium decays by emitting a beta particle, what is the atomic number of the resulting nucleus?

17. What change in atomic number occurs when a nucleus emits an alpha particle? A beta particle?

18. What is the long-range fate of all the uranium that exists in the world today?

The Shorter the Half-Life, the Greater the Radioactivity

19. What is meant by *radioactive half-life*?

20. What is the half-life of radium-226?

21. How does the decay rate of an isotope relate to its half-life?

Isotopic Dating Measures the Age of a Material

22. What do cosmic rays have to do with transmutation?

23. How is carbon-14 produced in the atmosphere?

24. Which is radioactive, carbon-12 or carbon-14?

25. Why is there more carbon-14 in living bones than in once-living ancient bones of the same mass?

26. Why is carbon-14 dating useless for dating old coins but not old pieces of cloth?

27. Why is lead found in all deposits of uranium ores?

28. What does the proportion of lead and uranium in rock tell us about the age of the rock?

Nuclear Fission Is the Splitting of the Atomic Nucleus

29. Why does a chain reaction not occur in uranium mines?

30. Is a chain reaction more likely to occur in two separate pieces of uranium-235 or in the same pieces stuck together?

31. How is a nuclear reactor similar to a conventional fossil-fuel power plant? How is it different?

32. What is the function of control rods in a nuclear reactor?

Nuclear Energy Comes from Nuclear Mass and Vice Versa

33. Is work required to pull a nucleon out of an atomic nucleus? Does the nucleon, once outside the nucleus, have more mass than it had inside the nucleus?

34. Does the mass of a nucleon after it has been pulled from an atomic nucleus depend on which nucleus it was extracted from?

35. How does the mass per nucleon in uranium compare with the mass per nucleon in the fission fragments of uranium?

6. If an iron nucleus split in two, would its fission fragments have more mass per nucleon or less mass per nucleon?

7. If a pair of iron nuclei were fused, would the product nucleus have more mass per nucleon or less mass per nucleon?

Nuclear Fusion Is the Combining of Atomic Nuclei

38. When a pair of hydrogen isotopes are fused, is the mass of the product nucleus more or less than the total mass of the hydrogen nuclei?

39. From where does the sun gets its energy?

40. How do the product particles of fusion reactions differ from the product particles of fission reactions?

41. What kind of containers are used to contain multimillion-degree plasmas?

Hands-On Chemistry Insights

Personal Radiation

Will the effects of the radiation you receive be passed on to your children? Only radiation received by your reproductive organs (testes in males and ovaries in females) has the potential of causing effects that might be passed on to future generations. All other radiation you receive is for your body only.

What percentage of your estimated annual radiation comes from natural sources? What adjustments might you be willing to make in order to decrease your annual exposure?

Radioactive Paper Clips

The unit of half-life in this simulation is *number of throws*. The element with the shorter half-life is considered to be the more radioactive one because it decays faster and in the process emits more radiation per unit time. For most students, this turns out to be legonium.

Uranium-238 has a half-life of 4.5 billion years, while polonium-214 has a half-life of 0.00016 second. So, which would you rather hold in your hands: 1 gram of uranium-238 or 1 gram of polonium-214? Perhaps, the most important point of this activity is

that radioactive decay is a statistical phenomenon. Follow any one of the paper clips, and you'll find that it may decay well before or after the half-life. Half-life is a predictable quantity only when a large number of particles are involved.

Exercises

1. Why is a sample of radium always a little warmer than its surroundings?

2. Is it possible for a hydrogen nucleus to emit an alpha particle? Defend your answer.

3. Why are alpha and beta rays deflected in opposite directions in a magnetic field? Why are gamma rays undeflected?

4. The alpha particle has twice the electric charge of the beta particle but deflects less in a magnetic field. Why?

5. Which type of radiation—alpha, beta, or amma—results in the greatest change in mass number? The greatest change in atomic number?

6. Which type of radiation—alpha, beta, or gamma—results in the least change in atomic mass number? The least change in the atomic number?

7. Which type of radiation—alpha, beta, or gamma—predominates on the inside of a high-flying commercial airplane? Why?

8. In bombarding atomic nuclei with proton "bullets," why must the protons be given large amounts of kinetic energy in order to make contact with the target nuclei?

9. Why would you expect alpha particles to be less able to penetrate materials than beta particles?

10. What evidence supports the hypothesis that, at short intranuclear distances, the strong nuclear force is stronger than the electric force?

11. The isotope cesium-137, which has a half-life of 30 years, is a product of nuclear power plants. How long will it take this isotope to decay to one-sixteenth its original amount?

12. When the isotope bismuth-213 emits an alpha particle, what new element results? What new element results if it instead emits a beta particle?

13. When $^{226}_{88}$Ra decays by emitting an alpha particle, what is the atomic number of the resulting nucleus? What is the resulting atomic mass?

14. What are the atomic number and atomic mass of the element formed when $^{218}_{84}$Po emits a beta particle? What are they if the polonium emits an alpha particle?

15. How is it possible for an element to decay "forward in the periodic table"—that is, decay to an element of higher atomic number?

16. Elements above uranium in the periodic table do not exist in any appreciable amounts in nature because they have short half-lives. Yet there are several elements below uranium in the table that have equally short half-lives but do exist in appreciable amounts in nature. How can you account for this?

17. You and a friend journey to the mountain foothills to get closer to nature and escape such things as radioactivity. While bathing in the warmth of a natural hot spring, she wonders aloud how the spring gets its heat. What do you tell her?

18. People who work around radioactivity wear film badges to monitor the amount of radiation that reaches their bodies. Each badge consists of a small piece of photographic film enclosed in a lightproof wrapper. What kind of radiation do these devices monitor, and how can they determine the amount of radiation the people receive?

19. Coal contains only minute quantities of radioactive materials, and yet there is more environmental radiation surrounding a coal-fired power plant than a fission power plant. What does this indicate about the shielding that typically surrounds these two types of plants?

20. A friend checks the local background radiation with a Geiger counter, which ticks audibly. Another friend, who normally fears most that which is understood least, makes an effort to keep away from the region of the Geiger counter and looks to you for advice. What do you say?

21. Why is carbon-14 dating not accurate for estimating the age of materials more than 50,000 years old?

22. The age of the Dead Sea Scrolls was determined by carbon-14 dating. Could this technique have worked if they had been carved on stone tablets? Explain.

23. A certain radioactive element has a half-life of 1 hour. If you start with a 1-gram sample of the element at noon, how much is left at 3:00 P.M.? At 6:00 P.M.? At 10:00 P.M.?

24. Why will nuclear fission probably never be used directly for powering automobiles? How could it be used indirectly?

25. Why does a neutron make a better nuclear bullet than a proton or an electron?

26. Does the average distance a neutron travels through fissionable material before escaping increase or decrease when two pieces of fissionable material are assembled into one piece? Does this assembly increase or decrease the probability of an explosion?

27. Why does plutonium not occur in appreciable amounts in natural ore deposits?

28. Uranium-235 releases an average of 2.5 neutrons per fission, while plutonium-239 releases an average of 2.7 neutrons per fission. Which of these elements might you therefore expect to have the smaller critical mass?

29. Why, after a uranium fuel rod reaches the end of its fuel cycle (typically three years), does most of its energy come from plutonium fission?

30. If a nucleus of $^{232}_{90}$Th absorbs a neutron and the resulting nucleus undergoes two successive beta decays, which nucleus results?

31. To predict the approximate energy release of either a fission or a fusion reaction, explain how a physicist uses a table of nuclear masses and the equation $E = mc^2$.

32. Which process would release energy from gold, fission or fusion? From carbon? From iron?

33. If a uranium nucleus were to fission into three segments of approximately equal size instead of two, would more energy or less energy be released? Defend your answer using Figure 4.30.

34. Explain how radioactive decay has always warmed the Earth from the inside and how nuclear fusion has always warmed the Earth from the outside.

35. Speculate about some worldwide changes likely to follow the advent of successful fusion reactors.

Suggested Readings and Web Sites

M. Mitchell Waldrop, "The Shroud of Turin: An Answer Is at Hand." *Science*, September 30, 1988.
Describes the events leading up to the dating of the shroud.

http://www.iaea.or.at/worldatom
The web site for the International Atomic Energy Agency, which monitors almost all issues related to nuclear technology. A good starting point for exploring applications of many of the concepts discussed in this chapter.

http://www.iter.org
The web site for the International Thermonuclear Experimental Reactor project. Explore this site for the latest on the science and politics of this important project.

http://www.rw.doe.gov/homejava/homejava.htm
Home page for the Office of Civilian Radioactive Waste Management, established in 1982 to develop and manage a federal system for disposing of spent nuclear fuel resulting from atomic energy defense activities. It's here that you'll find the official position of the U.S. government regarding Yucca Mountain, Nevada, as a potential nuclear waste repository.

Chapter 5
Atomic Models

Virtual Handles on the Very Real

The metal-containing compounds in fireworks emit colored light when the fireworks burn. Sodium compounds, for example, emit yellow light, strontium compounds emit red light, barium compounds emit green light, and copper compounds emit blue-green light. The color we see from any one of these compounds, however, consists of a number of overlapping colors. When viewed through a prism, the overlapping colors are separated. In the center of this chapter's opening photograph are the glowing sparks of an exploding firework. The adjacent diagonal stripes, created by a prismlike filter on the camera, reveal the color of that firework separated into a series of colors called a spectral pattern.

Each element emits its own characteristic spectral pattern, which can be used to identify the element just as a fingerprint can be used to identify a person. The spectral patterns of the opening photograph, for example, reveal the presence of strontium in the fireworks. As we discuss in this chapter, the spectral patterns of elements allowed scientists of the 1900s to develop models of the atom's internal structure and dynamics. Through these models, which continue to be refined even today, chemists gain a powerful understanding of the submicroscopic realm.

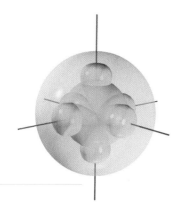

This chapter introduces some simplified atomic models, such as the one shown to the left. These models will help you gain a deeper understanding of the periodic table and give you a foundation for understanding how atoms react with one another to form new materials—an important topic of subsequent chapters. You'll learn why atomic models are useful for predicting how atoms behave but not for revealing what they "look like." Indeed, visual appearance has little meaning in the submicroscopic realm.

5.1 Models Help Us Visualize the Invisible World of Atoms

Atoms are so small that the number of them in a baseball is roughly equal to the number of Ping-Pong balls that could fit inside a hollow sphere as big as the Earth, as Figure 5.1 illustrates.

Atoms in
a baseball

Ping-Pong balls
in the Earth

Figure 5.1
If the Earth were filled with nothing but Ping-Pong balls, the number of balls would be roughly equal to the number of atoms in a baseball. Put differently, if a baseball were the size of the Earth, one of its atoms would be the size of a Ping-Pong ball.

This number is incredibly large—beyond our intuitive grasp. Atoms are so incredibly small that we can never *see* them in the usual sense. This is because light travels in waves, and atoms are smaller than the wavelengths of visible light, which is the light that allows the human eye to see things. We could stack microscope on top of microscope and still not see an individual atom. As illustrated in Figure 5.2, the diameter of an object visible under the highest magnification must be larger than the wavelengths of visible light.

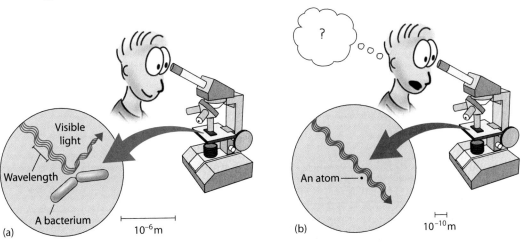

Visible
light

Wavelength

A bacterium

(a) 10^{-6} m

An atom — •

(b) 10^{-10} m

Figure 5.2
Microscopic objects can be seen through a microscope that works with visible light, but submicroscopic particles cannot. (a) A bacterium is visible because it is larger than the wavelengths of visible light. We can see the bacterium through the microscope because the bacterium reflects visible light. (b) An atom is invisible because it is smaller than the wavelengths of visible light and so does not reflect the light toward our eyes.

Although we cannot see atoms *directly*, we can generate images of them *indirectly*. In the mid 1980s, researchers developed the *scanning tunneling microscope* (STM), which produces images by dragging an ultrathin needle back and forth over the surface of a sample. Bumps the size of atoms on the surface cause the needle to move up and down. This vertical motion is detected and translated by a computer into a topographical image that corresponds to the positions of atoms on the surface (Figure 5.3). An STM can also be used to push individual atoms into desired positions. This ability opened up the field of nanotechnology, in which incredibly small electronic circuits and motors are built atom by atom.

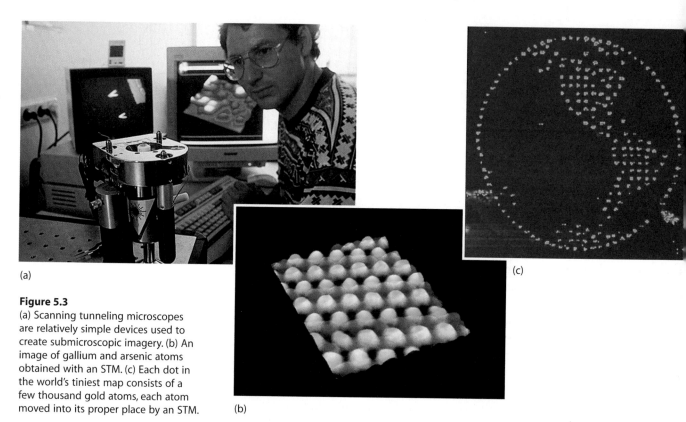

(a)

(b)

(c)

Figure 5.3
(a) Scanning tunneling microscopes are relatively simple devices used to create submicroscopic imagery. (b) An image of gallium and arsenic atoms obtained with an STM. (c) Each dot in the world's tiniest map consists of a few thousand gold atoms, each atom moved into its proper place by an STM.

Concept Check ✓

Why are atoms invisible?

Was this your answer? An individual atom is smaller than the wavelengths of visible light and so is unable to reflect that light. Atoms are invisible, therefore, because visible light passes right by them. The atomic images generated by STMs are not photographs taken by a camera. Rather, they are computer renditions generated from the movements of an ultrathin needle.

A very small or very large visible object can be represented with a **physical model**, which is a model that replicates the object at a more convenient scale. Figure 5.4a, for instance, shows a large-scale physical model

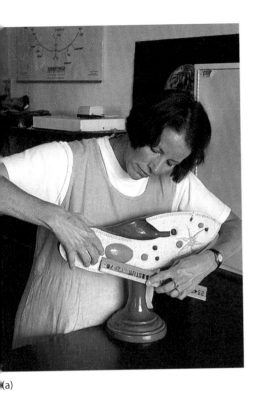

(a)

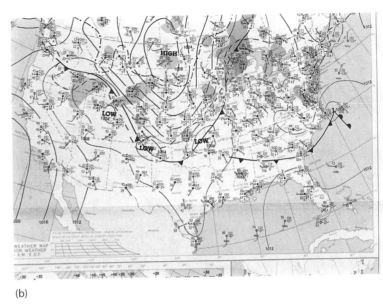

(b)

Figure 5.4
(a) This large-scale model of a microorganism is a physical model. (b) Weather forecasters rely on conceptual models such as this one to predict the behavior of weather systems.

of a microorganism that a biology student uses to study the microorganism's internal structure. Because atoms are invisible, however, we cannot use a physical model to represent them. In other words, we cannot simply scale up the atom to a larger size, as we might with a microorganism. (An STM merely shows the *positions* of atoms and not actual images of atoms, which do not have the solid surfaces implied in the STM images of Figure 5.3.) So, rather than describing the atom with a physical model, chemists use what is known as a **conceptual model** which describes a *system.* The more accurate a conceptual model, the more accurately it predicts the behavior of the system. The weather is best described using a conceptual model like the one shown in Figure 5.4b. Such a model shows how the various components of the system—humidity, atmospheric pressure, temperature, electric charge, the motion of large masses of air—interact with one another.

Other systems that can be described by conceptual models are the economy, population growth, the spread of diseases, and team sports.

Concept Check ✓

A basketball coach describes a playing strategy to her team by way of sketches on a game card. Do the illustrations represent a physical model or a conceptual model?

Was this your answer? The sketches are a conceptual model the coach uses to describe a system (the players on the court) with the hope of predicting an outcome (winning the game).

Like the weather, the atom is a complex system of interacting components, and it is best described with a conceptual model. You should therefore be careful not to interpret any visual representation of an atomic conceptual model as a re-creation of an actual atom. In Section 5.4, for example, you will be introduced to the planetary model of the atom wherein electrons are shown orbiting the atomic nucleus much as planets orbit the sun. This planetary model is limited, however, in that it fails to explain many properties of atoms. Thus newer and more accurate (and more complicated) conceptual models of the atom have since been introduced. In these models, electrons appear as a cloud hovering around the atomic nucleus, but even these models have their limitations. Ultimately, the best models of the atom are ones that are purely mathematical.

In this textbook, our focus is on conceptual atomic models that are easily represented by visual images, including the planetary model, the electron-cloud model, and a model in which electrons are grouped in units called *shells*. Despite their limitations, such images are excellent guides to learning chemistry, especially for the beginning student. These models were developed by scientists to help explain how atoms emit light. We begin our study of atomic models, therefore, by reviewing the fundamental nature of light.

5.2 Light Is a Form of Energy

Light is a form of energy known as *electromagnetic radiation*. It travels in waves that are analogous to the waves produced by a pebble dropped into a pond. Electromagnetic waves, however, are oscillations (vibrations) of electric and magnetic fields, not oscillations of a material medium like water. Most of the electromagnetic radiation we encounter is generated by electrons, which can oscillate at exceedingly high rates because of their small size.

As I idly tap this stick on the water surface, I generate waves that emanate outward from the point of contact. Similarly, as electrons oscillate back and forth in an atom, they generate electromagnetic waves that emanate from the atom.

The distance between two crests of an electromagnetic wave is called the **wavelength** of the wave. Electromagnetic wavelengths range from less than 1 nanometer (10^{-9} meter) for high-energy gamma rays to more than 1 kilometer (10^3 meters) for radio waves, which are low-energy electromagnetic radiation. Figure 5.5 labels two wavelengths—one very long, the other very short—on a fictitious wave drawn for illustration only.

Electromagnetic waves can also be characterized by their **wave frequency**, a measure of how rapidly they oscillate. The shorter the wavelength of an electromagnetic wave, the greater its wave frequency. Gamma rays, for example, have very short wavelengths, which means their wave frequencies are very high. Radio waves have very long wavelengths, which means their wave frequencies are very low.

The basic unit of wave frequency is the *hertz* (abbreviated Hz), where 1 hertz equals 1 cycle per second and *cycle* refers to one complete oscillation. Wave frequencies for electromagnetic radiation range from 10^{24} hertz for gamma rays to less than 10^3 hertz for radio waves. The higher the frequency of a wave, the greater its energy, which means that gamma rays are far more energetic than radio waves.

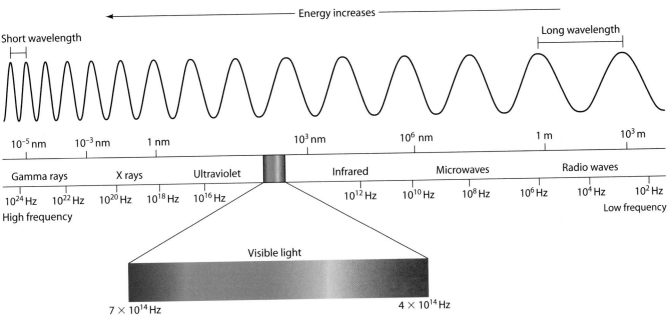

Figure 5.5
The electromagnetic spectrum is a continuous band of wave frequencies extending from high-energy gamma rays, which have short wavelengths and high frequencies, to low-energy radio waves, which have long wavelengths and low frequencies. The descriptive names of these regions are merely a historical classification, for all waves are the same in nature, differing only in wavelength and frequency.

Figure 5.5 shows the entire range of frequencies and wavelengths of electromagnetic radiation in a display known as the **electromagnetic spectrum.** The most energetic region of the electromagnetic spectrum consists of gamma rays. Next is the region of slightly lower energy where we find X rays, and next is the electromagnetic radiation we call ultraviolet light. Within a narrow region from about 7×10^{14} (700 trillion) hertz to about 4×10^{14} (400 trillion) hertz are the frequencies of electromagnetic radiation known as visible light. This region includes the rainbow of colors our eyes are able to detect, from violet at 700 trillion hertz to red at 400 trillion hertz. Lower in energy than visible light are infrared waves (detected by our skin as "heat waves"), then microwaves (used to cook foods), and finally radio waves (through which radio and television signals are sent), the waves of lowest energy.

Concept Check ✓

Can you see radio waves?

Was this your answer? Your eyes are equipped to see only the narrow range of frequencies of electromagnetic radiation from about 700 trillion to 400 trillion hertz—the range of visible light. Radio waves are one type of electromagnetic radiation, but their frequency is much lower than what your eyes can detect. Thus, you can't see radio waves. However, you can turn on an electronic gizmo called a radio, which translates radio waves into signals that drive a speaker to produce sound your ears can hear.

Figure 5.6
White light is separated into its color components by (a) a prism and (b) a diffraction grating.

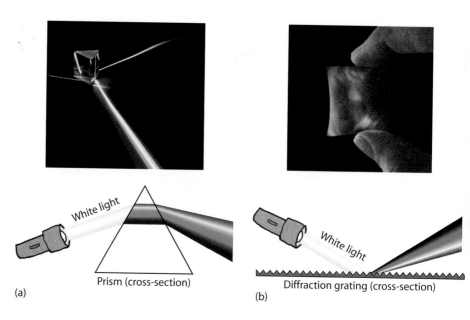

(a) Prism (cross-section)

(b) Diffraction grating (cross-section)

We see white light when all frequencies of visible light reach our eye at the same time. By passing white light through a prism or through a diffraction grating, which is a glass plate or plastic sheet with microscopic lines etched into it, the color components of the light can be separated, as shown in Figure 5.6. (Remember—each color of visible light corresponds to a different frequency.) A **spectroscope**, shown in Figure 5.7, is an instrument

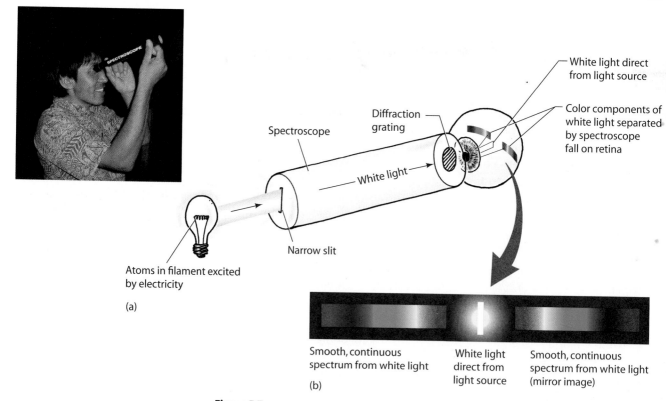

White light direct from light source

Color components of white light separated by spectroscope fall on retina

Diffraction grating

White light direct from light source

Spectroscope

White light

Narrow slit

Atoms in filament excited by electricity

(a)

Smooth, continuous spectrum from white light

White light direct from light source

Smooth, continuous spectrum from white light (mirror image)

(b)

Figure 5.7
(a) In a spectroscope, light emitted by atoms passes through a narrow slit before being separated into particular frequencies by a prism or (as shown here) a diffraction grating. (b) This is what the eye sees when the slit of a diffraction-grating spectroscope is pointed toward a white-light source. Spectra of colors appear to the left and right of the slit.

used to observe the color components of any light source. As we discuss in the following section, a spectroscope allows us to analyze the light emitted by elements as they are made to glow.

5.3 Atoms Can Be Identified by the Light They Emit

Light is given off by atoms subjected to various forms of energy, such as heat or electricity. The atoms of a given element emit only certain frequencies of light, however. As a consequence, each element emits a distinctive glow when energized.

Sodium atoms emit bright yellow light, which makes them useful as the light source in street lamps because our eyes are very sensitive to yellow light. Neon atoms emit a brilliant red-orange light, which makes them useful as the light source in neon signs. And as mentioned at the beginning of this chapter, glowing elements are also responsible for the colors of fireworks.

When we view the light from glowing atoms through a spectroscope, we see that the light consists of a number of discrete (separate from one another) frequencies rather than a continuous spectrum like the one shown in Figures 5.5 and 5.7. The pattern of frequencies formed by a given element—some of which are shown in Figure 5.8 on page 140—is referred to as that element's **atomic spectrum**. The atomic spectrum is an element's fingerprint. You can identify the elements in a light source by analyzing the light through a spectroscope and looking for characteristic patterns. If you don't have the opportunity to work with a spectroscope in your laboratory, check out the Hands-On Chemistry *Spectral Patterns* below.

Hands-On Chemistry: Spectral Patterns

Purchase some "rainbow" glasses from a nature, toy, or hobby store. The lenses of these glasses are diffraction gratings. Looking through them, you will see light separated into its color components. Certain light sources, such as the moon or a car's headlights, are separated into a continuous spectrum—in other words, all the colors of the rainbow appear in a continuous sequence from red to violet.

Other light sources, however, emit a distinct number of discontinuous colors. Examples include streetlights, neon signs, sparklers, and fireworks. The spectral patterns you see from these light sources are the atomic spectra of elements heated in the light sources. You'll be able to see the patterns best when you are at least 50 meters from the light source. This distance makes the spectrum appear as a series of dots like those of this chapter's opening photograph and similar to the series of lines shown in Figure 5.8.

The rainbow side of a compact disk can also be used for viewing spectral patterns. Holding the disk at eye level parallel to the ground, look over it at a light source, and observe the rainbow reflection. While focusing on the reflection, bring the disk as close as possible to your eye. Doing so will make the spectral pattern more apparent.

Share your rainbow glasses and disk with a friend on your next "night on the town." You'll find each type of light has its own signature pattern. How many different patterns are you able to observe?

Figure 5.8
Elements heated by a flame glow their characteristic color. This is commonly called a *flame test* and is used to test for the presence of an element in a sample. When viewed through a spectroscope, the color of each element is revealed to consist of a pattern of distinct frequencies known as an atomic spectrum.

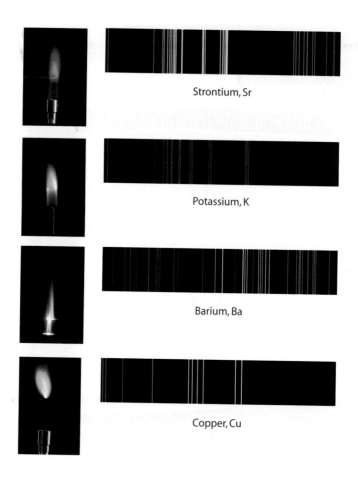

Strontium, Sr

Potassium, K

Barium, Ba

Copper, Cu

Concept Check ✓

How might you deduce the elemental composition of a star?

Was this your answer? Aim a well-built spectroscope at the star, and study its spectral patterns. In the late 1800s, this was done with our own star, the sun. Spectral patterns of hydrogen and some other known elements were observed, in addition to one pattern that could not be identified. Scientists concluded that this unidentified pattern belonged to an element not yet discovered on the Earth. They named this element *helium* after the Greek word for the "sun," *helios*.

Figure 5.9
A portion of the atomic spectrum for hydrogen. These frequencies are higher than those of visible light, which is why they are not shown in color.

Researchers in the 1800s noted that the lightest element, hydrogen, has a far more orderly atomic spectrum than the other elements. Figure 5.9 shows a portion of the hydrogen spectrum. Note that the spacing between successive lines decreases in a regular way. A Swiss schoolteacher, Johann Balmer (1825–1898), expressed these line positions by a mathematical formula. Another regularity in hydrogen's atomic spectrum was noticed by Johannes Rydberg (1854–1919)—the sum of the frequencies of two lines sometimes equals the frequency of a third line. For example,

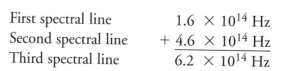

First spectral line	1.6×10^{14} Hz
Second spectral line	$+\ 4.6 \times 10^{14}$ Hz
Third spectral line	6.2×10^{14} Hz

The orderliness of hydrogen's atomic spectrum was most intriguing to Balmer, Rydberg, and other investigators of the time. However, as to why such orderliness should exist, these early workers were unable to formulate any hypothesis that agreed with any accepted atomic model of the day.

5.4 Niels Bohr Used the Quantum Hypothesis to Explain Atomic Spectra

An important step toward our present-day understanding of atoms and their spectra was taken by the German physicist Max Planck (1858–1947). In 1900, Planck hypothesized that light energy is *quantized* in much the same way matter is.

To understand what this interesting new term means, consider a gold brick. The mass of the brick equals some whole-number multiple of the mass of a single gold atom. Similarly, an electric charge is always some whole-number multiple of the charge on a single electron. Mass and electric charge are therefore said to be *quantized* in that they consist of some number of fundamental units.

What Planck did with his **quantum hypothesis** was to recognize that a beam of light energy is not the continuous (nonquantized) stream of energy we think it is. Instead the beam consists of zillions of small, discrete *packets* of energy, each packet called a **quantum**, as represented in Figure 5.10. A few years later, in 1905, Einstein recognized that these quanta of light behave much like tiny particles of matter. To emphasize their *particulate* nature, each quantum of light was called a **photon**, a name coined because of its similarity to the words *electron, proton,* and *neutron.*

Take a moment to let this amazing fact sink in: light as a stream of particles rather than a wave! And if that is so, why does Section 5.2 say light is an electromagnetic *wave*? Was that an error? A lie? Neither, for the truth of the matter is that light behaves as *both a wave and a particle,* and this is where the idea of conceptual models comes into play. When scientists study visible light (or any other electromagnetic radiation), they are free to choose the model that best fits their needs—light as wave or light as stream of particles.

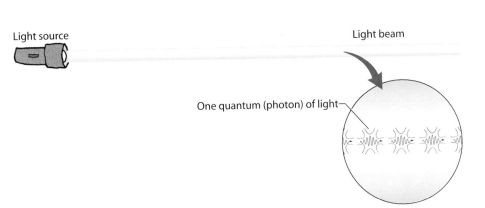

Light source

Light beam

One quantum (photon) of light

Figure 5.10
Light is quantized, which means it consists of a stream of energy packets. Each packet is called a quantum, also known as a photon.

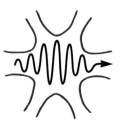

High-frequency,
high-energy
photon

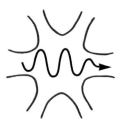

Low-frequency,
low-energy
photon

Figure 5.11
The greater the frequency of a photon of light, the greater the energy packed into that photon.

Depending on the model chosen, light has the properties of a wave or the properties of a particle. To represent this duality, photons are illustrated in this text as a burst of light with a wave drawn inside the burst.

As shown in Figure 5.11, the amount of energy in a photon increases with the frequency of the light. One photon of ultraviolet light, for example, possesses more energy than one photon of infrared light because ultraviolet light has higher frequency than the latter (as Figure 5.5 shows).

Using Planck's quantum hypothesis, the Danish scientist Niels Bohr (1885–1962) explained the formation of atomic spectra as follows. First, Bohr recognized that the potential energy of an electron in an atom depends on the electron's distance from the nucleus. This is analogous to the potential energy of an object held some distance above the Earth's surface. The object has more potential energy when it is held high above the ground than when it is held close to the ground. Likewise, an electron has more potential energy when it is far from the nucleus than when it is close to the nucleus. Second, Bohr recognized that when an atom absorbs a photon of light, it is absorbing *energy*. This energy is acquired by one of the electrons surrounding the atom's nucleus. Because this electron has gained energy, it must move away from the nucleus. In other words, absorption of a photon causes a low-potential-energy electron in an atom to become a high-potential-energy electron.

Bohr also realized that the opposite is true: when a high-potential-energy electron in an atom loses some of its energy, the electron moves closer to the nucleus and the energy lost from the electron is emitted from the atom as a photon of light. Both absorption and emission are illustrated in Figure 5.12.

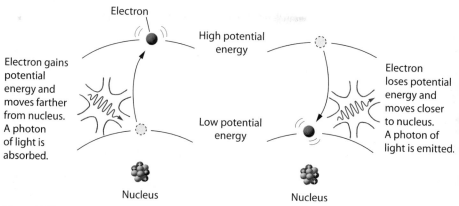

Figure 5.12
An electron is lifted away from the nucleus as the atom it is in absorbs a photon of light and drops closer to the nucleus as the atom releases a photon of light.

Concept Check ✓

Which has more energy: a photon of red light or a photon of infrared light?

Was this your answer? As shown in Figure 5.5, red light has a higher frequency than infrared light, which means a photon of red light has more energy than does a photon of infrared light. Recall that a photon is a single discrete packet (a *quantum*) of radiant energy.

Bohr reasoned that because light energy is quantized, the energy of an electron in an atom must also be quantized. In other words, an electron cannot have just any amount of potential energy. Rather, within the atom there must be a number of distinct *energy levels*, analogous to steps on a staircase. Where you are on a staircase is restricted to where the steps are—you cannot stand at a height that is, say, halfway between any two adjacent steps. Similarly, there are only a limited number of permitted energy levels in an atom, and an electron can never have an amount of energy between these permitted energy levels. Bohr gave each energy level a **principal quantum number n,** where n is always some integer. The lowest energy level has a principal quantum number $n = 1$. An electron for which $n = 1$ is as close to the nucleus as possible, and an electron for which $n = 2$, $n = 3$, and so forth is farther away from the nucleus.

Just as I can't stand between two adjacent steps, an electron can't exist between two energy levels.

Using these ideas, Bohr developed a conceptual model in which an electron moving around the nucleus is restricted to certain distances from the nucleus, with these distances determined by the amount of energy the electron has. Bohr saw this as similar to how the planets are held in orbit around the sun at given distances from the sun. The allowed energy levels for any atom, therefore, could be graphically represented as orbits around the nucleus, as shown in Figure 5.13. Bohr's quantized model of the atom thus became known as the *planetary model.*

Electron

$n = 4$
$n = 3$
$n = 2$
$n = 1$

Nucleus

Figure 5.13
Bohr's planetary model of the atom, in which electrons orbit the nucleus much like planets orbit the sun, is a graphical representation that helps us understand how electrons can possess only certain quantities of energy.

Bohr used his planetary model to explain why atomic spectra contain only a limited number of light frequencies. According to the model, photons are emitted by atoms as electrons move from higher-energy outer orbits to lower-energy inner orbits. The energy of an emitted photon is equal to the *difference* in energy between the two orbits. Because an electron is restricted to discrete orbits, only particular light frequencies are emitted, as atomic spectra show.

Interestingly, any transition between two orbits is always instantaneous. In other words, the electron doesn't "jump" from a higher to lower orbit the way a squirrel jumps from a higher branch in a tree to a lower one. Rather, it takes no time for an electron to move between two orbits.

Bohr was serious when he stated that electrons could *never* exist *between* permitted energy levels!

Bohr was also able to explain why the sum of two frequencies of light emitted by an atom often equals a third emitted frequency. If an electron is raised to the third energy level—that is, the third highest orbit, the one for which $n = 3$—it can return to the first orbit by two routes. As shown in Figure 5.14, it can return by a single transition from the third to the first orbit, or it can return by a double transition from the third orbit to the second and then to the first. The single transition emits a photon of frequency C, and the double transition emits two photons, one of frequency A and one of frequency B. These three photons of frequencies A, B, and C are responsible for three spectral lines. Note that the energy transition for A plus B is equal to the energy transition for C. Because frequency is proportional to energy, frequency A plus frequency B equals frequency C.

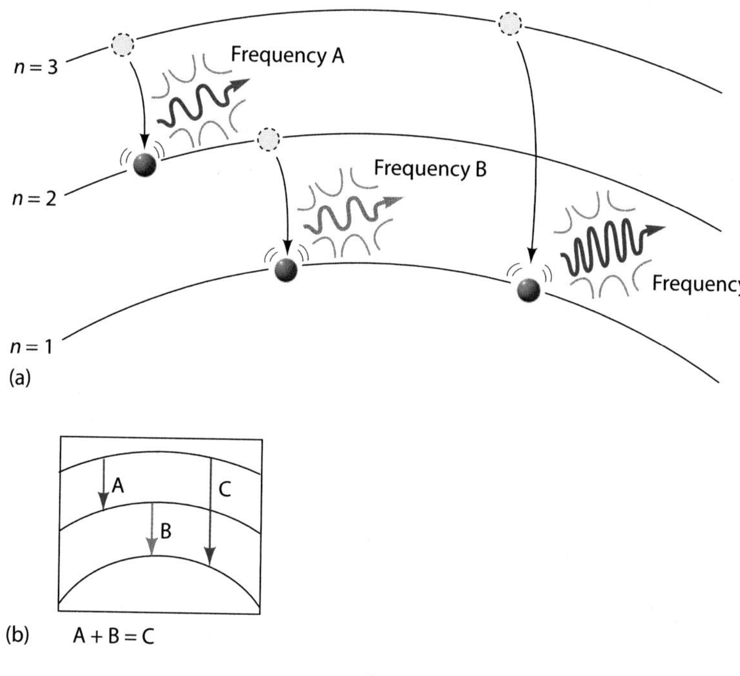

Figure 5.14
(a) The frequency of light emitted (or absorbed) by an atom is proportional to the energy difference between electron orbits. Because the energy differences between orbits are discrete, the frequencies of light emitted (or absorbed) are also discrete. The electron here can emit only three discrete frequencies of light—A, B, and C. The greater the transition, the higher the frequency of the photon emitted. (b) The sum of the energies (and frequencies) for transitions A and B equals the energy (and frequency) of transition C.

Concept Check ✓

Suppose the frequency of light emitted in Figure 5.14 is 5 billion hertz along path A and 7 billion hertz along path B. What frequency of light is emitted when an electron makes a transition along path C?

Was this your answer? Add the two known frequencies to get the frequency of path C: 5 billion hertz + 7 billion hertz = 12 billion hertz.

Bohr's planetary atomic model proved to be a tremendous success. By utilizing Planck's quantum hypothesis, Bohr's model solved the mystery of atomic spectra. Despite its successes, though, Bohr's model was limited because it did not explain why energy levels in an atom are quantized. Bohr himself was quick to point out that his model was to be interpreted only as a crude beginning, and the picture of electrons whirling about the nucleus like planets about the sun was not to be taken literally (a warning to which popularizers of science paid no heed).

5.5 Electrons Exhibit Wave Properties

If light has both wave properties and particle properties, why can't a material particle, such as an electron, also have both? This question was posed by the French physicist Louis de Broglie (1892–1987) while he was still a graduate student in 1924. His revolutionary answer was that every particle of matter is somehow endowed with a wave to guide it as it travels. The more slowly an electron moves, the more its behavior is that of a particle with mass. The more quickly it moves, however, the more its behavior is that of a wave of energy. This duality is an extension of Einstein's famous equation $E = mc^2$, which tells us that matter and energy are interconvertible (Section 4.9).

A practical application of the wave properties of fast-moving electrons is the electron microscope, which focuses not visible-light waves but electron waves. Because electron waves are much shorter than visible-light waves, electron microscopes are able to show far greater detail than optical microscopes, as Figure 5.15 shows.

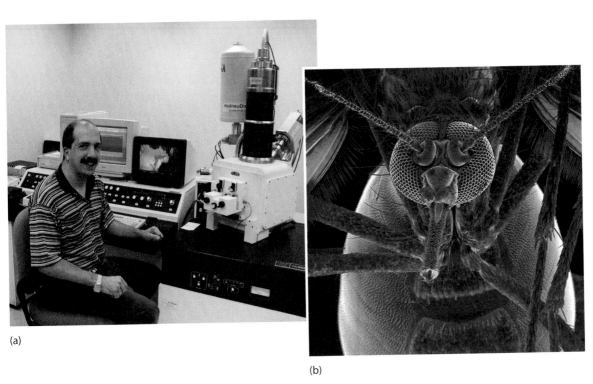

(a)

(b)

Figure 5.15
(a) An electron microscope makes practical use of the wave nature of electrons. The wavelengths of electron beams are typically thousands of times shorter than the wavelengths of visible light, and so the electron microscope is able to distinguish detail not visible with optical microscopes. (b) Detail of a female mosquito head as seen with an electron microscope at a "low" magnification of 200 times. Note the remarkable resolution.

In an atom, an electron moves at very high speeds—on the order of 2 million meters per second—and therefore exhibits many of the properties of a wave. An electron's wave nature can be used to explain why electrons in an atom are restricted to particular energy levels. Permitted energy levels are a natural consequence of electron waves closing in on themselves in a synchronized manner.

As an analogy, consider the wire loop shown in Figure 5.16. This loop is affixed to a mechanical vibrator that can be adjusted to create waves of different wavelengths in the wire. Waves passing through the wire that meet up with themselves, as shown in Figure 5.16b, form a stationary wave pattern called a *standing wave*. This pattern results because the peaks and valleys of successive waves are perfectly matched, which makes the waves reinforce one another. With other wavelengths, as shown in Figure 5.16c, successive waves are not synchronized. As a result, the waves do not build to great amplitude.

The only waves that an electron exhibits while confined to an atom are those that are self-reinforcing. These are the ones that resemble a standing wave centered on the atomic nucleus. Each standing wave corresponds to one of the permitted energy levels. Only the frequencies of light that match

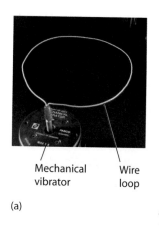

Mechanical   Wire
vibrator   loop

(a)

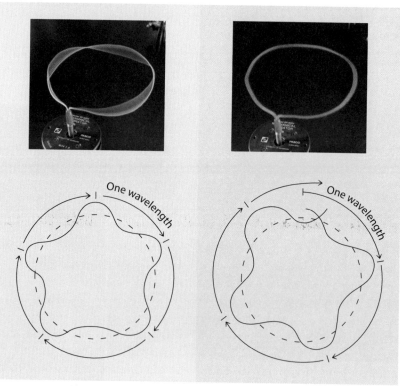

(b) Wavelength is self-reinforcing.   (c) Wavelength produces chaotic motion.

Figure 5.16
For the fixed circumference of a wire loop, only some wavelengths are self-reinforcing.
(a) The loop affixed to the post of a mechanical vibrator at rest. Waves are sent through the wire when the post vibrates. (b) Waves created by vibration at particular rates are self-reinforcing. (c) Waves created by vibration at other rates are not self-reinforcing.

Hands-On Chemistry: Rubber Waves

Stretch a rubber band between your two index fingers and pluck one length of it. Note that no matter where along the length you pluck, the area of greatest oscillation is always at the midpoint. This is a self-reinforcing wave that occurs as overlapping waves bounce back and forth from finger to finger.

Under regular light, it is difficult to see the waves traveling back and forth. For a better view, pluck the rubber band in front of a computer monitor or a television screen that uses a cathode ray tube. The light from these devices, which acts like a strobe light, makes the waves appear to slow down.

Vary the tension in the rubber band to see different effects.

the difference between any two of these permitted energy levels can be absorbed or emitted by an atom.

The wave nature of electrons also explains why they do not spiral closer and closer to the positive nucleus that attracts them. By viewing each electron orbit as a self-reinforcing wave, we see that the circumference of the smallest orbit can be no smaller than a single wavelength.

Concept Check ✓

What must an electron be doing in order to have wave properties?

Was this your answer? According to de Broglie, particles of matter behave like waves by virtue of their motion. An electron must therefore be *moving* in order to have wave properties. In atoms, electrons move on the order of 2 million meters per second, and so their wave nature is most pronounced.

Probability Clouds and Atomic Orbitals Help Us Visualize Electron Waves

Electron waves are three-dimensional, which makes them difficult to visualize, but scientists have come up with two ways of visualizing them: as *probability clouds* and as *atomic orbitals.*

As you saw if you just did the Hands-On exercise, when you pluck a stretched rubber band, the resulting waves are most intense at the midpoint of the plucked length and much weaker at the ends. In a similar fashion, standing electron waves in an atom are more intense in some regions than in others. In 1926, the Austrian–German scientist Erwin Schrodinger (1887–1961) formulated a remarkable equation from which the intensities of electron waves in an atom could be calculated. It was soon recognized that the intensity at any given location determined the probability of finding the electron at that location. In other words, the electron was most likely to be found where its wave intensity was greatest and least likely to be found where its wave intensity was smallest.

If we could plot the positions of an electron of a given energy over time as a series of tiny dots, the resulting pattern would resemble what is called a **probability cloud**. Figure 5.17a shows a probability cloud for hydrogen's electron. The denser a region of the cloud, the greater the probability of finding the electron in that region. The densest regions correspond to where the electron's wave intensity is greatest. A probability cloud is therefore a close approximation of the actual shape of an electron's three-dimensional wave.

An **atomic orbital**, like a probability cloud, specifies a volume of space where the electron is most likely to be found. By convention, atomic orbitals are drawn to delineate the volume inside which the electron is located 90 percent of the time. This gives the atomic orbital an apparent border, as shown in Figure 5.17b. This border is arbitrary, however, because the electron may exist on either side of it. Most of the time, though, the electron remains within the border.

Figure 5.17
(a) The probability cloud for hydrogen's electron. The more concentrated the dots, the greater the chance of finding the electron at that location. (b) The atomic orbital for hydrogen's electron. The electron is somewhere inside this spherical volume 90 percent of the time.

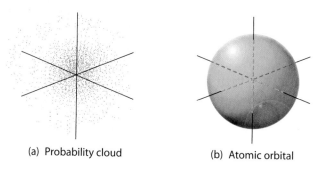

(a) Probability cloud   (b) Atomic orbital

Probability clouds and atomic orbitals are essentially the same thing. They differ only in that atomic orbitals specify an outer limit, which makes them easier to depict graphically.

As Table 5.1 shows, the first four atomic orbitals are classified by the letters *s*, *p*, *d*, and *f*.

Atomic orbitals come in a variety of shapes, some quite exquisite. The simplest orbital is the spherical *s* orbital (also shown in Figure 5.17). The *p* orbital consists of two lobes and resembles an hourglass. There are three kinds of *p* orbitals, and they differ from one another only by their orientation in three-dimensional space. The more complex *d* orbitals have five possible shapes, and the *f* orbitals have seven. Please do not feel compelled to memorize all the orbital shapes, especially the *d* and *f* ones. However, you should understand that each orbital represents a different region in which an electron of a given energy is most likely to be found.

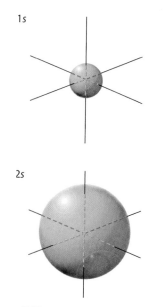

Figure 5.18
The 2s orbital is larger than the 1s orbital because the 2s accommodates electrons of greater energy.

Concept Check ✓

What is the relationship between an electron wave and an atomic orbital?

Was this your answer? The atomic orbital is an approximation of the shape of the standing electron wave surrounding the atomic nucleus.

In addition to a variety of shapes, atomic orbitals also come in a variety of sizes that correspond to different energy levels. In general, highly ener-

Table 5.1

The Four Major Types of Orbitals: *s, p, d, f*

Orbital Type	Spatial Orientations
s The *s* orbital has only one shape, which is spherical.	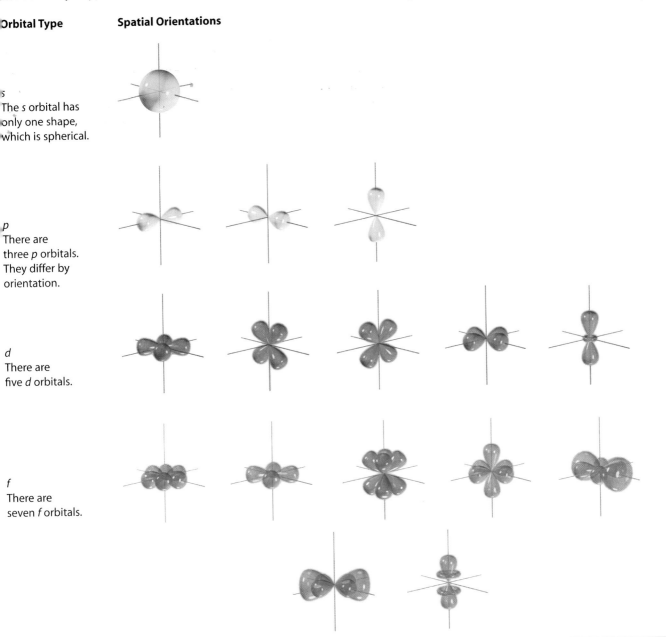
p There are three *p* orbitals. They differ by orientation.	
d There are five *d* orbitals.	
f There are seven *f* orbitals.	

gized electrons are able to extend farther away from the attracting nucleus, which means they are distributed over a greater volume of space. The higher the energy of the electron, therefore, the larger its atomic orbital. Because electron energies are quantized, however, the possible sizes of the atomic orbitals are quantized. The size of an orbital is thus indicated by Bohr's principal quantum number $n = 1, 2, 3, 4, 5, 6, 7$, or greater.

The first two *s* orbitals are shown in Figure 5.18. The smallest *s* orbital is the 1*s* (pronounced one-ess), where 1 is the principal quantum number. The next largest *s* orbital is the 2*s*, and so forth.

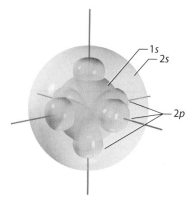

Figure 5.19
The fluorine atom has five overlapping atomic orbitals that contain its nine electrons, which are not shown.

An atomic orbital is simply a volume of space within which an electron may reside. Orbitals may therefore overlap one another in an atom. As shown in Figure 5.19, the electrons of a fluorine atom are distributed among its $1s$, $2s$, and three $2p$ orbitals.*

The hourglass-shaped p orbital illustrates the significance of the wave nature of the electron. Unlike the case with a real hourglass, the two lobes of this orbital are not open to each other, and yet an electron freely moves from one lobe to the other. To understand how this can happen, consider an analogy from the macroscopic world. A guitar player can gently tap a guitar string at its midpoint (the 12th fret) and pluck it elsewhere at the same time to produce a high-pitched tone called a harmonic. Close inspection of this string, shown in Figure 5.20, reveals that it oscillates everywhere along the string except at the point directly above the 12th fret. This point of zero oscillation is called a *node*. Although there is no motion at the node, waves nonetheless travel through it. Thus, the guitar string oscillates on both sides of the node when only one side is plucked. Similarly, the point between the two lobes of a p orbital is a node through which the electron may pass—but only by virtue of its ability to take on the form of a wave.

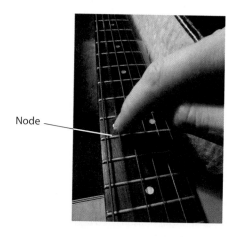

Node

Figure 5.20
The guitar string can oscillate on both sides of the 12th-fret node even when the string is plucked on only one side of the node. This occurs because waves can pass through the node.

Concept Check ✓

Distinguish between an *orbital* and one of Bohr's *orbits*.

Was this your answer? An orbit is a *distinct path* followed by an object in its revolution around another object. In Bohr's planetary model of the atom, he proposed an analogy between electrons orbiting the atomic nucleus and planets orbiting the sun.

An atomic orbital is a *volume of space* around an atomic nucleus where an electron of a given energy will most likely be found. What orbits and orbitals have in common is that they both use Bohr's principal quantum number to indicate energy levels in an atom.

A disadvantage of Bohr's planetary atomic model is that the restriction that electrons in an atom can have only discrete energy values is introduced arbitrarily in order to account for spectral data. Atomic models based on the electron's wave behavior, on the other hand, show that discrete electron

---

* For reasons that are beyond the scope of this text, the $1p$ orbital does not exist. The smallest p orbital is therefore the $2p$. Other nonexistent orbitals are the $1d$, $2d$, $1f$, $2f$, and $3f$.

Hands-On Chemistry: Quantized Whistle

You can "quantize" your whistle by whistling down a long tube, such as the tube from a roll of wrapping paper. First, without the tube, whistle from a high pitch to a low pitch. Do it in a single breath and as loud as you can. Next, try the same thing while holding the tube to your lips. Ah, ha! Note that some frequencies simply cannot be whistled, no matter how hard you try. These frequencies are forbidden because their wavelengths are not a multiple of the length of the tube.

Try experimenting with tubes of different lengths. To hear yourself more clearly, use a flexible plastic tube and twist the outer end toward your ear.

When your whistle is confined to the tube, the consequence is a quantization of its frequencies. When an electron wave is confined to an atom, the consequence is a quantization of the electron's energy.

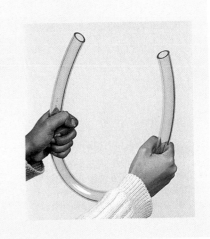

energy values are a natural consequence of the electron's confinement to the atom. While Bohr's planetary model accounts for the generation of light quanta, the wave model takes things a step further by treating light and matter in the same way—both behaving sometimes like a wave and sometimes like a particle. As abstract as the wave model may be, these successes indicate that it presents a more fundamental description of the atom than does Bohr's planetary model.

5.6 Energy-Level Diagrams Describe How Orbitals Are Occupied

Each orbital has a capacity for two, but no more than two, electrons. To understand how two electrically repelling electrons may coexist in the same region of space, we turn to physics. From physics we learn that the movement of any charged body generates a magnetic field. Electrons spin either clockwise or counterclockwise around an imaginary axis through their center. This spinning motion gives the electron north and south magnetic poles, as shown in Figure 5.21. Two electrons are able to pair together in the same

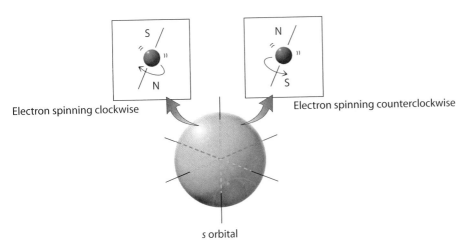

Electron spinning clockwise

Electron spinning counterclockwise

s orbital

Figure 5.21
Two electrons spinning in opposite directions may pair together in an atomic orbital because the opposite directions of spin create oppositely directed magnetic fields.

orbital when they spin in opposite directions because such spinning generates oppositely oriented magnetic fields that are mutually attractive and partly compensate for the electrical repulsion between the electrons.*

We can use the orbital model to "build" atoms electron by electron. This is done by using what is called an **energy-level diagram**, shown in Figure 5.22. Each box represents an orbital, each electron is represented by an arrow, and two electrons spinning in opposite directions in the same orbital are shown as two arrows pointing in opposite directions.

Figure 5.22
This energy-level diagram shows the relative energy levels of atomic orbitals in a multielectron atom (in this case rubidium, Rb, atomic number 37).

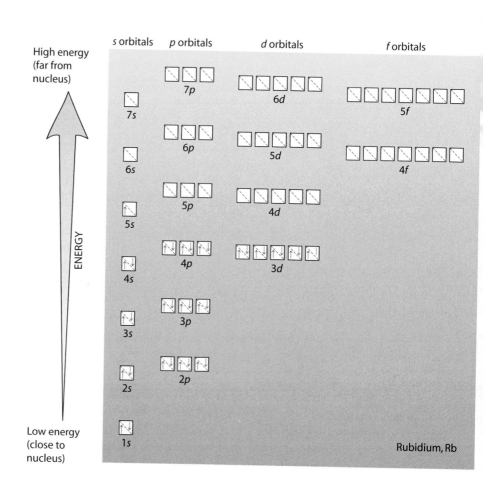

Consider the lithium atom, Li (atomic number 3), which has three electrons. In which orbitals do you suppose lithium's electrons are most likely to be found? As indicated in Figure 5.22, the lower a box is located in the diagram, the lower the energy of the orbital it represents. Low-energy orbitals are the ones that allow the electrons to get closest to the nucleus. Thus, these low-energy orbitals are the ones that tend to get filled first. Accordingly, a lithium atom in its lowest energy state, as depicted at left, has two electrons filling the 1s orbital and the third electron in the 2s orbital.

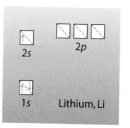

---

* This explanation is not fully accurate. A more accurate explanation, however, is beyond the scope of this text.

A boron atom, B (atomic number 5), in its lowest energy state has four of its five electrons filling the 1s and 2s orbitals. Its fifth electron may reside in any one of the 2p orbitals, all of which are at same energy level:

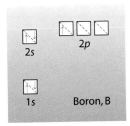

A carbon atom, C (atomic number 6), has six electrons. Five of them occupy the 1s, 2s, and 2p orbitals just as the electrons in boron do. Carbon's sixth electron, however, has a choice of either pairing up with the fifth electron in the same 2p orbital or entering a 2p orbital of its own:

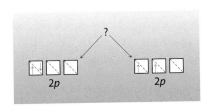

Because electrons have a natural repulsion for one another, they do not begin to pair up in the same orbital until all the other orbitals at the same energy level are singly occupied. Electrons in separate orbitals tend to spin in the same direction, and so the arrows should be shown all pointing in the same direction until pairing is necessary. For these reasons, the two 2p electrons of a carbon atom in its lowest energy state are in separate 2p orbitals and are drawn pointing in the same direction:

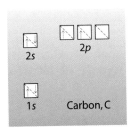

There is no pairing of 2p electrons in the nitrogen atom, N (atomic number 7), which has seven electrons. The oxygen atom, O (atomic number 8), however, has eight electrons, two of which are forced to pair up in one 2p orbital (it doesn't matter which one).

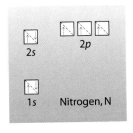
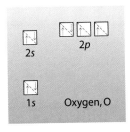

How electrons enter orbitals of the same energy level such as the three 2*p* orbitals is not unlike a bunch of strangers boarding a bus with double seats. These strangers—being an unfriendly bunch—prefer to occupy double seats alone. Only after all the seats are singly occupied do the strangers begin to pair up.

The arrangement of electrons in the orbitals of an atom is called the atom's **electron configuration**. The electron configuration of any atom can be shown in an energy-level diagram like Figure 5.22 by placing that atom's electrons in the orbitals in order of increasing energy level. Also, remember to pair electrons of opposite spin in an orbital only when necessary.

Concept Check ✓

1. How many 3*d* orbitals are there?
2. Fill in this energy-level diagram for sodium, Na (atomic number 11):

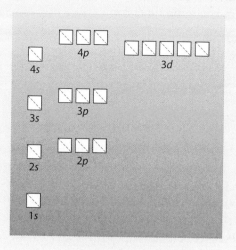

Were these your answers?

1. There are five 3*d* orbitals, each represented by one box in an energy-level diagram. These 3*d* orbitals differ from one another by their spatial orientations and shapes, as shown in Table 5.1.
2. Begin with the lowest-energy orbital, which is the 1*s*. Place two electrons in each orbital, using oppositely oriented arrows to represent the opposite spins of the electrons. Sodium's 11 electrons fill the 1*s*, 2*s*, and all three 2*p* orbitals. The 11th electron resides alone in the 3*s* orbital.

An abbreviated way of presenting electron configuration is to write the principal quantum number and letter of each occupied orbital and then use a superscript to indicate numbers of electrons in each orbital. The orbitals of each atom are then written in order of increasing energy levels. For the group 1 elements, this notation is

Hydrogen, H $1s^1$
Lithium, Li $1s^2 2s^1$
Sodium, Na $1s^2 2s^2 2p^6 3s^1$
Potassium, K $1s^2 2s^2 2p^6 3s^2 3p^6 4s^1$
Rubidium, Rb $1s^2 2s^2 2p^6 3s^2 3p^6 4s^2 3d^{10} 4p^6 5s^1$
Cesium, Cs $1s^2 2s^2 2p^6 3s^2 3p^6 4s^2 3d^{10} 4p^6 5s^2 4d^{10} 5p^6 6s^1$
Francium, Fr $1s^2 2s^2 2p^6 3s^2 3p^6 4s^2 3d^{10} 4p^6 5s^2 4d^{10} 5p^6 6s^2 4f^{14} 5d^{10} 6p^6 7s^1$

Note that all the superscripts for an atom must add up to the total number of electrons in the atom—1 for hydrogen, 3 for lithium, 11 for sodium, and so forth. Also note that the orbitals are not always listed in order of principal quantum number. The $4s$ orbital, for example, is lower in energy than the $3d$ orbitals as is indicated on the energy level diagram of Figure 5.22. The $4s$ orbital, therefore, appears *before* the $3d$ orbital.

The properties of an atom are determined mostly by its outermost electrons, the ones farthest from the nucleus. These are the electrons toward the "outer surface" of the atom and hence the ones in direct contact with the external environment. Elements that have similar electron configurations in their outermost orbitals, therefore, have similar properties. For example, in the alkaline metals of group 1, shown above, the outermost occupied orbital (shown in blue) is an s orbital containing a single electron. In general, elements in the same group of the periodic table have similar electron configurations in the outermost orbitals, which explains why elements in the same group have similar properties—a concept first presented in Section 2.6.

5.7 Orbitals of Similar Energies Can Be Grouped into Shells

Orbitals having comparable energies are grouped together. As shown in Figure 5.23 on page 156, no other orbital has energy similar to that of the $1s$ orbital, and so this orbital is grouped by itself. The energy level of the $2s$ orbital, however, is very close to the energy level of the three $2p$ orbitals, and so these four orbitals are grouped together. Likewise, the $3s$ and three $3p$ orbitals, the $4s$, five $3d$, and three $4p$ orbitals, and so on. The result is a set of seven distinct horizontal rows of orbitals.

The seven rows in Figure 5.23 correspond to the seven periods in the periodic table, with the bottom row corresponding to the first period, the next row up from the bottom corresponding to the second period, and so on. Furthermore, the maximum number of electrons each row can hold is equal to the number of elements in the corresponding period. The bottom row in Figure 5.23 can hold a maximum of two electrons, and so there are only two elements, hydrogen and helium, in the first period of the periodic table. The second and third rows up from the bottom each have a capacity

Figure 5.23
Orbitals of comparable energy levels can be grouped together to give rise to a set of seven rows of orbitals.

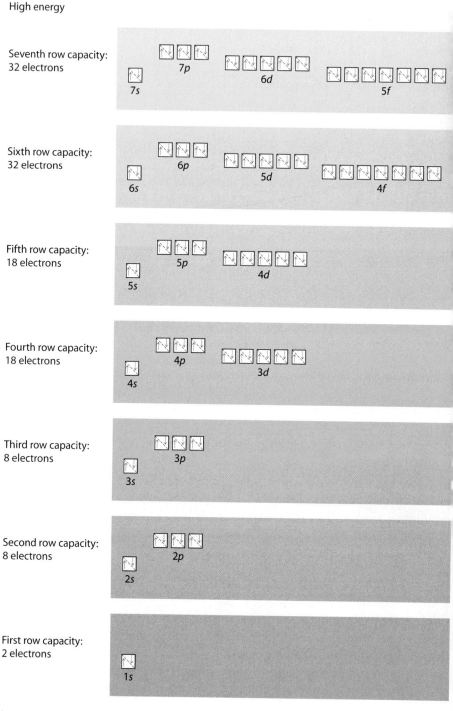

High energy

Seventh row capacity: 32 electrons

Sixth row capacity: 32 electrons

Fifth row capacity: 18 electrons

Fourth row capacity: 18 electrons

Third row capacity: 8 electrons

Second row capacity: 8 electrons

First row capacity: 2 electrons

Low energy

for eight electrons, and so eight elements are found in both the second and third periods. Continue analyzing Figure 5.23 in this way, and you will find 18 elements in the fourth and fifth periods, and 32 elements in the sixth and seventh periods. (As of this writing, only 29 of the seventh-period elements have been discovered.)

Recall from Section 5.5 that the higher the energy level of an orbital, the farther away an electron in that orbital is located from the nucleus. Electrons in the same row of orbitals in Figure 5.23, therefore, are roughly

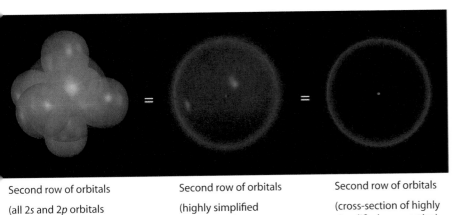

Figure 5.24
The second row of orbitals, which consists of the 2s and three 2p orbitals, can be represented either as a single smooth spherical shell or as a cross-section of such a shell.

Second row of orbitals
(all 2s and 2p orbitals combined)

Second row of orbitals
(highly simplified perspective)

Second row of orbitals
(cross-section of highly simplified perspective)

the same distance from the nucleus. Graphically, this can be represented by converging all the orbitals in a given row into a single three-dimensional hollow shell, as shown in Figure 5.24. Each is a graphic representation of a collection of orbitals of comparable energy in a multielectron atom. As you'll see in the next section, this *shell model* of the atom allows us to explain much about the organization of the periodic table.

The seven rows of orbitals in Figure 5.23 can thus be represented either by a series of seven concentric shells or by a series of seven cross-sectional circles of these shells, as shown in Figure 5.25. The number of electrons each shell can hold is equal to the number of orbitals it contains multiplied by two (because there can be two electrons per orbital).

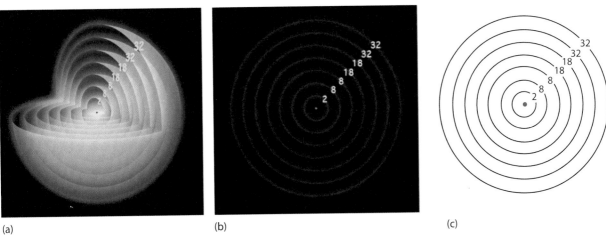

(a)   (b)   (c)

Figure 5.25
(a) A cutaway view of the seven shells, with the number of electrons each shell can hold indicated. (b) A two-dimensional, cross-sectional view of the shells. (c) An easy to draw cross-sectional view.

You fill in electrons in a shell diagram just as in an energy-level diagram—electrons first fill the shells closest to the nucleus. Also, in accordance with the strangers-on-a-bus analogy, electrons do not begin to pair in a shell until the shell is half filled. Figure 5.26 on page 158 shows how this works for the first three periods. As with energy-level diagrams, there is one shell for each period, and the number of elements in a period is equal to the maximum number of electrons the shells representing that period can hold.

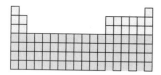

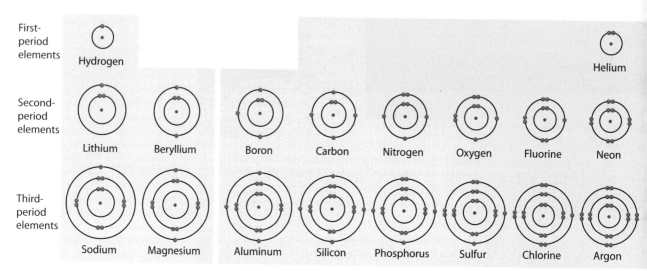

Figure 5.26
The first three periods of the periodic table according to the shell model. Elements in the same period have electrons in the same shells. Elements in the same period differ from one another by the number of electrons in the outermost shell.

Concept Check ✔

How many orbitals make up the fourth shell? What is the electron capacity of this shell?

Were these your answers? There are nine orbitals in the fourth shell. In order of increasing energy level, they are the one 4s orbital, the five 3d orbitals, and the three 4p orbitals. Because each orbital can hold two electrons, the total electron capacity of the fourth shell is $2 \times 9 = 18$ electrons, which is the same number of elements found in the fourth period of the periodic table.

In the next section, we explore how the shell model can be used to explain periodic trends. An even further simplified shell model, known as *electron-dot structure*, is then developed in Chapter 6 to assist you in understanding chemical bonding. As you use these models, please keep in mind that electrons are not really confined to the "surface" of one shell or another. Instead, any thorough description of electrons in an atom must involve the orbitals these shells represent. For the purpose of an elementary understanding of chemistry, however, the simplified shell model is very useful.

5.8 The Periodic Table Helps Us Predict Properties of Elements

Larger particles of sand can be separated from smaller particles by tossing the sand up and down over a wire-mesh screen. All particles larger than the holes in the screen stay above the screen, and all particles smaller than the oles pass through. Now imagine a membrane in which the pores (analogous to the holes in a screen) are so tiny that the membrane can be used to separate two different-sized molecules, say nitrogen, N_2, and oxygen, O_2. This would be an incredible feat because the diameters of these molecules differ by no more than 0.02 nanometer (2×10^{-11} meter). Which would you expect to pass through such a membrane more readily: nitrogen molecules or oxygen molecules?

To answer this question, you need look no further than the periodic table, which allows you to make fairly accurate predictions about the properties both of atoms and of the molecules they form. For instance, the farther to the left and lower down in the table an element is, the larger the atoms of that element are. Conversely, the farther to the right and higher up in the table an element is, the smaller the atoms of that element are. Knowing this, you can predict that oxygen atoms, being in the same row *but farther to the right*, are smaller than nitrogen atoms, which means oxygen molecules are smaller than nitrogen molecules. The smaller oxygen molecules, therefore, would pass through the membrane more readily. In fact, such membranes exist, and they are being developed as a cost-effective means of separating atmospheric nitrogen from oxygen, as shown in Figure 5.27.

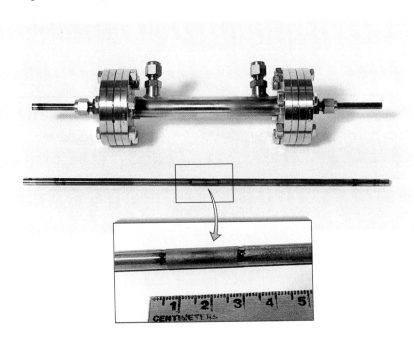

Figure 5.27
The composition of air passing through this membrane changes from 21 percent oxygen to up to 44 percent oxygen because the larger nitrogen molecules get left behind.

Recall from Chapter 2 that a gradual change in properties as we move in any direction in the periodic table is called a *periodic trend*. Most periodic trends can be understood from the perspective of the simplified shell model, and underlying most trends are two important concepts: *inner-shell shielding* and *effective nuclear charge*.

Imagine you are one of the two electrons in the shell of a helium atom. You share this shell with one other electron, but that electron doesn't affect your attraction to the nucleus because you both have the same "line of sight" to the nucleus. As shown in Figure 5.28, you and your neighbor electron sense a nucleus of two protons, and you are each equally attracted to it.

The situation is different for atoms beyond helium, which have more than one shell occupied by electrons. In these cases, inner-shell electrons

First shell

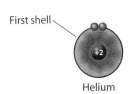

Helium

Figure 5.28
The two electrons in a helium atom have equal exposure to the nucleus; hence, they experience the same degree of attraction, represented by the pink shading in the space between the nucleus and the shell boundary.

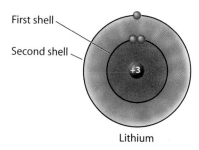

First shell
Second shell

Lithium

Figure 5.29
Lithium's two first-shell electrons shield the second-shell electron from the nucleus. The nuclear attraction, again represented by pink shading, is less intense in the second shell.

weaken the attraction between outer-shell electrons and the nucleus. Imagine, for example, you are that second-shell electron in the lithium atom shown in Figure 5.29. Looking toward the nucleus, what do you sense? Not just the nucleus but also the two electrons in the first shell. These two inner electrons, with their negative charge repelling your negative charge, have the effect of weakening your electrical attraction to the nucleus. This is **inner-shell shielding**—inner-shell electrons shield electrons farther out from some of the attractive pull exerted by the positively charged nucleus.

Because inner-shell electrons diminish the attraction outer-shell electrons have for the nucleus, the nuclear charge sensed by outer-shell electrons is always less than the actual charge of the nucleus. This diminished nuclear charge experienced by outer-shell electrons is called the **effective nuclear charge** and is abbreviated Z^* (pronounced zee star), where Z stands for the nuclear charge and the asterisk indicates this charge appears to be less than it actually is. The second-shell electron in lithium, for example, does not sense the full effect of lithium's +3 nuclear charge (there are three protons in the nucleus of lithium). Instead, the total charge on the first-shell electrons, −2, subtracts from the charge of the nucleus, +3, to give an effective nuclear charge of +1 sensed by the second-shell electron.

For most elements, subtracting the total number of inner-shell electrons from the nuclear charge provides a convenient estimate of the effective nuclear charge, as Figure 5.30 illustrates.

Figure 5.30
(a) A chlorine atom has three occupied shells. The 2 + 8 = 10 electrons of the inner two shells shield the 7 electrons of the third shell from the +17 nucleus. The third-shell electrons therefore experience an effective nuclear charge of 17 − 10 = +7. (b) In a potassium atom, the fourth-shell electron experiences an effective nuclear charge of 19 − 18 = +1.

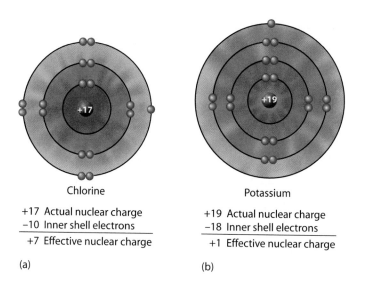

Chlorine

+17 Actual nuclear charge
−10 Inner shell electrons
_____
+7   Effective nuclear charge

(a)

Potassium

+19 Actual nuclear charge
−18 Inner shell electrons
_____
+1   Effective nuclear charge

(b)

The Smallest Atoms Are at the Upper Right of the Periodic Table

From left to right across any row of the periodic table, the atomic diameters get *smaller*. Let's look at this trend from the point of view of effective nuclear charge. Consider lithium's outermost electron, which experiences an effective nuclear charge of +1. Then look across period 2 to neon, where each outermost electron experiences an effective nuclear charge of +8, as Figure 5.31 shows. Because the outer-shell neon electrons experience a greater attraction to the nucleus, they are pulled in closer to it than is the outer-shell electron in lithium. So neon, although nearly three times as mas-

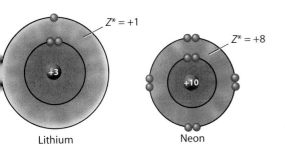

Figure 5.31
Lithium's outermost electron experiences an effective nuclear charge of $+1$, while those of neon experience an effective nuclear charge of $+8$. As a result, the outer-shell electrons in neon are closer to the nucleus than is the outer-shell electron in lithium, and so the diameter of the neon atom is smaller than the diameter of the lithium atom.

sive as lithium, has a considerably smaller diameter. In general, across any period from left to right, atomic diameters become smaller because of an increase in effective nuclear charge. Look carefully back to Figure 5.26 and you will see this illustrated for the first three periods.

Moving down a group, atomic diameters get larger because of an increasing number of occupied shells. Whereas lithium has a small diameter because it has only two occupied shells, francium has a much larger diameter because it has seven occupied shells. Figure 5.32 shows relative atomic diameters as estimated from experimental data. Note there are some exceptions to this trend, especially between groups 12 and 13.

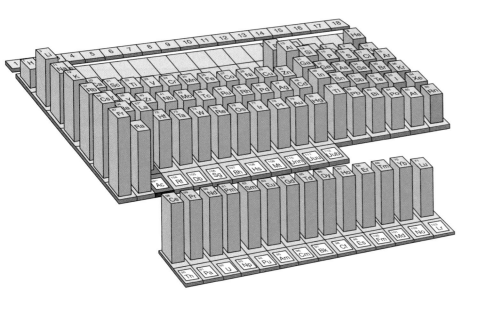

Figure 5.32
Relative atomic diameters indicated by height. Note that atomic size generally decreases in moving to the upper-right of the periodic table.

Concept Check ✓

Which is larger, a sulfur atom, S (atomic number 16), or an arsenic atom, As (atomic number 33)? Consult the periodic table that appears on the inside front cover of this textbook.

Was this your answer? The arsenic atom is larger because it is positioned closer to the lower left corner of the periodic table. Note that you didn't need to memorize some long list of atomic sizes nor look to Figure 5.32 in order to answer this question. Instead, you were able to use a common periodic table as a tool to help you find the answer.

The Smallest Atoms Have the Most Strongly Held Electrons

How strongly electrons are bound to an atom is another property that changes gradually across the periodic table. In general, the trend is that the smaller the atom, the more tightly bound its electrons.

As discussed earlier, effective nuclear charge increases in moving from left to right across any period. Thus not only are atoms toward the right in any period smaller, but their electrons are held more strongly. It takes about four times as much energy to remove an outer electron from a neon atom, for example, than to remove the outer electron from a lithium atom.

Moving down any group, the effective nuclear charge generally stays the same. The effective nuclear charges for all group 1 elements, for example, is about +1. Elements toward the bottom of a group, however, are larger, because of the greater number of shells, than are elements toward the top of the group. The electrons in the outermost shell are therefore farther from the nucleus by an appreciable distance. From physics we learn that the electric force weakens rapidly with increasing distance. As Figure 5.33 illustrates, an outer-shell electron in a larger atom, such as cesium, is not held as tightly as an outer-shell electron in a smaller atom, such as lithium. As a consequence, the energy needed to remove the outer electron from a cesium atom is about half the energy needed to remove the outer electron from a lithium atom.

The combination of increasing effective nuclear charge from left to right and increasing number of shells from top to bottom creates a periodic trend in which the electrons in atoms at the upper right of the periodic table are held the most strongly and the electrons in atoms at the lower left

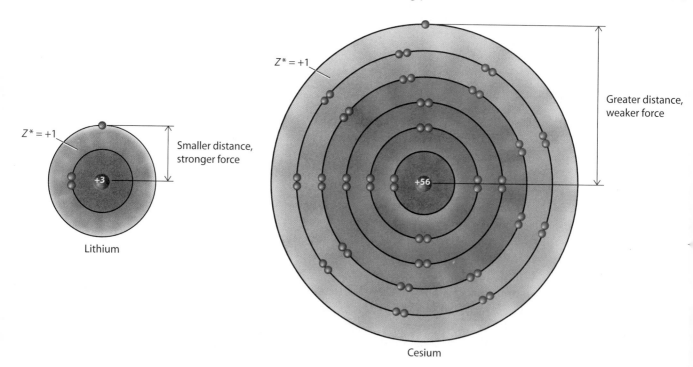

Figure 5.33
In both lithium and cesium, the outermost electron experiences an effective nuclear charge of +1. The outermost electron in a cesium atom, however, is not held as strongly to the nucleus because of its greater distance from the nucleus.

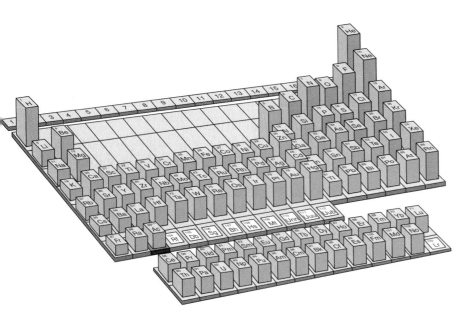

Figure 5.34
Ionization energy. The attraction an atomic nucleus has for the outermost electrons in an atom indicated by height. Note that atoms at the upper right tend to have the greatest ionization energy and those at the lower left the least.

are held least strongly. This is reflected in Figure 5.34, which shows **ionization energy**, the amount of energy needed to pull an electron away from an atom. The greater the ionization energy, the greater the attraction between the nucleus and its outermost electrons.

Concept Check ✔

Which loses one of its outermost electrons most easily: a francium, Fr, atom, or a helium, He, atom?

Was this your answer? A francium, Fr, atom loses electrons much more easily than does a helium, He, atom. Why? Because a francium atom's electrons are not held so tightly by its nucleus, which is buried deep beneath many layers of shielding electrons.

How strongly an atomic nucleus is able to hold on to the outermost electrons in an atom plays an important role in determining the atom's chemical behavior. What do you suppose happens when an atom that holds its outermost electrons only weakly comes into contact with an atom that has a very strong pull on its outermost electrons? As we explore in Chapter 6, either the atom that pulls strongly may swipe one or more electrons from the other atom or the two atoms may share electrons.

In this chapter we have gone into a fair amount of detail regarding atomic models, beginning with Bohr's planetary model and ending with the simplified shell model. Remember that these models are not to be interpreted as actual representations of the atom's physical structure. Rather, they serve as tools to help us understand and predict how atoms behave in various circumstances. These models, therefore, are the foundation of chemistry and the key to a richer understanding of the atomic and molecular environment that surrounds us.

Key Terms and Matching Definitions

_____ atomic orbital
_____ atomic spectrum
_____ conceptual model
_____ effective nuclear charge
_____ electromagnetic spectrum
_____ electron configuration
_____ energy-level diagram
_____ inner-shell shielding
_____ ionization energy
_____ photon
_____ physical model
_____ principal quantum number *n*
_____ probability cloud
_____ quantum
_____ quantum hypothesis
_____ spectroscope
_____ wave frequency
_____ wavelength

1. A representation of an object on a different scale.
2. A representation of a system that helps us predict how the system behaves.
3. The distance between two crests of a wave.
4. A measure of how rapidly a wave oscillates. The higher this value, the greater the amount of energy in the wave.
5. The complete range of waves, from radio waves to gamma rays.
6. A device that uses a prism or diffraction grating to separate light into its color components.
7. The pattern of frequencies of electromagnetic radiation emitted by the atoms of an element, considered to be an element's "fingerprint."
8. The idea that light energy is contained in discrete packets called quanta.
9. A small, discrete packet of light energy.
10 Another term for a single quantum of light, a name chosen to emphasize the particulate nature of light.
11. An integer that specifies the quantized energy level of an atomic orbital.
12. The pattern of electron positions plotted over time to show the likelihood of an electron being at a given position at a given time.
13. A region of space in which an electron in an atom has a 90 percent chance of being located.

14. Drawing used to arrange atomic orbitals in order of energy levels.
15. The arrangement of electrons in the orbitals of an atom.
16. The tendency of inner-shell electrons to partially shield outer-shell electrons from the nuclear charge.
17. The nuclear charge experienced by outer-shell electrons, diminished by the shielding effect of inner-shell electrons.
18. The amount of energy required to remove an electron from an atom.

Review Questions

Models Help Us Visualize the Invisible World of Atoms

1. If a baseball were the size of the Earth, about how large would its atoms be?

2. When we use a scanning tunneling microscope, do we see atoms directly or do we see them only indirectly?

3. Why are atoms invisible to visible light?

4. What is the difference between a physical model and a conceptual model?

5. What is the function of an atomic model?

Light Is a Form of Energy

6. Does visible light constitute a large or small portion of the electromagnetic spectrum?

7. Why does ultraviolet light cause more damage to our skin than visible light?

8. As the frequency of light increases, what happens to its energy?

9. What does a spectroscope do to the light coming from an atom?

Atoms Can Be Identified by the Light They Emit

10. What causes an atom to emit light?

11. Why do we say atomic spectra are like fingerprints of the elements?

12. What did Rydberg note about the atomic spectrum of hydrogen?

iels Bohr Used the Quantum Hypothesis
ɔ Explain Atomic Spectra

3. What was Planck's quantum hypothesis?

4. Which has more potential energy: an electron close to an atomic nucleus or one far from an atomic nucleus?

5. What happens to an electron as it absorbs a photon of light?

6. What is the relationship between the light emitted by an atom and the energies of the electrons in the atom?

7. Did Bohr think of his planetary model as an accurate representation of what an atom looks like?

Electrons Exhibit Wave Properties

18. About how fast does an electron travel around the atomic nucleus?

19. How does the speed of an electron change its fundamental nature?

20. Who developed the equation that relates the intensity of an electron's wave to the electron's most probable location?

21. How is an atomic orbital similar to a probability cloud?

Energy-Level Diagrams Describe
How Orbitals Are Occupied

22. How many electrons may reside in a single orbital?

23. How many $2p$ orbitals are there, and what is the total number of electrons they can hold?

24. What atom has the electron configuration $1s^2\ 2s^2\ 2p^6$?

25. Which electrons are most responsible for the physical and chemical properties of an atom?

26. Using the abbreviated notation, give the electron configuration for strontium, Sr (atomic number 38).

Orbitals of Similar Energies Can Be Grouped into Shells

27. What do the orbitals in a shell have in common?

28. The shell model presented in this book is not very accurate. Why then is it presented?

29. How many orbitals are there in the third shell?

30. How is the number of shells an atom of a given element contains related to the row of the periodic table in which that element is found?

31. What is the relationship between the maximum number of electrons each shell can hold and the number of elements in each period of the periodic table?

The Periodic Table Helps Us
Predict Properties of Elements

32. How would you know from looking at the periodic table that oxygen, O (atomic number 8), molecules are smaller than nitrogen, N (atomic number 7), molecules?

33. The nucleus of a carbon atom, C (atomic number 6), has a charge of +6, but this is not the charge sensed by electrons in carbon's outer shell. Why?

34. How many shells are occupied by electrons in a gold atom, Au (atomic number 79)?

35. Based on the periodic trend of atomic diameter, which should be larger, an atom of technetium, Tc (atomic number 43), or an atom of tantalum, Ta (atomic number 73)?

36. What is the effective nuclear charge for an electron in the outermost shell of a fluorine atom, F (atomic number 9)? How about one in the outermost shell of a sulfur atom, S (atomic number 16)?

37. Why is it more difficult for fluorine to lose an electron than for sulfur to do so?

Hands-On Chemistry Insights

Spectral Patterns

The diffraction gratings used in rainbow glasses have lines etched vertically and horizontally which makes the colors appear to the left and right, above and below, and in all corners as well. A compact disk behaves as a diffraction grating because its surface contains many rows of microscopic pits.

To the naked eye, a glowing element appears as only a single color. However, this color is an average of the many different visible frequencies the element is emitting. Only with a device such as a spectroscope are we able to discern the different frequencies. So when you look at an atomic spectrum, don't get confused and think that each frequency of light (color) corresponds to a different element. Instead, remember that what you are looking at is all the frequencies of light emitted by a single element as its electrons make transitions back and forth between energy levels.

Not all elements produce patterns in the visible spectrum. Tungsten, for example, produces the full spectrum of colors (white light), which makes it useful as the glowing component of a car's headlights, as shown in the photograph below. Also, the sunlight reflecting off the moon, also shown below, is so bright and contains the glow of many different elments that it too appears as a broad spectrum.

Rubber Waves

A self-reinforcing wave may sound beautiful on a guitar, but it can spell disaster for a bridge. In 1940, light winds across the Tacoma Narrows in the state of Washington caused the newly constructed Tacoma Narrows Bridge to start oscillating at a frequency that allowed the waves to be self-reinforcing. As the energy of the wind was absorbed by the bridge, the waves grew stronger (over the course of several days) to the point where the bridge collapsed. One of the tasks of building a durable structure, therefore, is to design it such that self-reinforcing waves are not likely to form.

Quantized Whistle

People watching you perform this activity may not believe that the audible "steps" of your whistling down the tube are not intentional. Explain quantization to them before allowing them to attempt this activity for themselves. Try to count the number of steps in your tubular whistle, understanding that each step is analogous to an energy level in an atom. Does a longer tube create fewer or more steps than a shorter tube? Why is it so difficult to whistle down a garden hose?

If you punch a few holes along the tube, you [a]lter the frequencies of the standing waves that can [f]orm in the tube, with the result that different [p]itches are produced. This is the underlying princi[p]le in such musical instruments as flutes and saxo[p]hones.

Exercises

1. With scanning tunneling microscopy (STM) technology, we see not actual atoms, but rather images of them. Explain.

2. Why is it not possible for an STM to make images of the inside of an atom?

3. Would you use a physical model or a conceptual model to describe the following: brain, mind, solar system, birth of universe, stranger, best friend, gold coin, dollar bill, car engine, virus, spread of sexually transmitted disease?

4. How might you distinguish a sodium-vapor lamp from a mercury-vapor lamp?

5. How can a hydrogen atom, which has only one electron, create so many spectral lines?

6. Suppose a certain atom has four energy levels. Assuming that all transitions between levels are possible, how many spectral lines will this atom exhibit? Which transition corresponds to the highest-energy light emitted? Which corresponds to the lowest-energy light emitted?

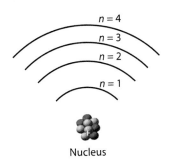

Nucleus

7. An electron drops from the fourth energy level in an atom to the third level and then to the first level. Two frequencies of light are emitted. How does their combined energy compare with the energy of the single frequency that would be emitted if the electron dropped from the fourth level directly to the first level?

8. Figure 5.14 shows three energy-level transitions that produce three spectral lines in a spectroscope. Note that the distance between the $n = 1$ and $n = 2$ levels is greater than the distance between the $n = 2$ and $n = 3$ levels. Would the number of spectral lines produced change if the distance between the $n = 1$ and $n = 2$ levels were exactly the same as the distance between the $n = 2$ and $n = 3$ levels?

9. Which color of light comes from a greater energy transition, red or blue?

10. How does the wave model of electrons orbiting the nucleus account for the fact that the electrons can have only discrete energy values?

11. What might the spectrum of an atom look like if the atom's electrons were not restricted to particular energy levels?

12. How does an electron get from one lobe of a p orbital to the other?

13. Light is emitted as an electron transitions from a higher-energy orbital to a lower-energy orbital. How long does it take for the transition to take place? At what point in time is the electron found between the two orbitals?

14. Why is there only one spatial orientation for the s orbital?

15. In which lobe of a p orbital is an electron more likely found?

16. Fill in these energy-level diagrams. Why do these three elements have such similar chemical properties?

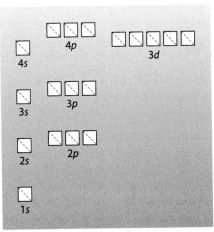

Oxygen, O

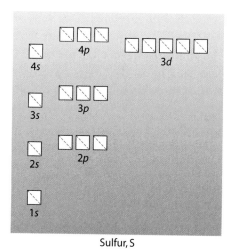

Sulfur, S

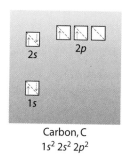

Selenium, Se

17. When does a carbon atom contain more energy—when its electrons are in the configuration on the left or when they are in the configuration on the right:

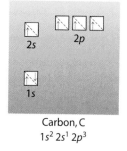

Carbon, C
$1s^2 \, 2s^2 \, 2p^2$

Carbon, C
$1s^2 \, 2s^1 \, 2p^3$

18. Write the electron configuration for uranium, U (atomic number 92), in abbreviated notation.

19. List these electron configurations for fluorine in order of increasing energy for the atom:

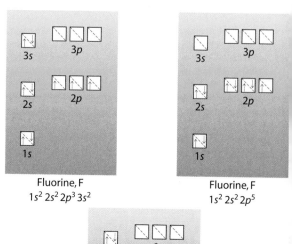

Fluorine, F
$1s^2 \, 2s^2 \, 2p^3 \, 3s^2$

Fluorine, F
$1s^2 \, 2s^2 \, 2p^5$

Fluorine, F
$1s^0 \, 2s^2 \, 2p^5 \, 3s^2$

20. What do the electron configurations for the group 18 noble gases have in common?

21. Place the proper number of electrons in each shell:

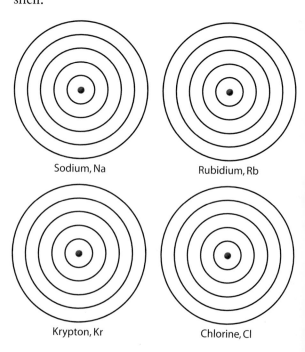

Sodium, Na

Rubidium, Rb

Krypton, Kr

Chlorine, Cl

2. Which element is represented in Figure 5.25 if all seven shells are filled to capacity?

3. Does an orbital or shell have to contain electrons in order to exist?

4. Why does an electron in a 7s orbital have more energy than one in a 1s orbital?

5. Neon, Ne (atomic number 10), has a relatively large effective nuclear charge, and yet it cannot attract any additional electrons. Why?

26. Which experiences a greater effective nuclear charge, an electron in the outermost shell of neon or one in the outermost shell of sodium? Why?

27. An electron in the outermost occupied shell of which element experiences the greatest effective nuclear charge?
    a. sodium, Na
    b. potassium, K
    c. rubidium, Rb
    d. cesium, Cs
    e. all experience the same effective nuclear charge

28. List the following atoms in order of increasing atomic size: thallium, Tl; germanium, Ge; tin, Sn; phosphorus, P:

    _____ < _____ < _____ < _____
    (smallest)   (largest)

29. Arrange the following atoms in order of increasing ionization energy: tin, Sn; lead, Pb; phosphorus, P; arsenic, As:

    _____ < _____ < _____ < _____
    (least)   (most)

30. Which of the following concepts underlies all the others: ionization energy, effective nuclear charge, atomic size?

31. It is relatively easy to pull one electron away from a potassium atom but very difficult to remove a second one. Use the shell model and the idea of effective nuclear charge to explain why.

32. Another interesting periodic trend is density. Osmium, Os (atomic number 76), has the greatest density of all elements, and, with some exceptions, the closer an element is to osmium in the periodic table, the greater its density. Use this trend to list the following elements in order of increasing density: copper, Cu; gold, Au; platinum, Pt; and silver, Ag:

    _____ < _____ < _____ < _____
    (least dense)   (most dense)

33. How is the following graphic similar to the energy-level diagram of Figure 5.23? Use it to explain why a gallium atom, Ga (atomic number 31), is larger than a zinc atom, Zn (atomic number 30):

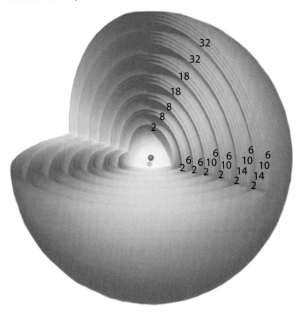

Suggested Readings and Web Sites

George Gamow, *Thirty Years That Shook Physics*. New York: Dover, 1985.

A historical tracing of quantum theory by someone who was part of its development.

G. J. Milburn, *Schrodinger's Machines*. New York: W. H. Freeman, 1997.

Our understanding of quantum theory has already led to a number of society-shaping inventions, such as the transistor, a basic component of all computers, and the laser, which scans everything from our groceries to our music. This book presents some of the newer and fantastic quantum technologies we can expect in the next 50 years.

http://www.achilles.net/~jtalbot/

A superb site for learning about the spectral patterns of stars and how they are used to study the universe.

http://www.achilles.net/~jtalbot/data/elements/index.htr

Here is where you will find high-resolution spectral patterns of a variety of elements.

http://www.physics.purdue.edu/nanophys

Site of the nanoscale physics laboratory of Purdue University, where they look at things that are really, really, really, really, really, really, really small. Lots of pretty pictures.

http://www.superstringtheory.com

If you think the wave nature of the electron is bizarre, explore this site for information on and references to the potentially revolutionary theory that particles, forces, space, and time are merely manifestations of incredibly tiny strings that exist in 11 dimensions.

Chapter 6
Chemical Bonding and Molecular Shapes

How Atoms Connect to One Another

Millions of years ago, the Great Plains of the United States were ocean. As sea levels fell and at the same time the North American continent rose, many isolated pockets of seawater, called saline lakes, formed. Over time these lakes evaporated, leaving behind the solutes that had been dissolved in the seawater. Most abundant was sodium chloride, which collected in cubic crystals referred to by mineralogists as the mineral *halite*. When conditions were right, halite crystals like the ones in this chapter's opening photograph would grow to be several centimeters across.

Why do halite crystals have such a distinct shape? As we explore in this chapter, the macroscopic properties of any substance can be traced to how its submicroscopic parts are held together. The sodium and chloride ions in a halite crystal, for example, are held together in a cubic orientation, and as a result the macroscopic object we know as a halite crystal is also cubic.

Similarly, the macroscopic properties of substances made of molecules are a result of how the atoms in the molecules are held together. For example, many of the properties of water are the result of how the hydrogen and oxygen atoms of each water molecule are held together at an angle. Because of this angled orientation, one side of the molecule has a slight negative charge and the opposite side has a slight positive charge. This charge separation in water molecules gives rise to such phenomena as the inability of water and oil to mix and water's high boiling temperature.

The force of attraction that holds ions or atoms together is the electric force, which is the force that occurs between oppositely charged particles. Chemists refer to this ion-binding or atom-binding force as a chemical bond. In this chapter we explore two types of chemical bonds: the *ionic bond*, which holds ions together in a crystal, and the *covalent bond*, which holds atoms together in a molecule.

6.1 An Atomic Model Is Needed to Understand How Atoms Bond

In Chapter 5, we discussed how electrons are arranged around an atomic nucleus. Rather than moving in neat orbits like planets around the sun, electrons are wavelike entities that swarm in various volumes of space called *atomic orbitals.* As discussed in Section 5.7, atomic orbitals of comparable energy levels can be grouped together and represented by a single *shell.* Such a shell should not be taken literally. Rather, the shell represents a region of space within which electrons of similar energy levels are most likely to be found.

As was shown in Figure 5.25, there are seven shells available to the electrons in any atom, and the electrons occupy these shells in order, from the innermost (lowest energy level) shell to the outermost (highest energy level). The maximum electron capacities for the seven shells are 2, 8, 8, 18, 18, 32, 32, and these numbers correspond to the number of elements in each period of the periodic table. Figure 6.1 shows how this model applies to the first four group 18 elements.

It is the electrons in the outermost occupied shell of any atom that are responsible for the atom's chemical properties, including the ability to form chemical bonds. To indicate their importance, these electrons that can participate in chemical bonding are called **valence electrons** (from the Latin *valentia,* "strength"), and the shell they occupy is called the **valence shell** of an atom. Valence electrons can be conveniently represented as a series of dots surrounding an atomic symbol. This notation is called an **electron-dot structure** or, sometimes, a *Lewis dot symbol* in honor of the American chemist G. N. Lewis, who first proposed the concepts of electron shells and valence electrons. Figure 6.2 shows the electron-dot structures for the atoms important in our discussions of ionic and covalent bonds. (Atoms of elements in groups 3 through 12 form *metallic bonds,* which we'll study in Chapter 18.)

If you look carefully at Figure 6.2, you may notice that for many elements not all the electrons in the outermost occupied shell are shown. For example, there are 18 electrons in the outermost occupied shell of krypton, Kr, but the electron-dot structure shows only 8. The reason some electrons seem to be missing is that the shell model illustrated in Figure 6.1 is highly simplified. A more accurate model would show that ten of the electrons in krypton's outermost occupied shell are not so available for playing a role in the chemistry of the atom. Thus, while all valence electrons reside in the outermost occupied shell of an atom, not all electrons in an outermost occupied shell are valence electrons. In this chapter, however, you need not concern yourself with this detail. Instead, you need only consult Figure 6.2 whenever you need to know how many valence electrons a given atom has.

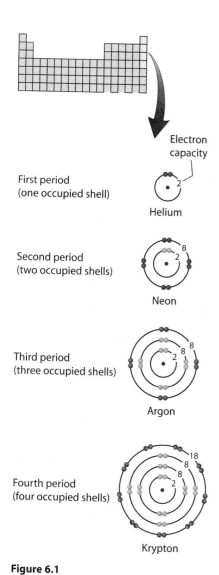

Figure 6.1
Occupied shells in the group 18 elements helium through krypton. Each of these elements has a filled outermost occupied shell, and the number of electrons in each outermost occupied shell corresponds to the number of elements in the period to which a particular group 18 element belongs.

Figure 6.2
The valence electrons of an atom are shown in its electron-dot structure. Note that the first three periods here parallel Figure 5.26.

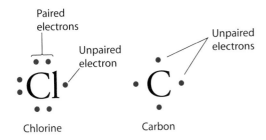

Figure 6.2 also shows that valence electrons can be either paired or unpaired. (Remember, the electrons can pair when they spin in opposite directions.) Chlorine, for example, has three sets of paired electrons and one unpaired electron, and carbon has four unpaired electrons:

Paired electrons

Unpaired electron

Unpaired electrons

:Cl·

· C ·

Chlorine

Carbon

Paired valence electrons are relatively stable entities, which means they usually do not form chemical bonds with other atoms. For this reason, electron pairs in an electron-dot structure are often referred to as **nonbonding pairs**. (Do not take this name literally, however, for in Chapter 10 you'll see that, under the right conditions, even "nonbonding" pairs can form a chemical bond.) As we discuss in Section 6.5, nonbonding pairs can have a significant influence on the shape of any molecule containing them.

Valence electrons that are unpaired, by contrast, have a strong tendency to participate in chemical bonding because by doing so, they become paired with an electron from another atom. The chemical bonds discussed in this chapter all result from either a transfer or a sharing of unpaired valence electrons.

Figure 6.3
Gilbert Newton Lewis (1875–1946) revolutionized chemistry with his theory of chemical bonding, which he published in 1916. He worked most of his life in the chemistry department of the University of California at Berkeley, where he was not only a productive researcher but also an exceptional teacher. Among his teaching innovations was the idea of providing students with problem sets as a follow-up to lectures and readings.

Concept Check ✔

What is a valence electron?

Was this your answer? A valence electron is any electron in the outermost occupied shell of an atom that is available to form a chemical bond with another atom.

6.2 Atoms Can Lose or Gain Electrons to Become Ions

When the number of protons in the nucleus of an atom equals the number of electrons in the atom, the charges balance and the atom is electrically neutral. If one or more electrons are lost or gained, as illustrated in Figures 6.4 and 6.5, the balance is upset and the atom takes on a net electric charge. Any atom having a net electric charge is referred to as an **ion**. If electrons are lost, protons outnumber electrons and the ion's net charge is positive. If electrons are gained, electrons outnumber protons and the ion's net charge is negative.

Chemists use a superscript to the right of the atomic symbol to indicate the magnitude and sign of an ion's charge. Thus, as shown in Figures 6.4 and 6.5, the positive ion formed from the sodium atom is written Na^{1+} and the negative ion formed from the fluorine atom is written F^{1-}. Usually the numeral *1* is omitted when indicating either a 1+ or 1− charge. Hence, these two ions are most frequently written Na^+ and F^-.

To give two more examples, a calcium atom that loses two electrons is written Ca^{2+}, and an oxygen atom that gains two electrons is written O^{2-}. (Note that the convention is to write the numeral before the sign, not after it: 2+, not +2.)

We can use the shell model to deduce the type of ion an atom tends to form. According to this model, *atoms tend to lose or gain electrons so that they end up with an outermost occupied shell that is filled to capacity.* Let's take a moment to consider this point, looking back to Figures 6.4 and 6.5 as visual guides.

If an atom has only one or a few electrons in its valence shell, it tends to lose these electrons so that the next shell inward, which is already filled, becomes the outermost occupied shell. The sodium atom of Figure 6.4, for example, has one electron in its valence shell, which is the third shell. In forming an ion, the sodium atom loses this electron, thereby making the second shell, which is already filled to capacity, the outermost occupied shell. Because the sodium atom has only one valence electron to lose, it tends to form the 1+ ion.

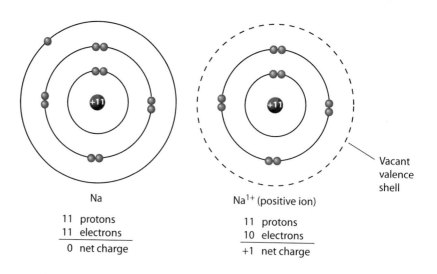

Na

11 protons
11 electrons
0 net charge

Na^{1+} (positive ion)

11 protons
10 electrons
+1 net charge

Vacant valence shell

Figure 6.4
An electrically neutral sodium atom contains 11 negatively charged electrons surrounding the 11 positively charged protons of the nucleus. When this atom loses an electron, the result is a positive ion.

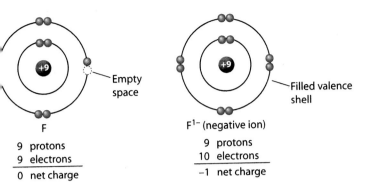

Figure 6.5
An electrically neutral fluorine atom contains nine protons and nine electrons. When this atom gains an electron, the result is a negative ion.

If the valence shell of an atom is almost filled, that atom attracts electrons from another atom and so forms a negative ion. The fluorine atom of Figure 6.5, for example, has one space available in its valence shell for an additional electron. After this additional electron is gained, the fluorine achieves a filled valence shell. Fluorine therefore tends to form the 1− ion.

You can use the periodic table as a quick reference when determining the type of ion an atom tends to form. As Figure 6.6 shows, each atom of any group 1 element, for example, has only one valence electron and so tends to form the 1+ ion. Each atom of any group 17 element has room for one additional electron in its valence shell and therefore tends to form the 1− ion. Atoms of the noble-gas elements tend not to form any type of ion because their valence shells are already filled to capacity.

Electrons are negatively charged. So gaining an electron results in a negative ion . . .

. . . and losing an electron results in a positive ion.

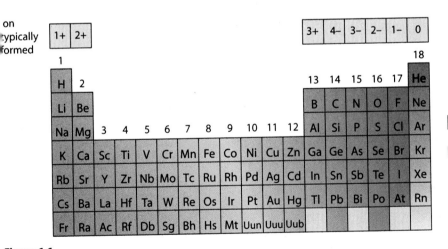

Figure 6.6
The periodic table is your guide to the types of ions atoms tend to form.

Concept Check ✓

What type of ion does the magnesium atom, Mg, tend to form?

Was this your answer? The magnesium atom (atomic number 12) is found in group 2 and has two valence electrons to lose (see Figure 6.3). It therefore tends to form the 2+ ion.

As was discussed in Chapter 5 and is indicated in Figure 6.6, the attraction an atom's nucleus has for its valence electrons is weakest for elements on the left in the periodic table and strongest for elements on the right. From sodium's position in the table, we see that a sodium atom's single valence electron is not held very strongly, which explains why it is so easily lost. The attraction the sodium nucleus has for its second-shell electrons, however, is much stronger, which is why the sodium atom rarely loses more than one electron.

At the other side of the periodic table, the nucleus of a fluorine atom holds on strongly to its valence electrons, which explains why the fluorine atom tends *not* to lose any electrons to form a positive ion. Instead, fluorine's nuclear pull on the valence electrons is strong enough to accommodate even an additional electron "imported" from some other atom.

The nucleus of a noble-gas atom pulls so strongly on its valence electrons that they are very difficult to lose. Because there is no room left in the valence shell of a noble-gas atom, no additional electrons are gained. Thus a noble-gas atom tends not to form an ion of any sort.

Concept Check ✓

Why does the magnesium atom tend to form the 2+ ion?

Was this your answer? Magnesium is on the left in the periodic table, and so atoms of this element do not hold on to the two valence electrons very strongly. The details of why this is so were explained in Section 5.8 using the concept of *inner-shell shielding*. For now, you need recognize only that, because these electrons are not held very tightly, they are easily lost, which is why the magnesium atom tends to form the 2+ ion.

Using the shell model to explain the formation of ions form works well for groups 1 and 2 and 13 through 18. This model is too simplified to work well for the transition metals of groups 3 through 12, however, or for the inner transition metals. In general, these metal atoms tend to form positive ions, but the number of electrons lost varies. Depending on conditions, for example, an iron atom may lose two electrons to form the Fe^{2+} ion, or it may lose three electrons to form the Fe^{3+} ion. Figuring out what type of ions metal atoms tend to be formed by transition or inner transition, therefore, must come from a more complex model of the atom or from laboratory experience. For the purposes of this text, all you need to understand is that the positive charge on any ion formed from an atom of a transition metal or inner transition metal is equal to the number of electrons lost.

6.3 Ionic Bonds Result from a Transfer of Electrons

When an atom that tends to lose electrons is placed in contact with an atom that tends to gain them, the result is an electron transfer and the formation of two oppositely charged ions. This is what happens when sodium and chlorine are combined. As shown in Figure 6.7, the sodium atom loses one of its electrons to the chlorine atom, resulting in the formation of a posive sodium ion and a negative chloride ion. The two oppositely charged ons are thus attracted to each other by the electric force, which holds them lose together. This electric force of attraction between two oppositely charged ions is called an **ionic bond**.

A sodium ion and a chloride ion together make the chemical compound sodium chloride, commonly known as table salt. This and all other chemical compounds containing ions are referred to as **ionic compounds**. All ionic compounds are completely different from the elements from which they are made. As discussed in Section 2.3, sodium chloride is not sodium, nor is it chlorine. Rather, it is a collection of sodium and chloride ions that form a unique material having its own physical and chemical properties.

Concept Check ✓

Is the transfer of an electron from a sodium atom to a chlorine atom a physical change or a chemical change?

Was this your answer? Recall from Chapter 2 that only a chemical change involves the formation of new material. Thus this or any other electron transfer, because it results in the formation of a new substance, is a chemical change.

As Figure 6.8 shows, ionic compounds typically consist of elements found on opposite sides of the periodic table. Also, because of how the metals and nonmetals are organized in the periodic table, positive ions are generally derived from metallic elements and negative ions are generally derived from nonmetallic elements.

For all ionic compounds, positive and negative charges must balance. In sodium chloride, for example, there is one sodium $1+$ ion for every chloride $1-$ ion. Charges must also balance in compounds containing ions

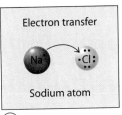
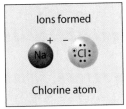
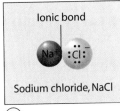

Figure 6.7
① An electrically neutral sodium atom loses its valence electron to an electrically neutral chlorine atom. ② This electron transfer results in two oppositely charged ions. ③ The ions are then held together by an ionic bond. The spheres drawn around the electron-dot structures here and in subsequent illustrations indicate the relative sizes of the atoms and ions. Note that the sodium ion is smaller than the sodium atom because the lone electron in the third shell is gone once the ion forms, leaving the ion with only two occupied shells. The chloride ion is larger than the chlorine atom because adding that one electron to the third shell makes the shell expand as a result of the repulsions among the electrons.

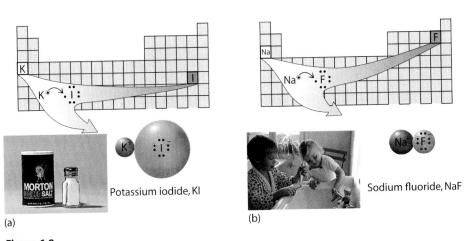

Potassium iodide, KI

(a)

Sodium fluoride, NaF

(b)

Figure 6.8
(a) The ionic compound potassium iodide, KI, is added in minute quantities to commercial salt because the iodide ion, I^-, it contains is an essential dietary mineral. (b) The ionic compound sodium fluoride, NaF, is often added to municipal water supplies and toothpastes because it is a good source of the tooth-strengthening fluoride ion, F^-.

that carry multiple charges. The calcium ion, for example, carries a charge of 2+, but the fluoride ion carries a charge of only 1−. Because two fluoride ions are needed to balance each calcium ion, the formula for calcium fluoride is CaF_2, as Figure 6.9 illustrates. Calcium fluoride occurs naturally in the drinking water of some communities, where it is a good source of the tooth-strengthening fluoride ion, F^-.

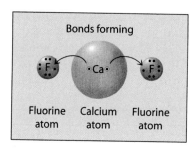

Figure 6.9

A calcium atom loses two electrons to form a calcium ion, Ca^{2+}. These two electrons may be picked up by two fluorine atoms, transforming the atoms to two fluoride ions. Calcium and fluoride ions then join to form the ionic compound calcium fluoride, CaF_2, which occurs naturally as the mineral fluorite.

An aluminum ion carries a 3+ charge, and an oxide ion carries a 2− charge. Together, these ions make the ionic compound aluminum oxide, Al_2O_3, the main component of such gemstones as rubies and sapphires. Figure 6.10 illustrates the formation of aluminum oxide. The three oxide ions in Al_2O_3 carry a total charge of 6−, which balances the total 6+ charge of the two aluminum ions. Interestingly, rubies and sapphires differ in color because of the impurities they contain. Rubies are red because of minor amounts of chromium ions, and sapphires are blue because of minor amounts of iron and titanium ions.

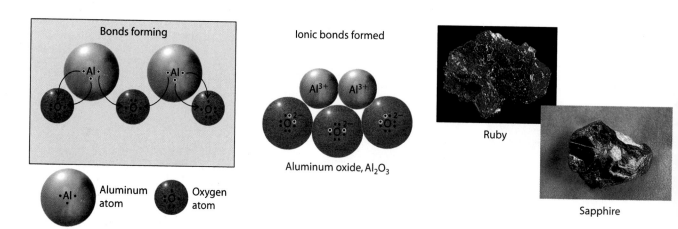

Figure 6.10

Two aluminum atoms lose a total of six electrons to form two aluminum ions, Al^{3+}. These six electrons may be picked up by three oxygen atoms, transforming the atoms to three oxide ions. The aluminum and oxide ions then join to form the ionic compound aluminum oxide, Al_2O_3.

Concept Check ✓

What is the chemical formula for the ionic compound magnesium oxide?

Was this your answer? Because magnesium is a group 2 element, you know a magnesium atom must lose two electrons to form an Mg^{2+} ion. Because oxygen is a group 16 element, an oxygen atom gains two electrons to form an O^{2-} ion. These charges balance in a one-to-one ratio, and so the formula for magnesium oxide is MgO.

An ionic compound typically contains a multitude of ions grouped together in a highly ordered three-dimensional array. In sodium chloride, for example, each sodium ion is surrounded by six chloride ions and each chloride ion is surrounded by six sodium ions, as shown in Figure 6.11. Overall there is one sodium ion for each chloride ion, but there are no identifiable sodium–chloride pairs. Such an orderly array of ions is known as an *ionic crystal*. On the atomic level, the crystalline structure of sodium chloride is cubic, which is why macroscopic crystals of table salt are also cubic. Smash a large cubic sodium chloride crystal with a hammer, and what do you get? Smaller cubic sodium chloride crystals!

Similarly, the crystalline structures of other ionic compounds, such as calcium fluoride and aluminum oxide, are a consequence of how the ions pack together.

● Sodium ion, Na^+

○ Chloride ion, Cl^-

Figure 6.11
Sodium chloride, as well as other ionic compounds, forms ionic crystals in which every internal ion is surrounded by ions of the opposite charge. (For simplicity, only a three-by-three ion array is shown here. A typical NaCl crystal involves millions and millions of ions.) A view of crystals of table salt through a microscope shows their cubic structure. The cubic shape is a consequence of the cubic arrangement of sodium and chloride ions.

Hands-On Chemistry: Up Close with Crystals

View crystals of table salt with a magnifying glass or, better yet, a microscope if one is available. If you do have a microscope, crush the crystals with a spoon and examine the resulting powder. Purchase some sodium-free salt, which is potassium chloride, KCl, and examine these ionic crystals, both intact and crushed. Sodium chloride and potassium chloride both form cubic crystals, but there are significant differences. What are they?

6.4 Covalent Bonds Result from a Sharing of Electrons

Imagine two children playing together and sharing their toys. A force that keeps the children together is their mutual attraction to the toys they share. In a similar fashion, two atoms can be held together by their mutual attraction for electrons they share. A fluorine atom, for example, has a strong attraction for one additional electron to fill its outermost occupied shell. As shown in Figure 6.12, a fluorine atom can obtain an additional electron by holding on to the unpaired valence electron of another fluorine atom. This results in a situation in which the two fluorine atoms are mutually attracted to the same two electrons. This type of electrical attraction in which atoms are held together by their mutual attraction for shared electrons is called a **covalent bond**, where *co-* signifies sharing and *-valent* refers to the valence electrons being shared.

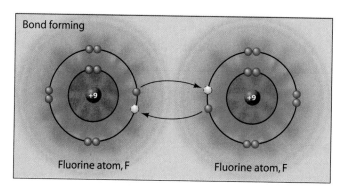
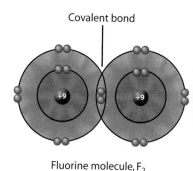

Figure 6.12
The effect of the positive nuclear charge (represented by red shading) of a fluorine atom extends beyond the atom's outermost occupied shell. This positive charge can cause the fluorine atom to become attracted to the unpaired valence electron of a neighboring fluorine atom. Then the two atoms are held together in a fluorine molecule by the attraction they both have for the two shared electrons. Each fluorine atom achieves a filled valence shell.

A substance composed of atoms held together by covalent bonds is a **covalent compound**. The fundamental unit of most covalent compounds is a **molecule**, which we can now formally define as any group of atoms held together by covalent bonds. Figure 6.13 uses the element fluorine to illustrate this principle.

Figure 6.13
Molecules are the fundamental units of the gaseous covalent compound fluorine, F_2. Notice that in this model of a fluorine molecule, the spheres overlap, whereas the spheres shown earlier for ionic compounds do not. Now you know that this difference in representation is because of the difference in bond types.

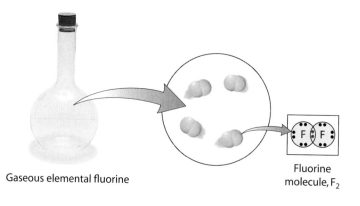

Gaseous elemental fluorine

Fluorine molecule, F_2

When writing electron-dot structures for covalent compounds, chemists often use a straight line to represent the two electrons involved in a covalent bond. In some representations, the nonbonding electron pairs are left out. This is done in instances where these electrons play no significant role in the process being illustrated. Here are two frequently used ways of showing the electron-dot structure for a fluorine molecule without using spheres to represent the atoms:

$$:\ddot{F}-\ddot{F}:\qquad F-F$$

Remember—the straight line in both versions represents two electrons, *one from each atom.* Thus we now have two types of electron pairs to keep track of. The term *nonbonding pair* refers to any pair that exists in the electron-dot structure of an individual atom, and the term *bonding pair* refers to any pair that results from formation of a covalent bond. In a nonbonding pair, both electrons come from the same atom; in a bonding pair, one electron comes from one of the atoms taking part in the covalent bond and the other electron comes from the other atom taking part in the bond.

Recall from Section 6.3 that an ionic bond is formed when an atom that tends to lose electrons is placed in contact with an atom that tends to gain them. A covalent bond, by contrast, is formed when two atoms that tend to gain electrons are brought into contact with each other. Atoms that tend to form covalent bonds are therefore primarily atoms of the nonmetallic elements in the upper right corner of the periodic table (with the exception of the noble-gas elements, which are very stable and tend not to form bonds).

Hydrogen tends to form covalent bonds because, unlike the other group 1 elements, it has a fairly strong attraction for an additional electron. Two hydrogen atoms, for example, covalently bond to form a hydrogen molecule, H_2, as shown in Figure 6.14.

The number of covalent bonds an atom can form is equal to the number of additional electrons it can attract, which is the number it needs to fill its valence shell. Hydrogen attracts only one additional electron, and so it forms only one covalent bond. Oxygen, which attracts two additional electrons, finds them when it encounters two hydrogen atoms and reacts with them to form water, H_2O, as Figure 6.15 shows. In water, not only does the oxygen atom have access to two additional electrons by covalently bonding to two hydrogen atoms, but each hydrogen atom has access to an additional electron by bonding to the oxygen atom. Each atom thus achieves a filled valence shell.

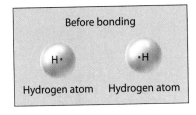

Before bonding

Hydrogen atom   Hydrogen atom

Covalent bond formed

Hydrogen molecule, H_2

Figure 6.14
Two hydrogen atoms form a covalent bond as they share their unpaired electrons.

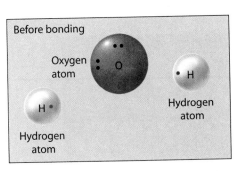

Before bonding

Oxygen atom

Hydrogen atom

Hydrogen atom

Covalent bonds formed

Water molecule, H_2O

Figure 6.15
The two unpaired valence electrons of oxygen pair with the unpaired valence electrons of two hydrogen atoms to form the covalent compound water.

Nitrogen attracts three additional electrons and is thus able to form three covalent bonds, as occurs in ammonia, NH_3, shown in Figure 6.16. Likewise, a carbon atom can attract four additional electrons and is thus able to form four covalent bonds, as occurs in methane, CH_4. Note that the number of covalent bonds formed by these and other nonmetal elements parallels the type of negative ions they tend to form (see Figure 6.5). This makes sense because covalent bond formation and negative ion formation are both applications of the same concept: nonmetallic atoms tend to gain electrons until their valence shells are filled.

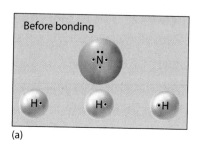

(a)

Figure 6.16
(a) A nitrogen atom attracts the three electrons in three hydrogen atoms to form ammonia, NH_3, a gas that can dissolve in water to make an effective cleanser. (b) A carbon atom attracts the four electrons in four hydrogen atoms to form methane, CH_4, the primary component of natural gas. In these and most other cases of covalent bond formation, the result is a filled valence shell for all the atoms involved.

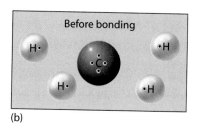

(b)

Diamond is a most unusual covalent compound consisting of carbon atoms covalently bonded to one another in four directions. The result is a *covalent crystal*, which, as shown in Figure 6.17, is a highly ordered three-dimensional network of covalently bonded atoms. The geometry of the bonding between the carbon atoms in diamond forms a very strong and rigid structure, which is why diamonds are so hard. Also, because a diamond is a group of atoms held together only by covalent bonds, it can be characterized as a single molecule! Unlike most other molecules, a diamond molecule is large enough to be visible to the naked eye, and so it is more appropriately referred to as a *macromolecule*.

Figure 6.17
The crystalline structure of diamond is best illustrated by using sticks to represent the covalent bonds. It is the molecular nature of diamond that is responsible for this material's unusual properties, such as its extreme hardness.

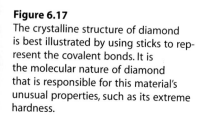
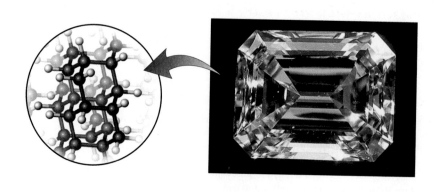

Concept Check ✓

How many electrons make up a covalent bond?

Was this your answer? Two—one from each participating atom.

It is possible to have more than two electrons shared between two atoms, and Figure 6.18 shows a few examples. Molecular oxygen, O_2, consists of two oxygen atoms connected by four shared electrons. This arrangement is called a *double covalent bond* or, for short, a *double bond*. As another example, the covalent compound carbon dioxide, CO_2, consists of two double bonds connecting two oxygen atoms to a central carbon atom.

Some atoms can form *triple covalent bonds*, in which six electrons—three from each atom—are shared. One example is molecular nitrogen, N_2.

Any double or triple bond is often referred to as a *multiple covalent bond*. Multiple bonds higher than these, such as the quadruple covalent bond, are not commonly observed.

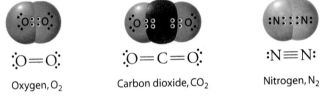

Oxygen, O_2 Carbon dioxide, CO_2 Nitrogen, N_2

Figure 6.18
Two representations of multiple covalent bonds in molecules of oxygen, O_2, and carbon dioxide, CO_2, both double covalent bonds, and nitrogen, N_2, a triple covalent bond.

6.5 Valence Electrons Determine Molecular Shape

Molecules are three-dimensional entities and therefore best depicted in three dimensions. We can translate the two-dimensional electron-dot structure representing a molecule into a more accurate three-dimensional rendering by using the model known as **valence shell electron-pair repulsion**, also called VSEPR (pronounced ves-per). According to this model, *any given pair of valence-shell electrons strives to get as far away as possible from all other electron pairs in the shell.* This includes both nonbonding pairs and any bonding pairs not taking part in a double or triple bond. (Pairs in a multiple bond stay together because of their mutual attractions for the same two nuclei.)

Note that the VSEPR model talks about the repulsions between pairs of electrons, not between the two electrons in a pair. (Recall that the electrons in a pair don't repel each other because of their opposite spins.) It is this striving for maximum separation distance between electron pairs that determines the geometry of any molecule.

The two-dimensional electron-dot structure for methane, CH_4, is

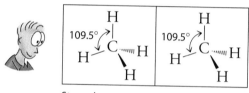

In this structure, the bonding electron pairs (shown as straight lines representing one electron from each atom) are set 90 degrees apart because that is the farthest apart they can be shown in two dimensions. When we extend to three dimensions, however, we can create a more accurate rendering in which the four bonding pairs are 109.5 degrees apart:

Stereo image

These two renderings of methane are *stereo images*—you can see them in three dimensions by looking at them cross-eyed so that they appear to overlap. The solid triangle represents a covalent bond coming out of the page, the dashed triangle represents a covalent bond falling behind the page, and the straight lines represent covalent bonds lying in the plane of the page.

You can think of this three-dimensional rendering of methane as the central carbon atom having one hydrogen atom sticking out of its top and supported on a tripod whose legs are formed by the three lower C–H bonds. Draw the four possible triangles having a hydrogen atom at each corner, and you'll see that the shape of the methane molecule is a pyramid that has a triangular base supporting three other triangles that meet at the pyramid apex. In geometry, a pyramid that has a triangular base is given the special name *tetrahedron*, and so chemists say that the methane molecule is *tetrahedral*:

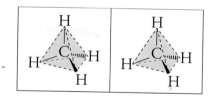

Stereo image of tetrahedral methane molecule

The VSEPR model allows us to use electron-dot structures to predict the three-dimensional geometry of simple molecules. This geometry is determined by considering the number of substituents surrounding the central atom. A **substituent** is any atom or nonbonding pair of electrons. The carbon of the methane molecule, for example, has four substituents—the four hydrogen atoms. The oxygen atom of a water molecule also has four substituents—two hydrogen atoms and two nonbonding pairs of electrons:

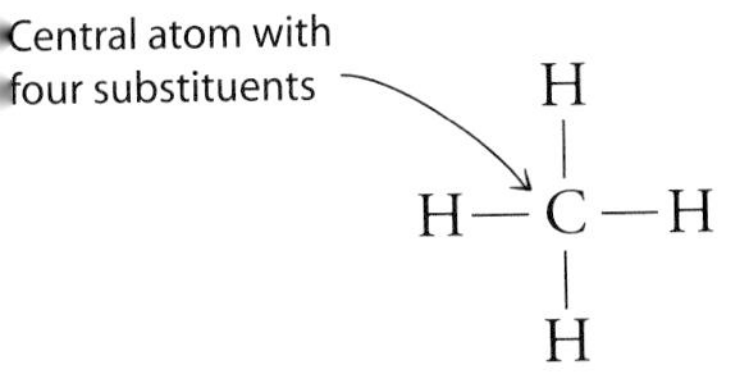

Central atom with
four substituents

$$H-\overset{\displaystyle H}{\underset{\displaystyle H}{\overset{|}{\underset{|}{C}}}}-H$$

Methane, CH_4

Central atom with
four substituents

Lobes used to indicate
space occupied by
nonbonding pair

$$:\!\overset{\displaystyle \cdot\cdot}{O}\!-\!H$$
$$\underset{\displaystyle H}{|}$$

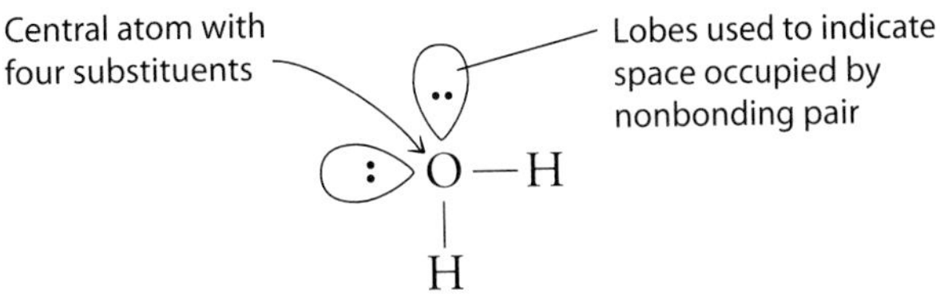

Water, H_2O

Note that each nonbonding pair is shown inside a lobe-shaped atomic orbital. As discussed in Chapter 5, an atomic orbital is the volume of space in which a pair of electrons may be found most of the time. These lobes are shown here to illustrate the role that nonbonding electron pairs play in determining the geometry of a molecule.

As shown in Table 6.1 on page 186, when a central atom has only two substituents, the geometry of the molecule is *linear*, meaning a single straight line may be drawn passing through both substituents and the central atom. Three substituents arrange themselves in a triangle the plane of which passes through the central atom, and so this molecular geometry is called *triangular planar*. Four substituents form a tetrahedron, as already discussed. Five substituents result in a *triangular bipyramidal* geometry, which, as you'll see when you do the Hands-On Chemistry activity on page 188, is two triangle-based pyramids sharing a base and having the two apexes pointing in opposite directions. Six substituents arrange themselves around the central atom in a geometry that, if it had a surface, would show eight sides. To indicate this eight-sided geometry, this structure is called *octahedral*.

Why these geometries? Simply put, these are the geometries that allow for maximum distance between substituents.

Concept Check ✔

Why are the two oxygen atoms in carbon dioxide, CO_2, spaced 180 degrees apart?

Was this your answer? If the two oxygen atoms were on the same side of the carbon atom, the bonding electrons would be relatively close to each other:

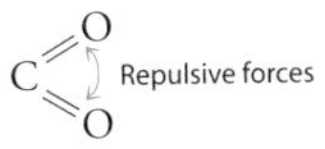

$$C\overset{\nearrow O}{\underset{\searrow O}{}}$$ Repulsive forces

Incorrect geometry for
carbon dioxide, CO_2

Because electron pairs repel one another, this is not a stable situation. Instead, the oxygen atoms position themselves so that the bonding pairs of the two double bonds are as far from each other as possible, which is on opposite sides of the carbon atom, 180 degrees apart, as shown in Table 6.1.

Table 6.1

Molecular Geometries

Number of Substituents	Three-Dimensional Geometry	Examples		
2	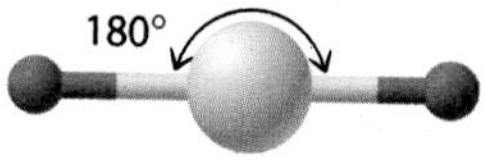 Linear	H—Be—H BeH_2	O=C=O CO_2	H—C≡N HCN
3	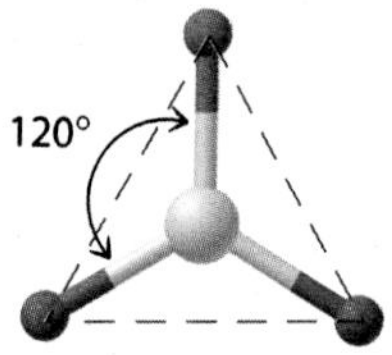 Triangular planar	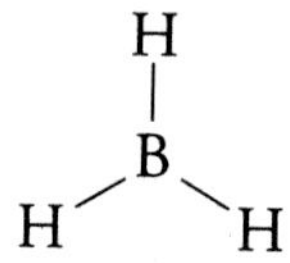 H, B, H, H BH_3	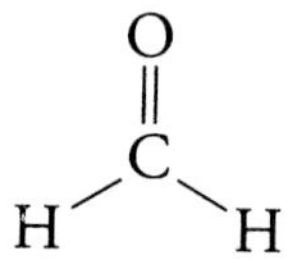 O, C, H, H H_2CO	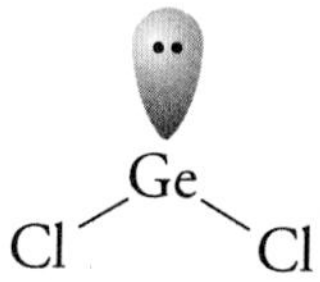 Ge, Cl, Cl $GeCl_2$
4	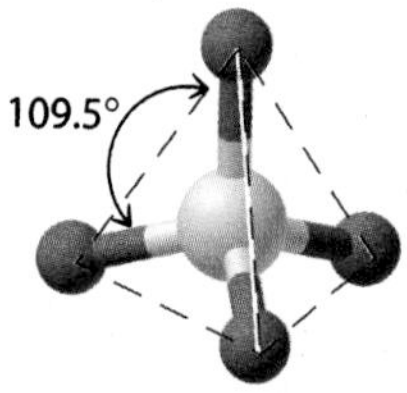 Tetrahedral	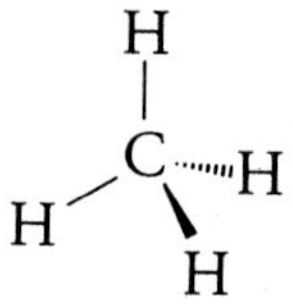 H, C, H, H, H CH_4	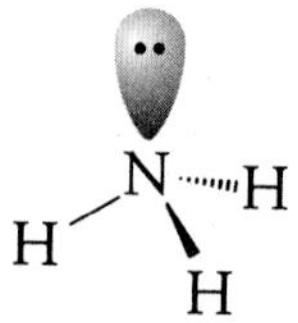 N, H, H, H NH_3	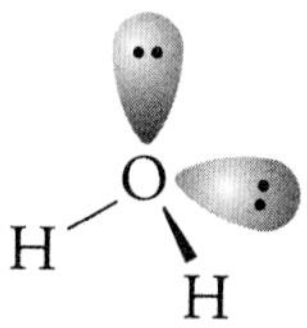 O, H, H H_2O
5	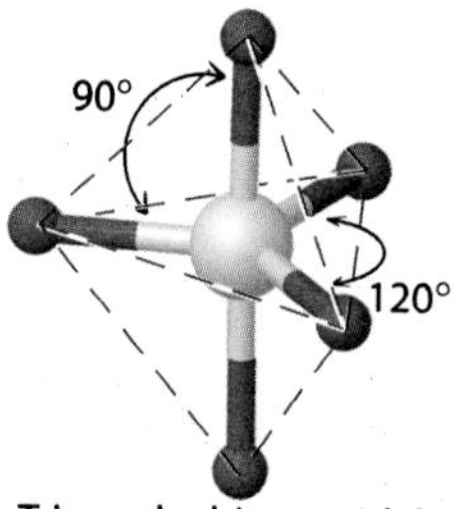 Triangular bipyramidal	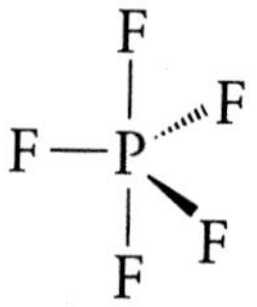 F—P, F, F, F, F PF_5	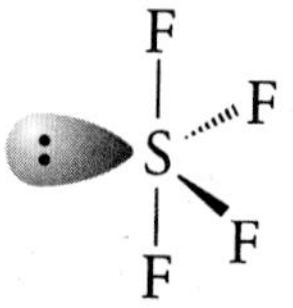 S, F, F, F, F SF_4	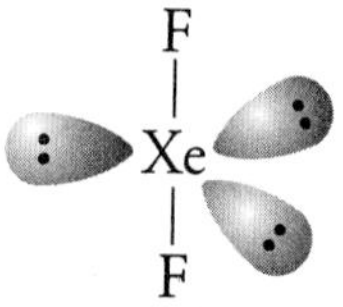 Xe, F, F XeF_2
6	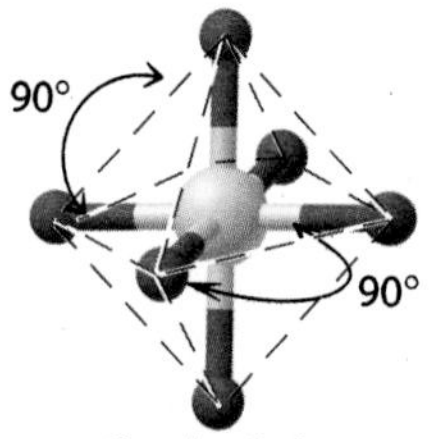 Octahedral	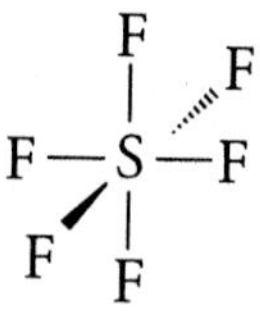 F—S—F, F, F, F, F SF_6	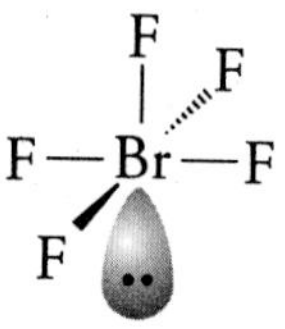 F—Br—F, F, F, F BrF_5	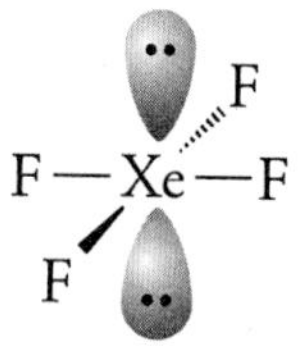 F—Xe—F, F, F XeF_4

Molecular Shape Is Defined by Where the Substituent Atoms Are

Now that you have learned how to use VSEPR to determine molecular *geometry*, you are ready to see how chemists figure out molecular *shape*. What's the difference, you ask? Just this: when chemists talk about molecular geometry, they are talking about the relative positions of *everything* surrounding a central atom in the molecule, both atoms and nonbonding pairs of electrons. When they talk about molecular shape, they are talking about the relative positions of *only the atoms surrounding a central atom.*

Figuring out a molecular shape is a two-step process. The first step is to use VSEPR to position all substituents, both atoms and nonbonding pairs, around a central atom. The second step is to "freeze" the orientations you've come up with so that no atom can change its position, remove all nonbonding pairs, and then decide what three-dimensional shape the atoms form. Let's work through a few examples from Table 6.1 to see what all this means.

In any molecule in which there are no nonbonding pairs around the central atom, the molecular shape is the same as the molecular geometry. Thus, to use the examples from Table 6.1, all three two-substituent molecules have both a linear geometry and a linear shape. Both BH_3 and H_2CO have a triangular planar shape, CH_4 has a tetrahedral shape, PF_5 a triangular bipyramidal shape, and SF_6 a square bipyramidal shape.

Now let's look at molecules that have nonbonding pairs, beginning with germanium chloride, $GeCl_2$, and its one nonbonding pair. The geometry is triangular planar, and to get the shape we ignore the nonbonding pair. This reveals the germanium and two chlorine atoms held together at an angle—a shape known as *bent.* Similarly, ignoring the two nonbonding pairs in a water molecule also reveals a bent shape. Now you know why water molecules are always depicted with the two hydrogen atoms close to each other like a set of mouse ears rather than as far apart as possible on opposite sides of the oxygen atom—there are two nonbonding pairs pushing them into this orientation.

Ignoring the nonbonding pair of the ammonia molecule, NH_3, in Table 6.1 means the shape is not tetrahedral because in a tetrahedron all four corners must be equally distant from the central atom. Ammonia's shape is thus more accurately defined as triangular pyramidal.

This same process of ignoring the nonbonding electron pairs reveals the shapes of the remaining molecules of Table 6.1, which are shown in Figure 6.19.

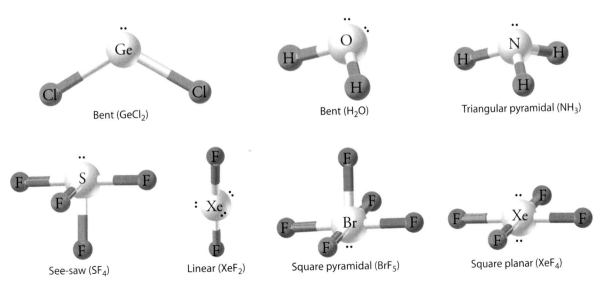

Bent ($GeCl_2$)   Bent (H_2O)   Triangular pyramidal (NH_3)

See-saw (SF_4)   Linear (XeF_2)   Square pyramidal (BrF_5)   Square planar (XeF_4)

Figure 6.19
The shapes of molecules from Table 6.1.

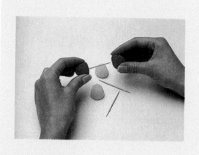

Hands-On Chemistry: Gumdrop Molecules

Use toothpicks and different colors of gumdrops or jelly beans to build models of the molecules shown in Figure 6.19, letting the different colors represent different elements.

Once you have become proficient at building these models, test your expertise by building models for difluoromethane, CH_2F_2; ethane, C_2H_6; hydrogen peroxide, H_2O_2; and acetylene, C_2H_2. Keep in mind that each carbon atom must have four covalent bonds, each oxygen must have two, and each fluorine and hydrogen must have only one.

No fair peeking at the Hands-On Chemistry Insights at the end of this chapter until you have made an honest attempt to build these molecules.

Concept Check ✓

What is the shape of a chlorine trifluoride molecule, ClF_3, which has a triangular bipyramidal geometry:

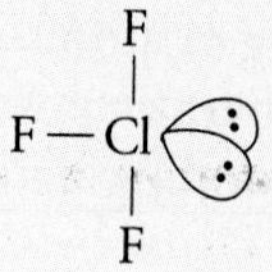

Was this your answer? Ignore the two nonbonding pairs, and the shape of the molecule is all four atoms in the same plane. They form a triangle having a fluorine atom at each corner and the chlorine atom sitting at the midpoint of one side:

Call it what you like—most chemists call it T-shaped. There are even more molecular shapes that can be derived from the geometries in Table 6.1. How many can you find? How might you name them? Curious? Talk with your instructor.

6.6 Polar Covalent Bonds Result from an Uneven Sharing of Electrons

If the two atoms in a covalent bond are identical, their nuclei have the same positive charge, and therefore the electrons are shared *evenly*. We can represent these electrons as being centrally located either by an electron-dot structure or by a probability cloud depiction (Chapter 5) that shows the most probable locations of the bonding electrons:

H : H 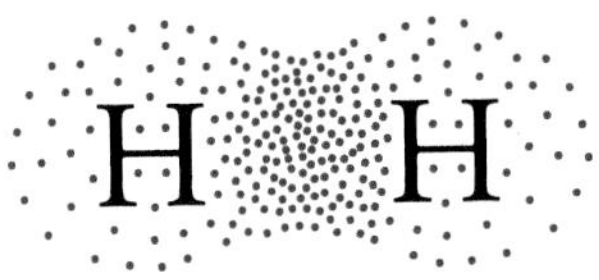

In a covalent bond between nonidentical atoms, the nuclear charges are different, and consequently the bonding electrons may be shared *unevenly*. This occurs in a hydrogen–fluorine bond, where electrons are more attracted to fluorine's greater nuclear charge:

H : F 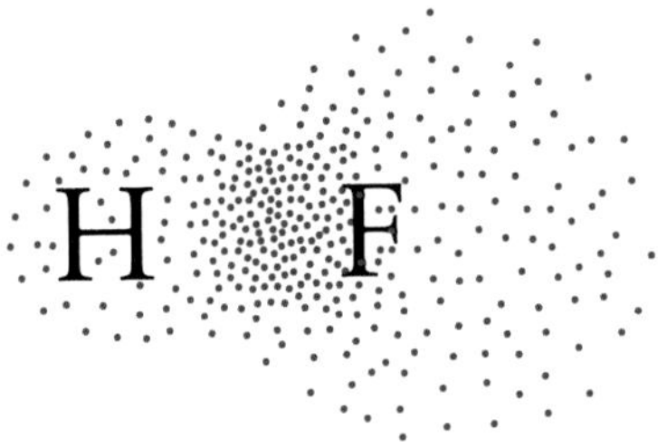

The bonding electrons spend more time around the fluorine atom. For this reason, the fluorine side of the bond is slightly negative and, because the bonding electrons have been drawn away from the hydrogen atom, the hydrogen side of the bond is slightly positive. This separation of charge is called a **dipole** (pronounced die-pole) and is represented either by the characters $\delta-$ and $\delta+$, read "slightly negative" and "slightly positive," respectively, or by a crossed arrow pointing to the negative side of the bond:

$$\overset{\delta+}{\mathrm{H}}-\overset{\delta-}{\mathrm{F}} \qquad \overset{+\!\!\longrightarrow}{\mathrm{H}-\mathrm{F}}$$

So, a chemical bond is a tug-of-war between atoms for electrons. How strongly an atom is able to tug on bonding electrons has been measured experimentally and quantified as the atom's **electronegativity**. The range of electronegativities runs from 0.7 to 3.98, as Figure 6.20 shows. The greater an atom's electronegativity, the greater its ability to pull electrons toward itself when bonded. Thus in hydrogen fluoride, fluorine has a greater electronegativity, or pulling power, than does hydrogen.

H 2.2																	He —
Li 0.98	Be 1.57											B 2.04	C 2.55	N 3.04	O 3.44	F 3.98	Ne —
Na 0.93	Mg 1.31											Al 1.61	Si 1.9	P 2.19	S 2.58	Cl 3.16	Ar —
K 0.82	Ca 1.0	Sc 1.36	Ti 1.54	V 1.63	Cr 1.66	Mn 1.55	Fe 1.83	Co 1.88	Ni 1.91	Cu 1.90	Zn 1.65	Ga 1.81	Ge 2.01	As 2.18	Se 2.55	Br 2.96	Kr —
Rb 0.82	Sr 0.95	Y 1.22	Zr 1.33	Nb 1.6	Mo 2.16	Tc 1.9	Ru 2.2	Rh 2.28	Pd 2.20	Ag 1.93	Cd 1.69	In 1.78	Sn 1.96	Sb 2.05	Te 2.1	I 2.66	Xe —
Cs 0.79	Ba 0.89	La 1.10	Hf 1.3	Ta 1.5	W 2.36	Re 1.9	Os 2.2	Ir 2.20	Pt 2.8	Au 2.54	Hg 2.00	Tl 2.04	Pb 2.33	Bi 2.02	Po 2.0	At 2.2	Rn —
Fr 0.7	Ra 0.9	Ac 1.1	Rf —	Db —	Sg —	Bh —	Hs —	Mt —	Uun —	Uuu —	Uub —						

Figure 6.20
The experimentally measured electronegativities of elements.

Electronegativity is greatest for elements at the upper right of the periodic table and lowest for elements at the lower left. Noble gases are not considered in electronegativity discussions because, with only a few exceptions, they do not participate in chemical bonding.

When the two atoms have the same electronegativity, no dipole is formed (as is the case with H_2) and the bond is classified as a **nonpolar bond**. When the electronegativity of the atoms differs, a dipole may form (as with HF) and the bond is classified as a **polar bond**. Just how polar a bond is depends on the difference between the electronegativity values of the two atoms—the greater the difference, the more polar the bond.

As can be seen in Figure 6.20, the farther apart two atoms are in the periodic table, the greater the difference in their electronegativities, and hence the greater the polarity of the bond between them. So a chemist need not even read the electronegativities to predict which bonds are more polar than others. To find out, he or she need only look at the relative positions of the atoms in the periodic table—the farther apart they are, especially when one is at the lower left and one is at the upper right, the greater the polarity of the bond between them.

Concept Check ✓

List these bonds in order of increasing polarity: P–F, S–F, Ga–F, Ge–F (F, fluorine, atomic number 9; P, phosphorus, atomic number 15; S, sulfur, atomic number 16; Ga, gallium, atomic number 31; Ge, germanium, atomic number 32):

(least polar) _____ < _____ < _____ < _____ < (most polar)

Was this your answer? *If you answered the question, or attempted to, before reading this answer, hooray for you! You're doing more than reading the text—you're learning chemistry.* The greater the *difference* in electronegativities between two bonded atoms, the greater the polarity of the bond, and so the order of increasing polarity is S–F < P–F < Ge–F < Ga–F.

Note that this answer can be obtained by looking only at the relative positions of these elements in the periodic table rather than by calculating their differences in electronegativities.

The magnitude of bond polarity is sometimes indicated by the size of the crossed arrow or $\delta+/\delta-$ symbol used to depict a dipole, as shown in Figure 6.21.

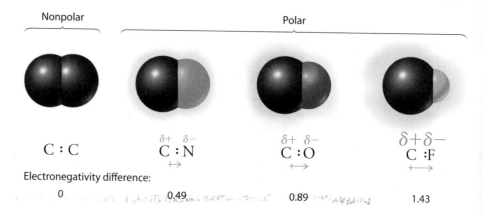

Figure 6.21
These bonds are in order of increasing polarity from left to right, a trend indicated by the larger and larger crossed arrows and $\delta+/\delta-$ symbols. Which of these pairs of elements are farthest apart in the periodic table?

Nonpolar   Polar

C : C   C : N   C : O   C : F

Electronegativity difference:

0   0.49   0.89   1.43

Note that the electronegativity difference between elements in an ionic bond can also be calculated. For example, the bond in NaCl has an electronegativity difference of 2.23, far greater than the difference of 1.43 shown for the C–F bond in Figure 6.21.

What is important to understand here is that there is no black-and-white distinction between ionic and covalent bonds. Rather, there is a gradual change from one to the other as the atoms that bond are located farther and farther apart in the periodic table. This continuum is illustrated in Figure 6.22. Atoms on opposite sides of the table have great differences in electronegativity, and hence the bonds between them are highly polar—in other words, ionic. Nonmetallic atoms of the same type have the same electronegativities, and so their bonds are nonpolar covalent. The polar covalent bond with its uneven *sharing* of electrons and slightly *charged* atoms is between these two extremes.

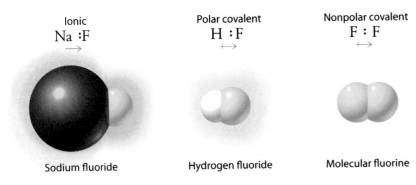

| Ionic | Polar covalent | Nonpolar covalent |
| Na :F | H :F | F : F |

Sodium fluoride   Hydrogen fluoride   Molecular fluorine

Figure 6.22
The ionic bond and the nonpolar covalent bond represent the two extremes of chemical bonding. The ionic bond involves a *transfer* of one or more electrons, and the nonpolar covalent bond involves the equitable *sharing* of electrons. The character of a polar covalent bond falls between these two extremes.

6.7 Molecular Polarity Results from an Uneven Distribution of Electrons

If all the bonds in a molecule are nonpolar, the molecule as a whole is also nonpolar—as is the case with H_2, O_2, and N_2. If a molecule consists of only two atoms and the bond between them is polar, the polarity of the molecule is the same as the polarity of the bond—as with HF, HCl, and ClF.

Complexities arise when assessing the polarity of a molecule containing more than two atoms. Consider carbon dioxide, CO_2, shown in Figure 6.23 on page 192. The cause of the dipole in either one of the carbon–oxygen bonds is oxygen's greater pull (because oxygen is more electronegative than carbon) on the bonding electrons. The second oxygen atom placed on the opposite side of the carbon pulls those electrons back to the carbon, however. The net result is an even distribution of bonding electrons around the whole molecule. So, dipoles that are of equal strength but pull in opposite

Figure 6.23
There is no net dipole in a carbon dioxide molecule, and so the molecule is nonpolar. This is analogous to two people in a tug-of-war. As long as they pull with equal forces but in opposite directions, the rope remains stationary.

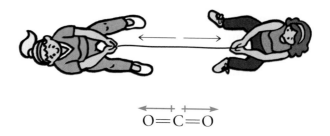

directions in a molecule effectively cancel each other, with the result that the molecule as a whole is nonpolar.

Figure 6.24 illustrates a similar situation in boron trifluoride, BF_3, where three fluorine atoms are oriented 120 degrees from one another around a central boron atom. Because the angles are all the same, and because each fluorine atom pulls on the electrons of its boron–fluorine bond with the same force, the resulting polarity of this molecule is zero.

Figure 6.24
The three dipoles of a boron trifluoride molecule oppose each other at 120-degree angles, which makes the overall molecule nonpolar. This is analogous to three people pulling with equal force on ropes attached to a central ring. As long as they all pull with equal force and all maintain the 120-degree angles, the ring remains stationary.

Nonpolar molecules have only relatively weak attractions to other nonpolar molecules. The covalent bonds in a carbon dioxide molecule, for example, are many times stronger than any forces of attraction that might occur between two adjacent carbon dioxide molecules. This lack of attraction between nonpolar molecules explains the low boiling points of many nonpolar substances. Recall from Section 1.7 that boiling is a process wherein the molecules of a liquid separate from one another as they go into the gaseous phase. When there are only weak attractions between the molecules of a liquid, less heat energy is required to liberate the molecules from one another and allow them to enter the gaseous phase. This translates into a relatively low boiling point for the liquid, as, for instance, in the nitrogen, N_2, shown in Figure 6.25. The boiling points of liquid hydrogen, H_2; oxy-

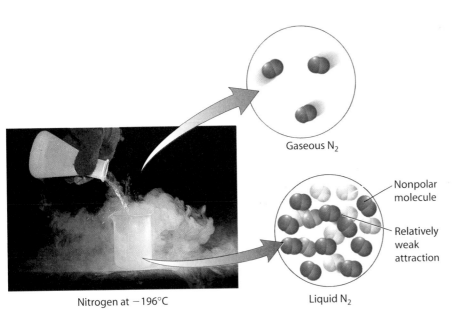

Gaseous N_2

Nonpolar molecule

Relatively weak attraction

Nitrogen at $-196°C$

Liquid N_2

Figure 6.25
Nitrogen is a liquid at temperatures below its chilly boiling point of $-196°C$. Nitrogen molecules are not very attracted to one another because they are nonpolar. As a result, the small amount of heat energy available at $-196°C$ is enough to separate them and allow them to enter the gaseous phase.

gen, O_2; carbon dioxide, CO_2; and boron trifluoride, BF_3, are also quite low for the same reason.

There are many instances in which the dipoles of different bonds in a molecule do not cancel each other. Reconsider the rope analogy of Figure 6.24. As long as everyone pulls equally hard, the ring stays put. Imagine, however, that one person begins to ease off on the rope. Now the pulls are no longer balanced, and the ring begins to move away from the person who is slacking off, as Figure 6.26 shows. Conversely, if one person began to pull harder, the ring would move away from the other two people.

A similar situation occurs in molecules where polar covalent bonds are not equal and opposite. Perhaps the most relevant example is water, H_2O. Each hydrogen–oxygen covalent bond is a relatively large dipole because of

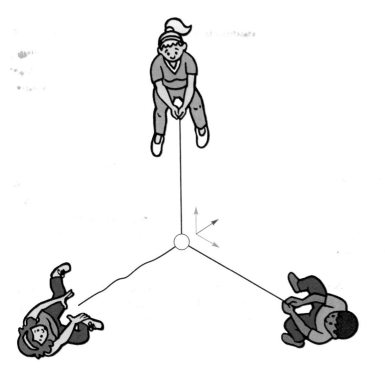

Figure 6.26
If one person eases off in a three-way tug-of-war but the other two continue to pull, the ring moves in the direction of the purple arrow.

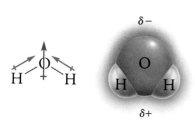

(a) (b)

Figure 6.27
(a) The individual dipoles in a water molecule add together to give a large overall dipole for the whole molecule, shown in purple. (b) The region around the oxygen atom is therefore slightly negative, and the region around the two hydrogens is slightly positive.

the great electronegativity difference. Because of the nonlinear geometry of the molecule, however, the two dipoles, shown in green in Figure 6.27, do not cancel each other the way the C=O dipoles in Figure 6.23 do. Instead, the dipoles in the water molecule work together to give an overall dipole, shown in purple, for the molecule.

Concept Check ✓

Which of these molecules is polar and which is nonpolar:

F   F   H   F
 \   /   \   /
  C=C   N   C=C   P
 /   \   /   \
F   F   H   F

Was this your answer? Symmetry is often the greatest clue for determining polarity. Because the molecule on the left is symmetrical, the dipoles on the two sides cancel each other. This molecule is therefore nonpolar:

F   F   H   F
 \   /   \   /
  C=C $\delta+$ C=C $\delta-$
 /   \   /   \
F   F   H   F

The molecule on the right is less symmetrical (more "lopsided") and so is the polar molecule. Because carbon is more electronegative than hydrogen, the dipoles of the two hydrogen–carbon bonds point toward the carbon. Similarly, fluorine is more electronegative than carbon, the dipoles of the carbon–fluorine bonds point toward the fluorines. Because the general direction of all dipole arrows is toward the fluorines, so is the average distribution of the bonding electrons. The fluorine side of the molecule is therefore slightly negative, and the hydrogen side is slightly positive.

Figure 6.28 illustrates how polar molecules electrically attract one another and as a result are relatively difficult to separate. In other words, polar molecules can be thought of as being "sticky." For this reason, substances composed of polar molecules typically have higher boiling points than sub-

Figure 6.28
Water molecules attract one another because each contains a slightly positive side and a slightly negative side. The molecules position themselves such that the positive side of one faces the negative side of a neighbor.

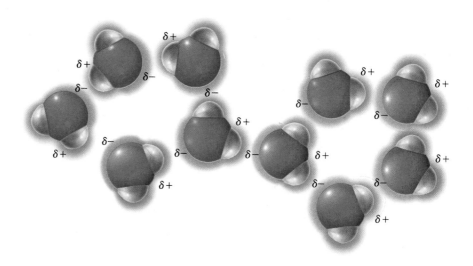

stances composed of nonpolar molecules because it takes more heat energy to separate the polar molecules into the gaseous phase, as Table 6.2 shows.

Table 6.2

Boiling Points of Some Polar and Nonpolar Substances

Substance	Boiling Point (°C)
Polar	
Hydrogen fluoride, HF	20
Water, H_2O	100
Ammonia, NH_3	-33
Nonpolar	
Hydrogen, H_2	-253
Oxygen, O_2	-183
Nitrogen, N_2	-196
Boron trifluoride, BF_3	-100
Carbon dioxide, CO_2	-79

Water, for example, boils at 100°C, whereas carbon dioxide boils at -79°C. This 179 C° difference is quite dramatic when you consider that a carbon dioxide molecule is more than twice as massive as a water molecule.

Because molecular "stickiness" can play a lead role in determining a substance's macroscopic properties, molecular polarity is a central concept of chemistry. Figure 6.29 describes an interesting example.

Figure 6.29
Oil and water are difficult to mix as is evident from this 1989 oil spill of the Exxon Valdez oil tanker in Alaska's Prince William Sound. It's not, however, that oil and water repel each other. Rather, water molecules are so attracted to themselves because of their polarity that they pull themselves together. The nonpolar oil molecules are thus excluded and left to themselves. Being less dense than water, oil floats on the surface where it poses great danger to wildlife.

Concept Check ✔

1. A substance made of polar molecules tends to have a higher boiling point than one made of nonpolar molecules. Why?
2. Consider two substances—one made of molecules like the one shown on the left, the other made of molecules like the one shown on the right. Which substance has the higher boiling point?

Were these your answers?

1. Polar molecules are attracted to one another, and so a lot of heat energy must be added to separate them into the gaseous phase. Therefore a substance made of polar molecules has a relatively high boiling point. There is less electrical attraction between nonpolar molecules, and so less heat energy is needed to separate them into the gaseous phase. Therefore a substance made of nonpolar molecules has a relatively low boiling point.

2. In the symmetrical CF_4 molecule, the four outward-pointing dipoles all cancel. This molecule is therefore nonpolar and likely to have a low boiling point. In the CH_2F_2 molecule, all the dipoles are directed toward the fluorine, which means the bonding electrons tend to be distributed toward this side of the molecule. This molecule has a significant polarity, and its boiling point should be relatively high.

The boiling point of CF_4 is $-129°C$, and that of CH_2F_2 is a much warmer $-52°C$.

In this chapter, we explored two types of chemical bonds: ionic and covalent. Ionic bonds are formed when one or more electrons move from one atom to another. In this way, the atoms become ions—one positive, the other negative—and are held together by the resulting electrical attraction. Covalent bonds form when atoms share electrons. When the sharing is completely equitable, the bond is nonpolar covalent. When one atom pulls more strongly on the electrons because of its greater electronegativity, the bond is polar covalent and a dipole may be formed.

We also looked at how the shape of a molecule can play a role in determining its polarity and how molecular polarity has a great influence on macroscopic behavior. Consider what the world would be like if the oxygen atom in a water molecule did not have its two nonbonding pairs of electrons. Instead of being bent, each water molecule would be linear, much like carbon dioxide. The dipoles of the two hydrogen–oxygen bonds would cancel each other, which would make water a nonpolar substance and give it a relatively low boiling point. Water would not be a liquid at the ambient temperatures of our planet, and we in turn would not be here discussing these concepts. Hooray for the two nonbonding pairs on the oxygen atom! Hooray for the insights we gain by thinking about the molecular realm!

Key Terms and Matching Definitions

_____ covalent bond
_____ covalent compound
_____ dipole
_____ electron-dot structure
_____ electronegativity
_____ ion
_____ ionic bond
_____ ionic compound
_____ molecule
_____ nonbonding pair
_____ nonpolar bond
_____ polar bond
_____ substituent
_____ valence electron
_____ valence shell
_____ valence-shell electron-pair repulsion

1. An electron that is located in the outermost occupied shell in an atom and can participate in chemical bonding.
2. The outermost occupied shell of an atom.
3. A shorthand notation of the shell model of the atom in which valence electrons are shown around an atomic symbol.
4. Two paired valence electrons that don't participate in a chemical bond and yet influence the shape of the molecule.
5. An electrically charged particle created when an atom either loses or gains one or more electrons.
6. A chemical bond in which an attractive electric force holds ions of opposite charge together.
7. Any chemical compound containing ions.
8. A chemical bond in which atoms are held together by their mutual attraction for two or more electrons they share.
9. An element or chemical compound in which atoms are held together by covalent bonds.
10. A group of atoms held tightly together by covalent bonds.
11. A model that explains molecular geometries in terms of electron pairs striving to be as far apart from one another as possible.
12. An atom or nonbonding pair of electrons surrounding a central atom.
13. A separation of charge that occurs in a chemical bond because of differences in the electronegativities of the bonded atoms.

14. The ability of an atom to attract a bonding pair of electrons to itself when bonded to another atom.
15. A chemical bond having no dipole.
16. A chemical bond having a dipole.

Review Questions

An Atomic Model Is Needed to Understand How Atoms Bond

1. How many shells are needed to account for the seven periods of the periodic table?
2. How many electrons can fit in the first shell? How many in the second shell?
3. How many shells are completely filled in an argon atom, Ar (atomic number 18)?
4. Which electrons are represented by an electron-dot structure?
5. How do the electron-dot structures of elements in the same group in the periodic table compare with one another?
6. How many nonbonding pairs are there in an oxygen atom? How many unpaired valence electrons?

Atoms Can Lose or Gain Electrons to Become Ions

7. How does an ion differ from an atom?
8. To become a negative ion, does an atom lose or gain electrons?
9. Do metals more readily gain or lose electrons?
10. How many electrons does the calcium atom tend to lose?
11. Why does the fluorine atom tend to gain only one electron?

Ionic Bonds Result from a Transfer of Electrons

12. Which elements tend to form ionic bonds?
13. Is an ionic compound an example of a chemical compound, or is a chemical compound an example of an ionic compound?
14. What is the electric charge on the calcium ion in the compound calcium chloride, $CaCl_2$?

15. What is the electric charge on the calcium ion in the compound calcium oxide, CaO?

16. Suppose an oxygen atom gains two electrons to become an oxygen ion. What is its electric charge?

17. What is an ionic crystal?

Covalent Bonds Result from a Sharing of Electrons

18. Which elements tend to form covalent bonds?

19. What force holds two atoms together in a covalent bond?

20. How many electrons are shared in a double covalent bond?

21. How many electrons are shared in a triple covalent bond?

22. How many additional electrons is an oxygen atom able to attract?

23. How many covalent bonds is an oxygen atom able to form?

Valence Electrons Determine Molecular Shape

24. What does *VSEPR* stand for?

25. How many faces are there on a tetrahedron?

26. What is meant by the term *substituent*?

27. When is the geometry of a molecule not the same as its shape?

28. How many substituents does the oxygen atom in a water molecule have?

Polar Covalent Bonds Result from an Uneven Sharing of Electrons

29. What is a dipole?

30. Which element of the periodic table has the greatest electronegativity? Which has the smallest?

31. Which is more polar: a carbon–oxygen bond or a carbon–nitrogen bond?

32. How is a polar covalent bond similar to an ionic bond?

Molecular Polarity Results from an Uneven Distribution of Electrons

33. How can a molecule be nonpolar when it consists of atoms that have different electro-negativities?

34. Why do nonpolar substances tend to boil at relatively low temperatures?

35. Which tends to have a greater degree of symmetry: a polar molecule or a nonpolar molecule?

36. Why don't oil and water mix?

37. Which would you describe as "stickier": a polar molecule or a nonpolar one?

Hands-On Chemistry Insights

Up Close with Crystals

One thing you probably noticed under the magnifying glass when you compared uncrushed crystals was sharp, angular edges in NaCl and rounded edges in KCl. Then you probably found it easier to grind the KCl crystals to powder. These differences have the same origin: a potassium ion, K^+, is larger than a sodium ion, Na^+.

The positive and negative ions in a crystal are attracted to one another by the attractive electric force between oppositely charged particles. The negative charge on a negative ion is, as we saw in Chapter 5, outside the nucleus, distributed among all the electrons. The positive charge on a positive ion, however, is all in the nucleus. This means the positive and negative charges of the ionic bond are farther apart in the compound containing the larger positive ion:

Shorter distance between positive and negative charges

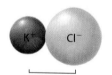

Longer distance between positive and negative charges

Because the electric force weakens with increasing distance between the opposite charges, the KCl ionic bond is weaker than the NaCl ionic bond. Weaker ionic bonds mean that KCl crystals are less resilient to tress and impact than are NaCl crystals, accounting for the rounder edges you observed in the KCl crystals and for the fact that it was easier to grind the KCl to a powder.

This difference in bond strength is also responsible for many other differences in the physical properties of these two substances. For instance, whereas the melting point of NaCl is 801°C, that of KCl is "only" 770°C. The 31°C difference is easy to explain in terms of what happens when a solid-to-liquid phase change occurs: the particles of the solid have to be pried apart from one another. The weaker ionic bonds in KCl means the ions separate more easily, and the macroscopic evidence of this is the lower melting point of KCl.

Gumdrop Molecules

Your molecular models should look like this:

Difluoromethane,
CH_2F_2,
tetrahedron

Ethane,
C_2H_6,
two tetrahedrons

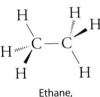

Hydrogen peroxide,
H_2O_2,
two bent shapes
stuck together

$H-C\equiv C-H$

Acetylene,
C_2H_2,
linear

Exercises

1. An atom loses an electron to another atom. Is this an example of a physical change or a chemical change?

2. Why is it so easy for a magnesium atom to lose two electrons?

3. Why doesn't the sodium atom gain seven electrons so that its third shell becomes the filled outermost shell?

4. Magnesium ions carry a 2+ charge, and chloride ions carry a 1− charge. What is the chemical formula for the ionic compound magnesium chloride?

5. Barium ions carry a 2+ charge, and nitrogen ions carry a 3− charge. What is the chemical formula for the ionic compound barium nitride?

6. Does an ionic bond have a dipole?

7. Why doesn't a neon atom tend to gain electrons?

8. Why doesn't a neon atom tend to lose electrons?

9. Why doesn't a hydrogen atom form more than one covalent bond?

10. What drives an atom to form a covalent bond: its nuclear charge or the need to have a filled outer shell? Explain.

11. Is there an abrupt change or a gradual change between ionic and covalent bonds? Explain.

12. Classify the following bonds as ionic, polar covalent, or nonpolar covalent (O, atomic number 8; F, atomic number 9; Na, atomic number 11; Cl, atomic number 17; Ca, atomic number 20; U, atomic number 92):

    O with F   _C - Polar_

    Ca with Cl   _Ionic_

    Na with Na   _C - Non_

    U with Cl   _C - Polar_

13. Nonmetal atoms form covalent bonds, but they can also form ionic bonds. How is this possible?

14. Metal atoms can form ionic bonds, but they are not very good at forming covalent bonds. Why?

15. Phosphine is a covalent compound of phosphorus, P, and hydrogen, H. What is its chemical formula?

16. Why is a germanium chloride molecule, $GeCl_2$, bent even though there are only two atoms surrounding the central germanium atom?

17. Write the electron-dot structure for the ionic compound calcium chloride, $CaCl_2$.

18. Write the electron-dot structure for the covalent compound ethane, C_2H_6.

19. Write the electron-dot structure for the covalent compound hydrogen peroxide, H_2O_2.

20. Write the electron-dot structure for the covalent compound acetylene, C_2H_2.

21. In two dimensions, sulfuric acid, H_2SO_4, is often written

$$
\begin{array}{c}
O \\
\parallel \\
HO - S - OH \\
\parallel \\
O
\end{array}
$$

What three-dimensional shape does this molecule most likely have?

22. Examine the three-dimensional geometries of PF_5 and SF_4 in Table 6.1. Which do you expect is the more polar compound?

23. What is the source of an atom's electronegativity?

24. Which bond is most polar: H–N, N–C, C–O, C–C, O–H, C–H?

25. Which molecule is most polar: S=C=S, O=C=O, O=C=S?

26. In each molecule, which atom carries the greater positive charge: H–Cl, Br–F, C≡O, Br–Br?

27. List these bonds in order of increasing polarity: N–N, N–F, N–O, H–F

_____ < _____ < _____ < _____
(least polar)   (most polar)

28. Which is more polar: a sulfur–bromine bond, S–Br, or a selenium–chlorine bond, Se–Cl?

29. Water, H_2O, and methane, CH_4, have about the same mass and differ by only one type of atom. Why is the boiling point of water so much higher than that of methane?

30. An individual carbon–oxygen bond is polar. Yet carbon dioxide, CO_2, which has two carbon–oxygen bonds, is nonpolar. Explain.

31. In each pair, which compound probably has the higher boiling point (atomic numbers: Cl 17, S 16, O 8, C 6, H 1):

(a)
$$
\begin{array}{cc}
Cl \quad\quad Cl & H \quad\quad Cl \\
\diagdown \quad / & \diagdown \quad / \\
C=C & C=C \\
/ \quad\quad \diagdown & / \quad\quad \diagdown \\
H \quad\quad H & Cl \quad\quad H
\end{array}
$$

(b) S=C=O   O=C=O

(c)
$$
\begin{array}{cc}
Cl & Cl \quad\quad H \\
\diagdown & \diagdown \quad / \\
C=O & C=C \\
/ & / \quad\quad \diagdown \\
Cl & Cl \quad\quad H
\end{array}
$$

32. Why is ammonia, NH_3, more polar than borane, BH_3?

Suggested Web Sites

http://www.ada.org/topics/fluoride.html
Fluoride page of the American Dental Association, with many links to information regarding fluorides and fluoridation of drinking water and toothpastes.

http://www.saltinstitute.org/idd.htm
Numerous reports in the literature demonstrate the effectiveness of iodized salt in controlling the medical condition called goiter. Check out this site for historical case studies that first pointed to this conclusion.

http://www.soils.wisc.edu/virtual_museum/
Home page of the Virtual Museum of Minerals and Molecules, curated by Phillip Barak of the University of Minnesota and Ed Nater of the University of Wisconsin. Through this site, you will find molecular models that you can manipulate in three dimensions. To do so, your browser will need to be equipped with the Chime plug-in, which you may download by following the hyperlinks to http://www.mdli.com/download/chimedown.html.

Chapter 7
Molecular Mixing

How Molecules Attract One Another

Can fish drown? To many people, this question may sound silly. Recall from Section 2.4, however, that fish do not "breathe" water. Rather, their gills are equipped to extract oxygen molecules mixed in with water. Fish therefore can drown if they are in water that contains an insufficient number of oxygen molecules. This is what happens when excessive amounts of organic wastes are discharged into a lake or river. As we explore in Chapter 16, the organic wastes are consumed by microorganisms that also utilize molecular oxygen. As these microorganisms thrive, the amount of molecular oxygen in the water drops to the point where fish and many other aquatic organisms drown.

The number of oxygen molecules that can mix with a given volume of water is amazingly low. Water that has been fully aerated at room temperature, for example, contains only about 1 oxygen molecule for every 200,000 water molecules, a ratio represented pictorially in the illustration to the right. The gills of a fish, therefore, must be highly efficient at extracting molecular oxygen from water.

This chapter explains how many of the physical properties of materials are a consequence of attractions among the submicroscopic particles making up the materials. Why only small amounts of oxygen can mix with water, for example, can be explained by the fact that the attractive forces between water molecules and oxygen molecules are very weak. We begin by looking at four types of electrical attractions that occur between submicroscopic particles.

7.1 Submicroscopic Particles Electrically Attract One Another

We can think of any pure substance as being made up of one type of submicroscopic particle. For an ionic compound, that particle is an ion; for covalent compound, it is a molecule; and for an element, it is an atom.

Table 7.1 lists four types of electrical attractions that can occur between these particles. The strength of even the strongest of these attractions is many times weaker than any chemical bond, however. The attraction between two adjacent water molecules, for example, is about 20 times weaker than the chemical bonds holding the hydrogen and oxygen atoms together in the water molecules. Although particle-to-particle attractions are relatively weak, you can see their profound effect on the substances around you.

We now explore these interparticle attractions in order of relative strength, beginning with the strongest.

Table 7.1

Electrical Attractions Between Submicroscopic Particles

Attraction	Relative Strength
Ion–dipole	Strongest
Dipole–dipole	
Dipole–induced dipole	
Induced dipole–induced dipole	Weakest

Ions and Polar Molecules Attract One Another

Recall from Chapter 6 that a *polar* molecule is one in which the bonding electrons are distributed unevenly. The side of the molecule on which these electrons tend to congregate carries a slight negative charge, and as a result the opposite side of the molecule carries a slight positive charge. This separation of charge is called a *dipole*.

So what happens when polar molecules, such as water molecules, approach an ionic compound, such as sodium chloride? The positive sodium ions are attracted to the negative side of the water molecules, and the negative chloride ions are attracted to the positive side of the water molecules, as illustrated in Figure 7.1. Such an attraction between an ion and the dipole of a polar molecule is called an *ion–dipole attraction*.

Ion–dipole attractions are much weaker than any ionic bond. A large number of ion–dipole attractions, however, can act collectively to disrupt an ionic bond, and this is what happens to sodium chloride in water. The

Figure 7.1
An ion–dipole attraction occurs between the slightly negative side (oxygen side) of a water molecule and the positively charged sodium ion of sodium chloride. Another ion–dipole attraction occurs between the slightly positive side (hydrogen side) of a water molecule and the negatively charged chloride ion. Electrical attractions are shown as a series of overlapping arcs. The blue arcs indicate negative charge, and the red arcs indicate positive charge.

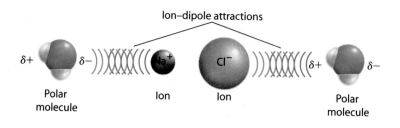

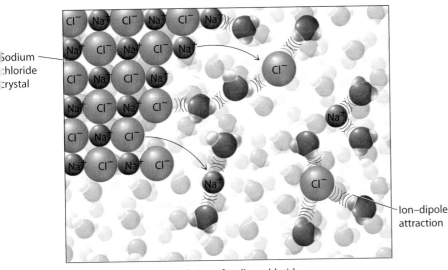

Aqueous solution of sodium chloride

Figure 7.2
Sodium and chloride ions tightly bound in a crystal lattice are separated from one another by the collective attraction exerted by many water molecules to form an aqueous solution of sodium chloride.

sodium and chloride ions are strongly held together by ionic bonds, but a multitude of ion–dipole attractions exerted by the water molecules break the ionic bonds and pull the ions apart. The result, represented in Figure 7.2, is a solution of sodium chloride in water. (A solution in water is called an *aqueous solution.*)

Polar Molecules Attract Other Polar Molecules

An attraction between two polar molecules is called a *dipole–dipole attraction.* For example, two molecules of dimethyl ether, C_2H_6O, because they are polar molecules, attract each other by a dipole–dipole attraction, as shown in Figure 7.3.

An unusually strong dipole–dipole attraction is the **hydrogen bond**. This attraction occurs between molecules that have a hydrogen atom covalently bonded to a highly electronegative atom, usually nitrogen, oxygen, or fluorine. As is shown in Figure 7.4, a hydrogen bond occurs when the hydrogen side of one such molecule (water in this example) is attracted to a pair of nonbonding electrons on the electronegative atom of the other molecule. How strong a given hydrogen bond is depends on two things: (1) the strength of the dipoles involved (which depends on the difference in electronegativity for the two atoms in either polar molecule) and (2) how strongly nonbonding electrons on one molecule can attract a hydrogen atom on a nearby molecule. Recent research has revealed that a small amount of true electron sharing occurs between the hydrogen and the nonbonding pair. Because electron sharing is the definition of covalent bond, the hydrogen bond is appropriately named a bond. However, any hydrogen bond is much weaker than the typical covalent bond, and so it is also appropriate to think of the hydrogen bond not as a bond but as an unusually strong dipole–dipole attraction between separate molecules.

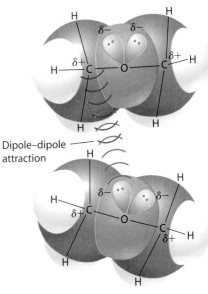

Figure 7.3
The dipole–dipole attraction between two dimethyl ether molecules involves a slightly positive carbon atom of one molecule and the slightly negative oxygen atom of the other molecule.

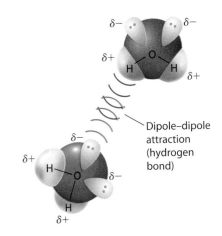

Figure 7.4
The dipole–dipole attraction between two water molecules is a hydrogen bond because it involves hydrogen atoms bonded to highly electronegative oxygen atoms.

The hydrogen bond is responsible for many of the unusual properties of water, as we explore in Chapter 8. The hydrogen bond is also of great importance in the chemistry of large biomolecules, such as DNA and proteins, discussed in Chapter 13.

Polar Molecules Can Induce Dipoles in Nonpolar Molecules

In many molecules, the electrons are distributed evenly, and so there is no dipole, as is the case with the oxygen molecule, O_2. Such a nonpolar molecule can be induced to become a temporary dipole, however, when it is brought close to a water molecule or any other polar molecule, as Figure 7.5 illustrates. The slightly negative side of the water molecule pushes the electrons in the oxygen molecule to the side of the molecule farthest from the water molecule. The result is a temporary uneven distribution of electrons called an **induced dipole**. The resulting attraction between the permanent dipole (water) and the induced dipole (oxygen) is a *dipole–induced dipole attraction*.

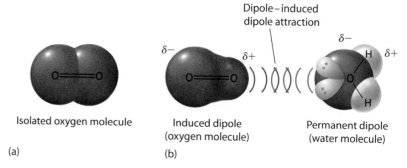

Figure 7.5
(a) An isolated oxygen molecule has no dipole; its electrons are distributed evenly. (b) An adjacent water molecule induces a redistribution of electrons in the oxygen molecule. (The slightly negative side of the oxygen molecule is shown larger than the slightly positive side because the slightly negative side contains more electrons.)

Concept Check ✓

How does the electron distribution in an oxygen molecule change when the hydrogen side of a water molecule is nearby?

Was this your answer? Because the hydrogen side of the water molecule is slightly positive, the electrons in the oxygen molecule are pulled *toward* the water molecule, inducing in the oxygen molecule a temporary dipole in which the larger side is nearest the water molecule (rather than as far away as possible as it was in Figure 7.5).

Remember—induced dipoles are only temporary. If the water molecule in Figure 7.5b were removed, the oxygen molecule would return to its normal, nonpolar state. As a consequence, dipole–induced dipole attractions are weaker than dipole–dipole attractions. They are strong enough to hold relatively small quantities of oxygen dissolved in water, however. As this

hapter's introduction discusses, this attraction between water and molecu-
r oxygen is vital for fish and other forms of aquatic life that rely on molec-
lar oxygen mixed in water.

Dipole–induced dipole attractions also occur between molecules of car-
on dioxide, which are nonpolar, and water. It is these attractions that keep
arbonated beverages (which are mixtures of carbon dioxide in water) from
osing their fizz too quickly after they've been opened. Dipole–induced
ipole attractions are also responsible for holding plastic wrap to glass, as
hown in Figure 7.6. These wraps are made of very long nonpolar mole-
ules that are induced to have dipoles when placed in contact with glass,
vhich is highly polar. As is discussed in the next section, the molecules of
nonpolar material, such as plastic wrap, can also induce dipoles among
hemselves. This explains how plastic wrap sticks not only to polar materi-
ls such as glass but also to itself.

Figure 7.6
Temporary dipoles induced in normally nonpolar molecules in plastic wrap makes it stick to glass.

Concept Check ✔

Distinguish between a dipole–dipole attraction and a dipole–induced dipole attraction.

Was this your answer? The dipole–dipole attraction is stronger and involves two permanent dipoles. The dipole–induced dipole attraction is weaker and involves a permanent dipole and a temporary one.

Atoms and Nonpolar Molecules Can Form Temporary Dipoles on Their Own

Individual atoms and nonpolar molecules, on average, have a fairly even distribution of electrons. Because of the randomness of electron motion, however, at any given moment the electrons in an atom or a nonpolar molecule may be bunched to one side. The result is a temporary dipole, as shown in Figure 7.7.

Just as the permanent dipole of a polar molecule can induce a dipole in a nonpolar molecule, a temporary dipole can do the same thing. This gives rise to the weakest particle-to-particle attraction: the *induced dipole–induced dipole attraction*, illustrated in Figure 7.8.

Nonpolar argon   Temporary dipole of argon

Figure 7.7
The electron distribution in an atom is normally even. At any given moment, however, the electron distribution may be less than even, resulting in a temporary dipole.

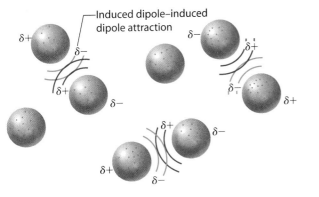

Induced dipole–induced dipole attraction

Figure 7.8
Because the normally even distribution of electrons in atoms can momentarily become uneven, atoms can be attracted to one another by induced dipole–induced dipole attractions.

Temporary dipoles are more significant for larger atoms. This is because the electrons in larger atoms have more space available for random motion and a greater likelihood of bunching together on one side. The electrons in smaller atoms are less able to bunch to one side because they are confined to a smaller space and the resulting greater electrical repulsion tends to keep them evenly spread. So it is larger atoms—and molecules made of larger atoms—that have the strongest induced dipole–induced dipole attractions. As shown in Figure 7.9, for example, nonpolar iodine molecules, I_2, because they are relatively large, have a greater attraction for one another than do relatively small nonpolar fluorine molecules, F_2. This explains why iodine molecules stick together as a solid at room temperature but at the same temperature fluorine molecules drift apart into the gaseous phase.

Fluorine is one of the smallest atoms, and nonpolar molecules made with fluorine atoms exhibit only very weak induced dipole–induced dipole attractions. This is the principle behind the Teflon nonstick surface. The Teflon molecule, part of which is shown in Figure 7.10, is a long chain of carbon atoms chemically bonded to fluorine atoms, and the fluorine atoms exert essentially no attractions on any material in contact with the Teflon surface—scrambled eggs in a frying pan, for instance.

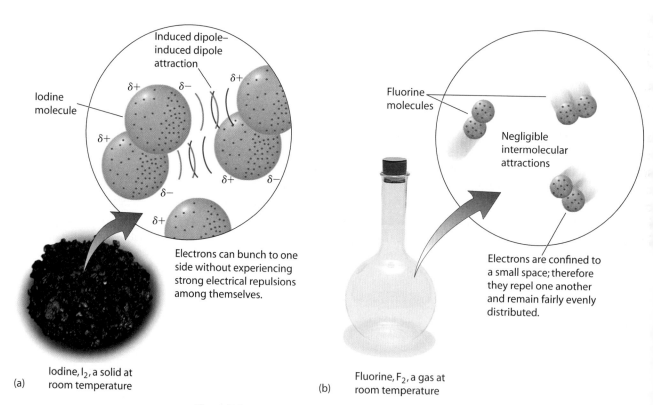

(a) Iodine, I_2, a solid at room temperature

(b) Fluorine, F_2, a gas at room temperature

Figure 7.9

(a) Temporary dipoles more readily form in larger atoms, such as those in an iodine molecule, because in larger atoms electrons bunched to one side are still relatively far apart from one another and not so repelled by the electric force. (b) In smaller atoms, such as those in a fluorine molecule, electrons cannot bunch to one side as well because the repulsive electric force gets greater as the electrons get closer together.

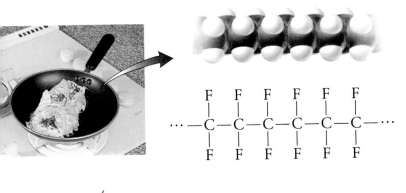

Figure 7.10
Few things stick to Teflon because of the high proportion of fluorine atoms it contains. The structure depicted here is only a portion of the full length of the molecule.

oncept Check ✓

Distinguish between a dipole–induced dipole attraction and an induced dipole–induced dipole attraction.

Was this your answer? The dipole–induced dipole attraction is stronger and involves a permanent dipole and a temporary one. The induced dipole–induced dipole attraction is weaker and involves two temporary dipoles.

Induced dipole–induced dipole attractions help explain why natural gas is a gas at room temperature but gasoline is a liquid. The major component of natural gas is methane, CH_4, and one of the major components of gasoline is octane, C_8H_{18}. We see in Figure 7.11 that the number of induced dipole–induced dipole attractions between two methane molecules is appreciably less than the number between two octane molecules. Have you ever noticed that two small pieces of Velcro are easier to pull apart than two long pieces? Like short pieces of Velcro, methane molecules can be pulled apart with little effort. That's why methane has a low boiling point, −161°C, and is a gas at room temperature. Octane molecules, like long strips of Velcro, are relatively hard to pull apart because of the larger number of induced dipole–induced dipole attractions. The boiling point of octane, 125°C, is therefore much higher than that of methane, and octane is a liquid at room temperature. (The greater mass of octane also plays a role in making its boiling point higher.)

Induced dipole–induced
dipole attractions

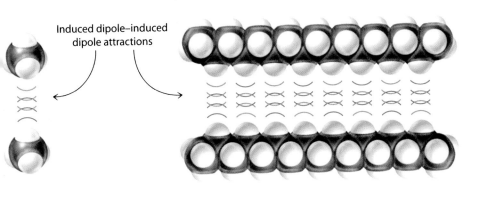

(a) Methane molecules   (b) Octane molecules

Figure 7.11
(a) Two nonpolar methane molecules are attracted to each other by induced dipole–induced dipole attractions, but there is only one attraction per molecule. (b) Two nonpolar octane molecules are similar to methane but longer. The number of induced ipole–induced dipole attractions between these two molecules is therefore greater.

Hands-On Chemistry: Circular Rainbows

Black ink contains pigments of many different colors, which together absorb all the frequencies of visible light. Because no light is reflected, the ink appears black. We can use electrical attractions to separate the components of black ink through a special technique called paper chromatography.

What You Need

Black felt-tip pen or black water-soluble marker; piece of porous paper, such as paper towel, table napkin, or coffee filter; solvent, such as water, acetone (fingernail polish remover), rubbing alcohol, or white vinegar.

Procedure

① Place a concentrated dot of ink at the center of the piece of porous paper.

② Carefully place one drop of solvent on top of the dot, and watch the ink spread radially with the solvent. Because the different components of the ink have different affinities for the solvent (based on the electrical attractions between component molecules and solvent molecules), they travel with the solvent at different rates.

③ Just after the drop of solvent is completely absorbed, add a second drop at the same place you put the first one, then a third, and so on until the ink components have separated to your satisfaction.

How the components separate depends on several factors, including your choice of solvent and your technique. It's also interesting to watch the leading edge of the moving ink under a strong magnifying glass or microscope.

Concept Check ✓

Methanol, CH_3OH, which can be used as a fuel, is not much larger than methane but is a liquid at room temperature. Suggest why.

Was this your answer? The polar oxygen–hydrogen covalent bond in each methanol molecule leads to hydrogen bonding between molecules. These relatively strong interparticle attractions hold methanol molecules together as a liquid at room temperature.

7.2 A Solution Is a Single-Phase Homogeneous Mixture

What happens when table sugar, known chemically as sucrose, is stirred into water? Is the sucrose destroyed? We know it isn't because it sweetens the water. Does the sucrose disappear because it somehow ceases to occupy space or because it fits within the nooks and crannies of the water? Not so, for the addition of sucrose changes the volume. This may not be noticeable at first, but continue to add sucrose to a glass of water and you'll see that the water level rises just as it would if you were adding sand.

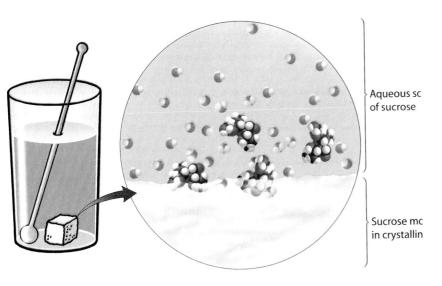

Aqueous sc
of sucrose

Sucrose mc
in crystallin

Figure 7.12
Water molecules pull the sucrose molecules in a sucrose crystal away from one another. They do not, however, effect the covalent bonds within each sucrose molecule, which is why each dissolved sucrose molecule remains intact as a single molecule.

Sucrose stirred into water loses its crystalline form. Each sucrose crystal consists of billions upon billions of sucrose molecules packed neatly together. When the crystal is exposed to water, as in Figure 7.12, an even greater number of water molecules pull on the sucrose molecules via hydrogen bonds formed between sucrose molecules and water molecules. With a little stirring, the sucrose molecules soon mix throughout the water. In place of sucrose crystals and water, we have a homogeneous mixture of sucrose molecules in water. As discussed in Section 2.5, homogeneous means that a sample taken from one part of a mixture is the same as a sample taken from any other part of the mixture. In our sucrose example, this means that the sweetness of the first sip of the solution is the same as the sweetness of the last sip.

Recall from Section 2.5 that a homogeneous mixture consisting of a single phase is called a *solution*. Sugar in water is a solution in the liquid phase. Solutions aren't always liquids, however. They can also be solid or gaseous, as Figure 7.13 shows. Gem stones are solid solutions. A ruby, for

(a)

(b)

(c)

Figure 7.13
Solutions may occur in (a) the solid phase, (b) the liquid phase, or (c) the gaseous phase.

example, is a solid solution of trace quantities of red chromium compounds in transparent aluminum oxide. A blue sapphire is a solid solution of trace quantities of light green iron compounds and blue titanium compounds in aluminum oxide. Another important example of solid solutions is metal alloys, which are mixtures of different metallic elements. The alloy known as brass is a solid solution of copper and zinc, for instance, and the alloy stainless steel is a solid solution of iron, chromium, nickel, and carbon.

An example of a gaseous solution is the air we breathe, which, by volume, is a solution of 78 percent nitrogen gas, 21 percent oxygen gas, and 1 percent other gaseous materials, including water vapor and carbon dioxide. The air we *exhale* is a gaseous solution of 75 percent nitrogen, 14 percent oxygen, 5 percent carbon dioxide, and around 6 percent water vapor.

In describing solutions, it is usual to call the component present in the largest amount the **solvent** and the other component(s) the **solute(s)**. For example, when a teaspoon of table sugar is mixed with 1 liter of water, we identify the sugar as the solute and the water as the solvent.

The process of a solute mixing in a solvent is called **dissolving**. To make a solution, a solute must *dissolve* in a solvent; that is, the solute and solvent must form a homogeneous mixture. Whether or not one material dissolves in another is a function of electrical attractions.

Concept Check ✔

What is the solvent in the gaseous solution we call air?

Was this your answer? Nitrogen is the solvent because it is the component present in the greatest quantity.

There is a limit to how much of a given solute can dissolve in a given solvent, as Figure 7.14 illustrates. When you add table sugar to a glass of water, for example, the sugar rapidly dissolves. As you continue to add sugar, however, there comes a point when it no longer dissolves. Instead, it collects at the bottom of the glass, even after stirring. At this point, the water is *saturated* with sugar, meaning the water cannot accept any more sugar. When this happens, we have what is called a **saturated solution**, defined as one in which no more solute can dissolve. A solution that has not reached the limit of solute that will dissolve is called an **unsaturated solution**.

Figure 7.14
A maximum of 200 grams of sucrose dissolves in 100 milliliters of water at 20°C. (a) Mixing 150 grams of sucrose in 100 milliliters of water at 20°C produces an unsaturated solution. (b) Mixing 200 grams of sucrose in 100 milliliters of water at 20°C produces a saturated solution. (c) If 250 grams of sucrose is mixed with 100 milliliters of water at 20°C, 50 grams of sucrose remains undissolved. (As we discuss later, the concentration of a saturated solution varies with temperature.)

(a) 150 g sucrose in 100 mL water at 20°C

(b) 200 g sucrose in 100 mL water at 20°C

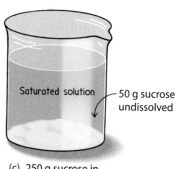

(c) 250 g sucrose in 100 mL water at 20°C

The quantity of solute dissolved in a solution is described in mathematical terms by the solution's **concentration**, which is the amount of solute dissolved per amount of solution:

$$\text{concentration of solution} = \frac{\text{amount of solute}}{\text{amount of solution}}$$

For example, a sucrose–water solution may have a concentration of 1 gram of sucrose for every liter of solution. This can be compared with concentrations of other solutions. A sucrose–water solution containing 2 grams of sucrose per liter of solution, for example, is more *concentrated*, and one containing only 0.5 gram of sucrose per liter of solution is less concentrated, or more *dilute*.

Chemists are often more interested in the number of solute particles in a solution rather than the number of grams of solute. Submicroscopic particles, however, are so very small that the number of them in any observable sample is incredibly large. To get around having to use cumbersome numbers, scientists use a unit called the mole. One **mole** of any type of particle is, by definition, 6.02×10^{23} particles (this superlarge number is about 602 billion trillion):

1 mole = 6.02×10^{23} particles
= 602,000,000,000,000,000,000,000 particles

One mole of pennies, for example, is 6.02×10^{23} pennies, 1 mole of marbles is 6.02×10^{23} marbles, and 1 mole of sucrose molecules is 6.02×10^{23} sucrose molecules.

Even if you've never heard the term *mole* in your life before now, you are already familiar with the basic idea the term is meant to convey, for it's just a shorthand way of saying "six point oh two times ten to the twenty-third." Just as *a couple of* means 2 of something and *a dozen of* means 12 of something, *a mole of* means 6.02×10^{23} of something. It's as simple as that:

- a couple of coconuts = 2 coconuts
- a dozen of donuts = 12 donuts
- a mole of mints = 6.02×10^{23} mints
- a mole of molecules = 6.02×10^{23} molecules

A stack containing 1 mole of pennies would reach a height of 903 quadrillion kilometers, which is roughly equal to the diameter of our Milky Way Galaxy. A mole of marbles would be enough to cover the entire land area of the 50 United States to a depth greater than 4 meters. Sucrose molecules are so small, however, that there are 6.02×10^{23} of them in only 342 grams of sucrose, which is about a cupful. Thus because 342 grams of sucrose contains 6.02×10^{23} molecules of sucrose, we can use our shorthand wording and say that 342 grams of sucrose contains 1 mole of sucrose. As Figure 7.15 shows, therefore, an aqueous solution that has a concentration of 342 grams of sucrose per liter of solution also has a concentration of 6.02×10^{23} sucrose molecules per liter of solution or, by definition, a concentration of 1 mole of sucrose per liter of solution.

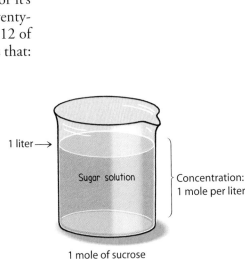

1 liter →

Sugar solution

Concentration: 1 mole per liter

1 mole of sucrose
equals
342 grams of sucrose
equals
6.02×10^{23} molecules of sucrose

Figure 7.15
An aqueous solution of sucrose that has a concentration of 1 mole of sucrose per liter of solution contains 6.02×10^{23} sucrose molecules (342 grams) in every liter of solution.

Calculation Corner: Calculating for Solutions

From the formula for the concentration of a solution, we can derive equations for amount of solute and amount of solution:

$$\text{concentration of solution} = \frac{\text{amount of solute}}{\text{amount of solution}}$$

$$\text{amount of solute} =$$

$$\text{concentration of solution} \times \text{volume of solution}$$

$$\text{amount of solution} = \frac{\text{amount of solute}}{\text{concentration of solution}}$$

In solving for any of these values, the units must always match. If concentration is given in grams per liter, for example, the amount of solute must be in grams and the amount of solution must be in liters.

Note that these equations are set up for calculating amount of *solution* rather than amount of *solvent.* The amount of solution is greater than the amount of solvent because in addition to containing the solvent, the solution also contains the solute. As discussed at the beginning of this section, for example, the volume of an aqueous solution of sucrose depends not only on the volume of water but also on the volume of dissolved sucrose.

Example 1

How much sucrose, in grams, is there in 3 liters of an aqueous solution that has a concentration of 2 grams of sucrose per liter of solution?

Answer 1

This question asks for amount of solute, and so you should use the second of the three formulas given above:

$$\text{amount of solute} = \frac{2\text{ g}}{1\text{ L}} \times 3\text{ L} = 6\text{ g}$$

Example 2

A solution you are using in an experiment has a concentration of 10 grams of solute per liter of solution. If you pour enough of this solution into an empty laboratory flask to make the flask contain 5 grams of the solute, how many liters of the solution have you poured into the flask?

Answer 2

This question asks for amount of solution, and so what you want is the third formula:

$$\text{amount of solution} = \frac{5\text{ g}}{10\text{ g/L}} = 0.5\text{ l}$$

Your Turn

1. At 20°C, a saturated solution of sodium chloride in water has a concentration of about 380 grams of sodium chloride per liter of solution. How much sodium chloride, in grams, is required to make 3 liters of a saturated solution?

2. A student is told to use 20 grams of sodium chloride to make an aqueous solution that has a concentration of 10 grams of sodium chloride per liter of solution. How many liters of solution does she end up with?

The number of grams tells you the *mass* of solute in a given solution, and the number of moles tells you the actual *number* of molecules. Translating a given mass to the number of molecules contained in that mass is something we explore further in Chapter 9.

A common unit of concentration used by chemists is **molarity**, which is the solution's concentration expressed in moles of solute per liter of solution:

$$\text{molarity} = \frac{\text{number of moles of solute}}{\text{liters of solution}}$$

A solution that contains 1 mole of solute per liter of solution has a concentration of 1 *molar*, which is often abbreviated 1 *M*. A more concentrated, 2-molar (2 *M*) solution contains 2 moles of solute per liter of solution.

The difference between referring to the number of molecules of solute and referring to the number of grams of solute can be illustrated by the following question. A saturated aqueous solution of sucrose contains 200 grams of sucrose and 100 grams of water. Which is the solvent: sucrose or water? As shown in Figure 7.16, there are 3.5×10^{23} molecules of sucrose in 200 grams of sucrose but almost 10 times as many molecules of water in 100 grams of water—3.3×10^{24} molecules. As defined earlier, the solvent is the component present in the largest amount, but what do we mean by *amount*? If amount means number of molecules, then water is the solvent. If amount means mass, then sucrose is the solvent. So, the answer depends on how you look at it. From a chemist's point of view, *amount* typically means the number of molecules, and so water is the solvent in this case.

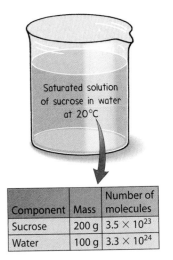

Saturated solution of sucrose in water at 20°C

Component	Mass	Number of molecules
Sucrose	200 g	3.5×10^{23}
Water	100 g	3.3×10^{24}

Figure 7.16
Although 200 grams of sucrose is twice as massive as 100 grams of water, there are about 10 times as many water molecules in 100 grams of water as there are sucrose molecules in 200 grams of sucrose. How can this be? Each water molecule is about 20 times less massive (and smaller) than each sucrose molecule, which means that about 10 times as many water molecules can fit within half the mass.

Concept Check ✔

1. How much sucrose, in moles, is there in 0.5 liter of a 2-molar solution? How many molecules of sucrose is this?
2. Does 1 liter of a 1-molar solution of sucrose in water contain 1 liter of water, less than 1 liter of water, or more than 1 liter of water?

Were these your answers?

1. First you need to understand that 2-molar means 2 moles of sucrose per liter of solution. Then you should multiply concentration by volume to obtain amount of solute:

    (2 moles/L)(0.5 L) = 1 mole

    which is the same as 6.02×10^{23} molecules.
2. The definition of molarity refers to the number of liters of *solution*, not liters of solvent. When sucrose is added to a given volume of water, the volume of the solution increases. So, if 1 mole of sucrose is added to 1 liter of water, the result is more than 1 liter of solution. Therefore, 1 liter of a 1-molar solution requires less than 1 liter of water.

Hands-On Chemistry: Overflowing Sweetness

Just because a solid dissolves in a liquid doesn't mean the solid no longer occupies space.

What You Need

Tall glass, warm water, container larger than the tall glass, 4 tablespoons table sugar

Procedure

① Fill the glass to its brim with the warm water, and then carefully pour all the water into the larger container.

② Add the sugar to the empty glass.

③ Return half of the warm water to the glass and stir to dissolve all the solid.

④ Return the remaining water, and as you get close to the top, ask a friend to predict whether the water level will be less than before, about the same as before, or more than before so that the water spills over the edge of the glass.

If your friend doesn't understand the result, ask him or her what would happen if you had added the sugar to the glass when the glass was full of water.

7.3 Solubility Is a Measure of How Well a Solute Dissolves

The **solubility** of a solute is its ability to dissolve in a solvent. As you might expect, this ability depends in great part on the submicroscopic attractions between solute particles and solvent particles. If a solute has any solubility in a solvent, then that solute is said to be **soluble** in that solvent.

Solubility also depends on attractions between solute particles and attractions between solvent particles. As shown in Figure 7.17, for exam-

Figure 7.17
A sucrose molecule contains many hydrogen–oxygen covalent bonds in which the hydrogen atoms are slightly positive and the oxygen atoms are slightly negative. These dipoles in any given sucrose molecule result in the formation of hydrogen bonds with neighboring sucrose molecules.

Sucrose

ole, there are many polar hydrogen–oxygen bonds in a sugar molecule. Sugar molecules, therefore, can form multiple hydrogen bonds with each other. These hydrogen bonds are strong enough to make sucrose a solid at room temperature and give it a relatively high melting point of 185°C. In order for sucrose to dissolve in water, the water molecules must first pull sucrose molecules away from one another. This puts a limit on the amount of sucrose that can dissolve in water—eventually a point is reached where there are not enough water molecules to separate the sucrose molecules from one another. As was discussed in Section 7.2, this is the point of saturation, and any additional sucrose added to the solution does not dissolve.

When the molecule-to-molecule attractions among solute molecules are comparable to the molecule-to-molecule attractions among solvent molecules, the result can be no practical point of saturation. As shown in Figure 7.18, for example, the hydrogen-bond among water molecules are about as strong as those among ethanol molecules. These two liquids therefore mix together quite well and in just about any proportion. We can even add ethanol to water until the ethanol rather than the water may be considered the solvent. In fact, ethanol and water stick so well to each other that, even after distillation (Section 2.4) of a water–ethanol solution, the purest ethanol we can get is 95 percent. To get 100 percent ethanol takes special procedures.

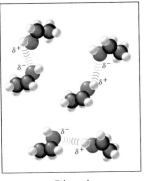

Ethanol

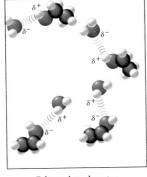

Ethanol and water

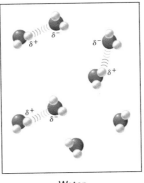

Water

Figure 7.18
Ethanol and water molecules are about the same size, and they both form hydrogen bonds. As a result, ethanol and water readily mix with each other.

A solute that has no practical point of saturation in a given solvent is said to be *infinitely soluble* in that solvent. Ethanol, for example, is infinitely soluble in water. Also, gases are generally infinitely soluble in each other because they can be mixed together in just about any proportion.

Let's now look at the other extreme of solubility, where a solute has very little solubility in a given solvent. An example is oxygen, O_2 in water. In contrast to sucrose, which has a solubility of 200 grams per 100 milliliters of water, only 0.004 gram of oxygen can dissolve in 100 milliliters of water. We can account for oxygen's low solubility in water by noting that the only electrical attractions that occur between oxygen molecules and water molecules are relatively weak dipole–induced dipole attractions. More important, however, is the fact that the stronger attraction of water molecules for one another—through the hydrogen bonds the water molecules form with one another—effectively excludes oxygen molecules from intermingling.

Figure 7.19
Glass is frosted by dissolving its
outer surface in hydrofluoric acid.

Figure 7.20
Is this cup melting or dissolving?

A material that does not dissolve in a solvent to any appreciable extent is said to be **insoluble** in that solvent. There are many substances we consider to be insoluble in water, including sand and glass. Just because a material is not soluble in one solvent, however, does not mean it won't dissolve in another. Sand and glass, for example, are soluble in hydrofluoric acid, HF, which is used to give glass the decorative frosted look shown in Figure 7.19. Also, although Styrofoam is insoluble in water, it is soluble in acetone, a solvent used in fingernail polish remover. Pour a little acetone into a Styrofoam cup, and the acetone soon dissolves the Styrofoam, as you can see in Figure 7.20.

Concept Check ✓

Why isn't sucrose infinitely soluble in water?

Was this your answer? The attraction between two sucrose molecules is much stronger than the attraction between a sucrose molecule and a water molecule. Because of this, sucrose dissolves in water only so long as the number of water molecules far exceeds the number of sucrose molecules. When there are too few water molecules to dissolve any additional sucrose, the solution is saturated.

Solubility Changes with Temperature

You probably know from experience that water-soluble solids usually dissolve better in hot water than in cold water. A highly concentrated solution of sucrose in water, for example, can be made by heating the solution almost to the boiling point. This is how syrups and hard candy are made.

Solubility increases with increasing temperature because hot water molecules have greater kinetic energy and therefore are able to collide with the solid solute more vigorously. The vigorous collisions facilitate the disruption of electrical particle-to-particle attractions in the solid.

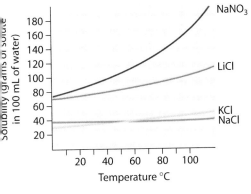

Figure 7.21
The solubility of many water-soluble solids increases with temperature, while the solubility of others is only very slightly affected by temperature.

Although the solubilities of some solid solutes—sucrose, to name just one example—are greatly affected by temperature changes, the solubilities of other solid solutes, such as sodium chloride, are only mildly affected, as Figure 7.21 shows. This difference has to do with a number of factors, including the strength of the chemical bonds in the solute molecules and the way those molecules are packed together.

When a solution saturated at a high temperature is allowed to cool, some of the solute usually comes out of solution and forms what is called a **precipitate**. When this happens, the solute is said to have *precipitated* from the solution. For example, at 100°C the solubility of sodium nitrate, $NaNO_3$, in water is 180 grams per 100 milliliters of water. As we cool this solution, the solubility of $NaNO_3$ decreases as shown in Figure 7.21, and this change in solubility causes some of the dissolved $NaNO_3$ to precipitate (come out of solution). At 20°C, the solubility of $NaNO_3$ is only 87 grams per 100 milliliters of water. So if we cool the 100°C solution to 20°C, 93 grams (180 grams − 87 grams) precipitates, as shown in Figure 7.22.

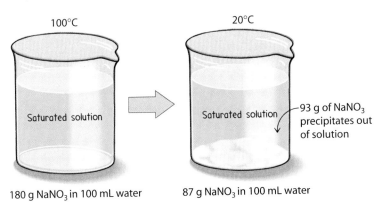

Figure 7.22
The solubility of sodium nitrate is 180 grams per 100 milliliters of water at 100°C but only 87 grams per 100 milliliters at 20°C. Cooling a 100°C saturated solution of $NaNO_3$ to 20°C causes 93 grams of the solute to precipitate.

Gases Are More Soluble at Low Temperatures and High Pressures

In contrast to the solubilities of most solids, the solubilities of gases in liquids *decrease* with increasing temperature, as Table 7.2 on page 218 shows. This is true because with an increase in temperature, the solvent molecules have more kinetic energy. This makes it more difficult for a gaseous solute to stay in solution because the solute molecules are literally being kicked out by the high-energy solvent molecules.

Perhaps you have noticed that warm carbonated beverages go flat faster than cold ones. The higher temperature causes the molecules of carbon dioxide gas to leave the liquid solvent at a higher rate.

Table 7.2

Temperature-Dependent Solubility of Oxygen Gas in Water at a Pressure of 1 Atmosphere

Temperature (°C)	O_2 Solubility (g O_2/L H_2O)
0	0.0141
10	0.0109
20	0.0092
25	0.0083
30	0.0077
35	0.0070
40	0.0065

The solubility of a gas in a liquid also depends on the pressure of the gas immediately above the liquid. In general, a higher gas pressure above the liquid means more of the gas dissolves. A gas at a high pressure has many, many gas particles crammed into a given volume. The "empty" space in an unopened soft drink bottle, for example, is crammed with carbon dioxide molecules in the gaseous phase. With nowhere else to go, many of these molecules dissolve in the liquid, as shown in Figure 7.23. Alternatively, we might say that the great pressure forces the carbon dioxide molecules into solution. When the bottle is opened, the "head" of highly pressurized carbon dioxide gas escapes. Now the gas pressure above the liquid is lower than it was. As a result, the solubility of the carbon dioxide drops and the carbon dioxide molecules once squeezed into the solution begin to escape into the air above the liquid.

The rate at which carbon dioxide molecules leave an opened soft drink is relatively slow. You can increase the rate by pouring in granulated sugar, salt, or sand. The microscopic nooks and crannies on the surface of the grains serve as *nucleation sites* where carbon dioxide bubbles are able to form rapidly and then escape by buoyant forces. Shaking the beverage also increases the surface area of the liquid-to-gas interface, making it easier for the carbon dioxide to escape from the solution. Once the solution is shaken, the rate at which carbon dioxide escapes becomes so great that the beverage froths over. You also increase the rate at which carbon dioxide escapes when you pour the beverage into your mouth, which abounds in nucleation sites. You can feel the resulting tingly sensation.

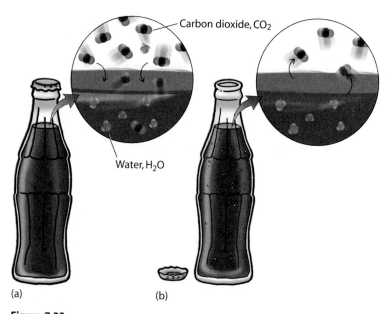

Figure 7.23
(a) The carbon dioxide gas above the liquid in an unopened soft drink bottle consists of many tightly packed carbon dioxide molecules that are forced by pressure into solution. (b) When the bottle is opened, the pressure is released and carbon dioxide molecules originally dissolved in the liquid can escape into the air.

Concept Check ✓

You open two cans of soft drink: one from a warm kitchen shelf, the other from the coldest depths of your refrigerator. Which provides more bubbles in the first gulp you take and why?

Was this your answer? The solubility of carbon dioxide in water decreases with increasing temperature. The warm drink will therefore fizz in your mouth more than does the cold one.

Hands-On Chemistry: Crystal Crazy

If a hot saturated solution is allowed to cool slowly and without disturbance, the solute may stay in solution. The result is a *supersaturated* solution. Supersaturated aqueous solutions of sucrose (table sugar) are fairly easy to make.

What You Need

Cooking pot, water, table sugar, butter knife or chopstick, string, weight (a nut or bolt works well), safety glasses to protect eyes from any hot liquid that may splatter

Procedure

① Fill the pot no more than 1 inch deep with water and heat the water to boiling.

② Lower the heat to medium–low. Slowly pour in sugar while carefully stirring to avoid splattering. Because sugar is very soluble in hot water, be prepared to add a volume of sugar equal to or greater than the volume of water you began with. Continue to add sugar until no more will dissolve even with persistent stirring.

③ Allow the solution to come back to a boil while stirring carefully. This should help dissolve any excess sugar added in step 2. Do not set the burner on high because doing so may make the sugar solution froth up and spill out of the pot. If sugar still doesn't fully dissolve after the solution is brought to a slow boil, add more water 1 teaspoon at a time. If the sugar dissolves after being brought to a slow boil, add more sugar 1 tablespoon at a time. Ideally, you want a boiling-hot sugar solution that is just below saturation, which may be difficult to assess without prior experience.

④ Remove the clear (no undissolved sugar) boiling sugar solution from the heat. Tie some string to the weight and lower the weight into the hot solution. Support the string with a butter knife or chopstick set across the rim of the pot so that the weight does not touch the bottom.

⑤ Leave the mixture undisturbed for about a week, but check it periodically. You will see large sugar crystals, also known as rock candy, form on the string and also along the sides of the pot. The longer you wait, the larger the crystals.

Nonpolar Gases Readily Dissolve in Perfluorocarbons

As was discussed earlier, good solubility can result when the particle-to-particle attractions in a solute are comparable to those in a solvent. This was the case with ethanol and water, and it is also the case with oxygen and certain *perfluorcarbons*, such as perfluorodecalin, which are molecules consisting of only carbon and fluorine atoms. Oxygen and perfluorodecalin molecules are both nonpolar. Because of the large size of the molecules, perfluorodecalin is a liquid at room temperature. Because they are nonpolar, both perfluorodecalin molecules and oxygen molecules experience induced dipole–induced dipole attractions. At room temperature, consequently, a significant amount of oxygen gas is able to dissolve in liquid perfluorodecalin, as is demonstrated by the mouse in Figure 7.24.

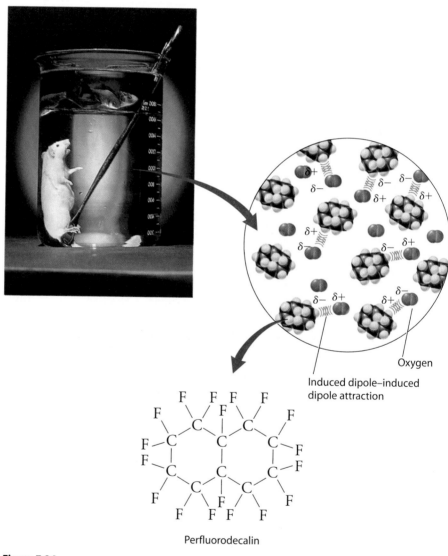

Oxygen

Induced dipole–induced dipole attraction

Perfluorodecalin

Figure 7.24
This mouse is alive and well, inhaling liquid perfluorodecalin saturated with oxygen gas.

Interestingly, a saturated solution of oxygen in a liquid perfluorocarbon contains about 20 percent more oxygen than does the atmosphere we breathe. When this perfluorocarbon solution is inhaled by a human or other animal, the lungs are able to absorb the oxygen in much the same way they absorb it from air. Because liquid perfluorocarbons are as inert as Teflon, which is a solid perfluorocarbon, negative side effects of having these liquids in the lungs are minimal.

Much research is currently being conducted on perfluorocarbons and their potential applications. For example, it is nearly impossible for babies born before seven months of gestation to breathe air. This is because their lungs have yet to develop an inner lining that prevents the moist walls from collapsing and sticking together like wet sheets of plastic food wrap. Researchers have found that premature infants can breathe oxygenated perfluorocarbons quite effectively. Adults may also benefit from inhaling perfluorocarbons because when the liquid is drained from the lungs, it carries with it foreign matter that has accumulated over time. Have you had your lungs cleaned lately?

Another exciting application of perfluorocarbons is their use as a blood substitute. Among the many advantages of *artificial blood* are that it can be stored for long periods of time without deteriorating and that it eliminates the transmission of such diseases as hepatitis and AIDS through blood transfusions. Please note, however, that because of precautionary measures taken by blood banks, our current blood supply is safe from these diseases. For example, the chance of dying from a blood transfusion is only about 1 in 100,000, whereas the chance of dying in a car accident is 2 in 100,000.

The need for a reliable blood substitute arises from frequent blood bank shortages. Currently less than 5 percent of the population donates blood, and this percentage is dropping as demand increases worldwide by about 7.5 million liters each year. The shortfall could become critical sometime in the next 30 years. Because there is still much research needed on perfluorocarbons, donating blood is still a *very* worthwhile thing to do.

7.4 Soap Works by Being Both Polar and Nonpolar

Dirt and grease together make *grime*. Because grime contains many nonpolar components, it is difficult to remove from hands or clothing using just water. To remove most grime, we can use a nonpolar solvent such as turpentine or trichloroethane, which dissolves the grime because of strong induced dipole–induced dipole attractions. Turpentine, also known as a paint thinner, is good for removing the grime left on hands after such activities as changing a car's motor oil. Trichloroethane is the solvent used to "dry clean" clothes—a process whereby dirty clothes are churned in a container full of this nonpolar solvent, which removes the toughest of nonpolar stains without the use of water.

Rather than washing our dirty hands and clothes with nonpolar solvents, however, we have a more pleasant alternative—soap and water. Soap works because soap molecules have both nonpolar and polar properties.

A typical soap molecule has two parts: a long *nonpolar tail* of carbon and hydrogen atoms and a *polar head* containing at least one ionic bond:

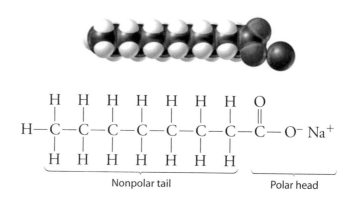

$$H-\overset{\overset{\displaystyle H}{|}}{\underset{\underset{\displaystyle H}{|}}{C}}-\overset{\overset{\displaystyle H}{|}}{\underset{\underset{\displaystyle H}{|}}{C}}-\overset{\overset{\displaystyle H}{|}}{\underset{\underset{\displaystyle H}{|}}{C}}-\overset{\overset{\displaystyle H}{|}}{\underset{\underset{\displaystyle H}{|}}{C}}-\overset{\overset{\displaystyle H}{|}}{\underset{\underset{\displaystyle H}{|}}{C}}-\overset{\overset{\displaystyle H}{|}}{\underset{\underset{\displaystyle H}{|}}{C}}-\overset{\overset{\displaystyle H}{|}}{\underset{\underset{\displaystyle H}{|}}{C}}-\overset{\overset{\displaystyle O}{||}}{C}-O^-\ Na^+$$

$\underbrace{\qquad\qquad\qquad\qquad}_{\text{Nonpolar tail}}\ \underbrace{\qquad\qquad}_{\text{Polar head}}$

Because most of a soap molecule is nonpolar, it attracts nonpolar grime molecules via induced dipole–induced dipole attractions, as Figure 7.25 illustrates. In fact, grime quickly finds itself surrounded in three dimensions by the nonpolar tails of soap molecules. This attraction is usually enough to lift the grime away from the surface being cleaned. With the nonpolar tails facing inward toward the grime, the polar heads are all directed outward, where they are attracted to water molecules by relatively strong ion–dipole attractions. If the water is flowing, the whole conglomeration of grime and soap molecules flows with it, away from your hands or clothes and down the drain.

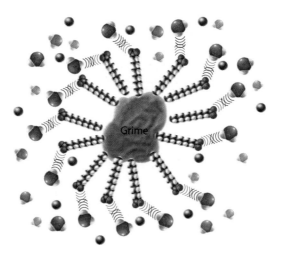

Figure 7.25
Nonpolar grime attracts and is surrounded by the nonpolar tails of soap molecules. The polar heads of the soap molecules are attracted by ion–dipole attractions to water molecules, which carry the soap–grime combination away.

For the past several centuries, soaps have been prepared by treating animal fats with sodium hydroxide, NaOH, also known as caustic lye. In this reaction, which is still used today, each fat molecule is broken down into three *fatty acid* soap molecules and one glycerol molecule:

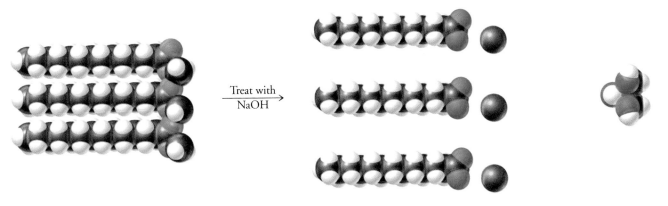

Fat molecule   Three fatty acid soap molecules   Glycerol molecule

Detergents Are Synthetic Soaps

In the 1940s, chemists began developing a class of synthetic soaps, known as *detergents*, that offer several advantages over soaps, such as stronger grease penetration and lower price.

The chemical structure of detergent molecules is similar to that of soap molecules in that both possess a polar head attached to a nonpolar tail. The polar head in a detergent molecule, however, typically consists of either a sulfate, $-OSO_3^-$, or a sulfonate, $-SO_3^-$, group, and the nonpolar tail can have an assortment of structures.

One of the most common sulfate detergents is sodium lauryl sulfate, a main ingredient of many toothpastes. A common sulfonate detergent is sodium dodecyl benzenesulfonate, also known as a linear alkylsulfonate, or LAS. You'll often find this compound in dishwashing liquids. Both these detergents are biodegradable, which means microorganisms can break down the molecules once they are released into the environment.

$$CH_3CH_2CH_2CH_2CH_2CH_2CH_2CH_2CH_2CH_2CH_2CH_2-O-\underset{\underset{O}{\|}}{\overset{\overset{O}{\|}}{S}}-O^-\ Na^+$$

Sodium lauryl sulfate

$$CH_3CH_2CH_2CH_2CH_2CH_2CH_2CH_2CH_2CH_2CH_2CH_2-$$

Sodium dodecyl benzenesulfonate

Concept Check ✓

What type of attractions hold soap or detergent molecules to grime?

Was this your answer? If you haven't yet formulated an answer, why not back up and re-read the question? You've only got four choices: Ion–dipole, dipole–dipole, dipole–induced dipole, and induced dipole–induced dipole. Induced dipole–induced dipole attractions, because the interaction is between two nonpolar entities—the grime and the nonpolar tail of a soap or detergent molecule.

Hard Water Makes Soap Less Effective

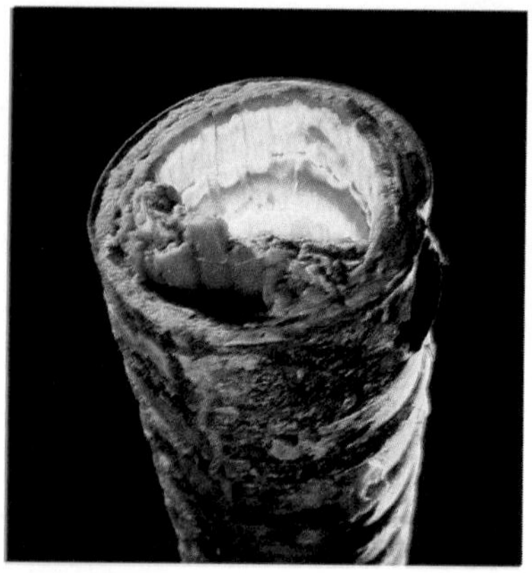

Water containing large amounts of calcium and magnesium ions is said to be *hard water*, and it has many undesirable qualities. For example, when hard water is heated, the calcium and magnesium ions tend to bind with negatively charged ions also found in the water to form solid compounds, like those shown in Figure 7.26, that can clog water heaters and boilers. You'll also find these calcium and magnesium compounds coated on the inside surface of a well-used tea kettle. Don't drink hard water if you have a problem with kidney stones because high intakes of calcium ions can contribute to kidney-stone formation.

Hard water also inhibits the cleansing actions of soaps and, to a lesser extent, detergents. The sodium ions of soap and detergent molecules carry a 1+ charge, and calcium and magnesium ions carry a 2+ charge (note their positions in the periodic table). The negatively charged portion of the polar head of a soap or detergent molecule is more attracted to the double positive charge of calcium and magnesium ions than to the single positive charge of sodium ions. Soap or detergent molecules therefore give up their sodium ions to selectively bind with calcium or magnesium ions:

Soap or detergent molecules bound to calcium or magnesium ions tend to be insoluble in water. As they come out of solution, they form a scum that can appear as a ring around the bathtub. Because the soap or detergent molecules are tied up with calcium and magnesium ions, more of the cleanser must be added to maintain cleaning effectiveness.

Many detergents today contain sodium carbonate, Na_2CO_3, commonly known as washing soda. The calcium and magnesium ions in hard water are more attracted to the carbonate ion with its two negative charges than to a soap or a detergent molecule with its single negative charge. With the calcium and magnesium ions bound to the carbonate ion, as shown in Figure 7.27, the soap or detergent is free to do its job. Because it removes the ions that make water hard, sodium carbonate is known as a *water-softening agent*.

In some homes, the water is so hard that it must be passed through a water-softening unit. In a typical unit, illustrated in Figure 7.28, hard water is passed through a large tank filled with tiny beads of a water-insoluble resin known as an *ion-exchange resin*. The surface of the resin contains many

Figure 7.26
Hard water causes calcium and magnesium compounds to build up on the inner surfaces of water pipes, especially those used to carry hot water.

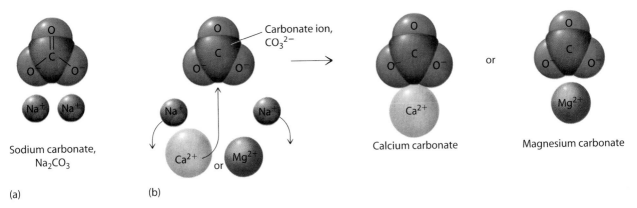

Figure 7.27
(a) Sodium carbonate is added to many detergents as a water-softening agent. (b) The doubly positive calcium and magnesium ions of hard water preferentially bind with the doubly negative carbonate ion, freeing the detergent molecules to do their job.

negatively charged ions bound to positively charged sodium ions. As calcium and magnesium ions pass over the resin, they displace the sodium ions and thereby become bound to the resin. The calcium and magnesium ions are able to do this because their positive charge (2+) is greater than that of the sodium ions (1+). The calcium and magnesium ions therefore have a greater attraction for the negative sites on the resin. The net result is that for every one calcium or magnesium ion that binds, two sodium ions are set loose. In this way, the resin *exchanges* one positively charged ion for another. The water that exits the unit is free of calcium and magnesium ions (but does contain sodium ions in their place).

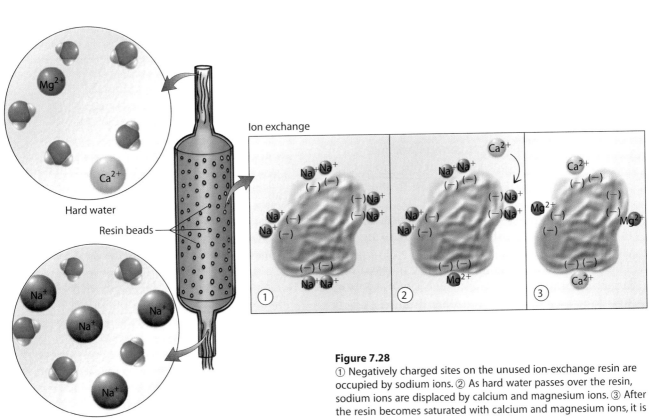

Figure 7.28
① Negatively charged sites on the unused ion-exchange resin are occupied by sodium ions. ② As hard water passes over the resin, sodium ions are displaced by calcium and magnesium ions. ③ After the resin becomes saturated with calcium and magnesium ions, it is no longer effective at softening water.

Eventually, all the sites for calcium and magnesium on the resin are filled, and then the resin needs to be either discarded or recharged. It is recharged by flushing it with a concentrated solution of sodium chloride, NaCl. The abundant sodium ions displace the calcium and magnesium ions (ions are *exchanged* once again), freeing up the binding sites on the resin.

We are now at a point in this textbook where you should have a firm understanding of how subatomic particles make atoms, how atoms make molecules, and how molecules interact with one another through relatively weak attractive electric forces. With this background, you are in a good position to understand and appreciate the real-world applications of chemistry, such as those that were discussed in the final section of this chapter. An important goal of *Conceptual Chemistry* is to give you an understanding of the submicroscopic basis of your macroscopic world. Toward this goal, the next chapter focuses on the macroscopic behavior of water and on how that behavior is determined by the properties of individual water molecules.

Key Terms and Matching Definitions

_____ concentration
_____ dissolving
_____ hydrogen bond
_____ induced dipole
_____ insoluble
_____ molarity
_____ mole
_____ precipitate
_____ saturated solution
_____ solubility
_____ soluble
_____ solute
_____ solvent
_____ unsaturated solution

1. A strong dipole–dipole attraction between a slightly positive hydrogen atom on one molecule and a pair of nonbonding electrons on another molecule.
2. A dipole temporarily created in an otherwise nonpolar molecule, induced by a neighboring charge.
3. The component in a solution present in the largest amount.
4. Any component in a solution that is not the solvent.
5. The process of mixing a solute in a solvent.
6. A solution containing the maximum amount of solute that will dissolve.
7. A solution that will dissolve additional solute if it is added.

8. A quantitative measure of the amount of solute in a solution.
9. 6.02×10^{23} of anything.
10. A unit of concentration equal to the number of moles of a solute per liter of solution.
11. The ability of a solute to dissolve in a given solvent.
12. Capable of dissolving to an appreciable extent in a given solvent.
13. Not capable of dissolving to any appreciable extent in a given solvent.
14. A solute that has come out of solution.

Review Questions

Submicroscopic Particles Electrically Attract One Another

1. What is the primary difference between a chemical bond and an attraction between two molecules?

2. Which is stronger, the ion–dipole attraction or the induced dipole–induced dipole attraction?

3. Why are water molecules attracted to sodium chloride?

4. How are ion–dipole attractions able to break apart ionic bonds, which are relatively strong?

5. Are electrons distributed evenly or unevenly in a polar molecule?

6. What is a hydrogen bond?

7. How are oxygen molecules attracted to water molecules?

8. Are induced dipoles permanent?

9. How can nonpolar atoms induce dipoles in other nonpolar atoms?

10. Why is it difficult to induce a dipole in a fluorine atom?

11. Why is the boiling point of octane, C_8H_{18}, so much higher than the boiling point of methane, CH_4?

A Solution Is a Single-Phase Homogeneous Mixture

12. What happens to the volume of a sugar solution as more sugar is dissolved in it?

13. Why is a ruby gemstone considered to be a solution?

14. Distinguish between a solute and a solvent.

15. What does it mean to say a solution is concentrated?

16. Distinguish between a saturated solution and an unsaturated solution.

17. How is the amount of solute in a solution calculated?

18. Is 1 mole of particles a very large number or a very small number of particles?

Solubility Is a Measure of How Well a Solute Dissolves

19. Why does oxygen have such a low solubility in water?

20. By what means are ethanol and water molecules attracted to each other?

21. What effect does temperature have on the solubility of a solid solute in a liquid solvent?

22. What effect does temperature have on the solubility of a gas solute in a liquid solvent?

23. How are supersaturated solutions made?

24. What does it mean to say that two materials are infinitely soluble in each other?

25. What kind of electrical attraction is responsible for oxygen dissolving in water?

26. What is the relationship between a precipitate and a solute?

27. Why does the solubility of a gas solute in a liquid solvent decrease with increasing temperature?

28. What do oxygen molecules and perfluorodecane molecules have in common?

Soap Works by Being Both Polar and Nonpolar

29. Which portion of a soap molecule is nonpolar?

30. Water and soap are attracted to each other by what type of electrical attraction?

31. Soap and grime are attracted to each other by what type of electrical attraction?

32. What is the difference between a soap and a detergent?

33. What component of hard water makes it hard?

34. Why are soap molecules so attracted to calcium and magnesium ions?

35. Calcium and magnesium ions are more attracted to sodium carbonate than to soap. Why?

Hands-On Chemistry Insights

Circular Rainbows

Paper chromatography was originally developed to separate plant pigments from one another. The separated pigments had different colors, which is how this technique got its name—*chroma* is Latin for "color." Mixtures need not be colored, however, to be separable by chromatography. All that's required is that the components have distinguishable affinities for the moving solvent and the stationary medium, such as paper, through which the solvent passes.

There are many other forms of chromatography besides paper chromatography. In *column chromatography*, the mixture to be separated is loaded at the top of a column of sandlike material. A solvent passing through the column pulls the components of the mixture through the material at different rates. As the purified components drip out the bottom of the column at different times, they can be collected in separate flasks.

In *gas chromatography*, a liquid mixture is injected into a long, narrow tube that has been heated to the point that the liquid mixture becomes a gaseous mixture. Each component of the gaseous mixture travels through the tube at its own rate, which is determined by the affinity that the component has for a stationary medium coating the inner surface of the tube. Gas chromatography can be used to isolate extremely small quantities, which makes it a valuable analytical tool for many purposes, such as drug testing.

Overflowing Sweetness

It can't be emphasized enough that a solute continues to occupy space whether or not it is dissolved in a liquid. The volume of water that spills over the edge of the glass in this activity is the volume of water displaced by the dissolved solid. As sugar dissolves in water, the sugar molecules are merely pulled out of the crystal lattice to become individual entities. Whether it is part of a lattice or free-floating, however, each sugar molecule occupies the same volume.

Crystal Crazy

Interesting crystals can also be made from supersaturated solutions of Epsom salts ($MgSO_4 \cdot 7\,H_2O$) and alum ($KAl(SO_4)_2 \cdot 12\,H_2O$), which is used for pickling and is available in the spice sections of some grocery stores. Crystal shape directly relates to how the ions or molecules of a substance pack together. In fact, substances are often characterized by the shape of the crystals they form. *Crystallography* is the study of mineral crystals and their shapes and structure.

If you try any experiments with Epsom salts or alum, note how different solutes give rise to different crystal shapes.

There are many good books and kits for making crystals. Check out Irene Trimble's book *Crystal Factory*, available from Addison-Wesley at 1-800-238-9682. The Space-Age Crystal-Growing Kit from the Kristal Corporation is also a real winner. Write to Kristal Corporation, 5355 Louie Lane, Reno, NV 89511-1810.

Exercises

1. Why are ion–dipole attractions stronger than dipole–dipole attractions?

2. Chlorine, Cl_2, is a gas at room temperature, but bromine, Br_2, is a liquid. Why?

3. Plastic wrap is made of nonpolar molecules and is able to stick well to polar surfaces, such as glass, by way of dipole–induced dipole attractions. Why does plastic wrap also stick to itself so well?

4. Dipole–induced dipole attractions exist between molecules of water and molecules of gasoline, and yet these two substances do not mix because water has such a strong attraction for itself. Which compound might best help these two substances mix into a single liquid phase:

(a)

(b) $Na^+ \, Cl^-$

(c)

5. Explain why, for these three substances, the solubility in 20°C water goes down as the molecules get larger but the boiling point goes up:

Substance	Boiling point/ Solubility
$CH_3{-}O{\diagup}^H$	65°C infinite
$CH_3CH_2CH_2CH_2{-}O{\diagup}^H$	117°C 8 g/100 mL
$CH_3CH_2CH_2CH_2CH_2{-}O{\diagup}^H$	138°C 2.3 g/100 mL

6. The boiling point of 1,4-butanediol is 230°C. Would you expect this compound to be soluble or insoluble in room-temperature water? Explain.

1,4-Butanediol

7. Based on atomic size, which would you expect to be more soluble in water: helium, He, or nitrogen, N_2?

8. If nitrogen, N_2, were pumped into your lungs at high pressure, what would happen to its solubility in your blood?

9. The air a scuba diver breathes is pressurized to counteract the pressure exerted by the water surrounding the diver's body. Breathing the high-pressure air causes excessive amounts of nitrogen to dissolve in body fluids, especially the blood. If a diver ascends to the surface too rapidly, the excessive nitrogen bubbles out of the body fluids (much like carbon dioxide bubbles out of a soda immediately after the container is opened). This results in a painful and potentially lethal medical condition known as the *bends*. Why does breathing a mixture of helium and oxygen rather than air help divers avoid getting the bends?

10. Why are noble gases infinitely soluble in other noble gases?

11. Describe two ways to tell whether a sugar solution is saturated or not.

12. Which solute in Figure 7.21 has a solubility in water that changes the least with increasing temperature?

13. At 10°C, which is more concentrated: a saturated solution of sodium nitrate, $NaNO_3$, or a saturated solution of sodium chloride, $NaCl$? (See Figure 7.21.)

14. A saturated aqueous solution of compound X has a higher concentration than a saturated aqueous solution of compound Y at the same temperature. Does it follow that compound X is more soluble in water than compound Y is?

15. The volume of many liquid solvents expands with increasing temperature. What happens to the concentration of a solution made with such a solvent as the temperature of the solution is increased?

16. Suggest why salt is insoluble in gasoline. Consider the electrical attractions.

17. Recall from Chapter 3 that the isotopes of an atom differ only in the number of neutrons in the nucleus. Two isotopes of hydrogen are the more common *protium* isotope, which has no neutrons, and the less common *deuterium* isotope, which has one neutron. Either isotope can

be used to make water molecules. Water made with deuterium is known as *heavy water* because each molecule is about 11 percent more massive than water made with protium. Might you also expect the boiling point of heavy water to be about 11 percent greater than the boiling point of regular water? Draw a picture of these two molecules if you need help visualizing the difference between them.

18. Which would you expect to have a higher melting point: sodium chloride, $NaCl$, or aluminum oxide, Al_2O_3? Why?

19. Hydrogen chloride, HCl, is a gas at room temperature. Would you expect this material to be very soluble or not very soluble in water?

20. Would you expect to find more dissolved oxygen in ocean water around the North Pole or tropical ocean water close to the equator? Why?

21. Of the two structures shown below, one is a typical gasoline molecule and the other is a typical motor oil molecule. Which is which? Base your reasoning not on memorization but rather on what you know about electrical attractions between molecules and the various physical properties of gasoline and motor oil.

Structure A

Structure B

22. What is the boiling point of a single water molecule? Why does this question not make sense?

23. Account for the observation that ethanol, C_2H_5OH, dissolves readily in water but dimethyl ether, CH_3OCH_3, which has the same number and kinds of atoms, does not.

Ethanol

Dimethyl ether

24. Why are the melting points of most ionic compounds far higher than the melting points of most covalent compounds?

25. An inventor claims to have developed a perfume that lasts a long time because it doesn't evaporate. Comment on this claim.

26. How necessary is soap for removing salt from your hands? Why?

27. When you set a pot of tap water on the stove to boil, you'll often see bubbles start to form well before boiling temperature is reached. Explain this observation.

28. Fish don't live very long in water that has been boiled and brought back to room temperature. Why?

29. Why might softened water not be good for persons trying to reduce their dietary sodium-ion intake?

Problems

1. How much sucrose, in grams, is there in 5 liters of an aqueous solution of sucrose that has a concentration of 0.5 gram of sucrose per liter of solution?

2. How much sodium chloride, in grams, is needed to make 15 L of a solution that has a concentration of 3.0 grams of sodium chloride per liter of solution?

3. If water is added to 1 mole of sodium chloride in a flask until the volume of the solution is 1 liter, what is the molarity of the solution? What is the molarity when water is added to 2 moles of sodium chloride to make 0.5 liter of solution?

4. A student is told to use 20.0 grams of sodium chloride to make an aqueous solution that has a concentration of 10.0 grams of sodium chloride per liter of solution. Assuming that 20.0 grams of sodium chloride has a volume of 7.5 milliliters, about how much water will she use in making this solution?

Answers to Calculation Corner

Calculating for Solutions

1. Multiply the solution concentration by the solution volume to obtain the amount of solute required:

$$(380 \text{ g/L})(3 \text{ L}) = 1140 \text{ g}$$

2. Divide the amount of solute by the solution concentration to obtain the volume of solution she prepared:

$$\frac{20 \text{ g}}{10 \text{ g/L}} = 2 \text{ L}$$

Suggested Web Sites

http://generalenv.com/
Use *hard water magnets* as a Web-search keyword to find a large number of Web sites, such as this one, that advertise the use of magnetic fields to prevent calcium buildup in plumbing. The proposed mechanism is that the magnetic field facilitates the formation of calcium carbonate crystals in the water rather than on the pipes. Does this method remove calcium from the tap water? How might such a method affect the cleaning abilities of soaps? Explore the related Federal Technology Alert at www.pnl.gov/fta/11_non.htm

http://www.med.umich.edu/liquid/Research.html
Use *perfluorocarbon* as a Web-search keyword and you will find references, most of them technical, to a variety of medical and other uses for liquid perfluorocarbons. The site listed here is that of the Liquid Ventilation Program at the University of Michigan. Scroll to the bottom of the home page for a list of useful links.

http://www.sugar.org/scoop/refine.html
This page sponsored by the Sugar Association takes you on a tour that follows sugar from cane field to table.

Chapter 8
Those Incredible Water Molecules

Hydrogen bond

Macroscopic Consequences of Molecular Stickiness

You are made of water, born into a world of water, and then forevermore dependent on water. You can survive for more than a month without food, but without fresh water you would perish in a matter of days. Little wonder when you consider that water makes up about 60 percent of your body mass. It's the ideal solvent for transporting nutrients through your body and for supporting the countless biochemical reactions that keep you alive. All living organisms we know of depend on water. It is the medium of life on our planet and arguably our most vital natural resource.

Water is so common in our lives that its many unusual properties easily escape our notice. Consider, for example, that water is the only chemical substance on our planet's surface that can be found abundantly in all three phases—solid, liquid, and gas. Another unique property of water is its great resistance to any change in temperature. As a result, the water in you moderates your body temperature just as the oceans moderate global temperatures. Water's resistance to a change in temperature is also why it takes so long for a pot of water to boil and why firewalkers benefit by walking on wet grass before stepping on red-hot coals. Consider also that, unlike most other liquids, which freeze from the bottom up, liquid water freezes from the top down. To the trained eye of a chemist, water is far from a usual substance. Rather, it's downright bizarre and exotic.

Almost all of the amazing properties of water are a consequence of the abilit of water molecules to cling tenaciously to one another by way of electrical attrac tions. Recall that each attraction, called a hydrogen bond, occurs between one of the positively charged hydrogen atoms of one water molecule and the negative charged oxygen atom of another water molecule. In this chapter we explore the physical behavior of water while diving into the details and consequences of the "stickiness" of water molecules. We begin by exploring first the properties of solid water (ice), then those of liquid water, and finally those of gaseous water, also known as water vapor.

8.1 Water Molecules Form an Open Crystalline Structure in Ice

Figure 8.1
A sealed glass jar is broken by the expansion of the freezing water inside.

Experience tells us not to place a sealed glass jar of liquid water in the freezer, for we know that water expands as it freezes. Trapped in the jar, the freezing water expands outward with a force strong enough to shatter the glass into a hazardous mess, or to pop the lid from a jar as shown in Figure 8.1. This expansion occurs because when the water freezes, the water molecules arrange themselves in a six-sided crystalline structure that contain many open spaces. As Figure 8.2 shows, a given number of water molecules in the liquid can get relatively close to one another and so occupy a certain volume. Water molecules in the crystalline structure of ice occupy a greater volume than in liquid water. Consequently, ice is less dense than liquid water, which is why ice floats in water. (Interestingly, the increase in volume that occurs when water freezes is equal to the volume of the ice floating above the liquid water's surface.)

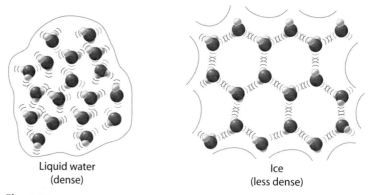

Liquid water
(dense)

Ice
(less dense)

Figure 8.2
Water molecules in the liquid phase are arranged more compactly than water molecules in the solid phase, where they form an open crystalline structure.

This property of expanding upon freezing is quite rare. As Figure 8.3 shows, the atoms or molecules of most frozen solids pack in such a way that the solid phase occupies a smaller volume than the liquid phase.

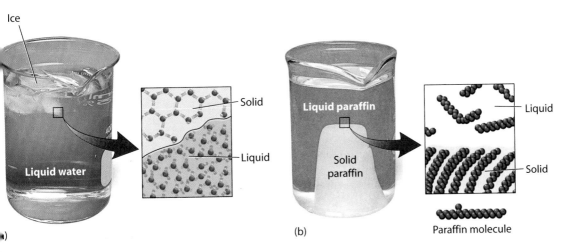

Figure 8.3

(a) Because water expands as it freezes, ice is less dense than liquid water and so floats in the water. (b) Like most other materials, paraffin is denser in its solid phase than in its liquid phase. Solid paraffin thus sinks in liquid paraffin.

Concept Check ✓

Are you interpreting correctly the illustration of water's open crystalline structure shown in Figure 8.2? If you are, you'll be able to answer this question: What's inside one of the open spaces?

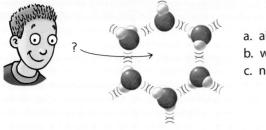

a. air
b. water vapor
c. nothing

Was this your answer? If there were air in the spaces, the illustration would have to show the molecules that make up air, such as O_2 and N_2, which are comparable in size to water molecules. Any water vapor in the spaces would have to be shown as free-roaming water molecules spaced relatively far apart. The open spaces shown here represent nothing but empty space. The answer is c.

The hexagonal crystalline structure of H_2O molecules in ice has some interesting effects. Most snowflakes, like the one in Figure 8.4, share a similar hexagonal shape, which is the microscopic consequence of this molecular geometry.

Applying pressure to ice causes the open spaces to collapse, which transforms a small amount of ice to liquid water. The effect is only temporary because, as soon as the pressure is removed, the liquid water refreezes. The pressure applied by the blades of an ice skater or an ice-sailing craft is sufficient to generate a temporary thin film of liquid water over which the blades glide, as shown in Figure 8.5 on page 234. (Melting is also a result

Figure 8.4
The six-sided geometry of ice crystals gives rise to the six-sided structure of snowflakes.

Figure 8.5
Skating blades cause a temporary melting of the ice, which generates a slippery thin film of liquid water.

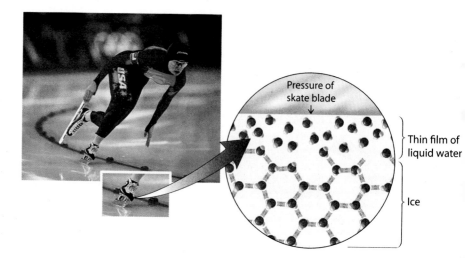

of the heat generated from the friction of the blade.) At temperatures well below 0°C, the water molecules in ice are held so firmly in the hexagonal structure that there is no noticeable melting from an applied pressure. For this reason, skating blades do not glide well in extremely cold weather.

Hands-On Chemistry: A Slice of Ice

The principle behind ice skating can be used to pass a metal wire through a block of ice.

What You Need

Brick-sized block of ice; flat board such as length of 2-by-4 or meterstick; metal wire about 1 meter long (copper works best); heavy weight, such as dumbbell or plastic milk jug filled with water

Procedure

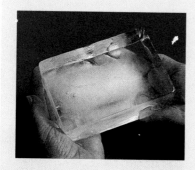

① Make the ice by freezing water in a plastic container of desired shape and size. To make a block that is fairly clear, use water that has just cooled down after being boiled.

② Attach the two ends of the wire to the heavy weight to form a long loop, pass the flat board through the loop, and support the two ends of the board so that the weight hangs free, as in the illustration.

③ Place the block of ice on the board and position the wire loop so that it sits on the top face of the ice. The ice just beneath the wire will melt because of the pressure exerted by the wire. The melted ice above the wire then refreezes, leaving a visible path if the ice is clear.

④ After a few minutes, the wire will have passed all the way through the ice block. Once that has happened, knock the ice with a hammer and see where it breaks. (In the days before refrigerators, this was the way large ice blocks were cut to size for the kitchen icebox.)

What do you suppose would happen if string were used instead of wire?

8.2 Freezing and Melting Go On at the Same Time

As Section 1.7 discussed, *melting* occurs when a substance changes from solid to liquid and *freezing* occurs when a substance changes from liquid to solid. When we view these processes from a molecular perspective, we see that melting and freezing occur simultaneously, as Figure 8.6 illustrates.

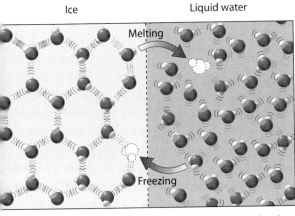

Ice   Liquid water

Melting

Freezing

Vibrating H₂O molecules
fixed in crystalline structure

Slowly moving H₂O molecules
near freezing temperature

Figure 8.6
At 0°C, ice crystals gain and lose water molecules simultaneously.

The temperature 0°C is both the melting temperature and the freezing temperature of water. At this temperature, water molecules in the liquid phase are moving slowly enough that they tend to clump together to form ice crystals—they freeze. At this same temperature, however, water molecules in ice are vibrating with great commotion, much more than they vibrate at colder temperatures. Many thus break loose from the crystalline structure to form liquid water—they melt. Thus melting and freezing occur simultaneously.

For water, 0°C is the special temperature at which the rate of ice formation equals the rate of liquid water formation. In other words, it is the temperature at which the opposite processes of melting and freezing counterbalance each other. This means that if a mixture of ice and liquid water is maintained at exactly 0°C, the two phases are able to coexist indefinitely.

Anytime we want a mixture of ice and liquid water at 0°C to freeze solid, we need to favor the rate of ice formation. This is accomplished by removing heat energy, a process that facilitates the formation of hydrogen bonds. As shown in Figure 8.7, when water molecules come together to form a hydrogen bond, heat energy is released. In order for the molecules to remain hydrogen bonded, this heat energy must be removed—otherwise, the heat energy can be reabsorbed by the molecules, causing them to separate. The removal of heat energy therefore allows hydrogen bonds to remain intact after they have formed. As a result, there is the tendency for the ice crystals to grow.

Conversely, we can get a mixture of ice and liquid water at 0°C to melt completely by adding heat energy. This heat energy goes into breaking apart

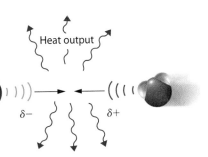

Heat output

$\delta-$ $\delta+$

Figure 8.7
As two water molecules come together to form a hydrogen bond, attractive electric forces cause them to accelerate toward each other. This results in an increase in their kinetic energies (the energy of motion), which is perceived on the macroscopic scale as heat energy.

Figure 8.8
Heat energy must be added in order to separate two water molecules held together by a hydrogen bond. This heat energy causes the molecules to vibrate so rapidly that the hydrogen bond breaks.

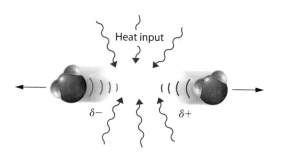

the hydrogen bonds that hold the water molecules together, as shown in Figure 8.8. Because more hydrogen bonds between water molecules are breaking, there is the tendency for the ice crystals to melt.

Solutes tend to inhibit crystal formation. Anytime a solute, such as salt or sugar, is added to water, the solute molecules take up space, as you learned in Section 7.2. When a solute is added to a mixture of ice and liquid water at 0°C, the solute molecules effectively decrease the number of liquid water molecules at the solid–liquid interface, as Figure 8.9 illustrates. With fewer liquid water molecules available to join the ice crystals, the rate of ice formation decreases. Because ice is a relatively pure form of water, the number of molecules moving from the solid phase to the liquid phase is not affected by the presence of solute. The net result is that the rate at which water molecules leave the solid phase is greater than the rate at which they enter the solid phase. This imbalance can be compensated for by decreasing the temperature to below 0°C. At lower temperatures, water molecules in the liquid phase move more slowly and have an easier time coalescing. Thus the rate of crystal formation is increased.

In general, adding anything to water lowers the freezing point. Antifreeze is a practical application of this process. The salting of icy roads is another.

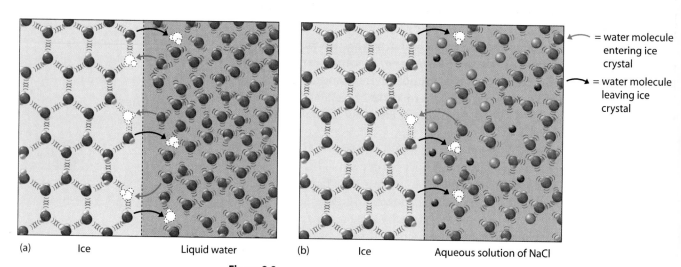

(a) Ice   Liquid water   (b) Ice   Aqueous solution of NaCl

= water molecule entering ice crystal

= water molecule leaving ice crystal

Figure 8.9
(a) In a mixture of ice and liquid water at 0°C, the number of H_2O molecules entering the solid phase is equal to the number of H_2O molecules entering the liquid phase. (b) Adding a solute, such as sodium chloride, decreases the number of H_2O molecules entering the solid phase because now there are fewer liquid H_2O molecules at the interface.

oncept Check ✓

On a day with normal traffic, a certain parking lot has cars entering and leaving at the same rate. If the traffic in the streets around the lot were suddenly to change so that about half of it was trucks and limousines too large to park in the lot, what would happen to the rate at which cars enter the lot? What would happen to the number of cars parked in the lot if this situation persisted for a couple of hours? How is this scenario analogous to what happens when a solute is added to a mixture of ice and liquid water at 0°C?

Were these your answers? With fewer cars on the streets, the rate at which cars enter the lot decreases. The rate at which cars leave the lot, however, initially stays the same. Eventually, fewer empted spaces get filled, and there is an overall decrease in the number of cars parked in the lot. This scenario is analogous to the ice–water case because the solute particles (trucks and limousines) lower the number of liquid water molecules (incoming cars) in contact with the ice (parking lot), thereby diminishing the rate at which water molecules (cars) enter the ice (parking lot). Freezing is thus deterred (fewer cars enter the lot), while melting continues unabated (cars leave the lot at the same rate).

Water Is Densest at 4°C

When the temperature of a substance is increased, its molecules vibrate faster and, on average, move farther apart. The result is that the substance expands. With few exceptions, all phases of matter—solids, liquids, and gases—expand when heated and contract when cooled. In many cases, these changes in volume are not very noticeable, but with careful observation you can usually detect them. Telephone wires, for instance, are longer and sag more on a hot summer day than on a cold winter day. Metal lids on glass jars can often be loosened by heating them under hot water. If one part of a piece of glass is heated or cooled more rapidly than adjacent parts, the expansion or contraction that results may break the glass.

Within any given phase, water also expands with increasing temperature and contracts with decreasing temperature. This is true of all three phases—ice, liquid water, and water vapor. For liquid water at near-freezing temperatures, however, there is an exception.

Liquid water at 0°C can flow just like any other liquid, but at 0°C the temperature is cold enough that microscopic crystals of ice are still able to form. These crystals slightly "bloat" the liquid water's volume, as shown in Figure 8.10. As the temperature is increased to above 0°C, more and more of the crystals collapse, and as a result the volume of the liquid water *decreases*.

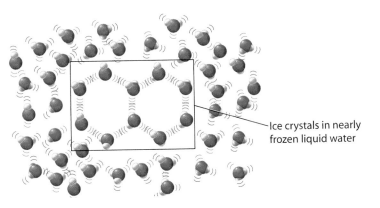

Ice crystals in nearly frozen liquid water

Figure 8.10
Within a few degrees of 0°C, liquid water contains crystals of ice. The open structure of these crystals makes the volume of the water slightly greater than it would be without the crystals.

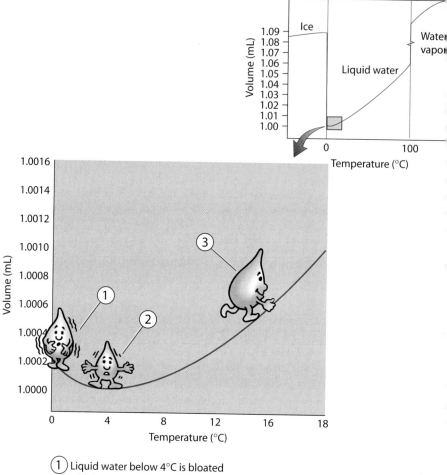

Figure 8.11
Between 0°C and 4°C, the volume of liquid water decreases as the temperature increases. Above 4°C, water behaves the way all other substances do: its volume increases as its temperature increases. The volumes shown here are for a 1-gram sample.

(1) Liquid water below 4°C is bloated with ice crystals.

(2) Upon warming, the crystals collapse, resulting in a smaller volume for the liquid water.

(3) Above 4°C, liquid water expands as it is heated because of greater molecular motion.

Figure 8.11 shows that between 0°C and 4°C liquid water *contracts* when its temperature is raised. This contraction, however, continues only up to 4°C. As near-freezing water is heated, there is a simultaneous tendency for the water to expand due to greater molecular motion. Between 0°C and 4°C, the decrease in volume caused by collapsing ice crystals is greater than the increase in volume caused by the faster-moving molecules. As a result, the water volume continues to decrease. At temperatures just above 4°C, expansion overrides contraction because most of the ice crystals have collapsed.

So, because of the effect of collapsing microscopic ice crystals, liquid water has its smallest volume and thus its greatest density at 4°C. (Recall from Section 1.8 that *density* is the amount of mass contained in a sample of anything divided by the volume of the sample.) By definition, 1 gram of pure liquid water at this temperature has a volume of 1.0000 milliliter. As seen in Figure 8.11, 1 gram of liquid water at 0°C has an only slightly larger volume of 1.0002 milliliters. By comparison, 1 gram of ice at 0°C has a vol-

me of 1.0870 milliliters. As can be seen in the small graph on the right in
figure 8.11, the volume of 1 gram of ice stays above 1.08 milliliters even
below 0°C, meaning that even when ice is cooled to temperatures well
below freezing, it is still always less dense than liquid water.

Although liquid water at 4°C is only slightly more dense than liquid
water at 0°C, this small difference is of great importance in nature. Consider that if water were densest at its freezing point, as is true of most other
liquids, the coldest water in a pond would settle to the bottom and the
pond would freeze from the bottom up, destroying living organisms in winter months. Fortunately this does not happen. As winter comes on and the
temperature of the water drops, its density also drops. The entire volume of
water in the pond does not cool all at once, however. Surface water cools
first because it is in direct contact with the cold air. Being cooler than the
underlying water, this surface water is denser and so sinks, with warmer
water rising to replace it. That new batch of surface water then cools to the
air temperature, gets denser as it does so, and sinks, only to be replaced by
warmer water that cools. This process continues on and on until the entire
body of water has been cooled to 4°C. Then, if the air temperature remains
below 4°C, the surface water also cools to below 4°C. This surface water
does not sink, however, because at this colder temperature it is now *less*
dense than the water below it. Thus cooler less-dense water says on the surface, where it can cool further, eventually reach 0°C, and turn to ice. While
this ice forms at the surface, the organisms that require a liquid environment are happily swimming below the ice in liquid water at a "warm" 4°C,
as Figure 8.12 illustrates.

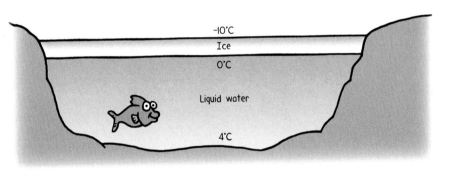

Figure. 8.12
As water cools to 4°C, it sinks. Then, as water at the surface is cooled to below 4°C, it floats on top and can freeze. Only after surface ice forms can temperatures lower than 4°C extend down into the pond. This does not happen very readily, however, because surface ice insulates the liquid water from the cold air.

An important effect of the vertical movement of water is the creation of
vertical currents that, to the benefit of organisms living in the water, transport oxygen-rich surface water to the bottom and nutrient-rich bottom
water to the surface. Marine biologists refer to this vertical cycling of water
and nutrients as *upwelling*.

Very deep bodies of fresh water are not ice-covered even in the coldest
of winters. This is because, as noted above, all the water must be cooled to
4°C before the temperature of the surface water can drop below 4°C. For
deep water, the winter is not long enough for this to occur.

If only some of the water in a pond is 4°C, this water lies on the bottom. Because of water's ability to resist changes in temperature (Section
8.6) and its poor ability to conduct heat, the bottom of deep bodies of
water in cold regions is a constant 4°C year round.

Concept Check ✓

What was the precise temperature at the bottom of Lake Michigan on New Year's Eve in 1901?

Was this your answer? If a body of water has 4°C water in it, then the temperature at the bottom of that body of water is 4°C, for the same reason that rocks are at the bottom. Both 4°C water and rocks are denser than water at any other temperature. If the body of water is deep and in a region of short summers, as is the case for Lake Michigan, the water at the bottom is 4°C year round.

8.3 The Behavior of Liquid Water Is the Result of the Stickiness of Water Molecules

In this section, we explore how water molecules in the liquid phase interact with one another via **cohesive forces**, which are forces of attraction between molecules of a single substance. For water, the cohesive forces are hydrogen bonds. We also explore how water molecules interact with other polar materials, such as glass, through **adhesive forces**, forces of attraction between molecules of two *different* substances.

Cohesive and adhesive forces involving water are dynamic. It is not one set of water molecules, for example, that holds a droplet of water to the side of a glass. Rather, the billions and billions of molecules in the droplet all take turns binding with the glass surface. Keep this in mind as you read this section and examine its illustrations, which, though informative, are merely freeze-frame depictions.

The Surface of Liquid Water Behaves like an Elastic Film

Gently lay a dry paper clip on the surface of some still water. If you're careful enough, the clip will rest on the surface, as shown in Figure 8.13. How can this be? Don't paper clips normally sink in water?

First, you should be aware that the paper clip is not floating *in* the water as a boat floats. Rather, the clip is resting *on* the water surface. The closeup view in Figure 8.13 reveals that the clip is indeed resting on the surface. The slight depression in the surface is caused by the weight of the clip, which pushes down on the water much like the weight of a child pushes down on

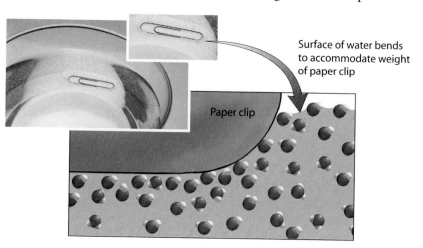

Surface of water bends to accommodate weight of paper clip

Paper clip

Figure 8.13
A paper clip rests on water, pushing the surface down slightly but not sinking.

Figure 8.14
A molecule at the surface is pulled only sideways and downward by neighboring molecules. A molecule beneath the surface is pulled equally in all directions.

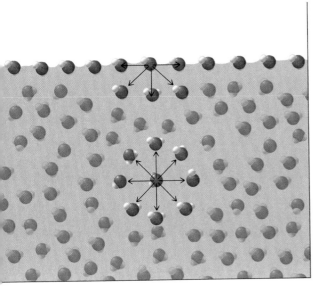

a trampoline. This elastic tendency found at the surface of a liquid, such as water, is known as **surface tension**.

Surface tension is caused by hydrogen bonds. As shown in Figure 8.14, beneath the surface, each water molecule is attracted in every direction by neighboring molecules, with the result that there is no tendency to be pulled in any preferred direction. A water molecule on the surface, however, is pulled only by neighbors to each side and those below; there is no pull upward. The combined effect of these molecular attractions is thus to pull the molecule from the surface into the liquid. This tendency to pull surface molecules into the liquid causes the surface to become as small as possible, and the surface behaves as if it were tightened into an elastic film. Lightweight objects that don't pierce the surface, such as a paper clip, are thus able to rest on the surface.

Surface tension accounts for the spherical shape of liquid drops. Raindrops, drops of oil, and falling drops of molten metal are all spherical because their surfaces tend to contract and this contraction forces each drop into the shape having the least surface area. This is a sphere, the geometric figure that has the least surface area for a given volume. In the weightless environment of an orbiting space shuttle, a blob of water takes on a spherical shape naturally, as is shown in Figure 8.15. Back on the Earth, the mist and dewdrops on spider webs or on the downy leaves of plants are also spherical, except for the distortions caused by the force of gravity.

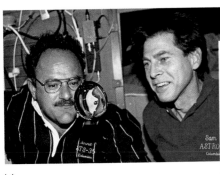

(a)

(b)

Figure 8.15
(a) The surface tension in a freely floating blob of water causes the water to take on a spherical shape. (b) Small blobs of water resting on a surface would also be spheres if it weren't for the force of gravity, which squashes them into beads.

Figure 8.16
Soap or detergent molecules align themselves at the surface of liquid water so that their nonpolar tails can escape the polarity of the water. This arrangement disrupts the water's surface tension.

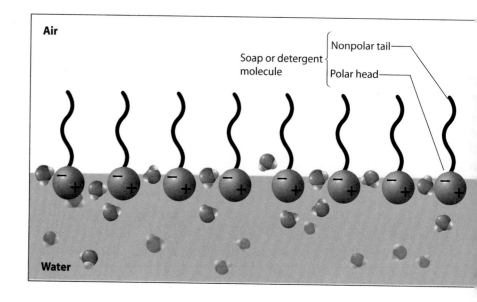

Surface tension is greater in water than in other common liquids because the hydrogen bonds in water are so relatively strong. The surface tension in water is dramatically reduced, however, by the addition of soap or detergent. Figure 8.16 shows that soap or detergent molecules tend to aggregate at the surface of water, with their nonpolar tails sticking out away from the water. At the surface, these molecules interfere with the hydrogen bonds between neighboring water molecules, thereby reducing the surface tension. Get a metal paper clip floating on the surface of some water and then carefully touch the water a few centimeters away with the corner of a bar of wet soap or a dab of liquid detergent. You will be amazed at how quickly the surface tension is destroyed.

It is the strong surface tension of water that prevents it from wetting materials with nonpolar surfaces, such as waxy leaves, umbrellas, and freshly polished automobiles. Rather than wetting (spreading out evenly), the water beads. This is good if the idea is to keep water away. If we want to clean, however, the idea is to get the object as wet as possible. This is another way in which soaps and detergents assist in cleaning, as Figure 8.17 illustrates. By destroying water's surface tension, they enhance its ability to wet. The nonpolar grime on dirty fabrics and dishes, for example, is penetrated by the water more rapidly, and cleaning is more efficient.

Figure 8.17
(a) Water beads on a surface that is clean and dry. (b) On a plate smeared with a thin film of detergent, water spreads evenly because the detergent has upset the water's surface tension.

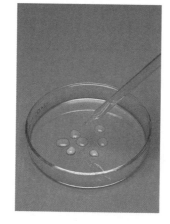

(a)

(b)

apillary Action Results from the Interplay
f Adhesive and Cohesive Forces

ecause glass is a polar substance, there are adhesive forces between glass and
vater. These adhesive forces are relatively strong, and the many water mole-
ules adjacent to the inner surface of a glass container compete to interact
vith the glass. They do so to the point of climbing up the inner surface of
he glass above the water surface. Take a close look at the tube of colored
vater in Figure 8.18, and you'll see that the water is curved up the sides of
he glass. We call the curving of the water surface (or the surface of any other
iquid) at the interface between it and its container a **meniscus**.

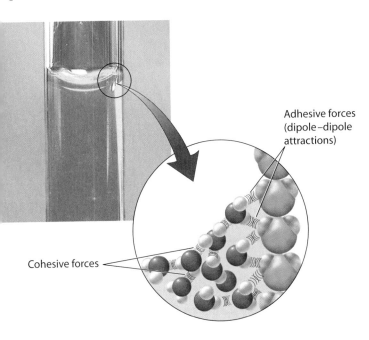

Adhesive forces
(dipole–dipole
attractions)

Cohesive forces

Figure 8.18
Adhesive forces between water and
glass cause water molecules to creep
up the sides of the glass, forming a
meniscus.

Figure 8.19 illustrates what happens when a small-diameter glass tube
is placed in water. ① Adhesive forces initially cause a relatively steep meniscus. ② As soon as the meniscus forms, the attractive cohesive forces among
water molecules respond to the steepness by acting to minimize the surface
area of the meniscus. The result is that the water level in the tube rises. ③
Adhesive forces then cause the formation of another steep meniscus. ④ This
is followed by the action of cohesive forces, which cause the steep meniscus
to be "filled in." This cycle is repeated until the upward adhesive force equals
the weight of the raised water in the tube. This rise in the liquid due to the
interplay of adhesive and cohesive forces is called **capillary action**.

Figure 8.19
Water is drawn up a narrow glass
tube by an interplay of adhesive and
cohesive forces.

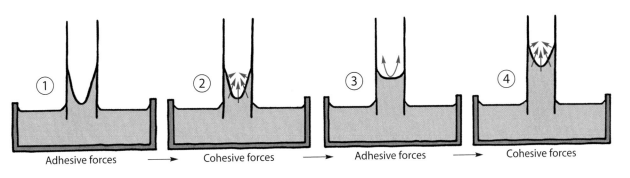

Adhesive forces ⟶ Cohesive forces ⟶ Adhesive forces ⟶ Cohesive forces

In a tube that has an internal diameter of about 0.5 millimeter, the water rises slightly higher than 5 centimeters. In a tube that has a smaller diameter, there is a smaller volume and less weight for a given height, and the water rises much higher, as Figure 8.20 illustrates.

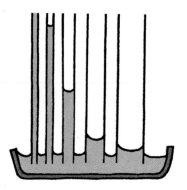

Figure 8.20
Capillary tubes. The smaller the diameter of the tube, the higher the liquid rises in it.

We see capillary action at work in many phenomena. If a paintbrush is dipped into water, the water rises into the narrow spaces between the bristles by capillary action. Hang your hair in the bathtub, and water seeps up to your scalp in the same way. This is how oil moves up a lamp wick and how water moves up a bath towel when one end hangs in water. Dip one end of a lump of sugar in coffee, and the entire lump is quickly wet. The capillary action occurring between soil particles is important in bringing water to the roots of plants.

Concept Check ✓

An astronaut sticks a narrow glass tube into a blob of floating water while in orbit, and the tube fills with water. Why?

Was this your answer? Capillary action causes the water to be drawn into the tube. In the free-fall environment of an orbiting spacecraft, however, there is no downward force to stop this capillary action. As a result, the water continues to creep along the inner surface of the tube until the tube is filled (and then starts spurting out the end).

8.4 Water Molecules Move Freely Between the Liquid and Gaseous Phases

Molecules of water in the liquid phase move about in all directions at different speeds. Some of these molecules may reach the liquid surface moving fast enough to overcome the hydrogen bonds and escape into the gaseous phase. As presented in Section 1.7, this process of molecules converting from the liquid phase to the gaseous phase is called *evaporation* (also sometimes called *vaporization*). The opposite of evaporation is *condensation*—the changing of a gas to a liquid. At the surface of any body of water, there is a constant exchange of molecules from one phase to the other, as illustrated in Figure 8.21.

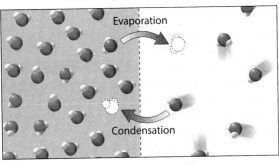
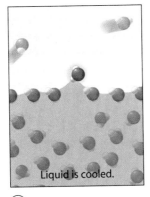

Figure 8.21
The exchange of molecules at the interface between liquid and gaseous water.

Evaporation

Condensation

Liquid water   Water vapor

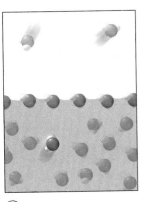
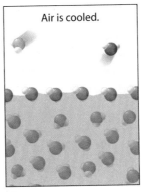

Air is cooled.

Liquid is cooled.

Figure 8.22
Evaporation is a cooling process.

① Liquid water molecule having sufficient kinetic energy to overcome surface hydrogen bonding approaches liquid surface.

② Liquid water cooled as it loses this high-speed water molecule.

③ Molecule enters gaseous phase, having lost kinetic energy in overcoming hydrogen bonding at the liquid surface. Air is cooled as it collects these slowly moving gaseous particles.

As evaporating molecules leave the liquid phase, they take their kinetic energy with them. This has the effect of lowering the average kinetic energy of all the molecules remaining in the liquid, and the liquid is cooled, as Figure 8.22 shows. Evaporation also has a cooling effect on the surrounding air because liquid molecules that escape into the gaseous phase are moving relatively slowly compared to other molecules in the air. This makes sense when you consider that these newly arrived molecules lost a fair amount of their kinetic energy in overcoming the hydrogen bonds of the liquid phase. Adding these slower molecules to the surrounding air effectively decreases the average kinetic energy of all the molecules making up the air, and the air is cooled. So no matter how you look at it, evaporation is a cooling process. Figure 8.23 shows a useful application of this cooling effect.

As the water cools, the rate of evaporation slows down because fewer molecules have sufficient energy to escape the hydrogen bonds of the liquid phase. A higher rate of evaporation can be maintained if the water is in contact with a relatively warm surface, such as your skin. Body heat then flows from you into the water. In this way the water maintains a higher temperature and evaporation continues at a relatively high rate. This is why you feel cool as you dry off after getting wet—you are losing body heat to the energy-requiring process of evaporation.

Figure 8.23
When wet, the cloth covering on this canteen promotes cooling. As the faster-moving water molecules evaporate from the wet cloth, its temperature decreases and cools the metal, which in turn cools the water in the canteen.

(b)

Figure 8.24
(a) Dogs have no sweat glands (except between their toes). They cool themselves by panting. In this way evaporation occurs in the mouth and the bronchial tract.
(b) Pigs have no sweat glands and therefore cannot cool by the evaporation of perspiration. Instead, they wallow in the mud to cool themselves.

(a)

When your body overheats, your sweat glands produce perspiration. The evaporation of perspiration cools you and helps maintain a stable body temperature. Many animals, such as the ones in Figure 8.24, do not have sweat glands and must cool themselves by other means.

Concept Check ✓

If water were less "sticky," would you be cooled more or less by its evaporation?

Was this your answer? Water molecules leave the liquid phase only when they have enough kinetic energy to overcome hydrogen bonding. If hydrogen bonding were not so strong, then at a given temperature, more molecules in the liquid phase would have sufficient kinetic energy to escape into the gaseous phase, carrying heat away from the liquid. The cooling power of evaporating water would therefore be greater. This is why less "sticky" substances, such as rubbing alcohol, have a noticeably greater cooling effect as they evaporate.

Warm water evaporates, but so does cool water. The only difference is that cool water evaporates at a slower rate. Even frozen water "evaporates." This form of evaporation, in which molecules jump directly from the solid phase to the gaseous phase, is called **sublimation**. Because water molecules are so firmly held in the solid phase, frozen water does not release molecules

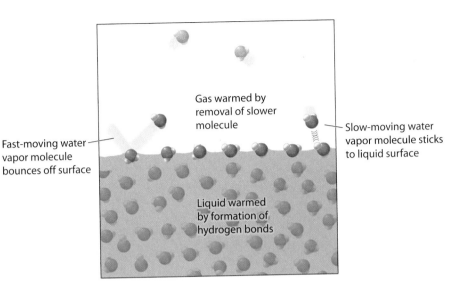

Figure 8.25
Condensation is a warming process.

Gas warmed by removal of slower molecule

Fast-moving water vapor molecule bounces off surface

Slow-moving water vapor molecule sticks to liquid surface

Liquid warmed by formation of hydrogen bonds

into the gaseous phase as readily as liquid water does. Sublimation, however, does account for the loss of significant portions of snow and ice, especially on sunny, dry mountain tops. It's also why ice cubes left in the freezer for a long time tend to get smaller.

At the surface of any body of water, there is condensation as well as evaporation, as Figure 8.21 indicates. Condensation occurs as slow-moving water vapor molecules collide with and stick to the surface of a body of liquid water. Fast-moving water vapor molecules tend to bounce off each other or off the liquid surface, losing little of their kinetic energy. Only the slowest gas molecules condense into the liquid phase, as Figure 8.25 illustrates. As this happens, energy is released as hydrogen bonds are formed. This energy is absorbed by the liquid and increases its temperature. Condensation involves the removal of slower-moving water vapor molecules from the gaseous phase. The average kinetic energy of the remaining water vapor molecules is therefore increased, which means that the water vapor is warmer. So no matter how you look at it, condensation is a warming process.

A dramatic example of the warming that results from condensation is the energy given up by water vapor when it condenses—a painful experience if it condenses on you. That's why a burn from 100°C water vapor is much more damaging than a burn from 100°C liquid water; the water vapor gives up considerable energy when it condenses to a liquid and wets the skin. This energy release by condensation is utilized in heating systems, such as the household radiator shown in Figure 8.26.

The water vapor in our atmosphere also gives up energy as it condenses. This is the energy source for many weather systems, such as hurricanes, which derive much of their energy from the condensation of water vapor contained in humid tropical air, as Figure 8.27 on page 248 illustrates. The formation of 1 inch of rain over an area of 1 square mile yields the energy equivalent of about 32,000 tons of exploded dynamite.

After you take a shower, even a cold one, you are warmed by the heat energy released as the water vapor in the shower stall condenses. You quickly

Figure 8.26
Heat is given up by water vapor when the vapor condenses inside the radiator.

Figure 8.27
As it condenses, the water vapor in humid tropical air releases ample quantities of heat. Continued condensation can sometimes lead to powerful storm systems, such as hurricanes.

Figure 8.28
If you're chilly outside the shower stall, step back inside and be warmed by the condensation of the excess water vapor there.

sense the difference if you step out of the stall, as the chilly guy in Figure 8.28 is finding out. Away from the moisture, net evaporation takes place quickly and you feel chilly. When you remain in the shower stall, the warming effect of condensation counteracts the cooling effect of evaporation. If as much moisture condenses as evaporates, you feel no change in body temperature. If condensation exceeds evaporation, you are warmed. If evaporation exceeds condensation, you are cooled. So now you know why you can dry yourself with a towel much more comfortably if you remain in the shower area. To dry yourself thoroughly, finish the job in a less moist area.

Spend a July afternoon in dry Tucson or Las Vegas, and you'll soon notice that the evaporation rate is appreciably greater than the condensation rate. The result of this pronounced evaporation is a much cooler feeling than you would experience in a same-temperature July afternoon in New York City or New Orleans. In these humid locations, condensation outpaces evaporation, and you feel the warming effect as water vapor in the air condenses on your skin.

Concept Check ✔

If the water level in a dish of water remains unchanged from one day to the next, can you conclude that no evaporation or condensation is taking place?

Was this your answer? Not at all, for there is much activity taking place at the molecular level. Both evaporation and condensation occur continuously and simultaneously. The fact that the water level remains constant indicates equal rates of evaporation and condensation—the number of H_2O molecules leaving the liquid surface by evaporation is equal to the number entering the liquid by condensation.

Boiling Is Evaporation Beneath a Liquid Surface

When liquid water is heated to a sufficiently high temperature, bubbles of water vapor form beneath the surface, as we saw in Section 1.7. These bubbles are buoyed to the surface, where they escape, and we say the liquid is *boiling*. As shown in Figure 8.29, bubbles can form only when the pressure of the vapor inside them is equal to or greater than the pressure exerted by

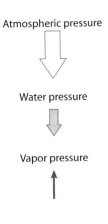

Atmospheric pressure

Water pressure

Vapor pressure

Figure 8.29
Boiling occurs when water molecules are moving fast enough to generate bubbles of water vapor beneath the surface of the liquid.

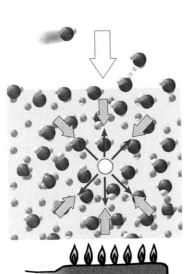

① As liquid water is heated, molecules gain enough energy to evaporate beneath the surface, forming bubbles of water vapor.

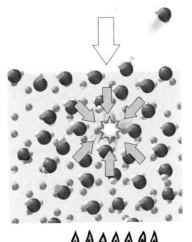

② Before the boiling point is reached, the pressure of the water vapor inside the bubbles is less than the sum of atmospheric pressure plus water pressure. As a result, the bubbles of water vapor collapse.

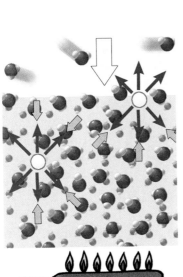

③ At the boiling point, the pressure of the water vapor inside the bubbles equals or exceeds the sum of atmospheric pressure plus water pressure. As a result, the bubbles of water vapor are buoyed to the surface and escape.

④ We see this evaporation as boiling.

Figure 8.30
The tight lid of a pressure cooker holds pressurized vapor above the water surface, and this inhibits boiling. In this way, the boiling temperature of the water is increased. Any food placed in this hotter water cooks more quickly than food placed in water boiling at 100°C.

the surrounding water, which is also pressed down upon by the atmosphere above. At the boiling point of the liquid, the pressure inside the bubbles equals or exceeds the combined pressure of the surrounding water and the atmosphere. At lower temperatures, the pressure inside the bubbles is not enough, and the surrounding pressure collapses any bubbles that form.

At what point boiling begins depends not only on temperature but also on pressure. As atmospheric pressure increases, the vapor molecules inside any bubbles that form must move faster in order to exert enough pressure from inside the bubble to counteract the additional atmospheric pressure. So increasing the pressure exerted on the surface of a liquid raises its boiling point. A cooking application of this effect of increased pressure is shown in Figure 8.30.

Conversely, lowered atmospheric pressure (as at high altitudes) decreases the boiling point of the liquid, as Figure 8.31 illustrates. In Denver, Colorado, the Mile-High City, for example, water boils at 95°C instead of the 100°C boiling temperature at sea level. If you try to cook food in boiling water that is cooler than 100°C, you must wait a longer time for proper cooking. A three-minute boiled egg in Denver is runny and undercooked. If the temperature of the boiling water were very low, food would not cook at all. As the German mountaineer Heinrich Harrer noted in his book *Seven Years in Tibet*, at an altitude of 4500 meters (15,000 feet) or higher, you can sip a cup of boiling tea without any danger of burning your mouth.

Figure 8.31
The boiling point of water (as well as other liquids) decreases with increasing altitude.

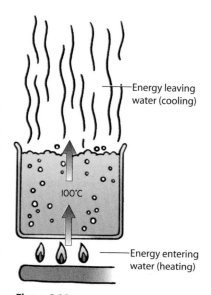

Figure 8.32
Heating warms the water from below, and boiling cools it from above. The net result is a constant temperature for the water.

Boiling, like evaporation, is a cooling process. At first thought, this may seem surprising—perhaps because we usually associate boiling with heating. But heating water is one thing; boiling it is another. As shown in Figure 8.32, boiling water is cooled by boiling as fast as it is heated by the energy from the heat source. So, boiling water remains at a constant temperature. If cooling did not take place, continued application of heat to a pot of boiling water would raise its temperature. The reason the pressure cooker in Figure 8.30 reaches higher temperatures is because boiling is forestalled by increased pressure, which in effect prevents cooling.

Concept Check ✓

Is boiling a form of evaporation or is evaporation a form of boiling?

Was this your answer? Boiling is evaporation that takes place beneath the surface of a liquid.

A simple experiment that dramatically shows the cooling effect of evaporation and boiling consists of a shallow dish of room-temperature water in a vacuum jar. When the pressure in the jar is slowly reduced by a vacuum pump, the water starts to boil. The boiling process takes heat away from the water, which consequently cools. As the pressure is further reduced, more and more of the slower-moving liquid molecules boil away. Continued boiling results in a lowering of the temperature until the freezing point of approximately 0°C is reached. Continued cooling by boiling causes ice to form over the surface of the bubbling water. Boiling and freezing take place at the same time! The frozen bubbles of boiling water in Figure 8.33 are a remarkable sight.

Spray some drops of coffee into a vacuum chamber, and they, too, boil until they freeze. Even after they are frozen, the water molecules continue to evaporate into the vacuum until all that is left to be seen are little crystals of coffee solids. This is how freeze-dried coffee is made. The low temperature of this process tends to keep the chemical structure of the coffee solids from changing. When hot water is added, much of the original flavor of the coffee is retained.

The refrigerator also employs the cooling effect of boiling. A liquid that has a low boiling point is pumped into the coils inside the refrigerator, where it boils (evaporates) and draws heat from the food stored there. The gas with its added energy is directed outside the refrigerator to coils located in the back, appropriately called condensation coils, where heat is given off to the air as the gas condenses to a liquid. A motor pumps the fluid through the system as it undergoes the cyclic process of vaporization and condensation. The next time you're near a refrigerator, place your hand near the condensation coils in the back and you'll feel the heat that has been extracted from inside.

An air conditioner employs the same principle, pumping heat energy from inside a building to outside. Turn the air conditioner around so that cold air is pumped to the outside, and the air conditioner becomes a type of heater known as a heat pump.

Figure 8.33
In a vacuum, water can freeze and boil at the same time.

8.5 It Takes a Lot of Energy to Change the Temperature of Liquid Water

Have you ever noticed that some foods stay hot much longer than others? The filling of a hot apple pie can burn your tongue while the crust will not, even when the pie has just been taken out of the oven. A piece of toast may be comfortably eaten a few seconds after coming from a hot toaster, whereas you must wait several minutes before eating hot soup.

Figure 8.34
It takes only 0.451 joule of heat to raise the temperature of 1 gram of iron by 1 C°. A 1-gram sample of water, by contrast, requires a whopping 4.184 joules for the same temperature change.

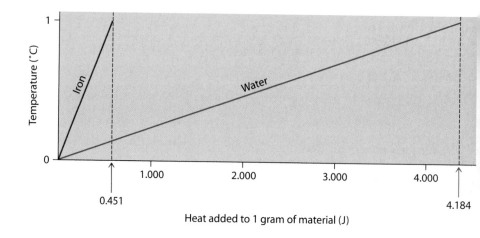

Heat added to 1 gram of material (J)

Different substances have different capacities for storing heat energy. This is because different materials absorb energy in different ways. The added energy may increase the jiggling motion of molecules, which raises the temperature, or it may pull apart the attractions among molecules and therefore go into potential energy, which does not raise the temperature. Generally there is a combination of the two ways.

It takes 4.184 joules of energy to raise the temperature of 1 gram of liquid water by 1°C. As you can see in Figure 8.34, it takes only about one-ninth as much energy to raise the temperature of 1 gram of iron by the same amount. In other words, water absorbs more heat than iron for the same change in temperature. We say water has a higher **specific heat capacity** (sometimes shortened to *specific heat*), defined as the quantity of heat required to change the temperature of 1 gram of the substance by 1°C.

We can think of specific heat capacity as thermal inertia. As you learned in Section 1.4, *inertia* is a term used in physics to signify the resistance of an object to a change in its state of motion. Specific heat capacity is like a thermal inertia because it signifies the resistance of a substance to a change in temperature. Each substance has its own characteristic specific heat capacity, which may be used to assist in identification. Some typical values are given in Table 8.1.

Table 8.1

Specific Heat Capacities for Some Common Materials

Material	Specific Heat Capacity (J/g · C°)
Ammonia, NH_3	4.70
Liquid water, H_2O	4.184
Ethylene glycol, $C_2H_6O_2$ (antifreeze)	2.42
Ice, H_2O	2.01
Water vapor, H_2O	2.0
Aluminum, Al	0.90
Iron, Fe	0.451
Silver, Ag	0.24
Gold, Au	0.13

Guess why water has such a high specific heat capacity. Once again, the answer is hydrogen bonds. When heat is applied to water, much of the heat is consumed in breaking hydrogen bonds. Broken hydrogen bonds are a form of potential energy (just as two magnets pulled apart are a form of potential energy). Much of the heat added to water, therefore, is stored as this potential energy. Consequently, less heat is available to increase the kinetic energy of the water molecules. Since temperature is a measure of kinetic energy, we find that as water is heated, its temperature rises slowly. By the same token, when water is cooled, its temperature drops slowly—as the kinetic energy decreases, molecules slow down and more hydrogen bonds are able to re-form. This in turn releases heat that helps to maintain the temperature.

Concept Check ✓

Hydrogen bonds are not broken as heat is applied to ice (providing the ice doesn't melt) or water vapor. Would you therefore expect ice and water vapor to have specific heat capacities that are greater or less than that of liquid water?

Was this your answer? As Table 8.1 shows, the specific heat capacities of ice and water vapor are about half that of liquid water. Only liquid water has a remarkable specific heat capacity. This is because the liquid phase is the only phase in which hydrogen bonds are continually breaking and re-forming.

Global Climates Are Influenced by Water's High Specific Heat Capacity

The tendency of liquid water to resist changes in temperature improves the climate in many places. For example, notice the high latitude of Europe in Figure 8.35. If water did not have a high specific heat capacity, the countries of Europe would be as cold as the northeastern regions of Canada, for

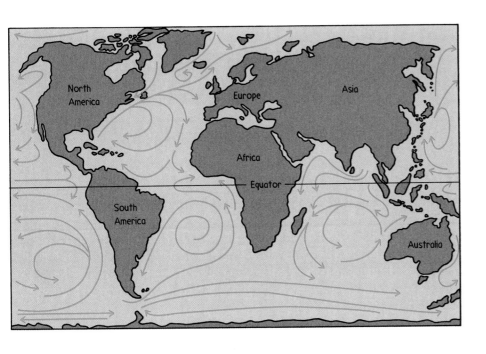

Figure 8.35
Many ocean currents, shown in blue, distribute heat from the warmer equatorial regions to the colder polar regions.

Calculation Corner: How Heat Changes Temperature

Heat must be applied to increase the temperature of a material. Conversely, heat must be withdrawn from a material in order to decrease its temperature. We can calculate the amount of heat required for a given temperature change from the equation

heat = specific heat capacity × mass
                        × temperature change

We can use this formula for any material provided there is no change of phase over the course of the temperature change. The value of the temperature change is obtained by subtracting the initial temperature T_i from the final temperature T_f.

Temperature change = $T_f - T_i$

Example 1
How much heat is required to increase the temperature of 1.00 gram of liquid water from an initial temperature of 30.0°C to a final temperature of 40.0°C?

Answer 1
The temperature change is $T_f - T_i = 40.0°C - 30.0°C = +10.0\ C°$. To find the amount of heat needed for this temperature change, multiply this positive temperature change by the water's specific heat capacity and mass:

$$\text{heat} = (4.184\ \text{J/g} \cdot C°)(1.00\ \text{g})(+10.0\ C°)$$
$$= 41.8\ \text{J}$$

The temperature decrease that occurs when heat is removed from a material is indicated by a negative sign, as is shown in the next example.

Example 2
A glass containing 10.0 grams of water at an initial temperature of 25.0°C is placed in a refrigerator. How much heat does the refrigerator remove from the water as the water is brought to a final temperature of 10.0°C?

Answer 2
The temperature change is $T_f - T_i = 10.0°C - 25.0°C = -15.0\ C°$. To find the heat removed, multiply this negative temperature change by the water's specific heat capacity and mass:

$$\text{heat} = (4.184\ \text{J/g} \cdot C°)(10.0\ \text{g})(-15.0\ C°)$$
$$= -628\ \text{J}$$

Your Turn

1. A residential water heater raises the temperature of 100,000 grams of liquid water (about 26 gallons) from 25.0°C to 55.0°C. How much heat was applied?

2. How much heat must be extracted from a 10.0-gram ice cube (specific heat capacity = 2.01 J/g · C°) in order to bring its temperature from a chilly −10.0°C to an even chillier −30.0°C?

both Europe and Canada get about the same amount of sunlight per square kilometer of surface area. An ocean current carries warm water northeast from the Caribbean. The water holds much of its heat long enough to reach the North Atlantic off the coast of Europe, where it then cools. The energy released, 4.184 joules per Celsius degree for each gram of water that cools, is carried by the westerly winds (winds that blow west to east) over the European continent.

The winds in the latitudes of North America are westerly. On the western coast of the continent, therefore, air moves from the Pacific Ocean to the land. Because of water's high specific heat capacity, ocean temperatures do not vary much from summer to winter. In winter, the water warms the air, which is then blown eastward over the coastal regions. In summer, the water cools the air and the coastal regions are cooled. On the eastern coast of the continent, the temperature-moderating effects of the Atlantic Ocean are significant, but because the winds blow from the west—over land—temperature ranges in the east are much greater than in the west. San Francisco, for example, is warmer in winter and cooler in summer than Washington, D.C., which is at about the same latitude.

Islands and peninsulas, because they are more or less surrounded by water, do not have the extremes of temperatures observed in the interior of a continent. The high summer temperatures and low winter temperatures common in Manitoba and the Dakotas, for example, are largely due to the absence of large bodies of water. Europeans, islanders, and people living near ocean air currents should be glad that water has such a high specific heat capacity.

Hands-On Chemistry: Racing Temperatures

This activity is a qualitative measure of the specific heat capacity of two common kitchen ingredients: rice and salt.

What You Need

Uncooked rice, table salt, 1-cup measuring cup, aluminum foil, baking sheet, two identical ceramic coffee mugs, thermometer (optional)

Procedure

1. Tear off two pieces of foil, each about half the size of the baking sheet. Place them side by side on the baking sheet.

2. Measure out 1 cup of rice and pour onto one of the foil sheets. Measure out 1 cup of salt and pour onto the other foil sheet.

3. Heat the rice and salt for 10 minutes in an oven preheated to 250°C, then pour the rice into one of the mugs and the salt into the other.

4. Use a thermometer to note which comes out of the oven at the higher temperature and which cools down faster. If you don't have a thermometer, leave the heated rice and salt on the aluminum foil and judge their cooling rates by cautious touch.

Which has the higher specific heat capacity? Why does the heated rice adhere to the sides of the mug?

Concept Check ✔

Which has a higher specific heat capacity, water or sand?

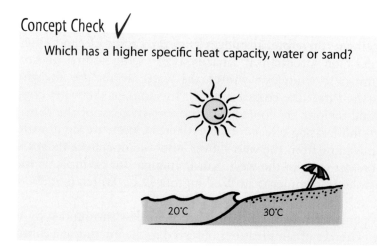

Was this your answer? As suggested by the illustration, the temperature of water increases less than the temperature of sand in the same sunlight. Water therefore has the higher specific heat capacity. Those who visit the beach frequently know that beach sand quickly turns hot on a sunny day while the water remains relatively cool. At night, however, the sand feels quite cool while the water's temperature feels about the same as it was during the day.

8.6 A Phase Change Requires the Input or Output of Energy

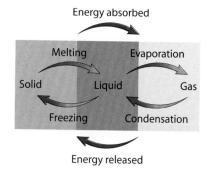

Figure 8.36
Energy changes with change of phase.

Any phase change involves the breaking or forming of molecular attractions. A substance changing from a solid to a liquid to a gas, for example, involves the breaking of molecular attractions. Phase changes in this direction therefore require the input of energy. Conversely, a substance changing from a gas to a liquid to a solid involves the forming of molecular attractions. Phase changes in this direction therefore result in the release of energy. Both these directions are summarized in Figure 8.36.

Consider a 1-gram piece of ice at −50°C put on a stove to heat. A thermometer in the container reveals a slow increase in temperature up to 0°C, as shown in Figure 8.37. At 0°C, the temperature stops rising, even though heat is still being added, for now all the added heat goes into melting the 0° ice, as indicated in Figure 8.38. This process of melting 1 gram of ice requires 335 joules. Only when all the ice has melted does the temperature begin to rise again. Then for every 4.184 joules absorbed, the water increases its temperature by 1 C° until the boiling temperature, 100°C, is reached. At

Figure 8.37
A graph showing the heat energy involved in converting 1 gram of ice initially at −50°C to water vapor. The horizontal portions of the graph represent regions of constant temperature.

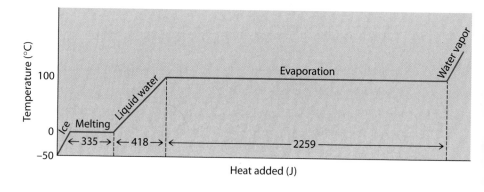

100°C, the temperature again stops rising even though heat is still being added, for now all the added heat is going into evaporating the liquid water to water vapor. The water must absorb a stunning 2259 joules of heat to evaporate all the liquid water. Finally, when all the liquid water has become vapor at 100°C, the temperature begins to rise once again and continues to rise as long as heat is added.

Notice in Figure 8.37 that the amounts of heat energy required to melt ice (335 joules per gram) and evaporate liquid water (2259 joules per gram) are the same amounts released when the phase changes are in the opposite direction. The processes are reversible.

Figure 8.38
Add heat to melting ice and there is no change in temperature. The heat is consumed in breaking hydrogen bonds.

Concept Check ✓

From Figure 8.37, deduce how much energy (in joules) is transferred when 1 gram of
  a. water vapor at 100°C condenses to liquid water at 100°C.
  b. liquid water at 100°C cools to liquid water at 0°C.
  c. liquid water at 0°C freezes to ice at 0°C.
  d. water vapor at 100°C turns to ice at 0°C.

Were these your answers?
a. 2259 joules   b. 418 joules   c. 335 joules
d. 3012 joules (2259 joules + 418 joules + 335 joules)

The amount of heat energy required to change a solid to a liquid is called the **heat of melting**, and the amount of heat energy released when a liquid freezes is called the **heat of freezing**. Water has a heat of melting of +335 joules per gram. The positive sign indicates that this is the amount of heat energy that must be *added to* ice to melt it. Water's heat of freezing is −335 joules per gram. The negative sign indicates that this is the amount of heat energy that is *released* from liquid water as it freezes—the same amount that was required to melt it.

The amount of heat energy required to change a liquid to a gas is called the **heat of vaporization**. For water, this is +2259 joules per gram. The amount of heat energy released when a gas condenses is called the **heat of condensation**. For water, this is −2259 joules per gram. These values are high relative to the heats of vaporization and condensation for most other substances. This is due to the relatively strong hydrogen bonds between water molecules that must be broken or formed during these processes.

Concept Check ✓

Can you add heat to ice without melting it?

Was this your answer? A common misconception is that ice cannot have a temperature lower than 0°C. In fact, ice can have any temperature below 0°C, down to absolute zero, −273°C. Adding heat to ice below 0°C raises its temperature—say from −200°C to −100°C. As long as its temperature stays below 0°C, the ice does not melt.

Figure 8.39
Water extinguishes a flame by wetting but also by absorbing much of the heat that the fire needs to sustain itself.

Figure 8.40
Tracy Suchocki walks with wetted bare feet across red-hot wood coals without harm.

Although water vapor at 100°C and liquid water at 100°C have the same temperature, the vapor contains an additional 2259 joules per gram of potential energy because the molecules are relatively far apart from one another. As the molecules bind together in the liquid phase, this 2259 joules per gram is released to the surroundings in the form of heat. In other words, the potential energy of the far-apart water vapor molecules transforms to heat as the molecules get closer together. This is like the potential energy of two attracting magnets separated from each other; when released, their potential energy is converted first to kinetic energy and then to heat as the magnets strike each other.

Water's high heat of vaporization allows you to *briefly* touch your *wetted* finger to a hot skillet or hot stove without harm. You can even touch it a few times in succession *as long as your finger remains wet.* This is because energy that ordinarily would go into burning your finger goes instead into changing the phase of the moisture on your finger from liquid to vapor. You can judge the hotness of a clothes iron in the same way—with a *wet* finger.

The firefighters in Figure 8.39 know that certain types of flames are best extinguished with a fine mist of water rather than a steady stream. The fine mist readily turns to water vapor and in doing so quickly absorbs heat energy and cools the burning material.

Water's high heat of vaporization makes walking barefooted on red-hot coals more comfortable, as shown in Figure 8.40. When your feet are wet, either from perspiration or because you are stepping off of wet grass, much

Figure 8.41
What remarkable properties of water can you find in this photograph?

of the heat from the coals is absorbed by the water and not by your skin. (Firewalking also relies on the fact that wood is a poor conductor of heat, even when it is in the form of red-hot coals.)

Many of the properties of water we have explored in this chapter at the molecular level are nicely summarized in the scene shown in Figure 8.41. First, notice that the massive bear is supported by the floating ice. The ice floats because hydrogen bonds hold the H_2O molecules in the ice together in an open crystalline structure that makes the ice less dense than the liquid water. Because so much energy is required both to melt ice and to evaporate liquid water, most of the Arctic ice, which builds up primarily from snowfall, remains in the solid phase throughout the year. Where the seawater is in contact with the ice, the temperature is lower than 0°C because salts dissolved in the seawater inhibit the formation of ice crystals and thereby lower the freezing point of the seawater. The high specific heat capacity of the Arctic ocean beneath the bear moderates the Arctic climate. It gets cold in the Arctic in winter, yes, but not as cold as it gets in Antarctica, where the specific heat capacity of the mile-thick ice is only half as great as that of the liquid water that predominates in the Arctic. Covered by a lower specific heat capacity material, Antarctica experiences much greater extremes in temperature than the Arctic.

The main focus of this chapter was the physical behavior of water molecules. In the previous chapter, the focus was the physical behavior of molecules and ions in general. For the next several chapters, we shift our attention to the chemical behavior of molecules and ions, which change their fundamental identities as they chemically react with one another.

Key Terms and Matching Definitions

_____ adhesive force
_____ capillary action
_____ cohesive force
_____ heat of condensation
_____ heat of freezing
_____ heat of melting
_____ heat of vaporization
_____ meniscus
_____ specific heat capacity
_____ sublimation
_____ surface tension

1. An attractive force between two identical molecules.
2. An attractive force between molecules of two different substances.
3. The elastic tendency found at the surface of a liquid.
4. The curving of the surface of a liquid at the interface between the liquid surface and its container.
5. The rising of liquid into a small vertical space due to the interplay of cohesive and adhesive forces.
6. The process of a material transforming from a solid to a gas.
7. The quantity of heat required to change the temperature of 1 gram of a substance by 1 Celsius degree.
8. The heat energy absorbed by a substance as it transforms from solid to liquid.
9. The heat energy released by a substance as it transforms from liquid to solid.
10. The heat energy absorbed by a substance as it transforms from liquid to gas.
11. The energy released by a substance as it transforms from gas to liquid.

Review Questions

Water Molecules Form an Open Crystalline Structure in Ice

1. What accounts for ice being less dense than water?

2. What is inside one of the open spaces of an ice crystal?

3. What happens to ice when great pressure is applied to it?

Freezing and Melting Go On at the Same Time

4. How is it possible for a substance to melt and freeze at the same time?

5. What is released when a hydrogen bond forms between two water molecules?

6. Why does extracting heat from a mixture of ice and liquid water at 0°C increase the rate of ice formation?

7. Why does adding heat to a mixture of ice and liquid water at 0°C increase the rate of water formation?

8. Why does water not freeze at 0°C when either ions or molecules other than H_2O are present?

9. Is the density of near-freezing water, which contains ice crystals, greater or less than the density of liquid water containing no ice crystals?

10. When the temperature of 0°C liquid water is increased slightly, does the water undergo a net expansion or a net contraction?

11. What happens to the amount of molecular motion in water, no matter what its phase, when its temperature is increased?

12. At what temperature do the competing effects of contraction and expansion produce the smallest volume for liquid water?

13. Why does ice form at the surface of a body of water instead of at the bottom?

The Behavior of Liquid Water Is the Result of the Stickiness of Water Molecules

14. What is the difference between cohesive forces and adhesive forces?

15. In what direction is a water molecule on the surface not pulled?

16. Why do liquids in which the molecular interactions are strong have greater surface tension than those in which the molecular interactions are weak?

17. Does liquid water rise higher in a narrow tube or a wide tube?

18. What determines the height that liquid water rises by capillary action?

Water Molecules Move Freely Between the Liquid and Gaseous Phases

9. Do all the molecules in a liquid have about the same speed?

20. Why is evaporation a cooling process? What does evaporation cool?

21. What phases are involved in sublimation?

22. Why is condensation a warming process? What does condensation warm?

23. Why is a burn from water vapor at 100°C more damaging than a burn from liquid water at the same temperature?

24. Why do we feel uncomfortably warm on a hot, humid day?

25. Is it the pressure on the food or the higher temperature that cooks food faster in a pressure cooker?

26. What condition permits liquid water to boil at a temperature below 100°C?

It Takes a Lot of Energy to Change the Temperature of Liquid Water

27. Why does liquid water have such a high specific heat capacity?

28. Is it easy or difficult to change the temperature of a substance that has a low specific heat capacity?

29. Does a substance that heats up quickly have a high or a low specific heat capacity?

30. How does the specific heat capacity of liquid water compare with the specific heat capacities of other common materials?

31. Northeastern Canada and much of Europe receive about the same amount of sunlight per unit surface area. Why then is Europe generally warmer in winter?

32. Why is the temperature fairly constant on islands and peninsulas?

A Phase Change Requires the Input or Output of Energy

33. When liquid water freezes, is heat released to the surroundings or absorbed from the surroundings?

34. Why doesn't the temperature of melting ice rise as the ice is heated?

35. How much heat is needed to melt 1 gram of ice? Give your answer in joules.

36. Is the food compartment in a refrigerator cooled by evaporation or condensation of the refrigerating fluid?

37. Why is it important that your finger be wet when you touch it briefly to a hot clothes iron?

38. Why does it take so much more energy to boil 10 grams of liquid water than to melt 10 grams of ice?

Hands-On Chemistry Insights

A Slice of Ice

Liquid water normally contains an appreciable amount of dissolved air. As the water freezes, this air comes out of solution and forms bubbles that can make the ice cloudy. Interestingly, liquid water in an ice tray begins to freeze along the perimeter of each cube. The dissolved gases are thus pushed inward toward the center of each cube, where freezing occurs last. This is why an ice cube is typically clear on its perimeter and cloudy in the middle. Water that has just been boiled has only small amounts of dissolved air, which is why it can be used to create fairly clear ice cubes.

It's interesting to consider this activity in light of Section 8.7. Note that changes in phase are occurring as the ice melts below the wire and the liquid water refreezes above. When the liquid water immediately above the wire refreezes, it gives up energy. How much? Enough to melt an equal amount of ice immediately under the wire. This energy must be conducted through the wire. Hence this demonstration requires that the wire be an excellent conductor of heat. String is a poor conductor of heat, which is why it does not work as a substitute for metal wire.

Ice skaters know that the sharper their blades, the easier it is for them to glide. A sharper blade has a smaller surface area in contact with the ice and is thus able to apply a greater pressure. Similarly, a thin wire is able to slice through a block of ice more quickly than a thick wire. A thin wire, however, is also weaker and so might not be able to hold a heavy weight without breaking.

Racing Temperatures

The first piece of evidence that the salt has a lower specific heat capacity is that it has a higher temperature when you take your samples out of the oven. The second piece of evidence is that, despite this initially higher temperature, the salt cools faster than the rice. One reason rice has the higher specific heat capacity is that each grain contains a fair amount of moisture. When you heat the rice, much of this moisture is released. Moisture continues to be released even after you take the rice out of the oven, which is why the grains adhere to the mug.

Some people exploit rice's ability to absorb moisture by placing grains of rice in their salt shakers. The rice absorbs any moisture that would otherwise cause the salt crystals to clump together. Most commercial salt contains water-absorbing silicates that achieve the same purpose. You can see these silicates as you try to dissolve commercial salt in water—the cloudiness you see is not from the salt but from the insoluble silicates.

You can put the high specific heat capacity of rice to practical use, either keeping warm on cold evenings or soothing painful cramps. Fill a clean sock three-quarters full with rice. Tie the open end closed with a string (don't use metal wire!) and cook in the microwave for a couple of minutes. (Don't use a conventional oven!!) The moisture in the grains becomes apparent when you take the sock out of the oven—the released moisture has made the sock slightly damp. Wrap the sock around your neck for instant gratification. Need a neck cooler? Store the rice-filled sock in the freezer. The moisture in the rice stays cold for a long time. These devices make great homemade gifts when a fancy fabric is used in place of the sock and a mild fragrance is added.

Exercises

1. Like water, hydrogen fluoride, HF, and ammonia, NH_3, have relatively high boiling points. Explain.

2. Ice floats in room-temperature water, but does it float in boiling water? Why or why not?

3. As an ice cube floating in a glass of water melts, what happens to the water level?

4. How does the combined volume of the billions and billions of hexagonal open spaces in the crystals in a piece of ice compare with the portion of the ice that floats above the water line?

5. Why is it important to protect water pipes in your home from freezing?

6. What happens to the freezing temperature of a solution of table salt in water as the solution becomes more concentrated?

7. Why does adding heat to an ice–water mixture decrease the rate of ice formation?

8. Suppose liquid water is used in a thermometer instead of mercury. If the temperature is initially 4°C and then changes, why can't the thermometer indicate whether the temperature is rising or falling?

9. Which graph most accurately represents the density of liquid water plotted against temperature:

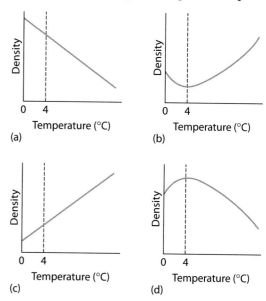

10. If cooling occurred at the bottom of a pond instead of at the surface, would a lake freeze from the bottom up? Explain.

11. Unlike fresh water, ocean water contracts as it cools to its freezing point, which is about −18°C. Why?

12. The polar ice cap that rests over the Arctic Ocean gets thicker each winter. Does it grow from above or below? Explain.

13. Consider a lake in which the water is uniformly 10°C. What happens to the oxygen-rich surface water as it cools to 4°C? What concurrently happens to the nutrient-rich deeper water?

14. Why are polar oceans far more fertile in autumn?

15. Nutrient-rich water tends to be murky. Why does tropical water tend to be so clear?

16. Capillary action causes water to climb up the internal walls of narrow glass tubes. Why does the water not climb as high when the glass tube is wider?

17. Mercury forms a convex meniscus with glass rather than the concave meniscus shown in Figure 8.18. What does this tell you about the cohesive forces between mercury atoms versus the adhesive forces between mercury atoms and glass? Which forces are stronger?

Convex meniscus   Concave meniscus

18. Can a glass be filled to above its brim with water without the water spilling over the edge? Try it and see. Explain your observations.

19. Would you expect the surface tension of water to increase or decrease with temperature? Defend your answer.

20. Dip a paper clip into water and then slowly pull it upward to the point where it is nearly free from the surface. You'll find that for a short distance, the water is brought up with the metal. Are these adhesive or cohesive forces at work?

21. Why does water bead on a freshly waxed surface?

22. Water coming out of volcanic sea vents at the bottom of the ocean can reach temperatures in excess of 300°C without boiling. Explain.

23. You can determine wind direction by wetting your finger and holding it up in the air. Explain.

24. Why does blowing over hot soup cool the soup?

25. Why will wrapping a bottle in a wet cloth produce a cooler bottle than placing the bottle in a bucket of cold water?

26. Could you cook an egg in water boiling in a vacuum? Explain.

27. An inventor friend proposes a design of cookware that will allow water to boil at a temperature lower than 100°C so that food can be cooked with less energy. Comment on this idea.

28. What is the gas inside a bubble of boiling water?

29. Your instructor hands you a closed flask partly filled with room-temperature water. When you hold it, the heat from your bare hands causes the water to boil. Quite impressive! How is this accomplished?

30. As an evaporating liquid cools, does something else get warm? If so, what?

31. A lid on a cooking pot filled with water shortens both the time it takes the water to come to a boil and the time the food takes to cook in the boiling water. Explain what is going on in each case.

32. If liquid water had a lower specific heat capacity, would ponds be more likely to freeze or less likely to freeze?

33. Should the specific heat capacity of your automobile's radiator liquid be as high as possible or as low as possible? Explain.

34. Would fevers run higher or lower if liquid water's specific heat capacity were not so high?

35. Bermuda is close to North Carolina, but unlike North Carolina it has a tropical climate year round. Why?

36. If the winds at the latitude of San Francisco and Washington, D.C., were from the east rather than from the west, why might San Francisco be able to grow cherry trees and Washington, D.C., palm trees?

37. To impart a hickory flavor to a roasted turkey, a cook places a pot of water containing hickory chips in the oven with the turkey. Why does the turkey take longer than expected to cook?

38. Why is it that in cold winters a large tub of liquid water placed in a farmer's canning cellar helps prevent canned food from freezing?

39. A great deal of heat is released when liquid water freezes. Why doesn't this heat simply remelt the ice?

40. Suppose 4 grams of liquid water at 100°C is spread over a large surface so that 1 gram evaporates rapidly. If evaporation of the 1 gram takes 2259 joules from the remaining 3 grams of water and no other heat transfer takes place, what are the temperature and phase of the remaining 3 grams once the 1 gram is evaporated?

Problems

1. A walnut stuck to a pin is burned beneath a can containing 100.0 grams of water at 21°C. After the walnut has completely burned, the water's final temperature is 28°C. How much heat energy came from the burning walnut?

2. How much heat is required to raise the temperature of 100,000 grams of iron by 30 C°?

3. By how much will the temperature of 5.0 grams of liquid water increase upon the addition of 230 joules of heat?

Answers to Calculation Corner

How Heat Changes Temperature

1. The temperature change is final temperature minus initial temperature: 55.0°C − 25.0°C = +30.0 C°. Multiply this positive temperature change by the water's specific heat capacity and mass:

$$\text{heat} = (4.184 \text{ J/g} \cdot \text{C}°)(100,000 \text{ g})(+30.0 \text{ C}°)$$
$$= 12,552,000 \text{ J}$$

This large number helps to explain how an electric water heater consumes about 25 percent of all household electricity. With the proper number of significant figures (see Appendix B), this answer should be expressed as 10,000,000 joules.

2. The temperature change is −30.0°C − (−10.0°C) = −20.0 C°. Multiply this negative temperature change by the ice's specific heat capacity and mass:

$$\text{heat} = (2.01 \text{ J/g} \cdot \text{C}°)(10.0 \text{ g})(−20.0 \text{ C}°)$$
$$= −402 \text{ J}$$

The next time you're near a refrigerator/freezer, place your hand near its back, and you'll feel the heat that has been extracted from the food inside.

Suggested Web Sites

http://madsci.wustl.edu/posts/archives/mar97/852921998.As.r.html

A discussion about the recent discovery of ice on the moon's south pole, with an explanation of how the ice can persist despite the absence of an atmosphere. See also http://www.nrl.navy.mil/clementine/.

http://seawifs.gsfc.nasa.gov/OCEAN_PLANET/HTML/oceanography_recently_revealed1.html

Volcanic vents at the bottom of the ocean spew out water at temperatures in excess of 300°C. In 1977, geologists exploring these vents discovered odd-looking animals surviving on the sunless sea floor.

Chapter 9
An Overview of Chemical Reactions

How Reactants React to Form Products

The heat of a lightning bolt causes many chemical reactions in the atmosphere, including one in which nitrogen and oxygen react to form nitrogen monoxide, NO. The nitrogen monoxide formed in this manner then reacts with atmospheric oxygen and water vapor to form nitric acid, HNO_3, and nitrous acid, HNO_2. These acids are carried by rain into the ground, where they form ions, which plants need for growth—a process that involves further chemical reactions.

Scientists have learned how to control chemical reactions to produce many useful materials—nitrates and other nitrogen-based fertilizers from atmospheric nitrogen, metals from rocks, plastics and pharmaceuticals from petroleum. These materials and the thousands of others produced by chemical reactions, as well as the abundant energy released when fossil fuels take part in the chemical reaction called combustion, have dramatically improved our living conditions.

The goal of this chapter is to give you a stronger handle on the basics of chemical reactions, which were introduced in Chapter 2. Then in the following chapters we'll look at specific classes of chemical reactions, such as acid-base reactions, oxidation-reduction reactions, and reactions involving organic chemicals.

9.1 Chemical Reactions Are Represented by Chemical Equations

During a chemical reaction, one or more new compounds are formed as result of the rearrangement of atoms. To represent a chemical reaction, w can write a **chemical equation**, which shows the substances about to reac called **reactants**, to the left of an arrow that points to the newly forme substances, called **products**:

reactants $\longrightarrow$ products

Typically, reactants and products are represented by their atomic o molecular formulas, but molecular structures or simple names may be use instead. Phases are also often shown: (s) for solid, (ℓ) for liquid, and (g) fo gas. Compounds dissolved in water are designated (aq) for aqueous. Lastl numbers are placed in front of the reactants or products to show the rati in which they either combine or form. These numbers are called **coeffi cients**, and they represent numbers of individual atoms and molecules. Fo instance, to represent the chemical reaction in which coal (solid carbon burns in the presence of oxygen to form gaseous carbon dioxide, we writ the chemical equation

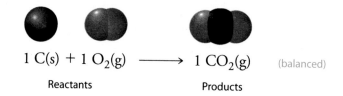

$$1\ C(s) + 1\ O_2(g) \longrightarrow 1\ CO_2(g) \quad \text{(balanced)}$$

Reactants   Products

One of the most important principles of chemistry is the *law of mas. conservation*, which states that matter is neither created nor destroyed dur ing a chemical reaction (Section 3.2). The atoms present at the beginning of a reaction merely rearrange to form new molecules. This means that nc atoms are lost or gained during any reaction. The chemical equation must therefore be *balanced*, which means each atom shown in the equation must appear on both sides of the arrow the same number of times. The preced ing equation for the formation of carbon dioxide is balanced because each side shows one carbon atom and two oxygen atoms. You can count the number of atoms in the space-filling models to see this for yourself.

In another chemical reaction, two hydrogen gas molecules, H_2, react with one oxygen gas molecule, O_2, to produce two molecules of water, H_2O, in the gaseous phase:

$$2\ H_2(g) + 1\ O_2(g) \longrightarrow 2\ H_2O(g) \quad \text{(balanced)}$$

This equation for the formation of water is also balanced—there are four hydrogen and two oxygen atoms before and after the arrow.

A coefficient in front of a chemical formula tells us the number of times that element or compound must be counted. For example, $2\ H_2O$ indicates two water molecules, which contain a total of four hydrogen atoms and two oxygen atoms.

By convention, the coefficient 1 is omitted so that the above chemical equations are typically written

$$C(s)\quad +\ O_2(g)\ \longrightarrow\quad CO_2(g)\qquad \text{(balanced)}$$

$$2\ H_2(g)\ +\ O_2(g)\ \longrightarrow\ 2\ H_2O(g)\qquad \text{(balanced)}$$

Concept Check ✔

How many oxygen atoms are indicated by the balanced equation

$$3\ O_2(g)\ \longrightarrow\ 2\ O_3(g)$$

Was this your answer? Before the reaction these six oxygen atoms are found in three O_2 molecules. After the reaction these same six atoms are found in two O_3 molecules.

You Can Balance Unbalanced Equations

An unbalanced chemical equation shows the reactants and products without the correct coefficients. For example, the equation

$$NO(g)\ \longrightarrow\ N_2O(g)\ +\ NO_2(g)\qquad \text{(not balanced)}$$

is not balanced because there is one nitrogen atom and one oxygen atom before the arrow but three nitrogen atoms and three oxygen atoms after the arrow.

You can balance unbalanced equations by adding or changing coefficients to produce correct ratios. (It's important **not to change subscripts**, however, because to do so changes the compound's identity—H_2O is water, but H_2O_2 is hydrogen peroxide!) For example, to balance the above equation, add a 3 before the NO:

$$3\ NO(g)\ \longrightarrow\ N_2O(g)\ +\ NO_2(g)\qquad \text{(balanced)}$$

Now there are three nitrogen atoms and three oxygen atoms on each side of the arrow, and the law of mass conservation is not violated.

There are many methods of balancing equations. For example, consider the following equation in which aluminum oxide, Al_2O_3, and carbon, C, react to form elemental aluminum, Al, and carbon dioxide, CO_2. Here is an unbalanced equation for this reaction:

$$\underline{\quad}\ Al_2O_3(s)\ +\ \underline{\quad}\ C(s)\ \longrightarrow\ \underline{\quad}\ Al(s)\ +\ \underline{\quad}\ CO_2(g)\qquad \text{(not balanced)}$$

Balancing an equation usually proceeds most efficiently when you balance one element at a time, starting with elements in the most complex reactant.

For this example, therefore, we can start by balancing the aluminum. This element can be balanced by placing a 2 in front of the product Al, so that there are two aluminum atoms before the arrow and two after.

$$\underline{}\ Al_2O_3(s) + \underline{}\ C(s) \longrightarrow 2\ Al(s) + \underline{}\ CO_2(g)$$

(aluminum balanced)
(oxygen not balanced)
(carbon balanced)

The oxygen can then be balanced by placing a 2 in front of the Al_2O_3 and a 3 in front of the CO_2:

$$2\ Al_2O_3(s) + \underline{}\ C(s) \longrightarrow 2\ Al(s) + 3\ CO_2(g)$$

(aluminum not balanced)
(oxygen balanced)
(carbon not balanced)

Doing this gives six oxygen atoms before and after the arrow. Ignore the fact that adding these coefficients upsets the balance of aluminum and carbon atoms. It is best to focus on one element at a time, and for the above our focus was on oxygen.

We've now worked with all the elements of the most complex reactant, Al_2O_3, and so it's time to balance the carbon, which can be done by placing a 3 in front of its symbol:

$$2\ Al_2O_3(s) + 3\ C(s) \longrightarrow 2\ Al(s) + 3\ CO_2(g)$$

(aluminum not balanced)
(oxygen balanced)
(carbon balanced)

Go through the equation again, focusing on one element at a time to make sure each is balanced. The number of aluminum atoms, for example, can be balanced by changing the coefficient on Al to 4:

$$2\ Al_2O_3(s) + 3\ C(s) \longrightarrow 4\ Al(s) + 3\ CO_2(g)$$

(aluminum balanced)
(oxygen balanced)
(carbon balanced)

As you will discover, you can follow many paths to balance a chemical equation. For the above example, you could have started by balancing the carbon first, though it's usually wisest to start with elements in the most complex reactant. If the coefficients start getting very large (beyond 12), you've likely chosen a path that is looping you around to no end. In such an event, start over.

Here is a summary of the steps used in our example:

1. Balance one element at a time. Modify the coefficients to make this element appear the same number of times on both sides of the arrow. Start with the reactant having the most complex formula and finish with the reactant having the simplest formula.

2. If you incidentally unbalance an element that you worked with previously, leave it alone and come back to it only after you have worked with all other elements.

3. After you have worked with each element, make another pass through the equation, changing coefficients as needed.

4. Repeat step 3 until all elements are balanced.

5. If necessary, minimize the coefficients by dividing by the lowest common denominator. The coefficients 2:4:2, for example, should be reduced to 1:2:1 by dividing by the lowest common denominator, which is 2.

Helpful Hints: Never, ever, EVER alter a subscript. Remember that a coefficient must appear before *a chemical compound, not within it. Use a pencil so that you can erase coefficients as needed.*

Concept Check ✔

Write a balanced equation for the reaction showing hydrogen gas and nitrogen gas forming ammonia gas below:

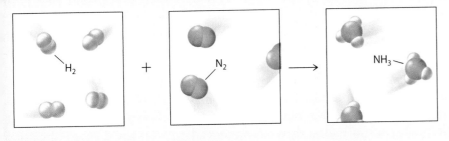

Was this your answer?   Start by writing the equation without the coefficients:

___ $H_2(g)$ + ___ $N_2(g)$ → ___ $NH_3(g)$

Then go through the steps outlined in the text. The balanced equation is

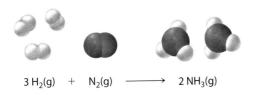

$3\,H_2(g)$ + $N_2(g)$ ⟶ $2\,NH_3(g)$

You can see that there are equal numbers of each kind of atom before and after the arrow. For more practice balancing equations, see the Exercises at the end of this chapter.

Practicing chemists develop a skill for balancing equations. This skill involves creative energy and, like other skills, improves with experience. There are some useful tricks of the trade for balancing equations, and maybe your instructor will share some with you. For brevity, however, this text introduces only the basics. More important than being an expert at balancing equations is knowing why they need to be balanced. And the reason is the law of mass conservation, which tells us that atoms are neither created nor destroyed in a chemical reaction—they are simply rearranged. So every atom present before the reaction must be present after the reaction, even though the groupings of atoms are different.

9.2 Chemists Use Relative Masses to Count Atoms and Molecules

In any chemical reaction, a specific number of reactant atoms or molecules react to form a specific number of product atoms or molecules. For example, when carbon and oxygen combine to form carbon dioxide, they always combine in the ratio of one carbon atom to one oxygen molecule. A chemist who wants to carry out this reaction in the laboratory would be wasting chemicals and money if she were to combine, say, four carbon atoms for every one oxygen molecule. The excess carbon atoms would have no oxygen molecules to react with and would remain unchanged.

How is it possible to measure out a specific number of atoms or molecules? Rather than counting these particles individually, chemists can use a scale that measures the mass of bulk quantities. Because different atoms and molecules have different masses, however, a chemist can't simply weigh out equal masses of each. Say, for example, he needs the same number of carbon atoms as oxygen molecules. Measuring equal masses of the two materials would not provide equal numbers.

You know that 1 kilogram of Ping-Pong balls contains more balls than 1 kilogram of golf balls, as Figure 9.1 illustrates. Likewise, because different atoms and molecules have different masses, there are different numbers of them in a 1-gram sample of each. Because carbon atoms are less massive than oxygen molecules, there are more carbon atoms in 1 gram of carbon than there are oxygen molecules in 1 gram of oxygen. So, clearly, weighing equal masses of these two particles does not yield equal numbers.

Equal masses

Figure 9.1
The number of balls in a given mass of Ping-Pong balls is very different from the number of balls in the same mass of golf balls.

If we know the *relative masses* of different materials, we can measure equal numbers. Golf balls, for example, are about 20 times more massive than Ping-Pong balls, which is to say the relative mass of Ping-Pong balls to golf balls is 20 to 1. Measuring out 20 times as much mass of golf balls as Ping-Pong balls, therefore, gives equal numbers of each, as is shown in Figure 9.2.

The mass of one Ping-Pong ball is 2 grams.

The mass of one golf ball is 40 grams.

A Ping-Pong ball is 2/40, or 1/20, as massive as a golf ball.

Number of Ping-Pong balls = Number of golf balls

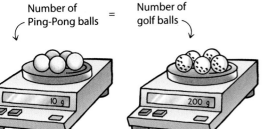

Figure 9.2
The number of golf balls in 200 grams of golf balls equals the number of Ping-Pong balls in 10 grams of Ping-Pong balls.

Concept Check ✓

A customer wants to buy a 1:1 mixture of blue and red jelly beans. Each blue bean is twice as massive as each red bean. If the clerk measures out 5 pounds of red beans, how many pounds of blue jelly beans must she measure out?

Was this your answer? Because each blue jelly bean has twice the mass of each red one, the clerk needs to measure out twice as much mass of blues in order to have the same count, which means 10 pounds of blues. If the clerk did not know that the blue beans were twice as massive as the red ones, she would not know what mass of blues was needed for the 1:1 ratio. Likewise, a chemist would be at a loss in setting up a chemical reaction if she did not know the relative masses of the reactants.

The periodic table tells us the relative masses of carbon and molecular oxygen; therefore, we can measure out equal numbers of their fundamental particles—atoms for carbon and molecules for oxygen. Figure 9.3 on page 272 illustrates this concept. The atomic mass of carbon is 12.011 atomic mass units. (As discussed in Section 3.6, 1 *atomic mass unit* (amu) = 1.661×10^{-24} gram.) The **formula mass** of a substance is the sum of the atomic masses of the elements in its chemical formula. Therefore, the formula mass of an oxygen molecule, O_2, is 15.999 atomic mass units + 15.999 atomic mass units ≈ 32 atomic mass units. A carbon atom, therefore, is about 12/32 = 3/8 as massive as an oxygen molecule. To measure out equal numbers of carbon atoms and oxygen molecules, we weigh out only three-eighths as much carbon. If we started with 8 grams of oxygen, we need 3 grams of carbon to have the same number of particles (because 3 is three-eighths of 8). Alternatively, if we started with 32 grams of oxygen, we need 12 grams of carbon to have the same number of particles (because 12 is three-eighths of 32).

Atomic mass of O = 15.999 amu
+ Atomic mass of O = 15.999 amu
Formula mass of O_2 ≈ 32 amu

Figure 9.3
To have equal numbers of carbon atoms and oxygen molecules requires weighing out three-eighths as much carbon as oxygen.

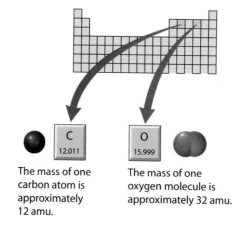

The mass of one carbon atom is approximately 12 amu.

The mass of one oxygen molecule is approximately 32 amu.

A carbon atom is $12/32$, or $3/8$, as massive as an oxygen molecule.

Number of   =   Number of
carbon atoms   oxygen molecules

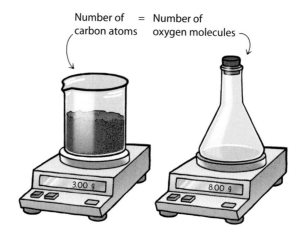

Concept Check ✓

1. Reacting 3 grams of carbon, C, with 8 grams of molecular oxygen, O_2, results in 11 grams of carbon dioxide, CO_2. Does it follow that 1.5 grams of carbon will react with 4 grams of oxygen to form 5.5 grams of carbon dioxide?

2. Would reacting 5 grams of carbon with 8 grams of oxygen also result in 11 grams of carbon dioxide?

Were these your answers?

1. The quantities are only half as much, but their ratio is the same as when 11 grams of carbon dioxide is formed: 1.5:4:5.5 = 3:8:11.

2. It is a common error of many students to think that no reaction will occur if the proper ratios of reactants are not provided. You should understand, however, that in a 5-gram sample of carbon, 3 grams of carbon is available for reacting. This 3 grams will react with the 8 grams of oxygen to form 11 grams of carbon dioxide. There will be 2 grams of carbon unreacted after the reaction. Reacting this remaining 2 grams of carbon would require more oxygen.

The Periodic Table Helps Us Convert Between Grams and Moles

Atoms and molecules react in specific ratios. In the laboratory, however, chemists work with bulk quantities of materials, which are measured by mass. Chemists therefore need to know the relationship between the mass of

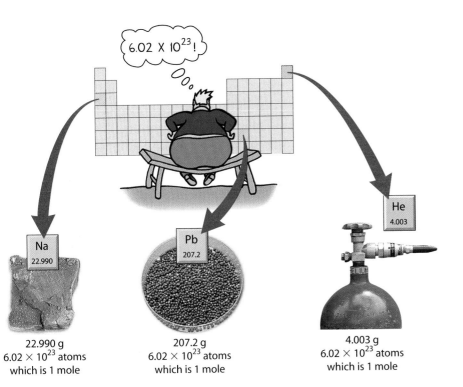

a given sample and the number of atoms or molecules contained in that mass. The key to this relationship is the *mole*. Recall from Section 7.2 that the mole is a unit equal to 6.02×10^{23}. This number is known as **Avogadro's number**, in honor of Amadeo Avogadro (Section 3.3).

As Figure 9.4 illustrates, if you express the numeric value of the atomic mass of any element in grams, the number of atoms in a sample of the element having this mass is always 6.02×10^{23}, which is 1 mole. For example, a 22.990-gram sample of sodium metal, Na (atomic mass 51.996 atomic mass units), contains 6.02×10^{23} sodium atoms, and a 207.2-gram sample of lead, Pb (atomic mass = 207.2 atomic mass units), contains 6.02×10^{23} carbon atoms.

The same concept holds for compounds. Express the numeric value of the formula mass of any compound in grams, and a sample having that mass contains 6.02×10^{23} molecules of that compound. For example, there are 6.02×10^{23} O_2 molecules in 31.998 grams of molecular oxygen, O_2 (formula mass 31.998 atomic mass units), and 6.02×10^{23} CO_2 molecules in 44.009 grams of carbon dioxide, CO_2 (formula mass 44.009 atomic mass units).

An explanation of this amazing relationship is beyond the scope of this book, but well within the range of questions you might ask your instructor.

Concept Check ✓

1. How many atoms are there in a 6.941-gram sample of lithium, Li (atomic mass 6.941 atomic mass units)?

2. How many molecules are there in a 18.015-gram sample of water, H_2O (formula mass 18.015 atomic mass units)?

Were these your answers?

1. Because this number of grams of lithium is numerically equal to the atomic mass, there are 6.02×10^{23} atoms in the sample, which is 1 mole of lithium atoms.
2. Because this number of grams of water is numerically equal to the formula mass, there are 6.02×10^{23} water molecules in the sample, which is 1 mole of water molecules.

The **molar mass** of any substance, be it element or compound, is defined as the mass of 1 mole of the substance. Thus the units of molar mass are grams per mole. For instance, carbon is 12.011 atomic mass units, which means that 1 mole of carbon has a mass of 12.011 grams, and we say that the molar mass of carbon is 12.011 grams per mole. The molar mass of molecular oxygen (O_2, formula mass 31.998 atomic mass units) is 31.998 grams per mole. For convenience, values such as these are often rounded off to the nearest whole number. The molar mass of carbon, therefore, might also be presented as 12 grams per mole, and that of molecular oxygen as 32 grams per mole.

Concept Check ✓

What is the molar mass of water (formula mass = 18 atomic mass units)?

Was this your answer? From the formula mass, you know that 1 mole of water has a mass of 18 grams. Therefore the molar mass is 18 grams per mole.

Because 1 mole of any substance always contains 6.02×10^{23} particles, the mole is an ideal unit for chemical reactions. For example, 1 mole of carbon (12 grams) reacts with 1 mole of molecular oxygen (32 grams) to give 1 mole of carbon dioxide (44 grams).

In many instances, the ratio in which chemicals react is not 1:1. As shown in Figure 9.5, for example, 2 moles (4 grams) of molecular hydrogen react with 1 mole (32 grams) of molecular oxygen to give 2 moles (36 grams) of water. Note how the coefficients of the balanced chemical equation can be conveniently interpreted as the number of moles of reactants or products. A chemist therefore need only convert these numbers of moles to grams in order to know how much mass of each reactant he or she should measure out to have the proper proportions.

Figure 9.5
Two moles of H_2 react with 1 mole of O_2 to give 2 moles of H_2O. This is the same as saying 4 grams of H_2 reacts with 32 grams of O_2 to give 36 grams of H_2O or, equivalently, that 12.04×10^{23} H_2 molecules react with 6.02×10^{23} O_2 molecules to give 12.04×10^{23} H_2O molecules.

$$2\,H_2 \quad + \quad 1\,O_2 \quad \longrightarrow \quad 2\,H_2O$$

2 moles	1 mole	2 moles
which is	which is	which is
4 grams	32 grams	36 grams
which is	which is	which is
12.04×10^{23} molecules	6.02×10^{23} molecules	12.04×10^{23} molecules

Calculation Corner: Figuring Masses of Reactants and Products

Using conversion factors (Section 1.3) and the relationship between grams and moles, you can perform some very high-powered calculations.

Example

What mass of water is produced when 16 grams of methane, CH_4 (formula mass 16 atomic mass units), burns in the reaction

$$CH_4 + 2\,O_2 \longrightarrow CO_2 + 2\,H_2O$$

Step 1. Convert the given mass to moles:

Conversion factor

$$(16\ \text{g}\ CH_4)\left(\frac{1\ \text{mole}\ CH_4}{16\ \text{g}\ CH_4}\right) = 1\ \text{mole}\ CH_4$$

Step 2. Use the coefficients of the balanced equation to find out how many moles of H_2O are produced from this many moles of CH_4:

Conversion factor

$$(1\ \text{mole}\ CH_4)\left(\frac{2\ \text{moles}\ H_2O}{1\ \text{mole}\ CH_4}\right) = 2\ \text{moles}\ H_2O$$

Step 3. Now that you know how many moles of H_2O are produced, convert this value to grams of H_2O:

Conversion factor

$$(2\ \text{moles}\ H_2O)\left(\frac{18\ \text{g}\ H_2O}{1\ \text{mole}\ H_2O}\right) = 36\ \text{g}\ H_2O$$

This method of converting from grams to moles (step 1), then from moles to moles (step 2), and then from moles to grams (step 3) is an important aspect of what is called *stoichiometry*—the science of calculating the amount of reactants or products in any chemical reaction. It is a method that is developed much further in general chemistry courses. For this course, all you need to do is be familiar with what stoichiometry is all about, which is keeping tabs on atoms and molecules as they react to form products. Nonetheless, for a special assignment, you might try your analytical thinking skills on the following problems. First try to deduce the answer based on what you know about the law of mass conservation, and then follow the steps given here to check your answers.

Your Turn

1. How many grams of ozone (O_3, 48 amu) can be produced from 64 grams of oxygen (O_2, 32 amu), in the reaction

$$3\,O_2 \longrightarrow 2\,O_3$$

2. What mass of nitrogen monoxide (NO, 30 amu) is formed when 28 grams of nitrogen (N_2, 28 amu) reacts with 32 grams of oxygen (O_2, 32 amu) in the reaction

$$N_2 + O_2 \longrightarrow 2\,NO$$

Cooking and chemistry are similar in that both require measuring ingredients. Just as a cook looks to a recipe to find the necessary quantities measured by the cup or the tablespoon, a chemist looks to the periodic table to find the necessary quantities measured by the number of grams per mole for each element or compound.

9.3 Reaction Rate Is Influenced by Concentration and Temperature

A balanced chemical equation helps us determine the amount of products that might be formed from given amounts of reactants. The equation, however, tells us little about what is taking place on the submicroscopic level during the reaction. In this and the following section, we explore that level to show how the *rate* of a reaction can be changed either by changing the concentration or temperature of the reactants or by adding what is known as a *catalyst*.

Some chemical reactions, such as the rusting of iron, are slow, while others, such as the burning of gasoline, are fast. The speed of any reaction is indicated by its reaction rate, which is an indicator of how quickly the reactants transform to products. As shown in Figure 9.6, initially a flask may contain only reactant molecules. Over time, these reactants form product molecules, and as a result, the concentration of product molecules increases. The **reaction rate**, therefore, can be defined either as how quickly the concentration of products increases or as how quickly the concentration of reactants decreases.

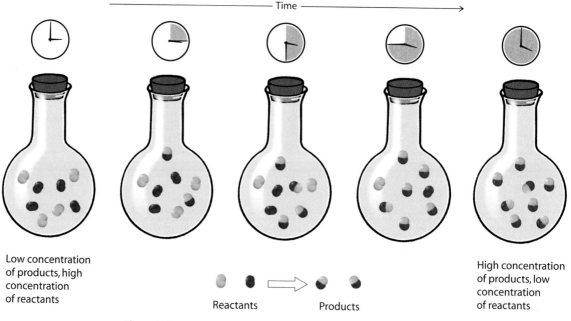

Figure 9.6
Over time, the reactants in this reaction flask may transform to products. If this happens quickly, the reaction rate is high. If this happens slowly, the reaction rate is low.

What determines the rate of a chemical reaction? The answer is complex, but one important factor is that reactant molecules must physically come together. Because molecules move rapidly, this physical contact is appropriately described as a collision. We can illustrate the relationship between molecular collisions and reaction rate by considering the reaction of gaseous nitrogen and gaseous oxygen to form gaseous nitrogen monoxide as shown in Figure 9.7.

Reactants ...   ...coming together ...   ...react upon colliding,...   ...resulting in the formation of product. Nitrogen monoxide, NO.

Nitrogen, N_2 Oxygen, O_2

Figure 9.7
During a reaction, reactant molecules collide with each other.

Because reactant molecules must collide in order for a reaction to occur, the rate of a reaction can be increased by increasing the number of collisions. An effective way to increase the number of collisions is to increase the concentration of the reactants. Figure 9.8 shows that, with higher concentrations, there are more molecules in a given volume, which makes collisions between molecules more probable. As an analogy, consider a bunch of people on a dance floor—as the number of people increases, so does the rate at which they bump into one another. An increase in the concentration of nitrogen and oxygen molecules, therefore, leads to a greater number of collisions between these molecules and hence a greater number of nitrogen monoxide molecules formed in a given period of time.

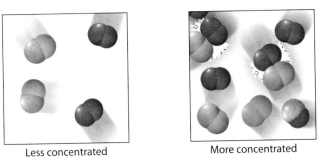

Less concentrated   More concentrated

Figure 9.8
The more concentrated a sample of nitrogen and oxygen, the greater the likelihood that N_2 and O_2 molecules will collide and form nitrogen monoxide.

Not all collisions between reactant molecules lead to products, however, because the molecules must collide in a certain orientation in order to react. Nitrogen and oxygen, for example, are much more likely to form nitrogen monoxide when the molecules collide in a parallel fashion, as shown in Figure 9.7. When they collide in a perpendicular fashion, as shown in Figure 9.9 on page 278, nitrogen monoxide does not form. For larger molecules, which can have numerous orientations, this orientation requirement is even more restrictive.

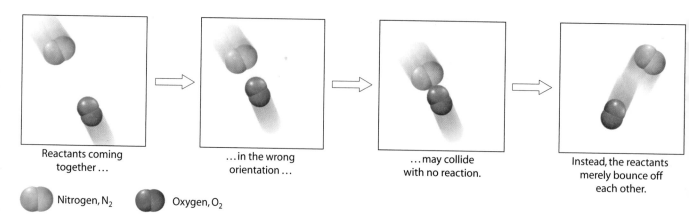

Nitrogen, N$_2$ Oxygen, O$_2$

Figure 9.9
The orientation of reactant molecules in a collision can determine whether or not a reaction takes place. A perpendicular collision between N$_2$ and O$_2$ does not tend to result in formation of a product molecule.

A second reason not all collisions lead to product formation is that the reactant molecules must also collide with enough kinetic energy to break their bonds. Only then is it possible for the atoms in the reactant molecules to change bonding partners and form product molecules. The bonds in N$_2$ and O$_2$ molecules, for example, are quite strong. In order for these bonds to be broken, collisions between the molecules must contain enough energy to break these bonds. As a result, collisions between slow-moving N$_2$ and O$_2$ molecules, even those that collide in the proper orientation, may not form NO, as is shown in Figure 9.10.

The higher the temperature of a material, the faster its molecules are moving and the more forceful the collisions between them. Higher temperatures, therefore, tend to increase reaction rates. The nitrogen and oxygen molecules that make up our atmosphere, for example, are always colliding with one another. At the ambient temperatures of our atmosphere, however, these molecules do not generally have sufficient kinetic energy to allow for the formation of nitrogen monoxide. The heat of a

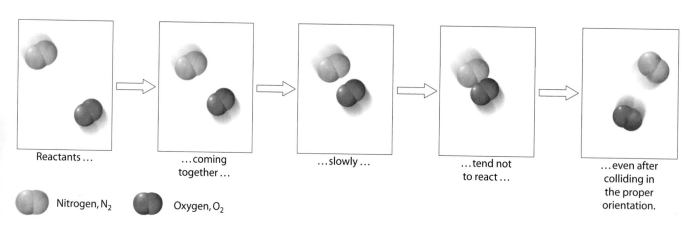

Nitrogen, N$_2$ Oxygen, O$_2$

Figure 9.10
Slow-moving molecules may collide without enough force to break bonds. In this case, they cannot react to form product molecules.

ightning bolt, however, dramatically increases the kinetic energy of these molecules, to the point that a large portion of the collisions in the vicinity of the bolt result in the formation of nitrogen monoxide. As discussed in the opening of this chapter, the nitrogen monoxide formed in this manner undergoes further atmospheric reactions to form chemicals known as nitrates that plants depend on to survive. This is an example of *nitrogen fixation*, which we explore in Chapter 15.

Concept Check ✓

An internal-combustion engine works by drawing a mixture of air and gasoline vapors into a chamber. The action of a piston then compresses these gases into a smaller volume prior to ignition by the spark of a spark plug. What is the advantage of squeezing the vapors to a smaller volume?

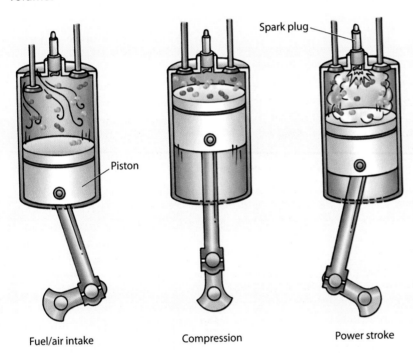

Fuel/air intake   Compression   Power stroke

Was this your answer? Squeezing the vapors to a smaller volume effectively increases their concentration and hence the number of collisions between molecules. This, in turn, promotes the chemical reaction.

The energy required to break bonds can also come from the absorption of electromagnetic radiation. As the radiation is absorbed by reactant molecules, the atoms in the molecules may start to vibrate so rapidly that the bonds between them are easily broken. In many instances, the direct absorption of electromagnetic radiation is all it takes to break chemical bonds and initiate a chemical reaction. As we discuss in Chapter 17, for example, the common atmospheric pollutant nitrogen dioxide, NO_2, may transform to nitrogen monoxide and atomic oxygen merely upon exposure to sunlight:

$$NO_2 + \text{sunlight} \longrightarrow NO + O$$

Whether the result of collisions, absorption of electromagnetic radiation, or both, broken bonds are a necessary first step in most chemical reactions. The energy required for this initial breaking of bonds can be viewed as an *energy barrier*. The minimum energy required to overcome this energy barrier is known as the **activation energy** E_a.

In the reaction between nitrogen and oxygen to form nitrogen monoxide, the energy barrier is so high (because the bonds in N_2 and O_2 are strong) that only the fastest-moving nitrogen and oxygen molecules possess sufficient energy to react. Figure 9.11 shows the energy barrier in this chemical reaction as a vertical hump.

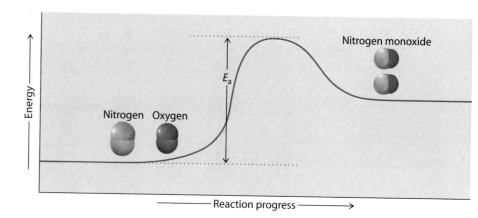

Figure 9.11
Reactant molecules must gain a minimum amount of energy, called the activation energy E_a, in order to transform to product molecules.

The activation energy of a chemical reaction is analogous to the energy a car needs to drive over the top of a hill. Without sufficient energy to climb to the top of the hill, there is no way for the car to get to the other side. Likewise, reactant molecules can transform to product molecules only if they possess an amount of energy equal to or greater than the activation energy.

At any given temperature, there is a wide distribution of kinetic energies in reactant molecules. Some are moving slowly and others quickly. As discussed in Chapter 1, the temperature of a material is simply the *average* of all these kinetic energies. The few fast-moving reactant molecules in Figure 9.12 are the first to transform to product molecules because these are the molecules that have enough energy to pass over the energy barrier.

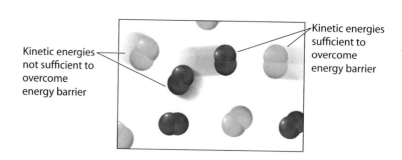

Figure 9.12
Fast-moving reactant molecules possess sufficient energy to pass over the energy barrier and hence are the first ones to transform to product molecules.

When the temperature of reactants is increased, the number of reactant molecules having sufficient energy to pass over the barrier also increases, which is why reactions are generally faster at higher temperatures. Conversely, at lower temperatures, there are fewer molecules having sufficient energy to pass over the barrier, which is why reactions are generally slower at lower temperatures.

Most chemical reactions are influenced by temperature in this manner, including those reactions occurring in living bodies. The body temperature of animals that regulate their internal temperature, such as humans, is fairly constant. However, the body temperature of some animals, such as the alligator shown in Figure 9.13, rises and falls with the temperature of the environment. On a warm day, the chemical reactions occurring in an alligator are "up to speed," and the animal can be most active. On a chilly day, however, the chemical reactions proceed at a lower rate, and as a consequence, the alligator's movements are unavoidably sluggish.

Figure 9.13
This alligator became immobilized on the pavement after being caught in the cold night air. By mid-morning, shown here, the temperature had warmed sufficiently to allow the alligator to get up and walk away.

Concept Check ✓

What kitchen device is used to lower the rate at which microorganisms grow on food?

Was this your answer? The refrigerator! Microorganisms, such as bread mold, are everywhere and difficult to avoid. By lowering the temperature of microorganism-contaminated food, the refrigerator decreases the rate of the chemical reactions that these microorganisms depend on for growth, thereby increasing the food's shelf life.

9.4 Catalysts Increase the Rate of Chemical Reactions

As discussed in the previous section, a chemical reaction can be made to go faster by increasing the concentration of the reactants or by increasing the temperature. A third way to increase the rate of a reaction is to add a **catalyst**, which is any substance that increases the rate of a chemical reaction by

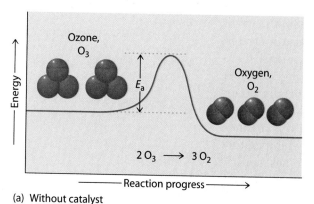

(a) Without catalyst

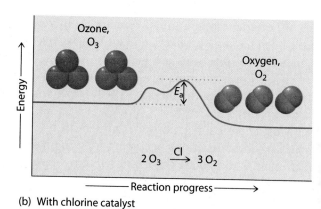

(b) With chlorine catalyst

Figure 9.14

(a) The relatively high energy barrier indicates that only the most energetic ozone molecules can react to form oxygen molecules. (b) Chlorine atoms lower the energy barrier, which means more reactant molecules have sufficient energy to form product. The chlorine allows the reaction to proceed in two steps, and the two smaller energy barriers correspond to these steps. (Note that the convention is to write the catalyst above the reaction arrow.)

lowering its activation energy. The catalyst may participate as a reactant, but it is then regenerated as a product and is thus available to catalyze subsequent reactions.

The conversion of ozone, O_3, to oxygen, O_2, is normally sluggish because the reaction has a relatively high energy barrier, as shown in Figure 9.14a. However, when chlorine atoms act as a catalyst, the energy barrier is lowered, as shown in Figure 9.14b, and the reaction is able to proceed faster.

Atomic chlorine lowers the energy barrier of this reaction by providing an alternate pathway involving intermediate reactions, each having a lower activation energy than the uncatalyzed reaction. This alternate pathway involves two steps. Initially, the chlorine reacts with the ozone to form chlorine monoxide and oxygen:

$$Cl \ + \ O_3 \ \longrightarrow \ ClO \ + \ O_2$$

Chlorine   Ozone   Chlorine   Oxygen
              monoxide

The chlorine monoxide then reacts with another ozone molecule to re-form the chlorine atom as well as produce two additional oxygen molecules:

$$ClO \ + \ O_3 \ \longrightarrow \ Cl \ + \ 2\,O_2$$

Chlorine   Ozone   Chlorine   Oxygen
monoxide

Although chlorine is used up in the first reaction, it is regenerated in the second reaction. As a result, there is no net consumption of chlorine. At the same time, however, a total of two ozone molecules are rapidly converted to three oxygen molecules. The chlorine is therefore a catalyst for the conversion of ozone to oxygen because the chlorine increases the speed of the reaction but is not consumed by the reaction.

Chlorine atoms in the stratosphere catalyze the destruction of the Earth's ozone layer. As we explore further in Chapter 17, evidence tells us

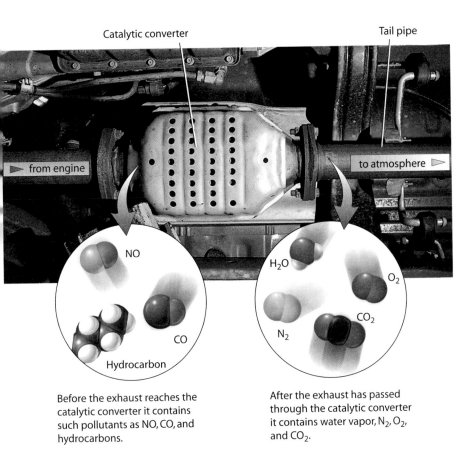

Catalytic converter

Tail pipe

from engine

to atmosphere ▷

NO

CO

Hydrocarbon

H₂O

O₂

CO₂

N₂

Before the exhaust reaches the catalytic converter it contains such pollutants as NO, CO, and hydrocarbons.

After the exhaust has passed through the catalytic converter it contains water vapor, N₂, O₂, and CO₂.

Figure 9.15
A catalytic converter reduces the pollution caused by automobile exhaust by converting such harmful combustion products as NO, CO, and hydrocarbons to harmless N_2, O_2, and CO_2. The catalyst is typically platinum, Pt, palladium, Pd, or rhodium, Rd.

that chlorine atoms are generated in the stratosphere as a by-product of human-made chlorofluorocarbons (CFCs), once widely produced as the cooling fluid of refrigerators and air-conditioners. Destruction of the ozone layer is a serious concern because of the role this layer plays in protecting us from the Sun's harmful ultraviolet rays. One chlorine atom in the ozone layer, it is estimated, can catalyze the transformation of 100,000 ozone molecules to oxygen molecules in the one or two years before the chlorine atom is removed by natural processes.

Chemists have been able to harness the power of catalysts for numerous beneficial purposes. The exhaust that comes from an automobile engine, for example, contains a wide assortment of pollutants, such as nitrogen monoxide, carbon monoxide, and uncombusted fuel vapors (hydrocarbons). To reduce the amount of these pollutants entering the atmosphere, most automobiles are equipped with a *catalytic converter*, shown in Figure 9.15. Metal catalysts in a converter speed up reactions that convert exhaust pollutants to less toxic substances. Nitrogen monoxide is transformed to nitrogen and oxygen, carbon monoxide is transformed to carbon dioxide, and unburned fuel is converted to carbon dioxide and water vapor. Because catalysts are not consumed by the reactions they facilitate, a single catalytic converter may continue to operate effectively for the lifetime of the car.

Catalytic converters, along with microchip-controlled fuel–air ratios, have led to a significant drop in the per-vehicle emission of pollutants. A typical car in 1960 emitted about 11 grams of uncombusted fuel, 4 grams

Figure 9.16
The exhaust from automobiles today is much cleaner than before the advent of the catalytic converter, but there are many more cars on the road. In 1960 there were 70 million registered motor vehicles in the United States. In 2000 there were more than 200 million.

of nitrogen oxide, and 84 grams of carbon monoxide per mile traveled. An improved vehicle in 2000 emitted less than 0.5 gram of uncombusted fuel, less than 0.5 gram of nitrogen oxide, and only about 3 grams of carbon monoxide per mile traveled. This improvement, however, has been offset by an increase in the number of cars being driven, exemplified by the traffic jam shown in Figure 9.16.

The chemical industry depends on catalysts because they lower manufacturing costs by lowering required temperatures and providing greater product yields without being consumed. Indeed, more than 90 percent of all manufactured goods are produced with the assistance of catalysts. Without catalysts, the price of gasoline would be much higher, as would be the price of such consumer goods as rubber, plastics, pharmaceuticals, automobile parts, clothing, and food grown with chemical fertilizers.

Living organisms rely on special types of catalysts known as *enzymes*, which allow exceedingly complex biochemical reactions to occur with ease. The nature and behavior of enzymes are discussed in Chapter 13.

Concept Check ✓

How does a catalyst lower the energy barrier of a chemical reaction?

Was this your answer? The catalyst provides an alternate and easier-to-achieve pathway along which the chemical reaction can proceed.

9.5 Chemical Reactions Can Be Either Exothermic or Endothermic

As the preceding two sections discuss, reactants must have a certain amount of energy in order to overcome the energy barrier so that a chemical reaction can proceed. Once a reaction is complete, however, there may be either a net release or a net absorption of energy. Reactions in which there is a net release of heat energy are called **exothermic**. Rocketships lift off into space and campfires glow red hot as a result of exothermic reactions. Reactions in which there is a net absorption of heat energy are called **endothermic**. Photosynthesis, for example, involves a series of endothermic reactions that are driven by the energy of sunlight. Both exothermic and endothermic reactions, illustrated in Figure 9.17, can be understood through the concept of bond energy.

During a chemical reaction, chemical bonds are broken and atoms rearrange to form new chemical bonds. Such breaking and forming of chemical bonds involves changes in energy. As an analogy, consider a pair of magnets. To separate them requires an input of "muscle energy." Conversely, when the two separated magnets collide, they become slightly warmer than they were, and this warmth is evidence of energy released. Energy must be absorbed by the magnets if they are to break apart, and energy is released as they come together. The same principle applies to atoms. To pull bonded atoms apart requires an energy input. When atoms combine, there is an energy output, usually in the form of faster-moving atoms and molecules, electromagnetic radiation, or both.

The amount of energy required to pull two bonded atoms apart is the same as the amount released when they are brought together. This energy absorbed as a bond breaks or released as one forms is called **bond energy**. Each chemical bond has its own characteristic bond energy. The hydrogen–hydrogen bond energy, for example, is 436 kilojoules per mole. This means that 436 kilojoules of energy is absorbed as 1 mole of hydrogen–hydrogen bonds break apart and 436 kilojoules of energy is released upon the formation of 1 mole of hydrogen–hydrogen bonds. Different bonds involving different elements have different bond energies. The oxygen–oxygen double bond has a bond energy of 498 kilojoules per mole, and the oxygen–hydrogen bond has a bond energy of 464 kilojoules per mole. These and some other bond energies are listed in Table 9.1. You can refer to Table 9.1 as you study this section, but please do not memorize these bond energies. Instead, focus on understanding what these bond energies mean.

Table 9.1

Selected Bond Energies

Bond	Bond Energy (kJ/mole)	Bond	Bond Energy (kJ/mole)
H–H	436	O–O	138
H–C	414	Cl–Cl	243
H–N	389	N–N	159
H–O	464	N=O	631
H–F	569	O=O	498
H–Cl	431	O=C	803
H–S	339	N≡N	946
C–C	347	C≡C	837

By convention, a positive bond energy represents the amount of energy absorbed as a bond breaks and a negative bond energy represents the amount of energy released as a bond forms. Thus when you are calculating the net energy released or absorbed during a reaction, you'll need to be careful about plus and minus signs. It is standard practice when doing such calculations to assign a plus sign to energy absorbed and a minus sign to energy released. For instance, when dealing with a reaction in which 1 mole of H–H bonds are broken, you'll write +436 kilojoules to indicate energy absorbed, and when dealing with the formation of 1 mole of H–H bonds, you'll write −436 kilojoules to indicate energy released. We'll do some sample calculations in a moment.

Figure 9.17
For the chemical reactions taking place in burning wood, there is a net release of energy. For those taking place in a photosynthetic plant, there is a net absorption of energy.

Concept Check ✓

Do all covalent single bonds have the same bond energy?

Was this your answer? Bond energy depends on the types of atoms bonding. The H–H single bond, for example, has a bond energy of 436 kilojoules per mole, but the H–O single bond has a bond energy of 464 kilojoules per mole. All covalent single bonds do not have the same bond energy.

I must supply energy to these magnets in order to pull them apart.

Energy is released when they come together!

An Exothermic Reaction Involves a Net Release of Energy

For any chemical reaction, the total amount of energy absorbed in breaking bonds in reactants is always different from the total amount of the energy released as bonds form in the products. Consider the reaction in which hydrogen and oxygen react to form water:

$$\text{H—H} \quad \text{H—H} + \text{O=O} \longrightarrow \text{H—O}_{\text{H}} \qquad \text{H}_{\diagdown}\text{O}_{\diagup}\text{H}$$

In the reactants, hydrogen atoms are bonded to hydrogen atoms and oxygen atoms are double-bonded to oxygen atoms. The total amount of energy absorbed as these bonds break is

Type of bond	Number of moles	Bond energy	Total energy
H–H	2	+436 kJ/mole	+872 kJ
O=O	1	+498 kJ/mole	+498 kJ
		Total energy absorbed	+1370 kJ

In the products there are four hydrogen–oxygen bonds. The total amount of energy released as these bonds form is

Type of bond	Number of moles	Bond energy	Total energy
H–O	4	−464 kJ/mole	−1856 kJ
		Total energy released	−1856 kJ

For this reaction the amount of energy released exceeds the amount of energy absorbed. The net energy of the reaction is found by adding the two quantities:

$$\begin{aligned}\text{net energy of reaction} &= \text{energy absorbed} + \text{energy released} \\ &= +1370 \text{ kJ} + (-1856 \text{ kJ}) \\ &= -486 \text{ kJ}\end{aligned}$$

The negative sign on the net energy indicates that there is a net *release* of energy, and so the reaction is exothermic. For any exothermic reaction, energy can be considered a product and is thus sometimes included after the arrow of the chemical equation:

$$2\,\text{H}_2 + \text{O}_2 \longrightarrow 2\,\text{H}_2\text{O} + \text{energy}$$

In an exothermic reaction, the potential energy of atoms in the product molecules is lower than their potential energy in the reactant molecules. This is illustrated in the reaction profile shown in Figure 9.18. The potential energy of the atoms is lower in the product molecules because they are held more tightly together. This is analogous to two attracting magnets,

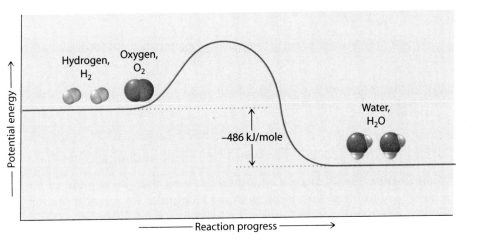

Figure 9.18
In an exothermic reaction, the product molecules are at a lower potential energy than the reactant molecules. The net amount of energy released by the reaction is equal to the difference in potential energies of the reactants and products.

whose potential energy decreases as they come closer together. The loss of potential energy is balanced by a gain in kinetic energy. As two free-floating magnets come together, they accelerate to higher speeds. Similarly, as reactants react to form products, the potential energy of the reactants is converted to kinetic energy, which can take the form of faster-moving atoms and molecules, electromagnetic radiation, or both. This kinetic energy is the energy released by the reaction, and it is equal to the difference between the potential energy of the reactants and the potential energy of the products, as is indicated in Figure 9.18.

It is important to understand that the energy released by an exothermic reaction is not created by the reaction. This is in accord with the *law of conservation of energy*, which states that energy is neither created nor destroyed in a chemical reaction. Instead, it is merely converted from one form to another. During an exothermic reaction, energy that was once in the form of the potential energy of chemical bonds is released as the kinetic energy of fast-moving molecules and/or electromagnetic radiation.

The amount of energy released in an exothermic reaction depends on the amount of reactants. For the formation of water, our earlier analysis shows that the reaction between 2 moles (4 grams) of H_2 and 1 mole (32 grams) of O_2 yields 486 kilojoules. With greater quantities of these reactants, correspondingly more energy is released. The reaction of large amounts of hydrogen and oxygen, for example, provide the energy to lift the space shuttle as shown in Figure 9.19 into orbit. There are two compartments in the large central tank to which the orbiter is attached—one filled with liquid hydrogen and the other with liquid oxygen. Upon ignition, these two liquids mix and react chemically to form water vapor, which produce the needed thrust as it is expelled out the rocket cones. Additional thrust is obtained by a pair of solid-fuel rocket boosters containing a mixture of ammonium perchlorate, NH_4ClO_4, and powdered aluminum. Upon ignition, these chemicals react to form products that are expelled out the back of the rocket. The balanced equation representing this reaction is

$$3\ NH_4ClO_4 + 3\ Al \longrightarrow Al_2O_3 + AlCl_3 + 3\ NO + 6\ H_2O + \text{energy}$$

Figure 9.19
A space shuttle uses exothermic chemical reactions to lift off from the Earth's surface.

Concept Check ✓

Where does the net energy released in an exothermic reaction go?

Was this your answer? This energy goes into making atoms and molecules move faster and/or into the formation of electromagnetic radiation.

An Endothermic Reaction Involves a Net Absorption of Energy

Many chemical reactions are endothermic, such that the amount of energy released as products form is *less* than the amount of energy absorbed in the breaking of bonds in the reactants. An example is the reaction of atmospheric nitrogen and oxygen to form nitrogen monoxide which is the same reaction used for many of the discussions earlier in this chapter:

$$N{\equiv}N + O{=}O \longrightarrow N{=}O + N{=}O$$

The amount of energy absorbed as the chemical bonds in the reactants break is

Type of bond	Number of moles	Bond energy	Total energy
N≡N	1	+946 kJ/mole	+946 kJ
O=O	1	+498 kJ/mole	+498 kJ
		Total energy absorbed	+1444 kJ

The amount of energy released upon the formation of bonds in the products is

Type of bond	Number of moles	Bond energy	Total energy
N=O	2	−631 kJ/mole	−1262 kJ
		Total energy released	−1262 kJ

As before, the net energy of the reaction is found by adding the two quantities:

$$\begin{aligned} \text{net energy of reaction} &= \text{energy absorbed} + \text{energy released} \\ &= +1444 \text{ kJ} + (-1262 \text{ kJ}) \\ &= +182 \text{ kJ} \end{aligned}$$

The positive sign indicates that there is a net *absorption* of energy, meaning the reaction is endothermic. For any endothermic reaction, energy can be considered a reactant and is thus sometimes included before the arrow of the chemical equation:

$$\text{energy} + N_2 + O_2 \longrightarrow 2\,NO$$

In an endothermic reaction, the potential energy of atoms in the product molecules is higher than their potential energy in the reactant molecules. This is illustrated in the reaction profile shown in Figure 9.20. Raising the potential energy of the atoms in the product molecules requires a net input of energy, which must come from some external source, such as electromagnetic radiation, electricity, or heat. Thus nitrogen and oxygen react to form nitrogen monoxide only with the application of much heat, as occurs adjacent to a lightning bolt or in an internal-combustion engine.

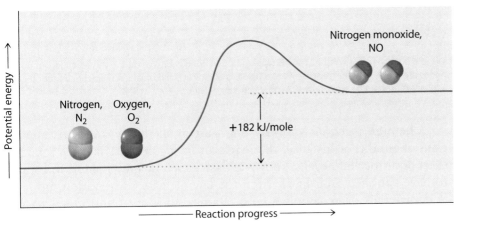

Figure 9.20
In an endothermic reaction, the product molecules are at a higher poten-tial energy than the reactant molecules. The net amount of energy absorbed by the reaction is equal to the difference in potential energies of the reactants and products.

Hands-On Chemistry: Warming and Cooling Water Mixtures

Recall from Section 7.1 that chemical bonds and intermolecular attractions are both consequences of the electric force, the difference being that chemical bonds are generally many times stronger than molecule-to-molecule attractions. So, just as the formation and breaking of chemical bonds involves energy, so does the formation and breaking of molecular attractions. For molecule-to-molecule attractions, the amount of energy absorbed or released per gram of material is relatively small. Physical changes involving the formation or breaking of molecule-to-molecule attractions, therefore, are much safer to perform, which makes them more suitable for a Hands-On Chemistry activity. Experience the exothermic and endothermic nature of physical changes for yourself by performing the following two activities.

① Hold some room-temperature water in the cupped palm of your hand over a sink. Pour an equal amount of room-temperature rubbing alcohol into the water. Is this mixing an exothermic or endothermic process? What's going on at the molecular level?

② Add lukewarm water to two plastic cups. (Do not use insulating Styrofoam cups.) Transfer the liquid back and forth between cups to ensure equal temperatures, ending up with the same amount of water in each cup. Add several tablespoons of table salt to one cup and stir. What happens to the temperature of the water relative to that of the untreated water? (Hold the cups up to your cheeks to tell.) Is this an exothermic or endothermic process? What's going on at the molecular level?

Concept Check ✓

> Without looking at bond energies, deduce whether the following reaction is exothermic or endothermic. Should energy be written as a reactant or as a product?

$$\underset{O^{\diagup}}{\overset{O}{\diagdown}} N - N \underset{\diagdown O}{\overset{\diagup O}{}} \longrightarrow \underset{O^{\diagdown}}{\overset{O}{\diagup}} N + N \underset{\diagdown O}{\overset{\diagup O}{}}$$

Was this your answer? The nitrogen–nitrogen bond is broken during this reaction, but no new bonds are formed. Because energy is absorbed as a chemical bond breaks, this reaction is endothermic, and energy should be written as a reactant: energy + N_2O_4 $\longrightarrow$ 2 NO_2.

Figure 9.21
Magic is in the eye of the beholder.

Chemical reactions are truly the heart of chemistry, and their applications abound. For instance, the magician in Figure 9.21 has just ignited a sheet of nitrocellulose, also known as flash paper. In a moment, it will appear to have vanished. You know from the law of mass conservation, however, that materials don't simply vanish. Rather, they are transformed to new materials. Sometimes we can't see the new materials, but that doesn't mean they don't exist. One of the reactions that occur as flash paper burns is

$$4\ C_6H_7N_5O_{16}(s) + 19\ O_2(g) \longrightarrow 24\ CO_2(g) + 20\ NO_2(g) + 14\ H_2O(g)$$

| A component of nitrocellulose | Oxygen | Carbon dioxide | Nitrogen dioxide | Water |

The equation shows 24 carbon, 28 hydrogen, 20 nitrogen, and 102 oxygen atoms before and after the reaction. The difference is in how these atoms are grouped together. The products formed in this case are all gaseous materials that quickly mix into the atmosphere, escaping our notice.

To make the flash paper, the magician would have had to mix the starting materials cellulose and nitric acid. He could determine the proper proportions by knowing the formula masses of these two substances. And although the flash paper may be bathed in an atmosphere of oxygen, it will not react with the oxygen until an initial amount of energy (from the spark of the magician's lighter) is provided to overcome the energy barrier. We know the burning of flash paper is exothermic because the amount of energy released as product bonds form is greater than the amount absorbed as reactant bonds break. The energy released is in the form of light and faster-moving molecules, which is why the air where the flash paper once was is now appreciably warmer. No true magic is involved, but it is enchanting all the same.

Key Terms and Matching Definitions

_____ activation energy
_____ Avogadro's number
_____ bond energy
_____ catalyst
_____ chemical equation
_____ coefficient
_____ endothermic
_____ exothermic
_____ formula mass
_____ molar mass
_____ product
_____ reaction rate
_____ reactant

1. A representation of a chemical reaction.
2. A starting material in a chemical reaction, appearing before the arrow in a chemical equation.
3. A new material formed in a chemical reaction, appearing after the arrow in a chemical equation.
4. A number used in a chemical equation to indicate either the number of atoms/molecules or the number of moles of a reactant or product.
5. The sum of the atomic masses of the elements in a chemical compound.
6. The number of particles—6.02×10^{23}—contained in 1 mole of anything.
7. The mass of 1 mole of a substance.
8. A measure of how quickly the concentration of products in a chemical reaction increases or the concentration of reactants decreases.
9. The minimum energy required in order for a chemical reaction to proceed.
10. Any substance that increases the rate of a chemical reaction without itself being consumed by the reaction.
11. A term that describes a chemical reaction in which there is a net release of energy.
12. A term that describes a chemical reaction in which there is a net absorption of energy.
13. The amount of energy either absorbed as a chemical bond breaks or released as a bond forms.

Review Questions

Chemical Reactions Are Represented by Chemical Equations

1. What is the purpose of coefficients in a chemical equation?

2. How many chromium atoms and how many oxygen atoms are indicated on the right side of this balanced chemical equation:

$$4\,Cr(s) + 3\,O_2(g) \longrightarrow 2\,Cr_2O_3(g)$$

3. What do the letters (s), (ℓ), (g), and (aq) stand for in a chemical equation?

4. Why is it important that a chemical equation be balanced?

5. Why is it important never to change a subscript in a chemical formula when balancing a chemical equation?

6. Which equations are balanced?
   a. $Mg(s) + 2\,HCl(aq) \longrightarrow MgCl_2(aq) + H_2(g)$
   b. $3\,Al(s) + 3\,Br_2(\ell) \longrightarrow Al_2Br_3(s)$
   c. $2\,HgO(s) \longrightarrow 2\,Hg(\ell) + O_2(g)$

Chemists Use Relative Masses to Count Atoms and Molecules

7. Why don't equal masses of golf balls and Ping-Pong balls contain the same number of balls?

8. Why don't equal masses of carbon atoms and oxygen molecules contain the same number of particles?

9. How does formula mass differ from atomic mass?

10. What is the mass of a sodium atom in atomic mass units?

11. What is the formula mass of nitrogen monoxide, NO, in atomic mass units?

12. If you had 1 mole of marbles, how many marbles would you have?

13. If you had 2 moles of pennies, how many pennies would you have?

14. How many moles of water are there in 18 grams of water?

15. How many molecules of water are there in 18 grams of water?

16. Why is saying you have 1 mole of water molecules the same as saying you have 6.02×10^{23} water molecules?

Reaction Rate Is Influenced by Concentration and Temperature

17. Why don't all collisions between reactant molecules lead to product formation?

18. What two aspects of a collision between two reactant molecules determine whether or not the collision results in the formation of product molecules?

19. What generally happens to the rate of a chemical reaction with increasing temperature?

20. Why does food take longer to spoil when it is placed in the refrigerator?

21. Which reactant molecules are the first to pass over the energy barrier?

22. What term is used to describe the minimum amount of energy required for a reaction to proceed?

Catalysts Increase the Rate of Chemical Reactions

23. What catalyst is effective in the destruction of atmospheric ozone, O_3?

24. Can a catalyst react with a reactant?

25. What is the purpose of a catalytic converter?

26. What does a catalyst do to the energy barrier of a reaction?

27. What net effect does a chemical reaction have on a catalyst?

28. Why are catalysts so important to our economy?

Chemical Reactions Can Be Either Exothermic or Endothermic

29. If it takes 436 kilojoules to break a bond, how many kilojoules are released when the same bond is formed?

30. Is there any energy consumed at any time during an exothermic reaction?

31. What is released by an exothermic reaction?

32. What is absorbed by an endothermic reaction?

33. Which is higher in an endothermic reaction: the potential energy of the reactants or the potential energy of the products?

Hands-On Chemistry Insights

Warming and Cooling Water Mixtures

1. The mixing of rubbing alcohol and water is an exothermic process, as evidenced by the warmth you feel upon combining the two. At the molecular level, hydrogen bonds are being formed between alcohol molecules and the water molecules. Recall from Section 7.1 that the hydrogen "bond" is a molecule-to-molecule attraction. It is the formation of these intermolecular attractions between alcohol and water molecules that results in the release of heat.

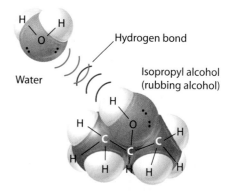

Water

Hydrogen bond

Isopropyl alcohol (rubbing alcohol)

2. You should have been able to feel that the salted water was cooler than the unsalted water, meaning the mixing of sodium chloride and water is an endothermic process. At the molecular level, two things are going on. First the ionic bonds between Na^+ and Cl^- in the solid salt break, a process that absorbs energy. Then the ions form ion–dipole attractions with water molecules, a process that releases energy. The amount of energy absorbed in the first step is greater than the amount released in the second step.

Commercial "cold packs" work by the same principle. Instead of sodium chloride, however, these packs are made with ammonium nitrate, which absorbs much more energy as it dissolves in water. In order for the pack to be activated, it must be punched. This breaks an inner seal and allows the ammonium nitrate to mix with water. As the ammonium nitrate dissolves, heat is absorbed and the temperature of anything in contact with the pack—including a sprained ankle—decreases.

Exercises

1. One trick of the trade in balancing chemical equations is to use a fraction as a coefficient. This works as long as you get rid of the fraction in your final step by multiplying the entire equation by the denominator of the fraction. You might use $\frac{1}{2}O_2$, for example, to indicate a single oxygen atom. To get rid of this fraction, you need to multiply each coefficient (including the $\frac{1}{2}$) by 2. Use this technique to balance this chemical equation:

   ____ Na_2SO_3 + ____ S_8 $\longrightarrow$ ____ $Na_2S_2O_3$

2. Is this chemical equation balanced:

   $2\ C_4H_{10}(g) + 13\ O_2(g) \longrightarrow$
   $\qquad\qquad 8\ CO_2(g) + 10\ H_2O(\ell)$

3. Balance these equations:

   a. ____ $Fe(s)$ + ____ $O_2(g)$ $\longrightarrow$
   $\qquad\qquad\qquad$ ____ $Fe_2O_3(s)$

   b. ____ $H_2(g)$ + ____ $N_2(g)$ $\longrightarrow$
   $\qquad\qquad\qquad$ ____ $NH_3(g)$

   c. ____ $Cl_2(g)$ + ____ $KBr(aq)$ $\longrightarrow$
   $\qquad\qquad$ ____ $Br_2(\ell)$ + ____ $KCl(aq)$

   d. ____ $CH_4(g)$ + ____ $O_2(g)$ $\longrightarrow$
   $\qquad\qquad$ ____ $CO_2(g)$ + ____ $H_2O(\ell)$

4. Balance these equations:

   a. ____ $Fe(s)$ + ____ $S(s)$ $\longrightarrow$ ____ $Fe_2S_3(s)$

   b. ____ $P_4(s)$ + ____ $H_2(g)$ $\longrightarrow$
   $\qquad\qquad\qquad$ ____ $PH_3(g)$

   c. ____ $NO(g)$ + ____ $Cl_2(g)$ $\longrightarrow$
   $\qquad\qquad\qquad$ ____ $NOCl(g)$

   d. ____ $SiCl_4(\ell)$ + ____ $Mg(s)$ $\longrightarrow$
   $\qquad\qquad$ ____ $Si(s)$ + ____ $MgCl_2(s)$

5. What are the formula masses of water, H_2O; propene, C_3H_6; and 2-propanol, C_3H_8O?

6. What is the formula mass of sulfur dioxide, SO_2?

7. Which has more atoms: 17.031 grams of ammonia, NH_3, or 72.922 grams of hydrogen chloride, HCl?

8. Which has more atoms: 64.058 grams of sulfur dioxide, SO_2, or 72.922 grams of hydrogen chloride, HCl?

9. Which has the greatest number of molecules:
   a. 28 grams of nitrogen, N_2
   b. 32 grams of oxygen, O_2
   · c. 32 grams of methane, CH_4
   d. 38 grams of fluorine, F_2

10. Which has the greatest number of atoms:
    a. 28 grams of nitrogen, N_2
    b. 32 grams of oxygen, O_2
    c. 16 grams of methane, CH_4
    d. 38 grams of fluorine, F_2

11. Hydrogen and oxygen always react in a 1:8 ratio by mass to form water. Early investigators took this to mean that oxygen was eight times more massive than hydrogen. What did these investigators assume about water's chemical formula?

12. Two atomic mass units equal how many grams?

13. What is the mass of an oxygen atom in atomic mass units?

14. What is the mass of a water molecule in atomic mass units?

15. What is the mass of an oxygen atom in grams?

16. What is the mass of a water molecule in grams?

17. Is it possible to have a sample of oxygen that has a mass of 14 atomic mass units? Explain.

18. Which is greater: 1.01 atomic mass units of hydrogen or 1.01 grams of hydrogen?

19. Which has the greater mass, 1.204×10^{24} molecules of molecular hydrogen or 1.204×10^{24} molecules of water?

20. You are given two samples of elements, and each sample has a mass of 10 grams. If the two samples contain the same number of atoms, what must be true of the two samples?

21. Does a refrigerator prevent or delay the spoilage of food? Explain.

22. The yeast used in bread dough feeds on sugar to produce carbon dioxide gas, which causes the dough to rise. Why is bread dough commonly left to rise in a warm area rather than in the refrigerator?

23. Why does a glowing splint of wood burn only slowly in air but burst into flames when placed in pure oxygen?

24. Why is heat often added to chemical reactions performed in the laboratory?

25. An Alka-Seltzer antacid tablet bubbles vigorously in water but only slowly in a solution of the same temperature containing a 50:50 mix of alcohol and water. Propose a probable explanation involving the relationship between reaction speed and the frequency of molecular collisions.

26. What can you deduce about the activation energy of a reaction that takes billions of years to go to completion? How about a reaction that takes only fractions of a second?

27. In the following reaction sequence for the catalytic formation of ozone from molecular oxygen, which chemical compound is the catalyst: nitrogen monoxide or nitrogen dioxide:

$$O_2 + 2\ NO \longrightarrow 2\ NO_2$$
$$2\ NO_2 \longrightarrow 2\ NO + 2\ O$$
$$2\ O + 2\ O_2 \longrightarrow 2\ O_3$$

28. What role do chlorofluorocarbons play in the catalytic destruction of ozone?

29. Many people hear about atmospheric ozone depletion and wonder why we don't simply replace that which has been destroyed. Knowing about chlorofluorocarbons and knowing how catalysts work, explain how this would not be a lasting solution.

30. Use the bond energies in Table 9.1 and the accounting format shown in Section 9.5 to determine whether these reactions are exothermic or endothermic:

$$H_2 + Cl_2 \longrightarrow 2\ HCl$$
$$2\ HC{\equiv}CH + 5\ O_2 \longrightarrow 4\ CO_2 + 2\ H_2O$$

31. Use the bond energies in Table 9.1 and the accounting format shown in Section 9.5 to

determine whether these reactions are exothermic or endothermic:

$$N_2H_4 \longrightarrow 2\ H_2 + N_2$$
$$2\ H_2O_2 \longrightarrow O_2 + 2\ H_2O$$

32. Note in Table 9.1 that bond energy increases going from H–N to H–O to H–F. Explain this trend based on the sizes of these atoms as deduced from their positions in the periodic table.

33. Are the chemical reactions that take place in a disposable battery exothermic or endothermic? What evidence supports your answer? Is the reaction going on in a rechargeable battery while it is recharging exothermic or endothermic?

34. Is the synthesis of ozone from oxygen exothermic or endothermic? How about the synthesis of oxygen from ozone?

Problems

1. How many molecules of aspirin (formula mass 180 atomic mass units) are there in a 0.250-gram sample?

2. Small samples of oxygen gas needed in the laboratory can be generated by any number of simple chemical reactions, such as

$$2\ KClO_3(s) \longrightarrow 2\ KCl(s) + 3\ O_2(g)$$

What mass of oxygen (in grams) is produced when 122.55 grams of $KClO_3$ (formula mass 122.55 atomic mass units) takes part in this reaction?

3. How many grams of water, H_2O, and propene, C_3H_6, can be formed from the reaction of 6.0 grams of 2-propanol, C_3H_8O?

2-Propanol

Propene

Water

4. How many moles of water, H_2O, can be produced from the reaction of 16 grams of methane, CH_4, with an unlimited supply of oxygen, O_2? How many grams of water is this? The reaction is

$$CH_4 + 2\,O_2 \longrightarrow CO_2 + 2\,H_2O$$

5. How many grams of calcium oxide, CaO, react with 64.058 grams of sulfur dioxide, SO_2, in the formation of calcium sulfite, $CaSO_3$? What mass of $CaSO_3$ is formed in this reaction? The molar masses are CaO 56.079 grams per mole, SO_2 64.058 grams per mole, $CaSO_3$ 120.137 grams per mole, and the balanced equation is

$$CaO + SO_2 \longrightarrow CaSO_3$$

Answers to Calculation Corner

Figuring Masses of Reactants and Products

1. According to the law of mass conservation, the amount of mass in the products must equal the amount of mass in the reactants. Given that this reaction involves only one reactant and one product, you should not be surprised to learn that 64 grams of reactant produces 64 grams of product:

   Step 1. Convert grams of O_2 to moles of O_2:

   $$(64 \text{ g } O_2)\left(\frac{1 \text{ mole } O_2}{32 \text{ g } O_2}\right) = 2 \text{ moles } O_2$$

   Step 2. Convert moles of O_2 to moles of O_3:

   $$(2 \text{ moles } O_2)\left(\frac{2 \text{ moles } O_3}{3 \text{ moles } O_2}\right) = 1.33 \text{ moles } O_3$$

   Step 3. Convert moles of O_3 to grams of O_3:

   $$(1.33 \text{ moles } O_3)\left(\frac{48 \text{ g } O_3}{1 \text{ mole } O_3}\right) = 64 \text{ g } O_3$$

2. There are several ways to answer this problem. One way would be to recognize that 28 grams

of N_2 is 1 mole of N_2 and 32 grams of O_2 is 1 mole of O_2. According to the balanced equation, combining 1 mole of N_2 with 1 mole of O_2 yields 2 moles of NO. The mass of 2 moles of NO is

$$(2 \text{ moles NO})\left(\frac{30 \text{ g NO}}{1 \text{ mole NO}}\right) = 60 \text{ g NO}$$

which is the sum of the masses of the reactants, as it must be because of the law of mass conservation.

Suggested Web Sites

http://www.thecatalyst.org/wwwchem.html
> This site has been developed as a resource for high school chemistry teachers, but anyone studying chemistry should find the links helpful. You might follow the link to the history of chemistry, for example, to learn more about Amadeo Avogadro and that huge number named after him.

http://artoo.gisd.k12.mi.us/~nmdf/
> The fun site of the National Mole Day Foundation, which sponsors the annual celebration of Mole Day on October 23 from 6:02 A.M. to 6:02 P.M. Proof that there's a Web site for everything imaginable.

http://www.wxumac.demon.co.uk/
http://www.powerpak.com/PowerGraphs/1998/February/Nitric.htm
> Nitrogen monoxide, also known as nitric oxide, NO, is a precursor to nitrate fertilizers and a common atmospheric pollutant, but it also plays a multitude of vital roles in our human biology. Use *nitric oxide* as a keyword in your internet search engine to find a plethora of Web sites devoted to the many roles this small but important molecule plays in our physiology and in various diseases, such as Alzheimer's, Parkinson's, asthma, heart disease, and infections.

Chapter 10
Acids and Bases

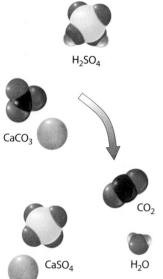

Transferring Protons

As rainwater falls, it absorbs atmospheric carbon dioxide. Once in the rainwater, the carbon dioxide reacts with water to form an acid known as carbonic acid, H_2CO_3, which, as we discuss in this chapter, makes rainwater naturally acidic. As the rainwater passes through the ground, the carbonic acid reacts with various basic minerals, such as limestone, to form products that are water-soluble and thus carried away by the underground flow of water. This washing-away action over the course of millions of years creates caves. The world's most extensive cave system is in western Kentucky in Mammoth Cave National Park, where more than 300 miles of networked caves have been mapped.

Although Mammoth Cave National Park has the most extensive network of caves, its cave chambers are much smaller than those in Carlsbad Caverns National Park in southeastern New Mexico. This chapter's opening photograph shows the largest chamber at Carlsbad, which measures 25 stories high and half a kilometer wide. The great size of the chambers at Carlsbad is due to the "limestone-eating" action of an acid known as sulfuric acid, H_2SO_4, which is much stronger than carbonic acid. This sulfuric acid forms from gaseous hydrogen sulfide, H_2S, and gaseous sulfur dioxide, SO_2, both of which rise up from oil and gas deposits buried deep in the Earth.

In this chapter, we explore acids and bases and the chemical reactions they undergo. We begin with a definition of these two important substances and then explore how some acids and bases are stronger than others. After learning about the pH scale, we close by looking at some environmental and physiological applications of acid–base concepts.

10.1 Acids Donate Protons, Bases Accept Them

The term *acid* comes from the Latin *acidus*, which means "sour." The sour taste of vinegar and citrus fruits is due to the presence of acids. Food is digested in the stomach with the help of acids, and acids are also essential in the chemical industry. Today, for instance, more than 85 billion pounds of sulfuric acid is produced annually in the United States, making this the number-one manufactured chemical. Sulfuric acid is used in fertilizers, detergents, paint dyes, plastics, pharmaceuticals, storage batteries, iron, and steel. It is so important in the manufacturing of goods that its production is considered a standard measure of a nation's industrial strength. Figure 10.1 shows only a very few of the acids we commonly encounter.

(a)

(b)

(c)

(d)

Figure 10.1
Examples of acids. (a) Citrus fruits contain many types of acids, including ascorbic acid, $C_6H_8O_8$, which is vitamin C. (b) Vinegar contains acetic acid, $C_2H_4O_2$, and can be used to preserve foods. (c) Many toilet bowl cleaners are formulated with hydrochloric acid, HCl. (d) All carbonated beverages contain carbonic acid, H_2CO_3, while many also contain phosphoric acid, H_3PO_4.

Bases are characterized by their bitter taste and slippery feel. Interestingly, bases themselves are not slippery. Rather, they cause skin oils to transform into slippery solutions of soap. Most commercial preparations for unclogging drains are composed of sodium hydroxide, NaOH (also known as lye), which is extremely basic and hazardous when concentrated. Bases are also heavily used in industry. Each year in the United States about 25 billion pounds of sodium hydroxide is manufactured for use in the production of various chemicals and in the pulp and paper industry. As was discussed in Section 2.6, solutions containing bases are often called *alkaline*, a term derived from the Arabic word for ashes (*al-qali*). Ashes are slippery when wet because of the presence of the base potassium carbonate, K_2CO_3. Figure 10.2 shows some common bases with which you are probably familiar.

(a)

(b)

(c)

(d)

Figure 10.2
Examples of bases. (a) Reactions involving sodium bicarbonate, $NaHCO_3$, make baked goods rise. (b) Ashes contain potassium carbonate, K_2CO_3. (c) Soap is made by reacting bases with animal or vegetable oils. The soap itself, then, is slightly alkaline. (d) Powerful bases, such as sodium hydroxide, NaOH, are used in drain cleaners.

Acids and bases may be defined in several ways. For our purposes, an appropriate definition is the one suggested in 1923 by the Danish chemist Johannes Brønsted (1879–1947) and the English chemist Thomas Lowry (1874–1936). In the Brønsted–Lowry definition, an **acid** is any chemical that donates a hydrogen ion, H^+, and a **base** is any chemical that accepts a hydrogen ion. Recall from Chapter 2 that, because a hydrogen atom consists of one electron surrounding a one-proton nucleus, a hydrogen ion formed from the loss of an electron is nothing more than a lone proton.

Thus, it is also sometimes said that an acid is a chemical that donates a proton and a base is a chemical that accepts a proton.

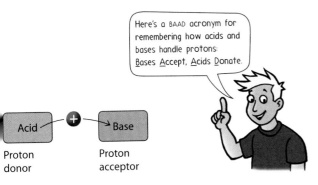

Here's a BAAD acronym for remembering how acids and bases handle protons: Bases Accept, Acids Donate.

Acid → + → Base
Proton donor   Proton acceptor

Consider what happens when hydrogen chloride is mixed into water:

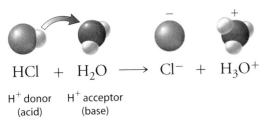

$$HCl + H_2O \longrightarrow Cl^- + H_3O^+$$

H$^+$ donor (acid)   H$^+$ acceptor (base)

Hydrogen chloride donates a hydrogen ion to one of the nonbonding electron pairs on a water molecule, resulting in a third hydrogen bonded to the oxygen. In this case, hydrogen chloride behaves as an acid (proton donor) and water behaves as a base (proton acceptor). The products of this reaction are a chloride ion and a **hydronium ion**, H_3O^+, which, as Figure 10.3 shows, is a water molecule with an extra proton.

Recall that a hydrogen ion with a positive charge is simply a lone proton.

Hydrogen atom   Positive hydrogen ion (lone proton)

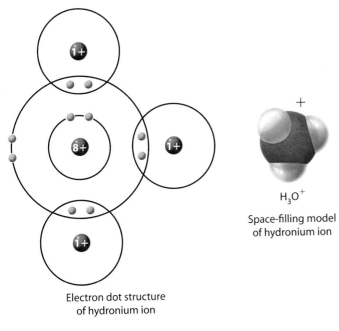

H_3O^+
Space-filling model of hydronium ion

Electron dot structure of hydronium ion

Total protons	11+
Total electrons	10−
Net charge	1+

Figure 10.3
The hydronium ion's positive charge is a consequence of the extra proton this molecule has acquired. Hydronium ions, which play a part in many acid–base reactions, are *polyatomic ions*—molecules that carry a net electric charge.

When added to water, ammonia behaves as a base by accepting a hydrogen ion from water, which, in this case, behaves as an acid:

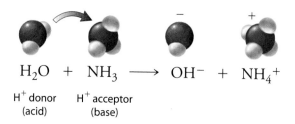

$$H_2O + NH_3 \longrightarrow OH^- + NH_4^+$$

H⁺ donor   H⁺ acceptor
(acid)   (base)

This reaction results in the formation of an ammonium ion and a **hydroxide ion**, which, as shown in Figure 10.4, is a water molecule without the nucleus of one of the hydrogen atoms.

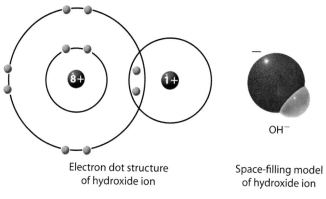

Electron dot structure
of hydroxide ion

Space-filling model
of hydroxide ion

Total protons	9+
Total electrons	10−
Net charge	1−

Figure 10.4
Hydroxide ions have a net negative charge, which is a consequence of having lost a proton. Like hydronium ions, they play a part in many acid–base reactions.

An important aspect of the Brønsted–Lowry definition is that it recognizes acid–base as a *behavior*. We say, for example, that hydrogen chloride *behaves* as an acid when mixed with water, which *behaves* as a base. Similarly, ammonia *behaves* as a base when mixed with water, which under this circumstance *behaves* as an acid. Because acid–base is seen as a behavior, there is really no contradiction when a chemical like water behaves as a base in one instance but as an acid in another instance. By analogy, consider yourself. You are who you are, but your behavior changes depending on whom you are with. Likewise, it is a chemical property of water to behave as a base (accept H^+) when mixed with hydrogen chloride and as an acid (donate H^+) when mixed with ammonia.

The products of an acid–base reaction can also behave as acids or bases. An ammonium ion, for example, may donate a hydrogen ion back to a hydroxide ion to re-form ammonia and water:

$$H_2O + NH_3 \longleftarrow OH^- + NH_4^+$$

H⁺ acceptor   H⁺ donor
(base)   (acid)

Forward and reverse acid–base reactions proceed simultaneously and can therefore be represented as occurring at the same time by using two oppositely facing arrows:

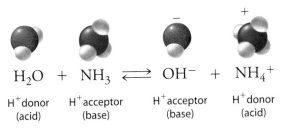

$$H_2O \; + \; NH_3 \; \rightleftharpoons \; OH^- \; + \; NH_4{}^+$$

H^+ donor (acid)	H^+ acceptor (base)	H^+ acceptor (base)	H^+ donor (acid)

When the equation is viewed from left to right, the ammonia behaves as a base because it accepts a hydrogen ion from the water, which therefore acts as an acid. Viewed in the reverse direction, the equation shows that the ammonium ion behaves as an acid because it donates a hydrogen ion to the hydroxide ion, which therefore behaves as a base.

Concept Check ✓

Identify the acid or base behavior of each participant in the reaction

$$H_2PO_4{}^- + H_3O^+ \; \rightleftharpoons \; H_3PO_4 + H_2O$$

Was this your answer? In the forward reaction (left to right), $H_2PO_4{}^-$ gains a hydrogen ion to become H_3PO_4. In accepting the hydrogen ion, $H_2PO_4{}^-$ is behaving as a base. It gets the hydrogen ion from the H_3O^+, which is behaving as an acid. In the reverse direction, H_3PO_4 loses a hydrogen ion to become $H_2PO_4{}^-$ and is thus behaving as an acid. The recipient of the hydrogen ion is the H_2O, which is behaving as a base as it transforms to H_3O^+.

A Salt Is the Ionic Product of an Acid–Base Reaction

In everyday language, the word *salt* implies sodium chloride, NaCl, table salt. In the language of chemistry, however, **salt** is a general term meaning any ionic compound formed from the reaction between an acid and a base. Hydrogen chloride and sodium hydroxide, for example, react to produce the salt sodium chloride and water:

$$HCl \; + \; NaOH \; \longrightarrow \; NaCl \; + \; H_2O$$

Hydrogen chloride (acid)	Sodium hydroxide (base)	Sodium chloride (salt)	Water

Similarly, the reaction between hydrogen chloride and potassium hydroxide yields the salt potassium chloride and water:

$$HCl \; + \; KOH \; \longrightarrow \; KCl \; + \; H_2O$$

Hydrogen chloride (acid)	Potassium hydroxide (base)	Potassium chloride (salt)	Water

Figure 10.5
"Salt-free" table-salt substitutes contain potassium chloride in place of sodium chloride. Caution is advised in using these products, however, because excessive quantities of potassium salts can lead to serious illness. Furthermore, sodium ions are a vital component of our diet and should never be totally excluded. For a good balance of these two important ions, you might inquire about commercially available half-and-half mixtures of sodium chloride and potassium chloride such as the one shown here.

Potassium chloride is the main ingredient in "salt-free" table salt, as noted in Figure 10.5.

Salts are generally far less corrosive than the acids and bases from which they are formed. A corrosive chemical has the power to disintegrate a material or wear away its surface. Hydrogen chloride is a remarkably corrosive acid, which makes it useful for cleaning toilet bowls and etching metal surfaces. Sodium hydroxide is a very corrosive base used for unclogging drains. Mixing hydrogen chloride and sodium hydroxide together in equal portions, however, produces an aqueous solution of sodium chloride—salt water, which is nowhere near as destructive as either starting material.

There are as many salts as there are acids and bases. Sodium cyanide, NaCN, is a deadly poison. "Salt peter," which is potassium nitrate, KNO_3, is useful as a fertilizer and in the formulation of gun powder. Calcium chloride, $CaCl_2$, is commonly used to de-ice roads, and sodium fluoride, NaF, prevents tooth decay. The acid–base reactions forming these salts are shown in Table 10.1.

The reaction between an acid and a base is called a **neutralization** reaction. As can be seen in the color-coding of the neutralization reactions in Table 10.1, the positive ion of a salt comes from the base and the negative ion comes from the acid. The remaining hydrogen and hydroxide ions join to form water.

Not all neutralization reactions result in the formation of water. In the presence of hydrogen chloride, for example, the drug cocaine behaves as a base by accepting H^+ from a hydrogen chloride. The negative Cl^- then attaches to form the salt cocaine hydrochloride, shown in Figure 10.6. This salt of cocaine is soluble in water and can be absorbed through the moist membranes of the nasal passages or mouth. The nonsalt form of cocaine,

Table 10.1

Acid–Base Reactions and The Salts Formed

Acid		Base		Salt		Water
HCN	+	NaOH	$\longrightarrow$	NaCN	+	H_2O
Hydrogen cyanide		Sodium hydroxide		Sodium cyanide		
HNO_3	+	KOH	$\longrightarrow$	KNO_3	+	H_2O
Nitric acid		Potassium hydroxide		Potassium nitrate		
2 HCl	+	$Ca(OH)_2$	$\longrightarrow$	$CaCl_2$	+	2 H_2O
Hydrogen chloride		Calcium hydroxide		Calcium chloride		
HF	+	NaOH	$\longrightarrow$	NaF	+	H_2O
Hydrogen fluoride		Sodium hydroxide		Sodium flouride		

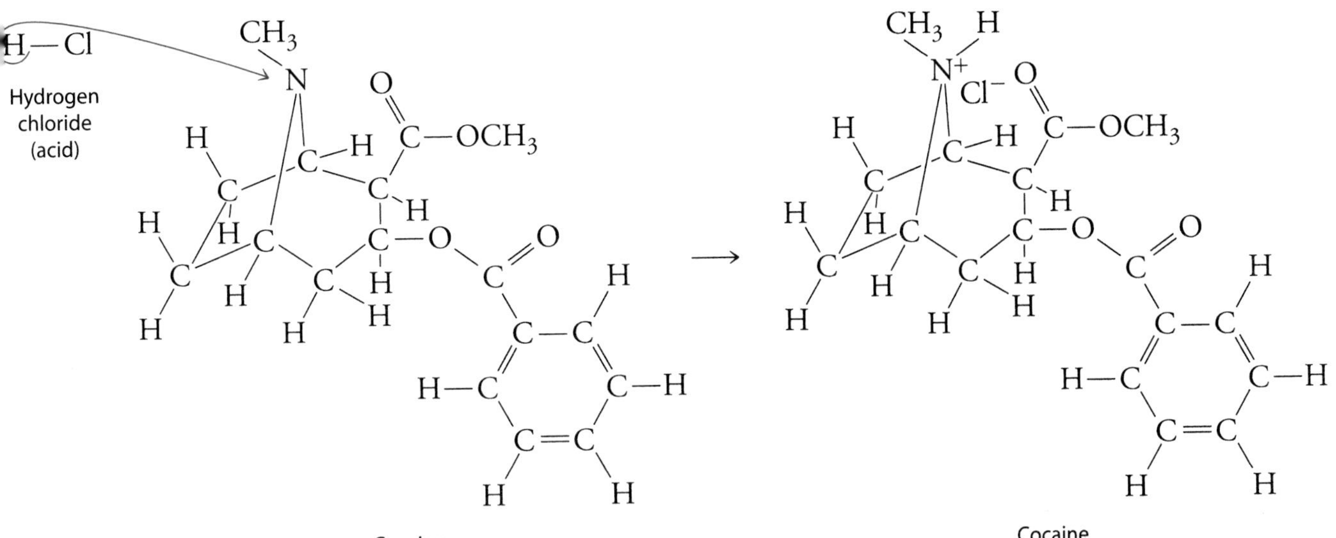

Figure 10.6
Hydrogen chloride and cocaine react to form the salt cocaine hydrochloride, which, because of its solubility in water, is readily absorbed into the body through moist membranes.

also known as "free-base cocaine" or "crack cocaine," is a nonpolar material that vaporizes easily when heated. Its vapors are inhaled directly into the lungs, resulting in dangerously high concentrations of cocaine in the bloodstream. We shall return to the actions of various drugs in Chapter 14.

Concept Check ✓

Is a neutralization reaction best described as a physical change or a chemical change?

Was this your answer? New chemicals are formed during a neutralization reaction, meaning the reaction is a chemical change.

10.2 Some Acids and Bases Are Stronger Than Others

In general, the stronger an acid, the more readily it donates hydrogen ions. Likewise, the stronger a base, the more readily it accepts hydrogen ions. An example of a strong acid is hydrogen chloride, HCl, and an example of a strong base is sodium hydroxide, NaOH. The corrosiveness of these materials is a result of their strength.

One way to assess the strength of an acid or base is to measure how much of it remains after it has been added to water. If little remains, the acid or base is strong. If a lot remains, the acid or base is weak. To illustrate this concept, consider what happens when the strong acid hydrogen chloride is added to water and what happens when the weak acid acetic acid, $C_2H_4O_2$ (the active ingredient of vinegar), is added to water.

Being an acid, hydrogen chloride donates hydrogen ions to water, forming chloride ions and hydronium ions. Because HCl is such a strong acid, nearly all of it is converted to these ions, as is shown in Figure 10.7.

Figure 10.7
Immediately after hydrogen chloride, which is a gaseous substance, is added to water, it reacts with the water to form hydronium ions and chloride ions. That very little HCl remains (none shown here) tells us that HCl is a strong acid.

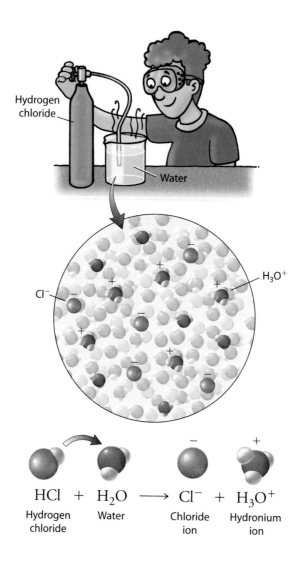

$$HCl + H_2O \longrightarrow Cl^- + H_3O^+$$

Hydrogen   Water   Chloride   Hydronium
chloride   ion   ion

Because acetic acid is a weak acid, it has much less tendency to donate hydrogen ions to water. When this acid is dissolved in water, only a small portion of the acetic acid molecules are converted to ions, which occurs as the polar O–H bonds are broken (the C–H bonds of acidic acid are unaffected by the water because of their nonpolarity). The majority of acetic acid molecules remain intact in their original nonionized form, as shown in Figure 10.8.

Figures 10.7 and 10.8 show the submicroscopic behavior of strong and weak acids in water. However, molecules and ions are too small to see. How then does a chemist measure the strength of an acid? One way is by measuring a solution's ability to conduct an electric current, as Figure 10.9 illustrates. In pure water there are practically no ions to conduct electricity. When a strong acid is dissolved in water many ions are generated, as indicated in Figure 10.7. The presence of these ions allows for the flow of a large electric current. A weak acid dissolved in water generates only a few ions, as indicated in Figure 10.8. The presence of fewer ions means there can be only a small electric current.

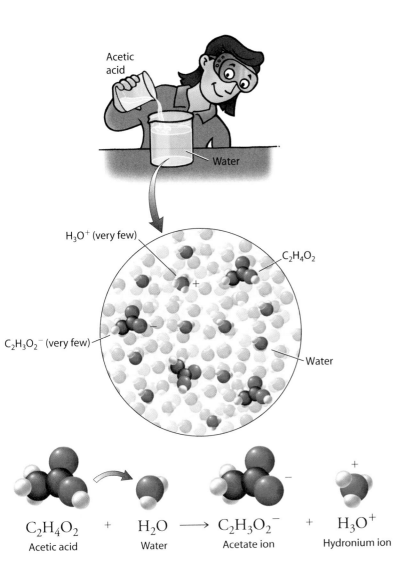

Acetic
acid

Water

H₃O⁺ (very few)

$C_2H_4O_2$

$C_2H_3O_2^-$ (very few)

Water

Figure 10.8
When liquid acetic acid is added to water, only a few acetic acid molecules react with water to form ions. The majority of the acetic acid molecules remain in their nonionized form, which tells us that acetic acid is a weak acid.

$$C_2H_4O_2 \quad + \quad H_2O \longrightarrow C_2H_3O_2^- \quad + \quad H_3O^+$$

Acetic acid   Water   Acetate ion   Hydronium ion

(a)

(b)

(c)

Figure 10.9
(a) The pure water in this circuit is unable to conduct electricity because it contains practically no ions. The light bulb in the circuit therefore remains unlit. (b) Because HCl is a strong acid, nearly all of its molecules break apart in water, giving a high concentration of ions, which are able to conduct an electric current that lights the bulb. (c) Acetic acid, $C_2H_4O_2$, is a weak acid, and in water only a small portion of its molecules break up into ions. Because fewer ions are generated, only a weak current exists and the bulb is dimmer.

This same trend is seen with strong and weak bases. Strong bases, for example, tend to accept hydrogen ions more readily than weak bases. In solution, a strong base allows the flow of a large electric current and a weak base allows the flow of a small electric current.

Concept Check ✓

According to the aqueous solutions illustrated here, which is the stronger base, NH_3 or NaOH:

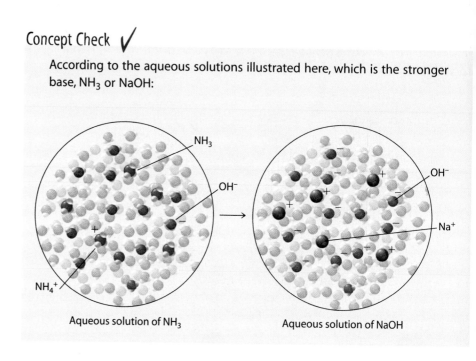

Aqueous solution of NH_3 Aqueous solution of NaOH

Was this your answer? The solution on the right contains the greater number of ions, meaning sodium hydroxide, NaOH, is the stronger base. Ammonia, NH_3, is the weaker base, indicated by the relatively few ions in the solution on the left.

Just because an acid or base is strong doesn't mean a solution of that acid or base is corrosive. The corrosive action of an acidic solution is caused by the hydronium ions rather than by the acid that generated those hydronium ions. Similarly, the corrosive action of a basic solution results from the hydroxide ions it contains, regardless of the base that generated those hydroxide ions. A *very* dilute solution of a strong acid or a strong base may have little corrosive action because in such solutions there are only a few hydronium or hydroxide ions. (Almost all the molecules of the strong acid or base break up into ions, but, because the solution is dilute, there are only a few acid or base molecules to begin with. As a result, there are only a few hydronium or hydroxide ions.) You shouldn't be too alarmed, therefore, when you discover that some toothpastes are formulated with small amounts of sodium hydroxide, one of the strongest bases known.

On the other hand, a concentrated solution of a weak acid, such as acetic acid, may be just as corrosive as or even more corrosive than a dilute solution of a strong acid, such as hydrogen chloride. The relative strengths of two acids in solution or two bases in solution, therefore, can be compared only when the two solutions have the same concentration.

10.3 Solutions Can Be Acidic, Basic, or Neutral

A substance whose ability to behave as an acid is about the same as its ability to behave as a base is said to be **amphoteric**. Water is a good example. Because it is amphoteric, water has the ability to react with itself. In behaving as an acid, a water molecule donates a hydrogen ion to a neighboring water molecule, which in accepting the hydrogen ion is behaving as a base. This reaction produces a hydroxide ion and a hydronium ion, which react together to re-form the water:

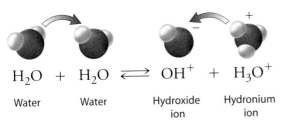

$$H_2O \;+\; H_2O \;\rightleftharpoons\; OH^+ \;+\; H_3O^+$$

| Water | Water | Hydroxide ion | Hydronium ion |

From this reaction we can see that, in order for a water molecule to gain a hydrogen ion, a second water molecule must lose a hydrogen ion. This means that for every one hydronium ion formed, there is also one hydroxide ion formed. In pure water, therefore, the total number of hydronium ions must be the same as the total number of hydroxide ions. Experiments reveal that the concentration of hydronium and hydroxide ions in pure water is extremely low—about 0.0000001 M for each, where M stands for molarity or moles per liter (Section 7.2). Water by itself, therefore, is a very weak acid as well as a very weak base, as evidenced by the unlit light bulb in Figure 10.9a.

Concept Check ✔

Do water molecules react with one another?

Was this your answer? Yes, but not to any large extent. When they do react, they form hydronium and hydroxide ions. (Note: Make sure you understand this point because it serves as a basis for most of the rest of the chapter.)

Further experiments reveal an interesting rule pertaining to the concentrations of hydronium and hydroxide ions in any solution that contains water. The concentration of hydronium ions in any aqueous solution multiplied by the concentration of the hydroxide ions in the solution always equals the constant K_w, which is a very, very small number:

concentration H_3O^+ × concentration OH^- = K_w
$$= 0.00000000000001$$

Concentration is usually given as molarity, which is indicated by abbreviating this equation using brackets:

$$[H_3O^+] \times [OH^-] = K_w = 0.00000000000001$$

The brackets mean this equation is read "the molarity of H_3O^+ times the molarity of OH^- equals K_w." Writing in scientific notation (see Appendix A), we have

$$[H_3O^+][OH^-] = K_w = 1.0 \times 10^{-14}$$

For pure water, the value of K_w is the concentration of hydronium ions, 0.0000001 M, multiplied by the concentration of hydroxide ions, 0.0000001 M, which can be written in scientific notation as

$$[1.0 \times 10^{-7}][1.0 \times 10^{-7}] = K_w = 1.0 \times 10^{-14}$$

The constant value of K_w is quite significant because it means that, *no matter what is dissolved in the water*, the product of the hydronium ion and hydroxide ion concentrations always equals 1.0×10^{-14}. This means that if the concentration of H_3O^+ goes up, the concentration of OH^- must go down so that the product of the two remains 1.0×10^{-14}.

Suppose, for example, that a small amount of HCl is added to pure water to increase the concentration of hydronium ions to 1.0×10^{-5} M. Be sure to see Appendix A if you're confused as to how 10^{-5} is larger than 10^{-7}. The hydroxide ion concentration decreases to 1.0×10^{-9} M so that the product of the two remains equal to $K_w = 1.0 \times 10^{-14}$:

$$[H_3O^+][OH^-] = K_w = 1.0 \times 10^{-14}$$

pure water $\quad [1.0 \times 10^{-7}][1.0 \times 10^{-7}] = K_w = 1.0 \times 10^{-14}$

HCl added $\quad [1.0 \times 10^{-5}][1.0 \times 10^{-9}] = K_w = 1.0 \times 10^{-14}$

The hydroxide ion concentration goes down because some of the hydroxide ions from the water are neutralized by the added hydronium ions from the HCl, as shown in Figure 10.10. In a similar manner, adding a base to water increases the hydroxide ion concentration. The response is a decrease in the hydronium ion concentration as hydronium ions from the water become neutralized by the added hydroxide ions from the base, as shown in Figure 10.10. The net result is that the product of the hydronium and hydroxide ion concentrations is always equal to the constant $K_w = 1.0 \times 10^{-14}$.

Concept Check ✓

1. In pure water, the hydroxide ion concentration is 1.0×10^{-7} M. What is the hydronium ion concentration?
2. What is the concentration of hydronium ions in a solution if the concentration of hydroxide ions is 1.0×10^{-3} M?

Were these your answers?

1. 1.0×10^{-7} M, because in pure water $[H_3O^+] = [OH^-]$.
2. 1.0×10^{-11} M, because $[H_3O^+][OH^-]$ must equal $1.0 \times 10^{-14} = K_w$.

Figure 10.10
Neutral water contains as many hydronium ions as hydroxide ions. When the acid HCl is added to water, hydronium ions from the added HCl neutralize hydroxide ions from the water, thereby decreasing the hydroxide ion concentration. When the base NaOH is added to water, the added hydroxide ions neutralize hydronium ions from the water, thereby decreasing the hydronium ion concentration.

An aqueous solution can be described as acidic, basic, or neutral, as Figure 10.11 summarizes. An **acidic solution** is one in which the hydronium ion concentration is higher than the hydroxide ion concentration. An acidic solution is made by adding an acid to water. The effect of this addition is to increase the concentration of hydronium ions, which necessarily decreases the concentration of hydroxide ions. A **basic solution** is one in which the hydroxide ion concentration is higher than the hydronium ion concentration. A basic solution is made by adding a base to water. This addition increases the concentration of hydroxide ions, which necessarily decreases the concentration of hydronium ions. A **neutral solution** is one in which the hydronium ion concentration equals the hydroxide ion concentration. Pure water is an example of a neutral solution—not because it contains so few hydronium and hydroxide ions but because it contains

In an **acidic** solution,
$[H_3O^+] > [OH^-]$.

In a **basic** solution,
$[H_3O^+] < [OH^-]$.

In a **neutral** solution,
$[H_3O^+] = [OH^-]$.

Figure 10.11
The relative concentrations of hydronium and hydroxide ions determine whether a solution is acidic, basic, or neutral.

equal numbers of them. A neutral solution is also obtained when equal quantities of acid and base are combined, which is why acids and bases are said to *neutralize* each other.

Concept Check ✓

How does adding ammonia, NH_3, to water make a basic solution when there are no hydroxide ions in the formula for ammonia?

Was this your answer? Ammonia indirectly increases the hydroxide ion concentration by reacting with water:

$$NH_3 + H_2O \longrightarrow NH_4^+ + OH^-$$

This reaction raises the hydroxide ion concentration, which has the effect of lowering the hydronium ion concentration. With the hydroxide ion concentration now higher than the hydronium ion concentration, the solution is basic.

The pH Scale Is Used To Describe Acidity

The *pH scale* is a numeric scale used to express the acidity of a solution. Mathematically, **pH** is equal to the negative logarithm of the hydronium ion concentration:

$$pH = -\log[H_3O^+]$$

Consider a neutral solution that has a hydronium ion concentration of 1.0×10^{-7} *M*. To find the pH of this solution, we first take the logarithm of this value, which is -7 (see the Calculation Corner on logarithms). The pH is by definition the negative of this value, which means $-(-7) = +7$. Hence, in a neutral solution, where the hydronium ion concentration equals 1.0×10^{-7} *M*, the pH is 7.

Acidic solutions have pH values less than 7. For an acidic solution in which the hydronium ion concentration is 1.0×10^{-4} *M*, for example, $pH = -\log(1.0 \times 10^{-4}) = 4$. The more acidic a solution is, the greater its hydronium ion concentration and the lower its pH.

Basic solutions have pH values greater than 7. For a basic solution in which the hydronium ion concentration is 1.0×10^{-8} *M*, for example, $pH = -\log(1.0 \times 10^{-8}) = 8$. The more basic a solution is, the smaller its hydroniium ion concentration and the higher its pH.

Figure 10.12 shows typical pH values of some familiar solutions, and Figure 10.13 shows two common ways of determining pH values.

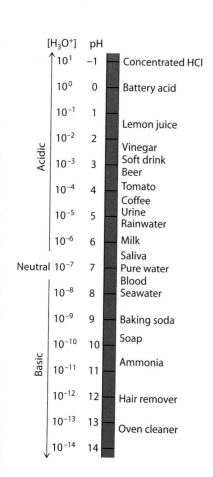

$[H_3O^+]$	pH	
10^1	-1	Concentrated HCl
10^0	0	Battery acid
10^{-1}	1	
		Lemon juice
10^{-2}	2	
		Vinegar
10^{-3}	3	Soft drink
		Beer
10^{-4}	4	Tomato
		Coffee
10^{-5}	5	Urine
		Rainwater
10^{-6}	6	Milk
		Saliva
10^{-7}	7	Pure water
		Blood
10^{-8}	8	Seawater
10^{-9}	9	Baking soda
10^{-10}	10	Soap
10^{-11}	11	Ammonia
10^{-12}	12	Hair remover
10^{-13}	13	Oven cleaner
10^{-14}	14	

Acidic · Neutral · Basic

Figure 10.12
The pH values of some common solutions.

Calculation Corner: Logarithms and pH

The logarithm of a number can be found on any scientific calculator by typing in the number and pressing the [log] button. What the calculator does is find the power to which 10 is raised to give the number.

The logarithm of 10^2, for example, is 2 because that is the power to which 10 is raised to give the number 10^2. If you know that 10^2 is equal to 100, then you'll understand that the logarithm of 100 also is 2. Check this out on your calculator. Similarly, the logarithm of 1000 is 3 because 10 raised to the third power, 10^3, equals 1000.

Any positive number, including a very small one, has a logarithm. The logarithm of $0.0001 = 10^{-4}$, for example, is -4 (the power to which 10 is raised to equal this number).

Example
What is the logarithm of 0.01?

Answer
The number 0.01 is 10^{-2} (see Appendix A), the logarithm of which is -2 (the power to which 10 is raised).

The concentration of hydronium ions in most solutions is typically much less than 1 M. Recall, for example, that in neutral water the hydronium ion concentration is 0.0000001 M (10^{-7} M). The logarithm of any number smaller than 1 (but greater than zero) is a negative number. The definition of pH includes the minus sign so as to transform the logarithm of the hydronium ion concentration to a positive number.

When a solution has a hydronium ion concentration of 1 M, the pH is 0 because 1 $M = 10^0$ M. A 10 M solution has a pH of -1 because 10 $M = 10^1$ M.

Example
What is the pH of a solution that has a hydronium ion concentration of 0.001 M?

Answer
The number 0.001 is 10^{-3}, and so

$$
\begin{aligned}
\text{pH} &= -\log[H_3O^+] \\
&= -\log 10^{-3} \\
&= -(-3) = 3
\end{aligned}
$$

Your Turn
1. What is the logarithm of 10^5?

2. What is the logarithm of 100,000?

3. What is the pH of a solution having a hydronium ion concentration of 10^{-9} M? Is this solution acidic, basic, or neutral?

(a)

(b)

Figure 10.13
(a) The pH of a solution can be measured electronically using a pH meter. (b) A rough estimate of the pH of a solution can be obtained with litmus paper, which is coated with a dye that changes color with pH.

Hands-On Chemistry: Rainbow Cabbage

The pH of a solution can be approximated with a *pH indicator*, which is any chemical whose color changes with pH. Many pH indicators are found in plants; the pigment of red cabbage is a good example. This pigment is red at low pH values (1 to 5), light purple around neutral pH values (6 to 7), light green at moderately alkaline pH values (8 to 11), and dark green at very alkaline pH values (12 to 14).

Safety Note

Wear safety glasses. Do not use bleach products because they will oxidize the pigment, rendering it insensitive to any changes in pH. You also do not want to run the risk of accidentally mixing a bleach solution with the toilet-bowl cleaner because the resulting solution would generate harmful chlorine gas.

What You Need

Head of red cabbage, small pot, water, four colorless plastic cups or drinking glasses, toilet-bowl cleaner, vinegar, baking soda, ammonia cleanser.

Procedure

① Shred about a quarter of the head of red cabbage and boil the shredded cabbage in 2 cups of water for about 5 minutes. Strain and collect the broth, which contains the pH-indicating pigment.

② Pour one-fourth of the broth into each cup. (If the cups are plastic, either allow the broth to cool before pouring or dilute with cold water.)

③ Add a small amount of toilet-bowl cleaner to the first cup, a small amount of vinegar to the second cup, baking soda to the third, and ammonia solution to the fourth.

④ Use the different colors to estimate the pH of each solution.

⑤ Mix some of the acidic and basic solutions together and note the rapid change in pH (indicated by the change in color).

10.4 Rainwater Is Acidic and Ocean Water Is Basic

Rainwater is naturally acidic. One source of this acidity is carbon dioxide, the same gas that gives fizz to soda drinks. There is 670 billion tons of CO_2 in the atmosphere, most of it from such natural sources as volcanoes and decaying organic matter but a growing amount from human activities.

Water in the atmosphere reacts with carbon dioxide to form *carbonic acid*:

$$CO_2(g) + H_2O(\ell) \longrightarrow H_2CO_3(aq)$$

Carbon   Water   Carbonic
dioxide   acid

Carbonic acid, as its name implies, behaves as an acid and lowers the pH of water. The CO_2 in the atmosphere brings the pH of rainwater to about

5.6—noticeably below the neutral pH value of 7. Because of local fluctuations, the normal pH of rainwater varies between 5 and 7. This natural acidity of rainwater may accelerate the erosion of land and, under the right circumstances, can lead to the formation of underground caves, as was discussed in this chapter's introduction.

By convention, *acid rain* is a term used for rain having a pH lower than 5. Acid rain is created when airborne pollutants such as sulfur dioxide are absorbed by atmospheric moisture. Sulfur dioxide is readily converted to sulfur trioxide, which reacts with water to form *sulfuric acid*:

$$2\ SO_2(g)\ +\ O_2(g)\ \longrightarrow\ 2\ SO_3(g)$$

Sulfur   Oxygen   Sulfur
dioxide   trioxide

$$SO_3(g)\ +\ H_2O(\ell)\ \longrightarrow\ H_2SO_4(aq)$$

Sulfur   Oxygen   Sulfuric
trioxide   acid

As noted at the beginning of the chapter, the sulfuric acid that helped create the great chambers of Carlsbad Caverns was generated from sulfur dioxide (and hydrogen sulfide) from subterranean fossil-fuel deposits. When we burn these fossil fuels, the reactants that produce sulfuric acid are emitted into the atmosphere. Each year, for example, about 20 million tons of SO_2 is released into the atmosphere by the combustion of sulfur-containing coal and oil. Sulfuric acid is much stronger than carbonic acid, and as a result rain laced with sulfuric acid eventually corrodes metal, paint, and other exposed substances. Each year the damage costs billions of dollars. The cost to the environment is also high. Many rivers and lakes receiving acid rain become less capable of sustaining life. Much vegetation that receives acid rain doesn't survive. This is particularly evident in heavily industrialized regions.

(b)

(a)

Figure 10.14
(a) The two photographs in (a) show the same obelisk before and after the effects of acid rain. (b) Many forests downwind from heavily industrialized areas, such as in the northeastern United States and in Europe, have been noticeably hard hit by acid rain.

Concept Check ✓

When sulfuric acid, H_2SO_4, is added to water, what makes the resulting aqueous solution corrosive?

Was this your answer? Because H_2SO_4 is a strong acid, it readily forms hydronium ions when dissolved in water. Hydronium ions are responsible for the corrosive action.

The environmental impact of acid rain depends on local geology, as Figure 10.15 illustrates. In certain regions, such as the midwestern United States, the ground contains significant quantities of the alkaline compound calcium carbonate (limestone), deposited when these lands were submerged under oceans 200 million years ago. Acid rain pouring into these regions is

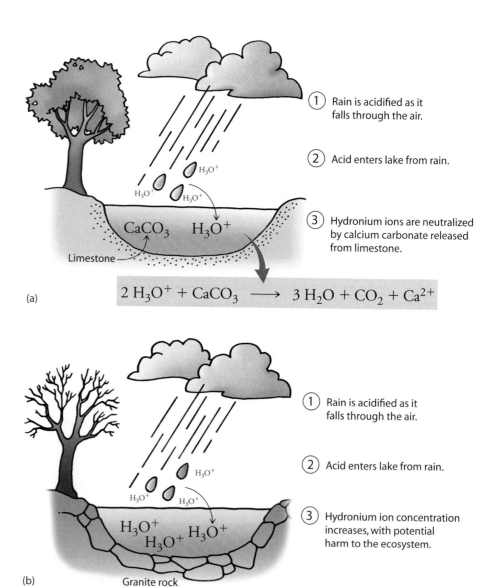

1. Rain is acidified as it falls through the air.

2. Acid enters lake from rain.

3. Hydronium ions are neutralized by calcium carbonate released from limestone.

$$2\ H_3O^+ + CaCO_3 \longrightarrow 3\ H_2O + CO_2 + Ca^{2+}$$

(a)

1. Rain is acidified as it falls through the air.

2. Acid enters lake from rain.

3. Hydronium ion concentration increases, with potential harm to the ecosystem.

(b)

Figure 10.15
(a) The damaging effects of acid rain do not appear in bodies of fresh water lined with calcium carbonate, which neutralizes any acidity. (b) Lakes and rivers lined with inert materials are not protected.

often neutralized by the calcium carbonate before any damage is done. (Figure 10.16 shows calcium carbonate neutralizing an acid.) In the northeastern United States and many other regions, however, the ground contains very little calcium carbonate and is composed primarily of chemically less reactive materials, such as granite. In these regions, the effect of acid rain on lakes and rivers accumulates.

One demonstrated solution to this problem is to raise the pH of acidified lakes and rivers by adding calcium carbonate—a process known as *liming.* The cost of transporting the calcium carbonate coupled with the need to monitor treated water systems closely limits liming to only a small fraction of the vast number of water systems already affected. Furthermore, as acid rain continues to pour into these regions, the need to lime also continues.

A longer-term solution to acid rain is to prevent most of the generated sulfur dioxide and other pollutants from entering the atmosphere in the first place. Toward this end, smokestacks have been designed or retrofitted to minimize the quantities of pollutants released. Though costly, the positive effects of these adjustments have been demonstrated, as we discuss in Section 18.2. An ultimate long-term solution, however, would be a shift from fossil fuels to cleaner energy sources, such as nuclear and solar energy, as we discuss in Chapter 19.

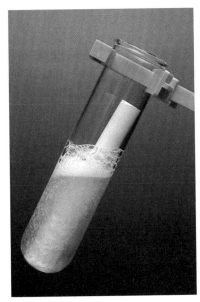

Figure 10.16
Most chalks are made from calcium carbonate, which is the same chemical found in limestone. The addition of even a weak acid, such as the acetic acid of vinegar, produces hydronium ions that react with the calcium carbonate to form several products, the most notable being carbon dioxide, which rapidly bubbles out of solution. Try this for yourself! If the bubbling is not as vigorous as shown here, then the chalk is made of other mineral components.

Concept Check ✔

What kind of lakes are protected against the negative effects of acid rain?

Was this your answer? Lakes that have a floor consisting of basic minerals, such as limestone, are more resistant to acid rain because the chemicals of the limestone (mostly calcium carbonate, $CaCO_3$) neutralize any incoming acid.

It should come as no surprise that the amount of carbon dioxide put into the atmosphere by human activities is growing. What is surprising, however, is that studies indicate that the atmospheric concentration of CO_2 is not increasing proportionately. A likely explanation has to do with the oceans and is illustrated in Figure 10.17 on page 316. When atmospheric CO_2 dissolves in any body of water—a raindrop, a lake, or the ocean—it forms carbonic acid. In fresh water, this carbonic acid transforms back to water and carbon dioxide, which is released back into the atmosphere. Carbonic acid in the ocean, however, is quickly neutralized by dissolved alkaline substances such as calcium carbonate (the ocean is alkaline, pH ≈ 8.2). The products of this neutralization eventually end up on the ocean floor as insoluble solids. Thus carbonic acid neutralization in the ocean prevents CO_2 from being released back into the atmosphere. The ocean therefore is a carbon dioxide *sink*—most of the CO_2 that goes in doesn't come out. So, pushing more CO_2 into our atmosphere means pushing more of it into our vast oceans. This is another of the many ways in which the oceans regulate our global environment.

Figure 10.17
Carbon dioxide forms carbonic acid upon entering any body of water. In fresh water, this reaction is reversible, and the carbon dioxide is released back into the atmosphere. In the alkaline ocean, the carbonic acid is neutralized to compounds such as calcium bicarbonate, Ca(HCO₃)₂, which precipitate to the ocean floor. As a result, most of the atmospheric carbon dioxide that enters our oceans stays there.

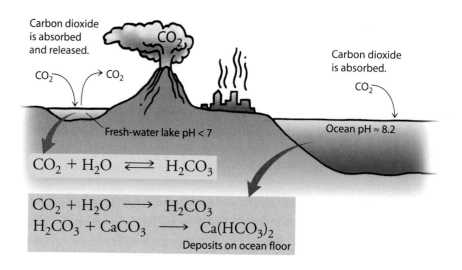

$$CO_2 + H_2O \rightleftharpoons H_2CO_3$$

$$CO_2 + H_2O \longrightarrow H_2CO_3$$
$$H_2CO_3 + CaCO_3 \longrightarrow Ca(HCO_3)_2$$
Deposits on ocean floor

Nevertheless, as Figure 10.18 shows, the concentration of atmospheric CO_2 *is* increasing. Carbon dioxide is being produced faster than the ocean can absorb it, and this may alter the Earth's environment. Carbon dioxide is a *greenhouse gas*, which means it helps keep the surface of the Earth warm by preventing infrared radiation from escaping into outer space. Without greenhouse gases in the atmosphere, the Earth's surface would average a frigid −18°C. However, with increasing concentration of CO_2 in the atmosphere, we might experience higher average temperatures. Higher temperatures may significantly alter global weather patterns as well as raise the average sea level as the polar ice caps melt and the volume of seawater increases because of thermal expansion. Global warming is explored in more detail in Section 18.4.

So we find that the pH of rain depends, in great part, on the concentration of atmospheric CO_2, which depends on the pH of the oceans. These systems are interconnected with global temperatures, which naturally connect to the countless living systems on the Earth. How true it is—all the parts are intricately connected, down to the level of atoms and molecules!

Figure 10.18
Researchers at the Mauna Loa Weather Observatory in Hawaii have recorded increasing concentrations of atmospheric carbon dioxide since they began collecting data in the 1950s. The oscillations of this graph reflect seasonal changes in CO_2 levels.

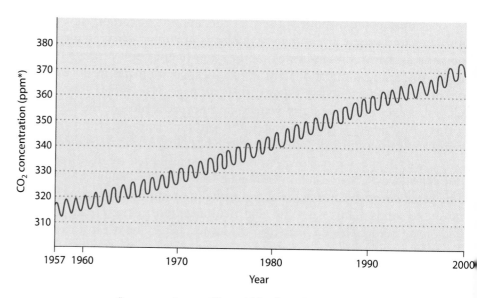

* ppm = parts per million, which tells us the number of carbon dioxide molecules for every million molecules of air.

10.5 Buffer Solutions Resist Changes in pH

A **buffer solution** is any solution that resists changes in pH. Buffer solutions work by containing two components. One component neutralizes any added base, and the other neutralizes any added acid. Effective buffer solutions can be prepared by mixing a weak acid with a salt of the weak acid. An example would be a mixture of acetic acid, $C_2H_4O_2$, and sodium acetate, $NaC_2H_4O_2$. This salt can be made by reacting acetic acid with sodium hydroxide.

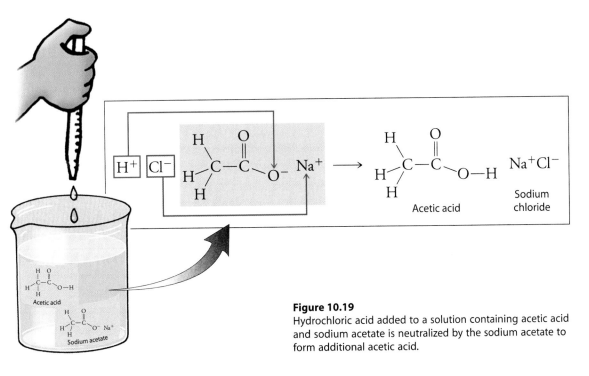

Acetic acid
(weak acid)

Sodium acetate
(salt of weak acid)

To make the buffer solution, a solution of acetic acid and a solution of sodium acetate are combined. To understand how this buffer solution resists changes in pH, first recall what happens when a strong acid is added to plain water, as in Figure 10.10b. The pH of the solution quickly *decreases* because the concentration of hydronium ions increases. Add a strong base to plain water, and you quickly *increase* the pH by decreasing the relative concentration of hydronium ions, as in Figure 10.10c.

Add the strong acid HCl to an acetic acid–sodium acetate buffer solution, however, and the H^+ ions produced by the HCl do not stay in solution to lower the pH because they react with the acetate ions, $C_2H_3O_2{}^-$, of sodium acetate to form acetic acid, as shown in Figure 10.19. (Remember

Figure 10.19
Hydrochloric acid added to a solution containing acetic acid and sodium acetate is neutralized by the sodium acetate to form additional acetic acid.

Figure 10.20
Sodium hydroxide added to a solution containing acetic acid and sodium acetate is neutralized by the acetic acid to form additional sodium acetate.

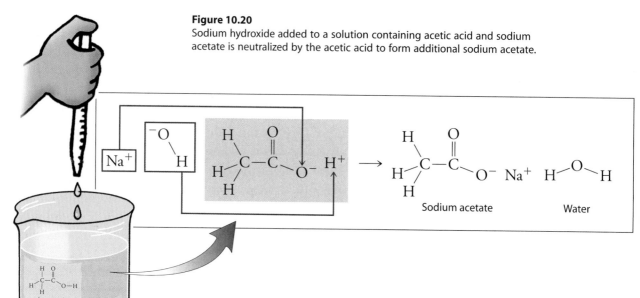

that acetic acid, being a weak acid, stays mostly in its molecular form, $HC_2H_3O_2$, and so does not contribute hydronium ions to the solution.) Add the strong base NaOH to the acetic acid–sodium acetate buffer solution, and the OH^- ions produced by the NaOH do not stay in solution to raise the pH because they combine with H^+ ions from the acetic acid to form water, as shown in Figure 10.20.

So, strong bases and acids are neutralized by the components of a buffer solution. This does not mean that the pH remains unchanged, however. When NaOH is added to the buffer system we are using as our example, sodium acetate is produced. Because sodium acetate behaves as a weak base (it accepts hydrogen ions but not very well), there is a slight increase in pH. When HCl is added, acetic acid is produced. Because acetic acid behaves as a weak acid, there is a slight decrease in pH. Buffer solutions therefore only resist *large* changes in pH.

Concept Check ✓

Why must a buffer solution consist of at least two dissolved components?

Was this your answer? One component is needed to neutralize any incoming acid, and the second component is needed to neutralize any incoming base.

There are many different buffer systems useful for maintaining particular pH values. The acetic acid–sodium acetate system is good for maintaining a pH around 4.8. Buffer solutions containing equal mixtures of a weak base and a salt of that weak base maintain alkaline pH values. For example, a buffer solution of the weak base ammonia, NH_3, and ammonium chloride, NH_4Cl is useful for maintaining a pH about 9.3.

Blood has several buffer systems that work together to maintain a narrow pH range between 7.35 and 7.45. A pH value above or below these levels can be lethal, primarily because cellular proteins become *denatured*, which is what happens to milk when vinegar is added to it.

The primary buffer system of the blood is a combination of carbonic acid and its salt sodium bicarbonate, shown in Figure 10.21. Any acid that builds up in the bloodstream is neutralized by the basic action of sodium bicarbonate, and any base that builds up is neutralized by the carbonic acid.

The carbonic acid in your blood is formed as the carbon dioxide produced by your cells enters the bloodstream and reacts with water—this is the same reaction that occurs in a raindrop, as we discussed earlier. You fine-tune the levels of blood carbonic acid, and hence your blood pH, by your breathing rate, as Figure 10.22 illustrates. Breathe too slowly or hold your breath and the amount of carbon dioxide (and hence carbonic acid) builds up, causing a slight but significant drop in pH. Hyperventilate and the carbonic acid level decreases, causing a slight but significant increase in pH. Your body uses this mechanism to protect itself from changes in blood pH. One of the symptoms of a severe overdose of aspirin, for example, is hyperventilation. Aspirin, also known as acetylsalicylic acid, is an acidic chemical that when taken in large amounts can overwhelm the blood buffering system, causing a dangerous drop in blood pH. As you hyperventilate, however, your body loses carbonic acid, which helps to maintain the proper blood pH despite the overabundance of the acidic aspirin.

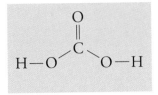

Carbonic acid
(weak acid)

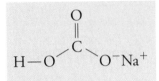

Sodium bicarbonate
(salt)

Figure 10.21
Carbonic acid and sodium bicarbonate.

(a)   (b)

Figure 10.22
(a) Hold your breath, and CO_2 builds up in your bloodstream. This increases the amount of carbonic acid, which lowers your blood pH. (b) Hyperventilate and the amount of CO_2 in your bloodstream decreases. This decreases the amount of carbonic acid, which raises your blood pH.

To summarize the concepts of this chapter, consider the gardener shown in Figure 10.23. Using a pH-measuring kit, the gardener has found that the soil pH is unacceptably low, perhaps because of local atmospheric pollutants, which may arise from natural or human-made sources. At this low pH, the soil contains an overabundance of hydronium ions, which react with many of the basic nutrients of the soil, such as ammonia, to form water-soluble salts. Because of their water solubility, these nutrients in their salt form are readily washed away with the rainwater, and as a result the soil becomes nutrient-poor. The mechanism by which plants absorb whatever nutrients do remain in the soil is also disturbed by the soil's low pH.

Figure 10.23
Raising the pH of garden soil by the addition of an alkaline mineral is known as liming.

As a result of all this, most plants do not grow well in acidic soil. To remedy this, the gardener spreads powdered limestone, a form of calcium carbonate, $CaCO_3$, which neutralizes the hydronium ions, thus raising the pH toward neutral.

Interestingly, the calcium carbonate reacts with the acidic soil to form carbon dioxide gas, which in the atmosphere helps to keep rainwater slightly acidic. This is the same gas that is generated by the cells of our bodies and tends to acidify our blood. The blood pH, however, is kept fairly constant at around 7.4 because it is buffered.

Key Terms and Matching Definitions

_____ acid
_____ acidic solution
_____ amphoteric
_____ base
_____ basic solution
_____ buffer solution
_____ hydronium ion
_____ hydroxide ion
_____ neutral solution
_____ neutralization
_____ pH
_____ salt

1. A substance that donates hydrogen ions.
2. A substance that accepts hydrogen ions.
3. A water molecule after accepting a hydrogen ion.
4. A water molecule after losing a hydrogen ion.
5. An ionic compound formed from the reaction between an acid and a base.
6. A reaction in which an acid and base combine to form a salt.
7. A description of a substance that can behave as either an acid or a base.
8. A solution in which the hydronium ion concentration is higher than the hydroxide ion concentration.
9. A solution in which the hydroxide ion concentration is higher than the hydronium ion concentration.
10. A solution in which the hydronium ion concentration is equal to the hydroxide ion concentration.
11. A measure of the acidity of a solution, equal to the negative of the base-10 logarithm of the hydronium ion concentration.
12. A solution that resists large changes in pH, made from either a weak acid and one of its salts or a weak base and one of its salts.

Review Questions

Acids Accept Protons, Bases Donate Them

1. What is the Brønsted–Lowry definition of an acid and a base?

2. When an acid is dissolved in water, what ion does the water form?

3. When a chemical loses a hydrogen ion, is it behaving as an acid or a base?

4. Does a salt always contain sodium ions?

5. What two classes of chemicals are involved in a neutralization reaction?

Some Acids and Bases Are Stronger Than Others

6. What does it mean to say that an acid is strong in aqueous solution?

7. What happens to most of the molecules of a strong acid when the acid is mixed with water?

8. Why does a solution of a strong acid conduct electricity better than a solution of a weak acid having the same concentration?

9. Which has a greater ability to accept hydrogen ions: a strong base or a weak base?

10. When can a solution of a weak base be more corrosive than a solution of a strong base?

Solutions Can Be Acidic, Basic, or Neutral

11. Is it possible for a chemical to behave as an acid in one instance and as a base in another instance?

12. Is water a strong acid or a weak acid?

13. Is K_w a very large or a very small number?

14. As the concentration of H_3O^+ ions in an aqueous solution increases, what happens to the concentration of OH^- ions?

15. What is true about the relative concentrations of hydronium and hydroxide ions in an acidic solution? How about a neutral solution? A basic solution?

16. What does the pH of a solution indicate?

17. As the hydronium ion concentration of a solution increases, does the pH of the solution increase or decrease?

Rainwater Is Acidic and Ocean Water Is Basic

18. What is the product of the reaction between carbon dioxide and water?

19. How can rain be acidic and yet not qualify as acid rain?

20. What does sulfur dioxide have to do with acid rain?

21. How do humans generate the air pollutant sulfur dioxide?

22. How does one lime a lake?

23. Why aren't atmospheric levels of carbon dioxide rising as rapidly as might be expected based on the increased output of carbon dioxide resulting from human activities?

Buffer Solutions Resist Changes in pH

24. What is a buffer solution?

25. A strong acid quickly drops the pH when added to water. Not so when added to a buffer solution. Why?

26. Do buffer solutions *prevent* or *inhibit* changes in pH?

27. Why is it so important that the pH of our blood be maintained within a narrow range of values?

28. Holding your breath causes the pH of your blood to decrease. Why?

Hands-On Chemistry Insights

Rainbow Cabbage

The change in color of a pH indicator is not permanent. Red cabbage juice brought to a pH of 4 turns red. This same solution brought to a pH of 8 turns green and then red again as it is brought back to a pH of 4. To demonstrate this, add a teaspoon of baking soda to the glass/cup to which you originally added the vinegar. The solution should turn green. (Why does this addition of baking soda also result in bubbling?) Add vinegar again to bring the color back to red.

Here is another interesting experiment. Boil a whole head of red cabbage for about 20 minutes to obtain a concentrated solution. Place several tablespoons of the concentrated broth in a large colorless glass container. Note the color and estimate the pH (the extract itself is acidic). Then quickly pour water into the container, carefully watching for any change in color. What does the changing color tell you about change in pH as you add the water? Does the pH go up or down? How can adding pure water change the pH of a solution?

Exercises

1. Suggest an explanation for why people once washed their hands with ashes.

2. What is the relationship between a hydroxide ion and a water molecule?

3. An acid and a base react to form a salt, which consists of positive and negative ions. Which forms the positive ions: the acid or the base? Which forms the negative ions?

4. Water is formed from the reaction between an acid and a base. Why is water not classified as a salt?

5. Identify the acid or base behavior of each substance in these reactions:
   a. $H_3O^+ + Cl \leftrightarrows H_2O + HCl$
   b. $H_2PO_4 + H_2O \leftrightarrows H_3O^+ + HPO_4^-$
   c. $HSO_4^- + H_2O \leftrightarrows H_3O^+ + SO_4^{2-}$

6. Identify the acid or base behavior of each substance in these reactions:
   a. $HSO_4^- + H_2O \leftrightarrows OH^- + H_2SO_4$
   b. $O^{2-} + H_2O \leftrightarrows OH^- + OH^-$

7. Sodium hydroxide, NaOH, is a strong base, which means it readily accepts hydrogen ions. What products are formed when sodium hydroxide accepts a hydrogen ion from a water molecule?

8. What happens to the corrosive properties of an acid and a base after they neutralize each other? Why?

9. What does the value of K_w say about the extent to which water molecules react with one another?

10. Why do we use the pH scale to indicate the acidity of a solution rather than simply stating the concentration of hydronium ions?

11. The amphoteric reaction between two water molecules is endothermic, which means the reaction requires the input of heat energy in order to proceed:

$$energy + H_2O + H_2O \longrightarrow H_3O^+ + OH^-$$

The warmer the water, the more heat energy is available for this reaction, and the more hydronium and hydroxide ions are formed.
   a. Does the value of K_w increase, decrease, or stay the same with increasing temperature?
   b. Which has a lower pH: pure water that is hot or pure water that is cold?
   c. Is it possible for water to be neutral but have a pH less than or greater than 7.0?

12. The pOH scale indicates the "basicity" of a solution, where $pOH = -\log[OH^-]$. For any solution, what is the sum pH + pOH always equal to?

13. When the hydronium ion concentration of a solution equals 1 mole per liter, what is the pH of the solution? Is the solution acidic or basic?

14. When the hydronium ion concentration of a solution equals 10 moles per liter, what is the pH of the solution? Is the solution acidic or basic?

15. What is the concentration of hydronium ions in a solution that has a pH of −3? Why is such a solution impossible to prepare?

16. When the pH of a solution decreases by 1, say from pH = 4 to pH = 3, by what factor does the hydronium ion concentration increase?

17. What happens to the pH of an acidic solution as pure water is added?

18. What happens to the pH of soda water as it loses its carbonation?

19. Why might a small piece of chalk be useful for alleviating acid indigestion?

20. How might you tell whether or not your toothpaste contained calcium carbonate, $CaCO_3$, or perhaps baking soda, $NaHCO_3$, without looking at the ingredients label?

21. Why do lakes lying in granite basins tend to become acidified by acid rain more readily than lakes lying in limestone basins?

22. Cutting back on the pollutants that cause acid rain is one solution to the problem of acidified lakes. Suggest another.

23. How might warmer oceans accelerate global warming?

24. Sodium bicarbonate, $NaHCO_3$,

Sodium bicarbonate
(salt)

is the active ingredient of baking soda. Compare this structure with those of the weak acids and weak bases presented in this chapter and explain how this compound by itself in solution moderates changes in pH.

25. Hydrogen chloride is added to a buffer solution of ammonia, NH_3, and ammonium chloride, NH_4Cl. What is the effect on the concentration of ammonia? On the concentration of ammonium chloride?

26. Sodium hydroxide is added to a buffer solution of ammonia, NH_3, and ammonium chloride, NH_4Cl. What is the effect on the concentration of ammonia? On the concentration of ammonium chloride?

27. At what point will a buffer solution cease to resist changes in pH?

28. Sometimes an individual going through a traumatic experience cannot stop hyperventilating. In such a circumstance, it is recommended that the individual breathe into a paper bag or cupped hands as a useful way to avoid an increase in blood pH, which can cause the person to pass out. Explain how this works.

Problems

1. What is the hydroxide ion concentration in an aqueous solution when the hydronium ion concentration is 1×10^{-10} mole per liter?

2. When the hydronium ion concentration of a solution is 1×10^{-10} mole per liter, what is the pH of the solution? Is the solution acidic or basic?

3. When the hydronium ion concentration of a solution is 1×10^{-4} mole per liter, what is the pH of the solution? Is the solution acidic or basic?

4. What is the hydroxide ion concentration in an aqueous solution having a pH of 5?

5. When the pH of a solution is 1, the concentration of hydronium ions is 10^{-1} $M = 0.1$ M. Assume that the volume of this solution is 500 mL and that the solution is not buffered. What is the pH after 500 mL of pure water is added? You will need a calculator with a logarithm function to answer this question.

Answers to Calculation Corner

Logarithms and pH

1. "What is the logarithm of 10^5?" can be rephrased as "To what power is 10 raised to give the number 10^5?" The answer is 5.

2. You should know that 100,000 is the same as 10^5. Thus the logarithm of 100,000 is 5.

3. The pH is 9, which means this is a basic solution:

$$
\begin{aligned}
pH &= -\log[H_3O^+] \\
&= -\log 10^{-9} \\
&= -(-9) \\
&= 9
\end{aligned}
$$

Suggested Web Sites

http://www.nps.gov/cave/
http://www.carlsbad.caverns.national-park.com/info.htm
http://www.nps.gov/maca/
http://www.mammoth.cave.national-park.com/info.htm
Check these official and unofficial sites for Carlsbad Caverns National Park and Mammoth Cave National Park for details on how these underground landmarks formed. Ample travel information is included.

http://www.epa.gov
Go to this home page for the Environmental Protection Agency and use *acid rain* as a keyword in their search engine to find numerous articles on this subject.

http://mloserv.mlo.hawaii.gov/mloinfo/program.htm
This address itemizes the atmospheric projects of the Climate Monitoring and Diagnostic Laboratory of the Mauna Loa Weather Observatory. Links to the Network for the Detection of Stratospheric Changes are included.

Chapter 11
Oxidation and Reduction

Transferring Electrons

In the previous chapter we discussed acid–base reactions, which are chemical reactions that involve the transfer of *protons* from one reactant to another. In this chapter, we explore reactions that involve the transfer of one or more *electrons* from one reactant to another. These are called **oxidation–reduction reactions**, and a common example is the burning of wood. Wood is mainly cellulose, a substance made up of carbon and hydrogen. As wood burns, its carbon–hydrogen bonds break and the carbon and hydrogen atoms form new bonds with oxygen molecules in the air to create carbon dioxide and water. The formation of these products involves the transfer of electrons from one atom to another and so is by definition an oxidation–reduction reaction.

We begin exploring oxidation–reduction reactions by defining necessary terms. With the background on chemical reactions given in Chapter 9, we are then ready to jump right into the various applications of oxidation–reduction reactions.

11.1 Oxidation Is the Loss of Electrons and Reduction Is the Gain of Electrons

Oxidation is the process whereby a reactant loses one or more electrons. **Reduction** is the opposite process whereby a reactant gains one or more electrons. Oxidation and reduction are complementary and simultaneous processes. They always occur together; you cannot have one without the other. The electrons lost by one chemical in an oxidation reaction don't simply disappear; they are gained by another chemical in a reduction reaction.

An oxidation–reduction reaction occurs when elemental sodium and chlorine react exothermically to form sodium chloride, as shown in Figure 11.1. The equation for this reaction is

$$2\ Na + Cl_2 \longrightarrow 2\ NaCl$$

To see how electrons are transferred in this reaction, we can look at each reactant individually. Each electrically neutral sodium atom changes to a positively charged ion—each atom loses an electron and is therefore oxidized:

$$2\ Na \longrightarrow 2\ Na^+ + 2\ e^- \quad \text{Oxidation}$$

Each electrically neutral chlorine molecule changes to two negatively charged ions—each atom gains an electron and is therefore reduced:

$$Cl_2 + 2\ e^- \longrightarrow 2\ Cl^- \quad \text{Reduction}$$

The net result is that the two electrons lost by the sodium atoms are transferred to the chlorine atoms. Therefore, the two equations shown above actually represent one process, called a **half reaction**. In other words, an electron won't be lost from a sodium atom without there being a chlorine atom available to pick up that electron. Both half reactions are required to represent the *whole* oxidation–reduction process. Half reactions are useful for showing which reactant loses electrons and which reactant gains them, which is why half reactions are used throughout this chapter.

Because the sodium causes reduction of the chlorine, the sodium is acting as a *reducing agent*, which is any reactant that causes another reactant to be reduced. Note that in behaving as a reducing agent, the sodium is oxidized—it loses electrons. Conversely, the chlorine causes oxidation of the sodium and so is acting as an *oxidizing agent*. Because it gains electrons as it causes another reactant to be oxidized, an oxidizing agent is reduced. Just remember that loss of **e**lectrons is **o**xidation, and **g**ain of **e**lectrons is **r**eduction. Here is a helpful mnemonic adapted from a once-popular children's story: **Leo** the lion went "**ger.**"

Figure 11.1
In the exothermic formation of sodium chloride, sodium metal is oxidized by chlorine gas, and chlorine gas is reduced by sodium metal.

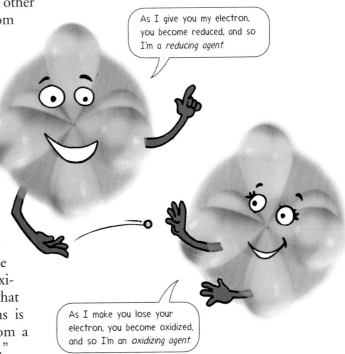

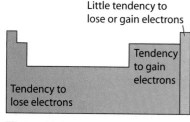

Little tendency to lose or gain electrons

Tendency to gain electrons

Tendency to lose electrons

■ More likely to behave as oxidizing agent (be reduced)

■ More likely to behave as reducing agent (be oxidized)

Figure 11.2
The ability of an atom to gain or lose electrons is a function of its position in the periodic table. Those at the upper right tend to gain electrons, and those at the lower left tend to lose them.

Different elements have different oxidation and reduction tendencies—some lose electrons more readily, while others gain electrons more readily, as Figure 11.2 illustrates. The tendency to do one or the other is a function of how strongly the atom's nucleus holds electrons. The greater the effective nuclear charge (Section 5.8), the greater the tendency of the atom to *gain* electrons. Because the atoms of elements at the upper right of the periodic table have the strongest effective nuclear charges (with the noble gases excluded), these atoms have the greatest tendency to gain electrons and hence behave as oxidizing agents. The atoms of elements at the lower left of the periodic table have the weakest effective nuclear charges and therefore the greatest tendency to *lose* electrons and behave as reducing agents.

Concept Check ✓

True or false:
1. Reducing agents are oxidized in oxidation–reduction reactions.
2. Oxidizing agents are reduced in oxidation–reduction reactions.

Were these your answers? Both statements are true.

11.2 Photography Works by Selective Oxidation and Reduction

Figure 11.3
A camera can be used to focus an image on wax paper as well as it does on photographic film.

Lay some wax paper on the back of an open unloaded camera as shown in Figure 11.3. Hold the shutter open, then focus. Voila! You have an image. Let the shutter close, however, and the image is gone. This is the same image that forms on the photographic film inside a loaded camera. The difference between the film and the wax paper is that the film is able to retain the image after the shutter has closed. How does it do that? The answer has to do with oxidation–reduction chemistry.

Follow the steps in Figure 11.4 as you read this simplified explanation of how a black-and-white photograph is produced.

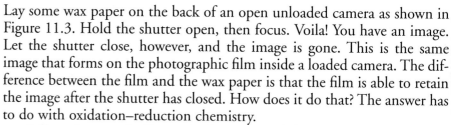

1. Unexposed black-and-white photographic film is a transparent strip of plastic coated with a gel containing microcrystals of silver bromide, AgBr. Light reflected from the subject being photographed passes through the camera lens and is focused on these microcrystals. The light causes many of the bromide ions in the microcrystals to oxidize. The electrons set loose by this oxidation are transferred to the silver ions, which are thereby reduced to opaque silver atoms. The more light received by a microcrystal, the greater the number of opaque silver atoms formed. In this way, the photographic image is encoded, and the film is said to have been *exposed*.

2. The light reflected from the subject does not typically result in the formation of enough silver atoms to make a visible image. The more silver atoms a microcrystal contains, however, the more susceptible it is to further oxidation–reduction reactions. To make a visible image, the

(1) The film is exposed.

(2) The film is developed.

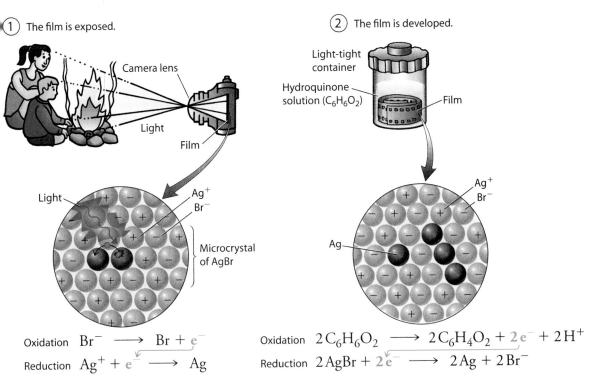

Oxidation $\quad Br^- \longrightarrow Br + e^-$

Reduction $\quad Ag^+ + e^- \longrightarrow Ag$

Oxidation $\quad 2\,C_6H_6O_2 \longrightarrow 2\,C_6H_4O_2 + 2\,e^- + 2\,H^+$

Reduction $\quad 2\,AgBr + 2\,e^- \longrightarrow 2\,Ag + 2\,Br^-$

(3) The film is fixed and washed.

Hypo solution $(Na_2S_2O_3)$ followed by water wash.

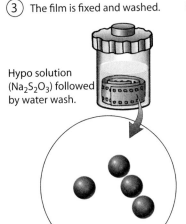

(4) The negative is dark where Ag^+ ions have been reduced to metallic silver.

(5) Light projected through the negative is captured on photographic paper as a positive image.

Figure 11.4
Black-and-white photography involves a series of oxidation–reduction reactions.

photographer puts the film in a light-tight container to prevent further exposure. Then the film is treated with a reducing agent, such as hydroquinone, $C_6H_6O_2$, which reveals the encoded image by causing the formation of many more opaque silver atoms. Through this step the image *develops*.

3. The reduction of silver ions by the hydroquinone developing solution is stopped by treating the film with a solution of sodium thiosulfate, $Na_2S_2O_3$, also called either *hypo* or *fixing solution*. The thiosulfate ion, $S_2O_3{}^{2-}$, binds with any unreduced silver ions to form a water-soluble salt. Subsequent washing with water removes everything

Hands-On Chemistry: Silver Lining

Tarnish on silverware is a coating of silver sulfide, Ag_2S, an ionic compound consisting of two silver ions, Ag^+, and one sulfide ion, S^{2-}. Tarnishing begins when silver atoms in the silverware come into contact with airborne hydrogen sulfide, H_2S, a smelly gas produced by the digestion of food in mammals and other organisms. The half reaction for the silver and hydrogen sulfide is

$$4\,Ag + 2\,H_2S \longrightarrow 4\,Ag^+ + 4\,H^+ + 2\,S^{2-} + 4\,e^- \qquad \text{Oxidation}$$

The silver ions and sulfide ions combine to form blackish silver sulfide, while at the same time the hydrogen ions and electrons combine with atmospheric oxygen to form water:

$$4\,H^+ + 4\,e^- + O_2 \longrightarrow 2\,H_2O \qquad \text{Reduction}$$

The balanced chemical equation for the tarnishing of silver is the combination of these two half reactions:

$$4\,Ag + 2\,H_2S + O_2 \longrightarrow 2\,Ag_2S + 2\,H_2O$$

From these equations we see that the hydrogen sulfide causes the silver to lose electrons to oxygen. To restore the silver to its shiny elemental state, we need to return the electrons it lost. The oxygen won't relinquish electrons back to silver, but with the proper connection, aluminum atoms will.

What You Need

Very clean aluminum pot (or non-aluminum pot and aluminum foil), water, baking soda, piece of tarnished silver

Procedure

① Put about a liter of water and several heaping tablespoons of baking soda in the aluminum pot or the non-aluminum pot containing aluminum foil.

② Bring the water to boiling and then remove the pot from the heat source.

③ Slowly immerse the tarnished silver; you'll see an immediate effect as the silver and aluminum make contact. (Add more baking soda if you don't.) Also, as the silver ions accept electrons from the aluminum and are thereby reduced to shiny silver atoms, the sulfide ions are free to re-form hydrogen sulfide gas, which is released back into the air. You may smell it!

The baking soda serves as a conductive ionic solution that permits electrons to move from the aluminum atoms to the silver ions. What is the advantage of this approach over polishing the silver with an abrasive paste?

except the silver atoms adhering to the film, which are most abundant where the greatest amount of light hit the film when the photograph was taken. The film is now *fixed.*

4. Because the silver atoms are opaque, the film appears as a *negative*, which is dark where the subject was light and light where the subject was dark.

5. Light is projected through the negative onto photographic paper, which is developed using the same reactions that produced the negative. The resulting developed image is a negative of the negative—in other words, a positive print.

Color photographic film is coated with a variety of chemicals that respond to light of different frequencies (colors). There are more oxidation–reduction reactions involved in the developing of a color photograph, but the basic principle is the same—the selective reduction of only those chemicals exposed to light. Digital photography, by contrast, is an outgrowth of photovoltaic cells, which are made of metalloids, such as silicon, that lose electrons upon exposure to light. We explore photovoltaic cells in Chapter 19 in our discussion of energy sources.

Concept Check ✓

Would a photographic negative be mostly transparent or mostly opaque if the camera shutter remained open too long and too much light fell on the film? What would the positive print from this negative look like?

Were these your answers? The more light that hits the film, the greater the number of silver ions reduced by the bromide ions or hydroquinone. The reduction of the silver ions results in opaque silver atoms that adhere to the film. Such an overexposed negative, therefore, would be mostly opaque because of all the opaque silver atoms.

The positive print would be very light because there would be very little light passing through the negative to sensitize the silver ions in the photographic paper.

11.3 The Energy of Flowing Electrons Can Be Harnessed

Electrochemistry is the study of the relationship between electrical energy and chemical change. It involves either the use of an oxidation–reduction reaction to produce an electric current or the use of an electric current to produce an oxidation–reduction reaction.

To understand how an oxidation–reduction reaction can generate an electric current, consider what happens when a reducing agent is placed in direct contact with an oxidizing agent: Electrons flow from the reducing agent to the oxidizing agent. This flow of electrons is an electric current, which is a form of kinetic energy that can be harnessed for useful purposes.

Iron, Fe, for example, is a better reducing agent than the copper ion Cu^{2+}. So when a piece of iron metal and a solution containing copper ions are placed in contact with each other, electrons flow from the iron to the copper ions, as Figure 11.5 on page 330 illustrates. The result is the oxidation of iron and the reduction of copper ions.

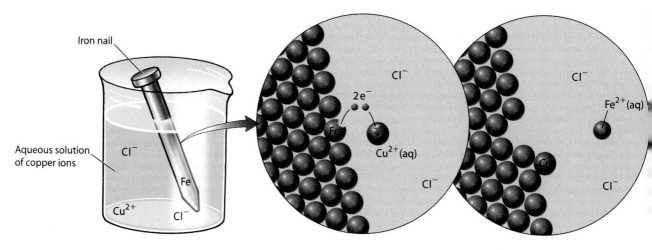

Iron nail

Aqueous solution of copper ions

Cl^-

Fe

Cu^{2+}

Cl^-

Cl^-

$2e^-$

Fe

$Cu^{2+}(aq)$

Cl^-

Cl^-

$Fe^{2+}(aq)$

Cu

Cl^-

Figure 11.5
A nail made of iron placed in a solution of Cu^{2+} ions oxidizes to Fe^{2+} ions, which dissolve in the water. At the same time, copper ions are reduced to metallic copper, which coats the nail. (Negatively charged ions, such as chloride ions, Cl^-, must also be present to balance these positively charged ions in solution.)

Oxidation $\quad Fe \longrightarrow Fe^{2+} + 2\,e^-$

Reduction $\quad Cu^{2+} + 2\,e^- \longrightarrow Cu$

The elemental iron and copper ions need not be in physical contact in order for electrons to flow between them. If they are in separate containers but bridged by a conducting wire, the electrons can flow from the iron to the copper ions through the wire. The resulting electric current in the wire could be attached to some useful device, such as a light bulb. But alas, an electric current is not sustained by this arrangement.

The reason the electric current is not sustained is shown in Figure 11.6. An initial flow of electrons through the wire immediately results in a buildup of electric charge in both containers. The container on the left builds up positive charge as it accumulates Fe^{2+} ions from the nail. The container on the right builds up negative charge as electrons accumulate on

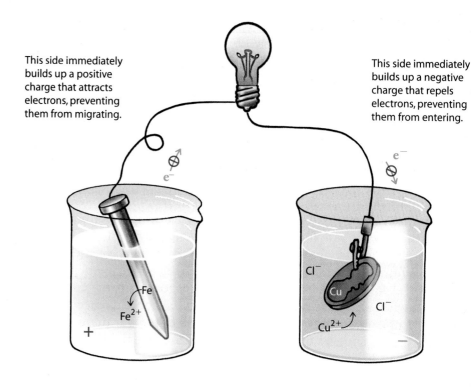

This side immediately builds up a positive charge that attracts electrons, preventing them from migrating.

This side immediately builds up a negative charge that repels electrons, preventing them from entering.

e^-

e^-

Fe

Fe^{2+}

$+$

Cl^-

Cu

Cl^-

Cu^{2+}

$-$

Figure 11.6
An iron nail is placed in water and connected by a conducting wire to a solution of copper ions. Nothing happens because this arrangement results in a buildup of charge that prevents the further flow of electrons.

his side. This situation prevents any further migration of electrons through he wire. Recall that electrons are negative, and so they are repelled by the negative charge in the right container and attracted to the positive charge in the left container. The net result is that the electrons do not flow through he wire, and the bulb remains unlit.

The solution to this problem is to allow ions to migrate into either container so that neither builds up any positive or negative charge. This is accomplished with a *salt bridge*, which may be a U-shaped tube filled with a salt, such as sodium nitrate, $NaNO_3$, and closed with semiporous plugs. Figure 11.7 shows how a salt bridge allows the ions it holds to enter either container, permitting the flow of electrons through the conducting wire and creating a complete electric circuit.

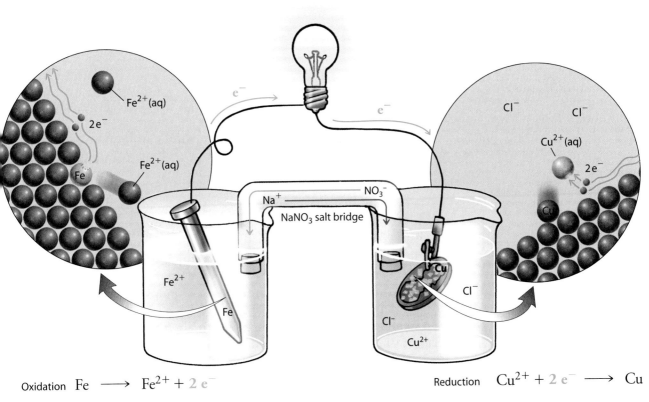

Oxidation $Fe \longrightarrow Fe^{2+} + 2\,e^-$ Reduction $Cu^{2+} + 2\,e^- \longrightarrow Cu$

Figure 11.7
The salt bridge completes the electric circuit. Electrons freed as the iron is oxidized pass through the wire to the container on the right. Nitrate ions, NO_3^-, from the salt bridge flow into the left container to balance the positive charges of the Fe^{2+} ions that form and prevent any buildup of positive charge. Meanwhile, Na^+ ions from the salt bridge enter the right container to balance the Cl^- ions "abandoned" by the Cu^{2+} ions as the Cu^{2+} ions pick up electrons to become metallic copper.

The Electricity of a Battery Comes from Oxidation–Reduction Reactions

So we see that with the proper setup it is possible to harness electrical energy from an oxidation–reduction reaction. The apparatus shown in Figure 11.7 is one example. Such devices are called *voltaic cells*. Instead of two containers, a voltaic cell can be an all-in-one, self-contained unit, in which case it is called a *battery*. Batteries are either disposable or rechargeable, and

Figure 11.8
A common dry-cell battery with a graphite rod immersed in a paste of ammonium chloride, manganese dioxide, and zinc chloride.

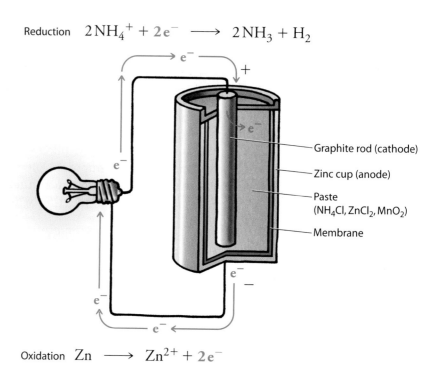

Reduction $2\,NH_4^+ + 2\,e^- \longrightarrow 2\,NH_3 + H_2$

- Graphite rod (cathode)
- Zinc cup (anode)
- Paste (NH_4Cl, $ZnCl_2$, MnO_2)
- Membrane

Oxidation $Zn \longrightarrow Zn^{2+} + 2\,e^-$

here we explore some examples of each. Although the two types differ in design and composition, they function by the same principle: Two materials that oxidize and reduce each other are connected by a medium through which ions travel to balance an external flow of electrons.

Let's look at disposable batteries first. The common *dry-cell battery* was invented in the 1860s and is still used today as probably the cheapest disposable energy source for flashlights, toys, and the like. The basic design consists of a zinc cup filled with a thick paste of ammonium chloride, NH_4Cl, zinc chloride, $ZnCl_2$, and manganese dioxide, MnO_2. Immersed in this paste is a porous stick of graphite that projects to the top of the battery, as shown in Figure 11.8.

Graphite is a good conductor of electricity, and it is at the graphite stick that the chemicals in the paste receive electrons and so are reduced. The reaction for the ammonium ions, for instance, is

$$2\,NH_4^+(aq) + 2\,e^- \longrightarrow 2\,NH_3(g) + H_2(g) \qquad \text{Reduction}$$

An **electrode** is any material that conducts electrons into or out of a medium in which electrochemical reactions are occurring. The electrode where chemicals are reduced is called a **cathode**. For any battery, such as the one shown in Figure 11.8, the cathode is always positive ($+$), which indicates that electrons are naturally attracted to this location. The electrons gained by chemicals at the cathode originate at the **anode**, which is the electrode where chemicals are oxidized. For any battery, the anode is always negative ($-$), which indicates that electrons are streaming away from this location. The anode in Figure 11.8 is the zinc cup, where zinc atoms lose electrons to form zinc ions:

$$Zn(s) \longrightarrow Zn^{2+}(aq) + 2\,e^- \qquad \text{Oxidation}$$

The reduction of ammonium ions in a dry-cell battery produces two gases—ammonia, NH_3, and hydrogen, H_2—that need to be removed to avoid a pressure buildup and a potential explosion. Removal is accomplished by having the ammonia and hydrogen react with the zinc chloride and manganese dioxide:

$$ZnCl_2(aq) + 2\,NH_3(g) \longrightarrow Zn(NH_3)_2Cl_2(s)$$

$$2\,MnO_2(s) + H_2(g) \longrightarrow Mn_2O_3(s) + H_2O(\ell)$$

The life of a dry-cell battery is relatively short. Oxidation causes the zinc cup to deteriorate, and eventually the contents leak out. Even while the battery is not operating, the zinc corrodes as it reacts with ammonium ions. This zinc corrosion can be inhibited by storing the battery in a refrigerator. As discussed in Chapter 9, chemical reactions slow down with decreasing temperature. Chilling a battery therefore slows down the rate at which the zinc corrodes, which increases the life of the battery.

Another type of disposable battery, the more expensive *alkaline battery*, shown in Figure 11.9, avoids many of the problems of dry-cell batteries by operating in a strongly alkaline paste. In the presence of hydroxide ions, the zinc oxidizes to insoluble zinc oxide:

$$Zn(s) + 2\,OH^-(aq) \longrightarrow ZnO(s) + H_2O(\ell) + 2\,e^- \quad \text{Oxidation}$$

while at the same time manganese dioxide is reduced:

$$2\,MnO_2(s) + H_2O(\ell) + 2\,e^- \longrightarrow Mn_2O_3(s) + 2\,OH^-(aq) \quad \text{Reduction}$$

Note how these two reactions avoid the use of the zinc-corroding ammonium ion (which means alkaline batteries last a lot longer than dry-cell batteries) and the formation of any gaseous products. Furthermore, these reactions are better-suited to maintaining a given voltage during longer periods of operation.

The small mercury and lithium disposable batteries used for calculators and cameras are variations of the alkaline battery. In the mercury battery, mercuric oxide, HgO, is reduced rather than manganese dioxide. Manufacturers are phasing out these batteries because of the environmental hazard posed by mercury, which is poisonous. In the lithium battery, lithium metal is used as the source of electrons rather than zinc. Not only is lithium able to maintain a higher voltage than zinc, it is about 13 times less dense, which allows for a lighter battery.

Disposable batteries have relatively short lives because electron-producing chemicals are consumed. The main feature of rechargeable batteries is the reversibility of the oxidation and reduction reactions. In your car's rechargeable lead storage battery, for example, electrical energy is produced as lead dioxide, lead, and sulfuric acid are consumed to form lead sulfate and water. The elemental lead is oxidized to Pb^{2+}, and the oxygen in the lead dioxide is reduced from the O^- state to the O^{2-} state. Combining the two half reactions gives the complete oxidation–reduction reaction:

$$PbO_2 + Pb + 2\,H_2SO_4 \longrightarrow 2\,PbSO_4 + 2\,H_2O + \text{electrical energy}$$

Figure 11.9
Alkaline batteries last a lot longer than dry-cell batteries and give a steadier voltage, but they are expensive.

Figure 11.10
(a) Electrical energy from the battery forces the starter motor to start the engine. (b) The combustion of fuel keeps the engine running and provides energy to spin the alternator, which recharges the battery. Note that the battery has a reversed cathode–anode orientation during recharging.

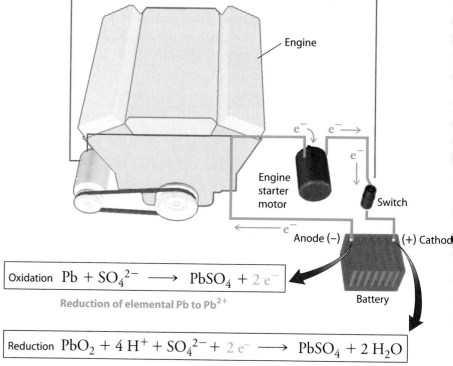

Oxidation $Pb + SO_4^{2-} \longrightarrow PbSO_4 + 2\,e^-$

Reduction of elemental Pb to Pb^{2+}

Reduction $PbO_2 + 4\,H^+ + SO_4^{2-} + 2\,e^- \longrightarrow PbSO_4 + 2\,H_2O$

Oxidation of elemental Pb^{4+} to Pb^{2+}

(a)

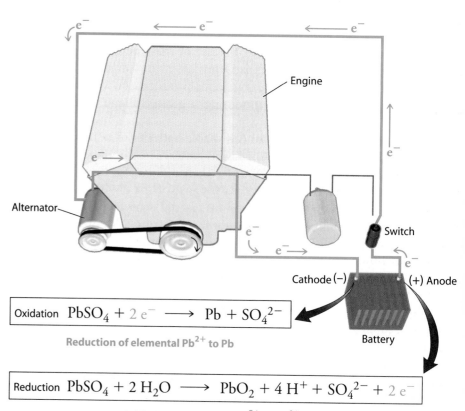

Oxidation $PbSO_4 + 2\,e^- \longrightarrow Pb + SO_4^{2-}$

Reduction of elemental Pb^{2+} to Pb

Reduction $PbSO_4 + 2\,H_2O \longrightarrow PbO_2 + 4\,H^+ + SO_4^{2-} + 2\,e^-$

Oxidation of elemental Pb^{2+} to Pb^{4+}

(b)

This reaction can be reversed by supplying electrical energy, as Figure 11.10 shows. This is the task of the car's alternator, which is powered by the engine:

$$\text{electrical energy} + 2 \; PbSO_4 + 2 \; H_2O \longrightarrow PbO_2 + Pb + 2 \; H_2SO_4$$

So running the engine maintains concentrations of lead dioxide, lead, and sulfuric acid in the battery. With the engine turned off, these reactants stand ready to supply electric power as needed to start the engine, operate the emergency blinkers, or play the radio.

Concept Check ✓

What is recharged in a car battery?

Was this your answer? When the battery is being recharged, electrical energy from a source (the alternator) outside the battery is used to regenerate reactants that were earlier transformed to products during the oxidation–reduction reaction that produced the electrical energy needed to start the engine. The reactants being regenerated are lead dioxide, elemental lead, and sulfuric acid.

Many rechargeable batteries smaller than car batteries are made of compounds of nickel and cadmium (ni–cad batteries). As with the lead storage battery, ni–cad reactants are replenished by supplying electrical energy from some external source, such as an electrical wall outlet. Like mercury batteries, ni–cad batteries pose an environmental hazard because cadmium is toxic to humans and other organisms. For this reason, alkaline batteries designed to be rechargeable are rapidly gaining a place in the market.

Fuel Cells Are Highly Efficient Sources of Electrical Energy

A *fuel cell* is a device that changes the chemical energy of a fuel to electrical energy. Fuel cells are by far the most efficient means of generating electricity. A hydrogen–oxygen fuel cell is shown in Figure 11.11 on page 336. It has two compartments, one for entering hydrogen fuel and the other for entering oxygen fuel, separated by a set of porous electrodes. Hydrogen is oxidized upon contact with hydroxide ions at the hydrogen-facing electrode (the anode). The electrons from this oxidation flow through an external circuit and provide electric power before meeting up with oxygen at the oxygen-facing electrode (the cathode). The oxygen readily picks up the electrons (in other words, the oxygen is reduced) and reacts with water to form hydroxide ions. To complete the circuit, these hydroxide ions migrate across the porous electrodes and through an ionic paste of potassium hydroxide, KOH, to meet up with hydrogen at the hydrogen-facing electrode.

As the oxidation equation shown at the top of Figure 11.11 demonstrates, the hydrogen and hydroxide ions react to produce steam as well as electrons. This steam may be used for heating or to generate electricity in a steam turbine. Furthermore, the water that condenses from the steam is pure water, suitable for drinking!

Oxidation $2H_2 + 4OH^- \longrightarrow 4H_2O + 4e^-$

Reduction $4e^- + O_2 + 2H_2O \longrightarrow 4OH$

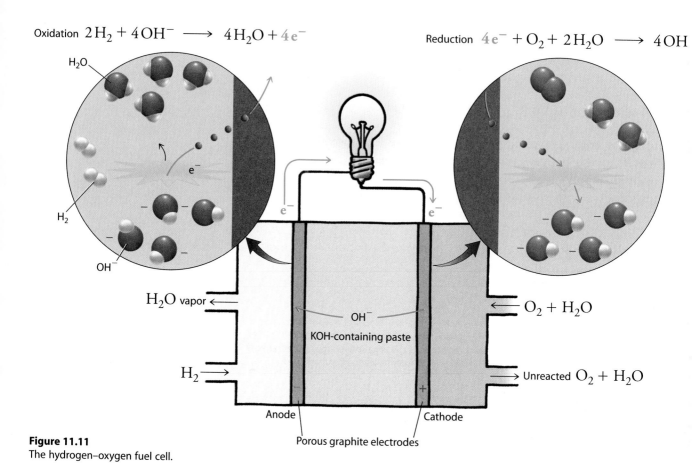

H₂O

H₂

OH⁻

e^-

e^-

e^-

H_2O vapor ←

OH^-
KOH-containing paste

H_2 →

← $O_2 + H_2O$

→ Unreacted $O_2 + H_2O$

Anode

Cathode

Porous graphite electrodes

Figure 11.11
The hydrogen–oxygen fuel cell.

Fuel cells are similar to dry-cell batteries, but fuel cells don't run down as long as fuel is supplied. The space shuttle uses hydrogen–oxygen fuel cells to meet its electrical needs. The cells also produce more than 100 gallons of drinking water for the astronauts during a typical week-long mission. Back on the Earth, researchers are developing fuel cells for buses and automobiles. As shown in Figure 11.12, experimental fuel-cell buses are already operating in several cities, such as Vancouver, British Columbia,

Figure 11.12
Because this bus is powered by a fuel cell, its tail pipe emits mostly water vapor.

and Chicago, Illinois. These vehicles produce very few pollutants and can run much more efficiently than those that run on fossil fuels.

In the future, commercial buildings as well as individual homes may be outfitted with fuel cells as an alternative to receiving electricity (and heat) from regional power stations. Researchers are also working on miniature fuel cells that could replace the batteries used for portable electronic devices, such as cellular phones and laptop computers. Such devices could operate for extended periods of time on a single "ampule" of fuel available at your local supermarket.

Amazingly, a car powered by a hydrogen–oxygen fuel cell requires only about 3 kilograms of hydrogen to travel 500 kilometers. However, this much hydrogen gas at room temperature and atmospheric pressure would occupy a volume of about 36,000 liters, the volume of about four midsize cars! Thus the major hurdle to the development of fuel-cell technology lies not with the cell but with the fuel. This volume of gas could be compressed to a much smaller volume, as it is on the experimental buses in Vancouver.

Compressing a gas takes energy, however, and as a consequence the inherent efficiency of the fuel cell is lost. Chilling hydrogen to its liquid phase, which occupies much less volume, poses similar problems. Instead, researchers are looking for novel ways of providing fuel cells with hydrogen. In one design, hydrogen is generated within the fuel cell from chemical reactions involving liquid hydrocarbons, such as methanol, CH_3OH. Alternatively, certain porous materials, including the recently developed carbon nanofibers shown in Figure 11.13, can hold large volumes of hydrogen on their surfaces, behaving in effect like hydrogen "sponges." The hydrogen is "squeezed" out of these materials on demand by controlling the temperature—the warmer the material, the more hydrogen released. We explore hydrogen as a fuel source in Chapter 19, in our discussions of sustainable energy sources.

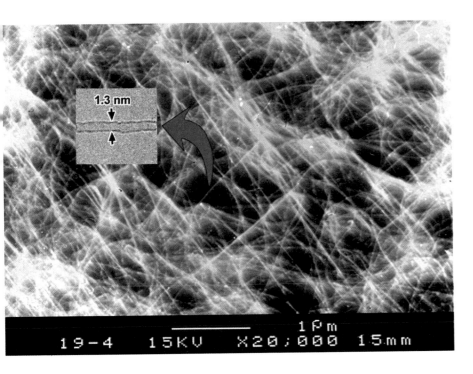

Figure 11.13
Carbon nanofibers consist of near-submicroscopic tubes of carbon atoms. They outclass most all other known materials in their ability to absorb hydrogen molecules. With carbon nanofibers, for example, a volume of 36,000 liters of hydrogen can be reduced to a mere 35 liters. Carbon nanofibers are a recent discovery, however, and much research is still required to confirm their applicability to hydrogen storage and to develop the technology.

Concept Check ✓

> As long as fuel is available to it, a given fuel cell can supply electrical energy indefinitely. Why can't batteries do the same?

Was this your answer? Batteries generate electricity as the chemical reactants they contain are reduced and oxidized. Once these reactants are consumed, the battery can no longer generate electricity. A rechargeable battery can be made to operate again, but only after the energy flow is interrupted so that the reactants can be replenished.

Electrical Energy Can Produce Chemical Change

Electrolysis is the use of electrical energy to produce chemical change. The recharging of a car battery is an example of electrolysis. Another, shown in Figure 11.14, is passing an electric current through water, a process that breaks the water down into its elemental components:

$$\text{electrical energy} + 2\,H_2O \longrightarrow 2\,H_2(g) + O_2(g)$$

Electrolysis is used to purify metals from metal ores. An example is aluminum, the third most abundant element in the Earth's crust. Aluminum occurs naturally bonded to oxygen in an ore called *bauxite*. Aluminum metal wasn't known until about 1827, when it was prepared by reacting bauxite with hydrochloric acid. This gave the aluminum ion, Al^{3+}, which was reduced to aluminum metal with sodium metal acting as the reducing agent:

$$Al^{3+} + 3\,Na \longrightarrow Al + 3\,Na^{+}$$

This chemical process was expensive. The price of aluminum at that time was about $100,000 per pound, and it was considered a rare and precious metal. In 1855, aluminum dinnerware and other items were exhibited in Paris with the crown jewels of France. Then, in 1886, two men working independently, Charles Hall (1863–1914) in the United States and Paul Heroult (1863–1914) in France, almost simultaneously discovered a process whereby aluminum could be produced from aluminum oxide, Al_2O_3, a main component of bauxite. In what is now known as the Hall–Heroult process, shown in Figure 11.15, a strong electric current is passed through a molten mixture of aluminum oxide and cryolite, Na_3AlF_6, a naturally occurring mineral. The fluoride ions of the cryolite react with the aluminum oxide to form various aluminum fluoride ions, such as $AlOF_3^{2-}$, which are then oxidized to the aluminum hexafluoride ion, AlF_6^{3-}. The Al^{3+} in this ion is then reduced to elemental aluminum, which collects at the bottom of the reaction chamber. This process, which is still in use today, greatly facilitated mass production of aluminum metal, and by 1890 the price of aluminum had dropped to about $2 per pound.

Today, worldwide production of aluminum is about 16 million tons annually. For each ton produced from ore, about 16,000 kilowatt-hours of electrical energy is required, as much as a typical American household consumes in 18 months. Processing recycled aluminum, on the other hand,

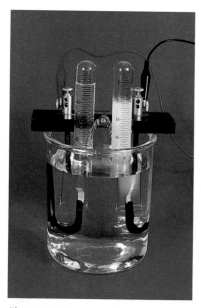

Figure 11.14
The electrolysis of water produces hydrogen gas and oxygen gas in a 2:1 ratio by volume, which is in accordance with the chemical formula for water: H_2O. For this process to work, ions must be dissolved in the water so that the electricity can be conducted between the electrodes.

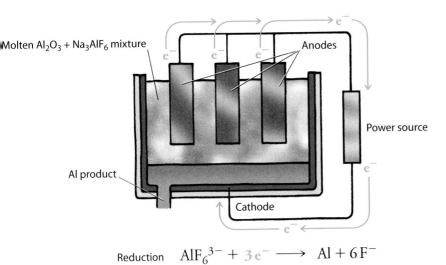

Oxidation $\quad 2\,AlOF_3^{2-} + 6\,F^- + C \longrightarrow 2\,AlF_6^{3-} + CO_2 + 4\,e^-$

Molten $Al_2O_3 + Na_3AlF_6$ mixture

Anodes

Al product

Cathode

Power source

Reduction $\quad AlF_6^{3-} + 3\,e^- \longrightarrow Al + 6\,F^-$

Figure 11.15
The melting point of aluminum oxide (2030°C) is too high for it to be efficiently electrolyzed to aluminum metal. When the oxide is mixed with the mineral cryolite, the melting point of the oxide drops to a more reasonable 980°C. A strong electric current passed through the molten aluminum oxide–cryolite mixture generates aluminum metal at the cathode, where aluminum ions pick up electrons and so are reduced to elemental aluminum.

consumes only about 700 kilowatt-hours for every ton. Thus recycling aluminum not only reduces litter but also helps reduce the load on power companies, which in turn reduces air pollution.

For a nerve-wracking experience involving the oxidation of elemental aluminum, bite a piece of aluminum foil with a tooth filled with dental amalgam. (If you don't have any dental fillings, hooray for you! You'll need to ask a less fortunate friend what this activity is like.) The aluminum behaves as an anode and releases electrons to the amalgam (a mix of silver, tin, and mercury). The amalgam behaves as a cathode by transferring these electrons to oxygen, which then combines with hydrogen ions to form water. The slight current that results produces a jolt of . . . ouch . . . pain.

Concept Check ✓

Is the reaction that goes on in a hydrogen–oxygen fuel cell an example of electrolysis?

Was this your answer? During electrolysis, electrical energy is used to produce chemical change. In the hydrogen–oxygen fuel cell, chemical change is used to produce electrical energy. Therefore, the answer to the question is no.

Hands-On Chemistry: Splitting Water

You can see the electrolysis of water by immersing the top of a disposable 9-volt battery in salt water. The bubbles that form contain hydrogen gas produced as the water decomposes. Why does this activity work better with salt water than with tap water? Why does this activity quickly ruin the battery (which should therefore not be used again)?

11.4 Oxygen Is Responsible for Corrosion and Combustion

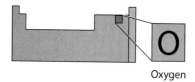

Oxygen

Look to the upper right of the periodic table, and you will find one of the most common oxidizing agents—oxygen. In fact, if you haven't guessed already, the term *oxidation* is derived from this element. Oxygen is able to pluck electrons from many other elements, typically those that lie at the lower left of the periodic table. Two common oxidation–reduction reactions involving oxygen as the oxidizing agent are *corrosion* and *combustion*.

Concept Check ✓

Oxygen is a good oxidizing agent, but so is chlorine. What does this tell you about their relative positions in the periodic table?

Was this your answer? Chlorine and oxygen must lie in the same area of the periodic table. Both have strong effective nuclear charges, and both are strong oxidizing agents.

Figure 11.16
Rust itself is not harmful to the iron structures on which it forms. Rather it is the loss of metallic iron that ruins the structural integrity.

Corrosion is the process whereby a metal deteriorates. Corrosion caused by atmospheric oxygen is a widespread and costly problem. About one-quarter of the steel produced in the United States, for example, goes into replacing corroded iron at a cost of billions of dollars annually. Iron corrodes when it reacts with atmospheric oxygen and water to form iron oxide trihydrate—the naturally occurring reddish-brown substance you know as *rust*, shown in Figure 11.16:

$$4\,Fe \ + \ 3\,O_2 \ + \ 3\,H_2O \ \longrightarrow \ 2\,Fe_2O_3 \cdot 3\,H_2O$$

Iron   Oxygen   Water   Rust

We can better understand rusting by considering this equation in steps, as shown in Figure 11.17. ① Iron loses electrons to form the Fe^{2+} ion. ② Oxygen accepts these electrons and then reacts with water to form hydroxide ions, OH^-. ③ Iron ions and hydroxide ions combine to form iron hydroxide, $Fe(OH)_2$, which is further oxidized by oxygen to form rust, $Fe_2O_3 \cdot 3\,H_2O$.

Another common metal oxidized by oxygen is aluminum. The product of aluminum oxidation is aluminum oxide, Al_2O_3, which is water-insoluble. Because of its water insolubility, aluminum oxide forms a protective coat that shields aluminum from further oxidation. This coat is so thin that it's transparent, which is why aluminum maintains its metallic shine.

A protective water-insoluble oxidized coat is the principle underlying a process called *galvanization*. Zinc has a slightly greater tendency to oxidize than does iron. For this reason, many iron articles, such as the nails pictured in Figure 11.18, are *galvanized* by coating them with a thin layer of zinc. The zinc oxidizes to zinc oxide, an inert, insoluble substance that protects the inner iron from rusting.

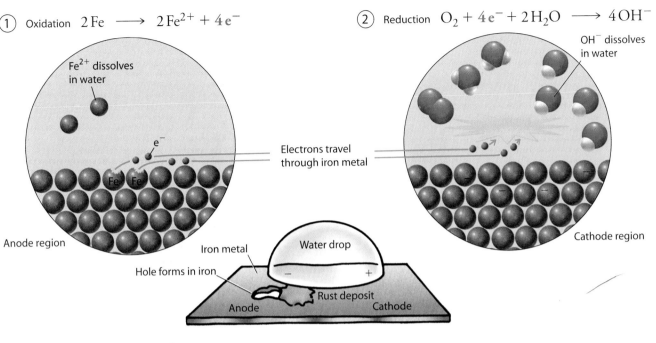

① Oxidation $2\,Fe \longrightarrow 2\,Fe^{2+} + 4\,e^-$

② Reduction $O_2 + 4\,e^- + 2\,H_2O \longrightarrow 4\,OH^-$

OH^- dissolves in water

Fe^{2+} dissolves in water

e^-

Electrons travel through iron metal

Fe Fe

Anode region

Cathode region

Iron metal

Water drop

Hole forms in iron

Rust deposit

Anode

Cathode

③ Fe^{2+} and OH^- react in aqueous solution to form iron hydroxide, $Fe(OH)_2$, which reacts with H_2O and O_2 to form rust, $Fe_2O_3 \cdot 3\,H_2O$.

Figure 11.17
Rusting begins when iron atoms lose electrons to form Fe^{2+} ions. These electrons are lost to oxygen atoms, which are thereby reduced to hydroxide ions, OH^-. One region of the iron behaves as the anode while another region behaves as the cathode. Rust forms only in the region of the anode, where iron atoms lose electrons. The loss of elemental iron in this region causes a hole to form in the metal. The formation of rust, however, is not as much of a problem as is the loss of metallic iron, which results in a loss of structural integrity.

In a technique called *cathodic protection*, iron structures can be protected from oxidation by placing them in contact with metals, such as zinc or magnesium, that have a greater tendency to oxidize. This forces the iron to accept electrons, which means it is behaving as a cathode—recall from Figure 11.17 that rusting occurs only where iron behaves as an anode. Ocean tankers, for example, are protected from corrosion by strips of zinc affixed to their hulls, as shown in Figure 11.19. Similarly, outdoor steel pipes are protected by being connected to magnesium rods inserted into the ground.

Yet another way to protect iron and other metals from oxidation is to coat them with a corrosion-resistant metal, such as chromium, platinum, or gold. *Electroplating* is the operation of coating one metal with another by electrolysis, and it is illustrated in Figure 11.20 on page 342. The object to be electroplated is connected to a negative battery terminal and then submerged in a solution containing ions of the metal to be used as the coating. The positive terminal of the battery is connected to an electrode made of the coating metal. The circuit is completed when this electrode is submerged in the solution. Dissolved metal ions are attracted to the negatively charged object, where they pick up electrons and are deposited as metal atoms. The ions in solution are replenished by the forced oxidation of the coating metal at the positive electrode.

Figure 11.18
The galvanized nail (bottom) is protected from rusting by the sacrificial oxidation of zinc.

Figure 11.19
Zinc strips help protect the iron hull of an oil tanker from oxidizing. The zinc strip shown here is attached to the hull's interior surface.

Figure 11.20
As electrons flow into the hubcap and give it a negative charge, positively charged chromium ions move from the solution to the hubcap and are reduced to chromium metal, which deposits as a coating on the hubcap. The solution is kept supplied with ions as chromium atoms in the cathode are oxidized to Cr^{2+} ions.

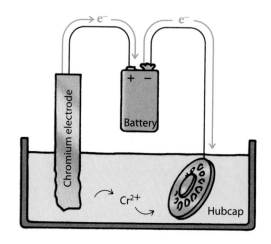

Combustion is an oxidation–reduction reaction between a nonmetallic material and molecular oxygen. Combustion reactions are characteristically exothermic (energy-releasing). A violent combustion reaction is the formation of water from hydrogen and oxygen. As discussed in Section 9.5, the energy from this reaction is used to power rockets into space. More common examples of combustion include the burning of wood and fossil fuels. The combustion of these and other carbon-based chemicals forms carbon dioxide and water. Consider, for example, the combustion of methane, the major component of natural gas:

$$CH_4 \;+\; 2\,O_2 \;\longrightarrow\; CO_2 \;+\; 2\,H_2O \;+\; \text{energy}$$

    Methane   Oxygen   Carbon   Water
                               dioxide

In combustion, electrons are transferred as polar covalent bonds are formed in place of nonpolar covalent bonds, or vice versa. This is in contrast to the other examples of oxidation–reduction reactions presented in this chapter, which involve the formation of ions from atoms or, conversely, atoms from ions. This concept is illustrated in Figure 11.21, which compares the electronic structures of the combustion starting material molecular oxygen and the combustion product water. Molecular oxygen is a non-

Figure 11.21
(a) Neither atom in an oxygen molecule is able to preferentially attract the bonding electrons. (b) The oxygen atom of a water molecule pulls the bonding electrons away from the hydrogen atoms on the water molecule, making the oxygen slightly negative and the two hydrogens slightly positive.

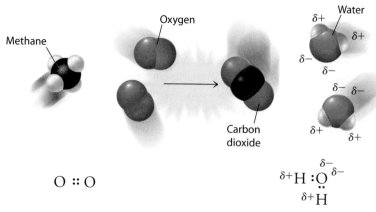

(a) Reactant oxygen atoms share electrons equally in O_2 molecules.

(b) Product oxygen atoms pull electrons away from H atoms in H_2O molecules and are reduced.

polar covalent compound. Although each oxygen atom in the molecule has a fairly strong electronegativity, the four bonding electrons are pulled equally by both atoms and thus are unable to congregate on one side or the other. After combustion, however, the electrons are shared between the oxygen and hydrogen atoms in a water molecule and are pulled to the oxygen. This gives the oxygen a slight negative charge, which is another way of saying it has gained electrons and has thus been reduced. At the same time, the hydrogen atoms in the water molecule develop a slight positive charge, which is another way of saying they have lost electrons and have thus been oxidized. This gain of electrons by oxygen and loss of electrons by hydrogen is an energy-releasing process. Typically, the energy is released either as molecular kinetic energy (heat) or as light (the flame).

Interestingly, the same sort of oxidation–reduction reaction occurs in your body. You can visualize a simplified model of your metabolism by reviewing Figure 11.21 and substituting a food molecule for the methane. Food molecules relinquish their electrons to the oxygen molecules you inhale. The products are carbon dioxide, water vapor, and energy. Both the carbon dioxide and water vapor you exhale. Much of the energy from the reaction is used to keep your body warm and to drive the many other biochemical reactions necessary for living.

Key Terms and Matching Definitions

_____ anode
_____ cathode
_____ combustion
_____ corrosion
_____ electrochemistry
_____ electrode
_____ electrolysis
_____ half reaction
_____ oxidation
_____ oxidation–reduction reaction
_____ reduction

1. A reaction involving the transfer of electrons from one reactant to another.
2. The process whereby a reactant loses one or more electrons.
3. The process whereby a reactant gains one or more electrons.
4. One portion of an oxidation–reduction reaction, represented by an equation showing electrons as either reactants or products.
5. The branch of chemistry concerned with the relationship between electrical energy and chemical change.
6. Any material that conducts electrons into or out of a medium in which electrochemical reactions are occurring.
7. The electrode where reduction occurs.
8. The electrode where oxidation occurs.
9. The use of electrical energy to produce chemical change.
10. The deterioration of a metal, typically caused by atmospheric oxygen.
11. An exothermic oxidation–reduction reaction between a nonmetallic material and molecular oxygen.

Review Questions

Oxidation Is the Loss of Electrons and Reduction Is the Gain of Electrons

1. Which elements have the greatest tendency to behave as oxidizing agents?

2. Write an equation for the half reaction in which a potassium atom, K, is oxidized.

3. Write an equation for the half reaction in which a bromine atom, Br, is reduced.

4. What is the difference between an oxidizing agent and a reducing agent?

5. What happens to a reducing agent as it reduces?

Photography Works by Selective Oxidation and Reduction

6. What special property of silver bromide makes it so useful for photography?

7. What gets reduced as bromine ions, Br^-, on photographic film are oxidized by light?

8. What role does hydroquinone play in the development of a black-and-white photograph?

The Energy of Flowing Electrons Can Be Harnessed

9. What is electrochemistry?

10. What is the purpose of the manganese dioxide in a dry-cell battery?

11. What chemical reaction is forced to occur while a car battery is being recharged?

12. Why don't the electrodes of a fuel cell deteriorate the way the electrodes of a battery do?

13. What is electrolysis, and how does it differ from what goes on inside a battery?

Oxygen Is Responsible for Corrosion and Combustion

14. Why is oxygen such a good oxidizing agent?

15. What do the oxidation of zinc and the oxidation of aluminum have in common?

16. What is electroplating, and how is it accomplished?

17. What are some differences between corrosion and combustion?

18. What are some similarities between corrosion and combustion?

Hands-On Chemistry Insights

Silver Lining

This is one of the better party tricks you can perform for any willing dinner host burdened with a cabinet full of tarnished silver pieces. Forewarn, however, that many pieces coming out of the treatment are still in need of some buffing with silver polish. Lively conversation is guaranteed, especially concerning the source of the tarnishing hydrogen sulfide gas.

Polishing with an abrasive paste removes both the thin layer of tarnish and some silver atoms. Silver-plated pieces are therefore susceptible to losing their thin coating of silver. The aluminum method, by contrast, restores the silver lost to the tarnishing.

For pieces too large to fit in the pot, try rubbing lightly with a paste of baking soda and water, using aluminum foil as your rubbing cloth.

Splitting Water

Try this activity with tap water instead of salt water to see the difference dissolved ions can make—the ions are needed to conduct electricity between the two electrodes.

The primary reaction occurs at the negative electrode, where water molecules accept electrons to form hydrogen gas and hydroxide ions. Recall from Chapter 10 that an increase in hydroxide ion concentration causes the pH of the solution to rise. You can track the production of hydroxide ions by adding a pH indicator to the solution. The indicator of choice is phenolphthalein, which you might obtain from your instructor. Alternatively, you might use the red cabbage extract discussed in Chapter 10. Whichever indicator you use, note the swirls of color forming at the negative electrode as hydroxide ions are generated.

The battery is quickly ruined because placing it in the conducting liquid short-circuits the terminals, which results in a large drain on the battery.

You may be wondering why oxygen gas is not generated along with the hydrogen gas. For reasons beyond the scope of this text, oxygen gas is generated only when the positive electrode is made of certain metals, such as gold or platinum. The steel electrode of the 9-volt battery does not suffice.

Exercises

1. Which atom is oxidized, ● or ● :

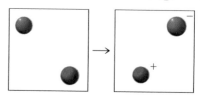

2. In the previous exercise, which atom behaves as the oxidizing agent, ● or ● ?

3. What correlation might you expect between an element's electronegativity (Section 6.6) and its ability to behave as an oxidizing agent? How about its ability to behave as a reducing agent?

4. What correlation might you expect between an element's ionization energy (Section 5.8) and its ability to behave as an oxidizing agent? How about its ability to behave as a reducing agent?

5. Based on their relative positions in the periodic table, which might you expect to be a stronger oxidizing agent, chlorine or fluorine? Why?

6. How does an atom's electronegativity relate to its ability to become oxidized?

7. Iron is a better reducing agent than the copper ion Cu^{2+}. In which direction do electrons flow when an iron nail is submerged in a solution of Cu^{2+} ions?

8. What is the purpose of the salt bridge in Figure 11.7?

9. Why is the anode of a battery indicated with a minus sign?

10. Is sodium metal oxidized or reduced in the production of aluminum?

11. Why is the formation of iron hydroxide, $Fe(OH)_2$, from Fe^{2+} and OH^- not considered an oxidation–reduction reaction?

12. Your car lights were left on while you were shopping, and now your car battery is dead. Has the pH of the battery fluid increased or decreased?

13. Sketch a voltaic cell that uses the oxidation–reduction reaction

$$Mg(s) + Cu^{2+}(aq) \longrightarrow Mg^{2+}(aq) + Cu(s)$$

Which atom or ion is reduced? Which atom or ion is oxidized?

14. Jewelry is often manufactured by electroplating an expensive metal such as gold over a cheaper metal. Sketch a setup for this process.

15. Some car batteries require the periodic addition of water. Does adding the water increase or decrease the battery's ability to provide electric power to start the car? Explain.

16. Why does a battery that has thick zinc walls last longer than one that has thin zinc walls?

17. The oxidation of iron to rust is a problem structural engineers need to be concerned about, but the oxidation of aluminum to aluminum oxide is not. Why?

18. How many electrons are transferred from iron atoms to oxygen atoms in the formation of two molecules of iron hydroxide, $Fe(OH)_2$? See Figure 11.17.

19. Why are combustion reactions generally exothermic?

20. Which element is closer to the upper right corner of the periodic table, ⬤ or ⬤:

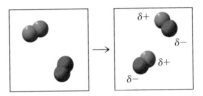

21. Water is 88.88 percent oxygen by mass. Oxygen is exactly what a fire needs to grow brighter and stronger. So why doesn't a fire grow brighter and stronger when water is added to it?

22. Clorox is a laundry bleaching agent used to remove stains from white clothes. Suggest why the name begins with *Clor-* and ends with *-ox*.

23. Iron has a greater tendency to oxidize than does copper. Is this good news or bad news for a home in which much of the plumbing consists of iron and copper pipes connected together? Explain.

24. Copper has a greater tendency to be reduced than iron does. Was this good news or bad news for the Statue of Liberty, whose copper exterior was originally held together by steel rivets?

25. One of the products of combustion is water. Why doesn't this water extinguish the combustion?

Suggested Web Sites

http://www.aluminum.org/

The Web site of the Aluminum Association, Inc., where you will find basic facts about the aluminum industry, recycling efforts, and the impact of our aluminum use on the environment.

http://www.kodak.com/aboutKodak/kodakHistory/kodakHistory.shtml

The Eastman Kodak Company was founded in the late 1800s and was the first company to offer easy-to-use photography services to the general public. Explore this site for some of this history, and be sure to check out the link to "About Film and Imaging" to read about the chemistry and engineering required for the manufacture of photographic film.

http://www.duracell.com/Fun_Learning/index.html

An excellent site to explore the chemistry and history of the battery. Also included is a Battery IQ Test you should take. Any questions you miss are prompted by a link to help you find the correct answers. Remember: **Leo** the lion went "**ger**."

http://www.internationalfuelcells.com/
http://www.fuelcellworld.org/

Use *fuel cells* as a search keyword and you will find a number of private companies and organizations, such as the two named here, that are dedicated to improving the efficiency of fuel cells and publicizing their use. Fuel cells are certainly a wave of the future.

Chapter 12
Organic Compounds

A Survey of Carbon-Based Molecules

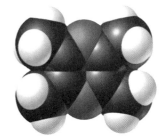

Vanillin

Tetramethylpyrazine

Carbon atoms have the ability to link together and thereby form molecules made up of many carbon atoms. Add to this the fact that any of the carbon atoms in such a chain can also bond with atoms of other elements, and you see the possibility of an endless number of different carbon-based molecules. Each molecule has its own unique set of physical, chemical, and biological properties. The flavor of vanilla, for example, is perceived when the compound *vanillin* is absorbed by the sensory organs in the mouth and nose. This compound consists of a ring of carbon atoms with oxygen atoms attached in a particular fashion. Vanillin is the essential ingredient in anything having the flavor of vanilla—without vanillin, there is no vanilla flavor. The flavor of chocolate, on the other hand, is generated when not just one but a wide assortment of carbon-based molecules are absorbed in the mouth and nose. One of the more significant of these molecules is *tetramethylpyrazine*, which has a ring of nitrogen and carbon atoms attached in a particular fashion.

Life is based on carbon's ability to bond with other carbon atoms to form diverse structures. Reflecting this fact, the branch of chemistry that is the study of carbon-containing compounds has come to be known as **organic chemistry**. The term *organic* is derived from *organism* and is not necessarily related to the environment-friendly form of farming discussed in Chapter 15. Today, more than 13 million organic compounds are known, and about 100,000 new ones are added to the list each year. This includes those discovered in nature and those synthesized in the laboratory. (By contrast, there are only 200,000 to 300,000 known *inorganic* compounds, those based on elements other than carbon.)

Because organic compounds are so closely tied to living organisms and because they have many applications—from flavorings to fuels, polymers, medicines, agriculture, and more—it is important to have a basic understanding of them. We begin with the simplest organic compounds—those consisting of only carbon and hydrogen.

12.1 Hydrocarbons Contain Only Carbon and Hydrogen

Organic compounds that contain only carbon and hydrogen are **hydrocarbons**, which differ from one another by the number of carbon and hydrogen atoms they contain. The simplest hydrocarbon is methane, CH_4, with only one carbon per molecule. Methane is the main component of natural gas. The hydrocarbon octane, C_8H_{18}, has eight carbons per molecule and is a component of gasoline. The hydrocarbon polyethylene contains hundreds of carbon and hydrogen atoms per molecule. Polyethylene is a plastic used to make many items, including milk containers and plastic bags.

Methane, CH_4

Octane, C_8H_{18}

Polyethylene

Hydrocarbons also differ from one another in the way the carbon atoms connect to each other. Figure 12.1 shows the three hydrocarbons *n*-pentane, *iso*-pentane, and *neo*-pentane. These hydrocarbons all have the same molecular formula, C_5H_{12}, but are structurally different from one another. The carbon framework of *n*-pentane is a chain of five carbon atoms. In *iso*-pentane, the carbon chain branches, so that the framework is a *four*-carbon chain branched at the second carbon. In *neo*-pentane, a central carbon atom is bonded to four surrounding carbon atoms.

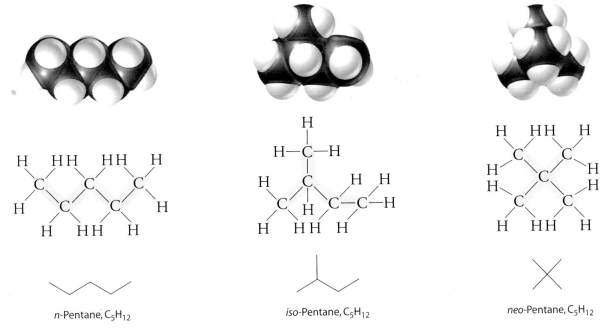

Figure 12.1
These three hydrocarbons all have the same molecular formula. We can see their different structural features by highlighting the carbon framework in two dimensions. Easy-to-draw stick structures that use lines for all carbon–carbon covalent bonds can also be used.

We can see the different structural features of *n*-pentane, *iso*-pentane, and *neo*-pentane more clearly by drawing the molecules in two dimensions, as shown in the middle row of Figure 12.1. Alternatively, we can represent them by the *stick structures* shown in the bottom row. A stick structure is a commonly used, shorthand notation for representing an organic molecule. Each line (stick) represents a covalent bond, and carbon atoms are understood to be wherever two or more straight lines meet and at the end of any line (unless another type of atom is drawn at the end of the line). Any hydrogen atoms bonded to the carbons are also typically not shown. Instead, their presence is implied so that the focus can remain on the skeletal structure formed by the carbon atoms.

When every carbon atom in a hydrocarbon except the two terminal ones is bonded to only two other carbon atoms, the molecule is called a *straight-chain hydrocarbon*. (Do not take this name literally, for, as the *n*-pentane structures in Figure 12.1 show, this is a straight-chain hydrocarbon despite the zigzag nature of the drawings representing it.) When one or more carbon atoms in a hydrocarbon is bonded to either three or four carbon atoms, the molecule is a *branched hydrocarbon*. Both *iso*-pentane and *neo*-pentane are branched hydrocarbons.

Molecules such as *n*-pentane, *iso*-pentane, and *neo*-pentane, which have the same molecular formula but different structures, are known as **structural isomers**. Structural isomers have different physical and chemical properties. For example, *n*-pentane has a boiling point of 36°C, *iso*-pentane's boiling point is 30°C, and *neo*-pentane's is 10°C.

The number of possible structural isomers for a chemical formula increases rapidly as the number of carbon atoms increases. There are 3 structural isomers for compounds having the formula C_5H_{12}, 18 for C_8H_{18}, 75 for $C_{10}H_{22}$, and a whopping 366,319 for $C_{20}H_{42}$! Carbon-based molecules can have different spatial orientations called **conformations.** Flex your wrist, elbow, and shoulder joints, and you'll find your arm passing through a range of conformations. Likewise, organic molecules can twist and turn about their carbon–carbon single bonds and thus have a range of conformations. The structures in Figure 12.2, for example, are different conformations of *n*-pentane.

Figure 12.2
Three conformations for a molecule of *n*-pentane. The molecule looks different in each conformation, but the five-carbon framework is the same in all three conformations. In a sample of liquid *n*-pentane, the molecules are found in all conformations—not unlike a bucket of worms.

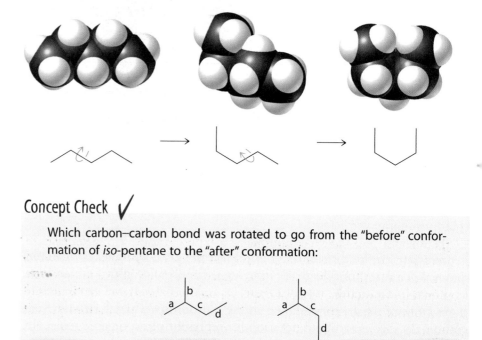

Concept Check ✔

Which carbon–carbon bond was rotated to go from the "before" conformation of *iso*-pentane to the "after" conformation:

Before   After

Was this your answer? The best way to answer any question about the conformation of a molecule is to play around with molecular models that you can hold in your hand. In this case, bond c rotates in such a way that the carbon at the right end of bond d comes up out of the plane of the page, momentarily points straight at you, and then plops back into the plane of the page below bond c. This rotation is similar to that of the arm of an arm wrestler who, her arm just above the table as she is on the brink of losing, suddenly gets a surge of strength and swings her opponent's arm (and her own) through a half-circle arc and wins.

Before   After

Hydrocarbons are obtained primarily from coal and petroleum, both formed when plant and animal matter decays in the absence of oxygen. Most of the coal and petroleum that exist today were formed between 280 and 395 million years ago. At that time, there were extensive swamps that,

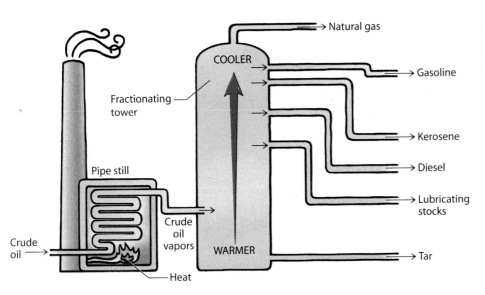

Figure 12.3
A schematic for the fractional distillation of petroleum into its useful hydrocarbon components.

because they were close to sea level, periodically became submerged. The organic matter of the swamps was buried beneath layers of marine sediments and was eventually transformed to either coal or petroleum.

Coal is a solid mineral containing many large, complex hydrocarbon molecules. As is discussed in Chapters 18 and 19, most of the coal mined today is used for the production of steel and for generating electricity at coal-burning power plants.

Petroleum, also called crude oil, is a liquid readily separated into its hydrocarbon components through a process known as *fractional distillation,* shown in Figure 12.3. The crude oil is heated in a pipe still to a temperature high enough to vaporize most of the components. The hot vapor flows into the bottom of a fractionating tower, which is warmer at the bottom than at the top. As the vapor rises in the tower and cools, the various components begin to condense. Hydrocarbons that have high boiling points, such as tar and lubricating stocks, condense first at warmer temperatures. Hydrocarbons that have low boiling points, such as gasoline, travel to the cooler regions at the top of the tower before condensing. Pipes drain the various liquid hydrocarbon fractions from the tower. Natural gas, which is primarily methane, does not condense. It remains a gas and is collected at the top of the tower.

Differences in the strength of molecular attractions explain why different hydrocarbons condense at different temperatures. As discussed in Section 7.1, in our comparison of induced dipole–induced dipole attractions in methane and octane, larger hydrocarbons experience many more of these attractions than smaller hydrocarbons do. For this reason, the larger hydrocarbons condense readily at high temperatures and so are found at the bottom of the tower. Smaller molecules, because they experience fewer attractions to neighbors, condense only at the cooler temperatures found at the top of the tower.

The gasoline obtained from the fractional distillation of petroleum consists of a wide variety of hydrocarbons having similar boiling points. Some of these components burn more efficiently than others in a car engine. The straight-chain hydrocarbons, such as *n*-hexane, tend to burn too quickly, causing what is called *engine knock*, as illustrated in Figure 12.4 on page 352. Gasoline hydrocarbons that have more branching, such as *iso*-octane,

Figure 12.4
(a) A straight-chain hydrocarbon, such as *n*-hexane, can be ignited from the heat generated as gasoline is compressed by the piston—before the spark plug fires. This upsets the timing of the engine cycle, giving rise to a knocking sound. (b) Branched hydrocarbons, such as *iso*-octane, burn less readily and are ignited not by compression alone but only when the spark plug fires.

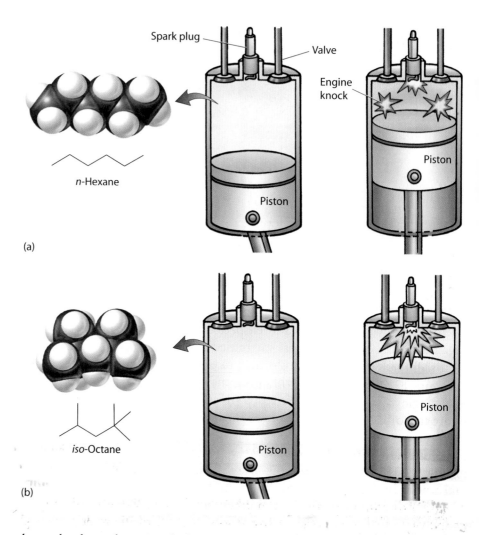

n-Hexane

(a)

iso-Octane

(b)

Figure 12.5
Octane ratings are posted on gasoline pumps.

burn slowly, and as a result the engine runs more smoothly. These two compounds, *n*-hexane and *iso*-octane, are used as standards in assigning *octane ratings* to gasoline. An octane number of 100 is arbitrarily assigned to *iso*-octane, and *n*-hexane is assigned an octane number of 0. The antiknock performance of a particular gasoline is compared with that of various mixtures of *iso*-octane and *n*-hexane, and an octane number is assigned. Figure 12.5 shows octane information on a typical gasoline pump.

Concept Check ✔

Which structural isomer in Figure 12.1 should have the highest octane rating?

Was this your answer? The structural isomer with the greatest amount of branching in the carbon framework will likely have the highest octane rating, making *neo*-pentane the clear winner. Just for the record, the ratings are

Compound	Octane rating
n-Pentane	61.7
iso-Pentane	92.3
neo-Pentane	116

12.2 Unsaturated Hydrocarbons Contain Multiple Bonds

Recall from Section 6.1 that carbon has four unpaired valence electrons. As shown in Figure 12.6, each of these electrons is available for pairing with an electron from another atom, such as hydrogen, to form a covalent bond.

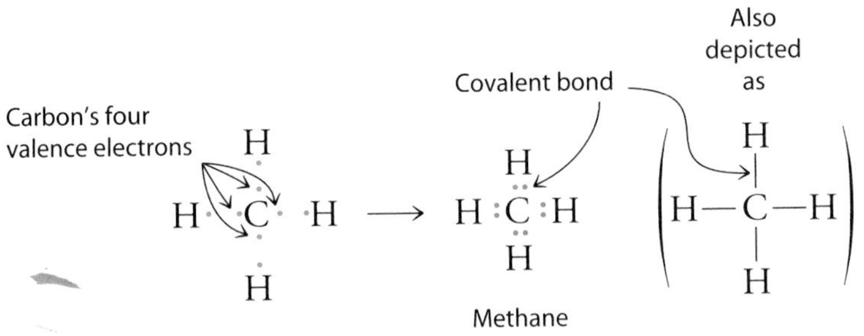

Figure 12.6
Carbon has four valence electrons. Each electron pairs with an electron from a hydrogen atom in the four covalent bonds of methane.

In all the hydrocarbons discussed so far, including the methane shown in Figure 12.6, each carbon atom is bonded to four neighboring atoms by four single covalent bonds. Such hydrocarbons are known as **saturated hydrocarbons**, where the term *saturated* means that each carbon has as many atoms bonded to it as possible. We now explore cases where one or more carbon atoms in a hydrocarbon are bonded to fewer than four neighboring atoms. This occurs when at least one of the bonds between a carbon and a neighboring atom is a multiple bond.

A hydrocarbon containing a multiple bond—either double or triple—is known as an **unsaturated hydrocarbon**. Because of the multiple bond, two of the carbons are bonded to fewer than four other atoms. These carbons are thus said to be *unsaturated*.

Figure 12.7 compares the saturated hydrocarbon *n*-butane with the unsaturated hydrocarbon 2-butene. The number of atoms bonded to each of the two middle carbons of *n*-butane is four, whereas each of the two middle carbons of 2-butene is bonded to only three other atoms—a hydrogen and two carbons.

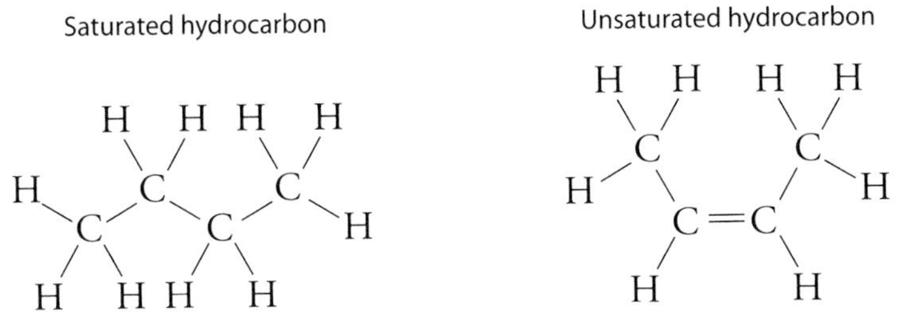

Figure 12.7
The carbons of the hydrocarbon *n*-butane are *saturated*, each being bonded to four other atoms. Because of the double bond, two of the carbons of the unsaturated hydrocarbon 2-butene are bonded to only three other atoms, which makes the molecule an unsaturated hydrocarbon.

An important unsaturated hydrocarbon is benzene, C_6H_6, which may be drawn as three double bonds contained within a flat hexagonal ring, as is shown in Figure 12.8a. Unlike the double-bond electrons in most other unsaturated hydrocarbons, however, the electrons of the double bonds in benzene are not fixed between any two carbon atoms. Instead, these electrons are able to move freely around the ring. This is commonly represented by drawing a circle within the ring, as shown in Figure 12.8b, rather than the individual double bonds.

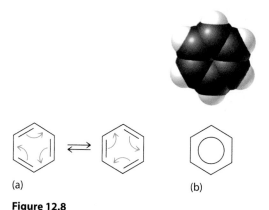

(a)   (b)

Figure 12.8
(a) The double bonds of benzene, C_6H_6, are able to migrate around the ring. (b) For this reason, they are often represented by a circle within the ring.

Many organic compounds contain one or more benzene rings in their structure. Because many of these compounds are fragrant, any organic molecule containing a benzene ring is classified as an **aromatic compound** (even if it is not particularly fragrant). Figure 12.9 shows a few examples. Toluene, a common solvent used as paint thinner, is toxic and gives airplane glue its distinctive odor. Some aromatic compounds, such as naphthalene, contain two or more benzene rings fused together. At one time, mothballs were made of naphthalene. Most mothballs sold today, however, are made of the less toxic 1,4-dichlorobenzene.

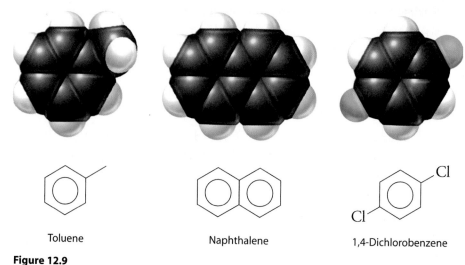

Toluene   Naphthalene   1,4-Dichlorobenzene

Figure 12.9
The structures for three odoriferous organic compounds containing one or more benzene rings: toluene, naphthalene, and 1,4-dichlorobenzene.

An example of an unsaturated hydrocarbon containing a triple bond is acetylene, C_2H_2. A confined flame of acetylene burning in oxygen is hot enough to melt iron, which makes acetylene a choice fuel for the welding shown in Figure 12.10.

H—C≡C—H
Acetylene

Figure 12.10
The unsaturated hydrocarbon acetylene, C_2H_2, burned in this torch produces a flame hot enough to melt iron.

Hands-On Chemistry: Twisting Jellybeans

Two carbon atoms connected by a single bond can rotate relative to each other. As we discussed in Section 12.1, this ability to rotate can give rise to numerous conformations (spatial orientations) of an organic molecule. Is it also possible for carbon atoms connected by a double bond to rotate relative to each other? Perform this quick activity to see for yourself.

What You Need

Jellybeans (or gumdrops), round toothpicks

Procedure

① Attach one jellybean to each end of a single toothpick. Hold one of the jellybeans firmly with one hand while rotating the second jellybean with your other hand. Observe how there is no restriction on the different orientations of the two jellybeans relative to each other.

② Hold two toothpicks side by side and attach one jellybean to each end such that each jellybean has both toothpicks poked into it. As before, hold one jellybean while rotating the other. What kind of rotations are possible now?

Relate what you observe to the carbon–carbon double bond. Which structure of Figure 12.7 do you suppose has more possible conformations: *n*-butane or 2-butene? What do you suppose is true about the ability of atoms connected by a carbon–carbon triple bond to twist relative to each other?

Concept Check ✓

Prolonged exposure to benzene has been found to increase the risk of developing certain cancers. The structure of aspirin contains a benzene ring. Does this necessarily mean that prolonged exposure to aspirin will increase a person's risk of developing cancer?

Benzene ring

Aspirin

Was this your answer? No. Although benzene and aspirin both contain a benzene ring, these two molecules have different overall structures, which means the properties of one are quite different from the properties of the other. Each carbon-containing organic compound has its own set of unique physical, chemical, and biological properties. While benzene may cause cancer, aspirin is a safe remedy for headaches.

12.3 Organic Molecules Are Classified by Functional Group

Carbon atoms can bond to one another and to hydrogen atoms in many ways, which results in an incredibly large number of hydrocarbons. But carbon atoms can bond to atoms of other elements as well, further increasing the number of possible organic molecules. In organic chemistry, any atom other than carbon or hydrogen in an organic molecule is called a **heteroatom**, where *hetero-* means "different from either carbon or hydrogen."

A hydrocarbon structure can serve as a framework to which various heteroatoms can be attached. This is analogous to a Christmas tree serving as the scaffolding on which ornaments are hung. Just as the ornaments give character to the tree, so do heteroatoms give character to an organic molecule. In other words, heteroatoms can have profound effects on the properties of an organic molecule.

Consider ethane, C_2H_6, and ethanol, C_2H_6O, which differ from each other by only a single oxygen atom. Ethane has a boiling point of $-88°C$, making it a gas at room temperature, and it does not dissolve in water very well. Ethanol, by contrast, has a boiling point of $+78°C$, making it a liquid at room temperature. It is infinitely soluble in water and is the active ingredient of alcoholic beverages. Consider further ethylamine, C_2H_7N, which has a nitrogen atom on the same basic two-carbon framework. This compound is a corrosive, pungent, highly toxic gas—most unlike either ethane or ethanol.

Organic molecules are classified according to the functional groups they contain, where a **functional group** is defined as a combination of atoms that behave as a unit. Most functional groups are distinguished by the heteroatoms they contain, and some common groups are listed in Table 12.1.

Ethane

Ethanol

Ethylamine

Table 12.1

Functional Groups in Organic Molecules

General Structure	Name	Class
$-\overset{\vert}{\underset{\vert}{C}}-OH$	Hydroxyl group	Alcohols
$-\overset{\vert}{C}\overset{C=C}{\underset{C-C}{\diagdown}}C-OH$	Phenolic group	Phenols
$-\overset{\vert}{\underset{\vert}{C}}-O-\overset{\vert}{\underset{\vert}{C}}-$	Ether group	Ethers
$-\overset{\vert}{\underset{\vert}{C}}-N\diagup$	Amine group	Amines
$-\overset{\vert}{\underset{\vert}{C}}\overset{\overset{O}{\|}}{C}\overset{\vert}{\underset{\vert}{C}}-$	Ketone group	Ketones
$\overset{\overset{O}{\|}}{C}\diagdown_H$	Aldehyde group	Aldehydes
$\overset{\overset{O}{\|}}{C}\diagdown_{N}\diagup$	Amide group	Amides
$\overset{\overset{O}{\|}}{C}\diagdown_{OH}$	Carboxyl group	Carboxylic acids
$\overset{\overset{O}{\|}}{C}\diagdown_{O}-\overset{\vert}{\underset{\vert}{C}}-$	Ester group	Esters

The remainder of this section introduces the classes of organic molecules shown in Table 12.1. The role heteroatoms play in determining the properties of each class is the underlying theme. As you study this material, focus on understanding the chemical and physical properties of the various classes of compounds, for doing so will give you a greater appreciation of the remarkable diversity of organic molecules and their many applications.

Concept Check ✔

What is the significance of heteroatoms in an organic molecule?

Was this your answer? Heteroatoms largely determine an organic molecule's "personality."

Alcohols Contain the Hydroxyl Group

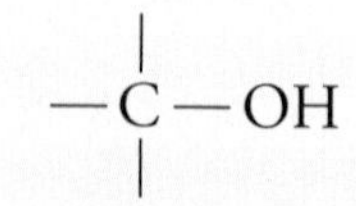

Hydroxyl group

Alcohols are organic molecules in which a *hydroxyl group* is bonded to a saturated carbon. The hydroxyl group consists of an oxygen bonded to a hydrogen. Because of the polarity of the oxygen–hydrogen bond, low-formula-mass alcohols are often soluble in water, which is itself very polar. Some common alcohols and their melting and boiling points are listed in Table 12.2.

Table 12.2

Some Simple Alcohols

Structure	Scientific Name	Common Name	Melting Point (°C)	Boiling Point (°C)
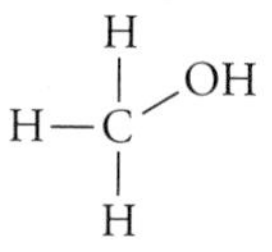 Methanol structure	Methanol	Methyl alcohol	−97	65
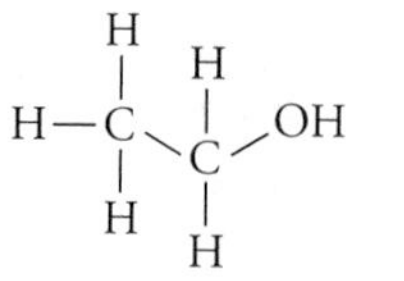 Ethanol structure	Ethanol	Ethyl alcohol	−115	78
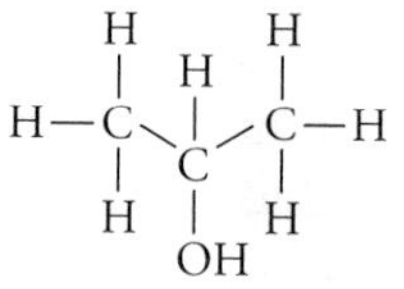 2-Propanol structure	2-Propanol	Isopropyl alcohol	−126	97

More than 11 billion pounds of methanol, CH_3OH, is produced annually in the United States. Most of it is used for making formaldehyde and acetic acid, important starting materials in the production of plastics. In addition, methanol is used as a solvent, an octane booster, and an anti-icing agent in gasoline. Sometimes called wood alcohol because it can be obtained from wood, methanol should never be ingested because in the body it is metabolized to formaldehyde and formic acid. Formaldehyde is harmful to the eyes, can lead to blindness, and was once used to preserve dead biological specimens. Formic acid, the active ingredient in an ant bite, can lower the pH of the blood to dangerous levels. Ingesting only about 15 milliliters of methanol may lead to blindness, and about 30 milliliters can cause death.

Ethanol, C_2H_5OH, is one of the oldest chemicals manufactured by humans. The "alcohol" of alcoholic beverages, ethanol is prepared by feeding the sugars of various plants to certain yeasts, which produce ethanol through a biological process known as *fermentation.* Ethanol is widely used as an industrial solvent. For many years, ethanol intended for this purpose

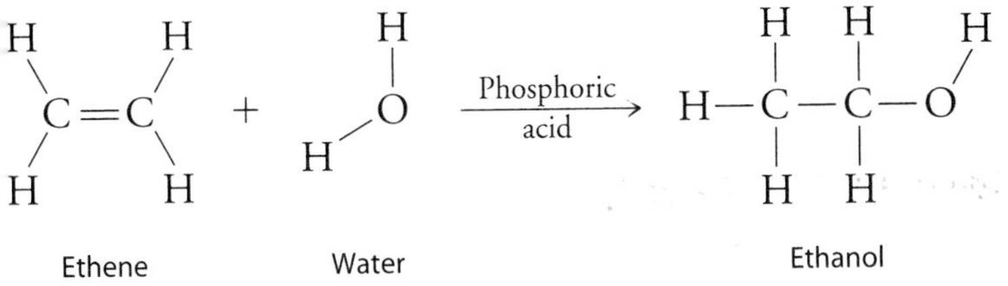

Figure 12.11
Ethanol can be synthesized from the unsaturated hydrocarbon ethene, with phosphoric acid as a catalyst.

was made by fermentation, but today industrial-grade ethanol is more cheaply manufactured from petroleum byproducts, such as ethene, as Figure 12.11 illustrates.

The liquid produced by fermentation has an ethanol concentration no greater than about 12 percent because at this concentration the yeast begin to die. This is why most wines have an alcohol content of 11 or 12 percent—they are produced solely by fermentation. To attain the higher ethanol concentrations found in such "hard" alcoholic beverages as gin and vodka, the fermented liquid must be distilled. In the United States, the ethanol content of alcoholic beverages is measured as *proof*, which is twice the percent ethanol. An 86-proof whiskey, for example, is 43 percent ethanol by volume. The term *proof* evolved from a crude method once employed to test alcohol content. Gunpowder was wetted with a beverage of suspect alcohol content. If the beverage was primarily water, the powder would not ignite. If the beverage contained a significant amount of ethanol, the powder would burn, thus providing "proof" of the beverage's worth.

A third well-known alcohol is isopropyl alcohol, also called 2-propanol. This is the rubbing alcohol you buy at the drugstore. Although 2-propanol has a relatively high boiling point, it readily evaporates, leading to a pronounced cooling effect when applied to skin—an effect once used to reduce fevers. (Isopropyl alcohol is very toxic if ingested. Washcloths wetted with cold water are nearly as effective in reducing fever and far safer.) You are probably most familiar with the use of isopropyl alcohol as a topical disinfectant.

Phenols Contain an Acidic Hydroxyl Group

Phenols contain a phenolic group, which consists of a hydroxyl group attached to a benzene ring. Because of the presence of the benzene ring, the hydrogen of the hydroxyl group is readily lost in an acid–base reaction, which makes the phenolic group mildly acidic.

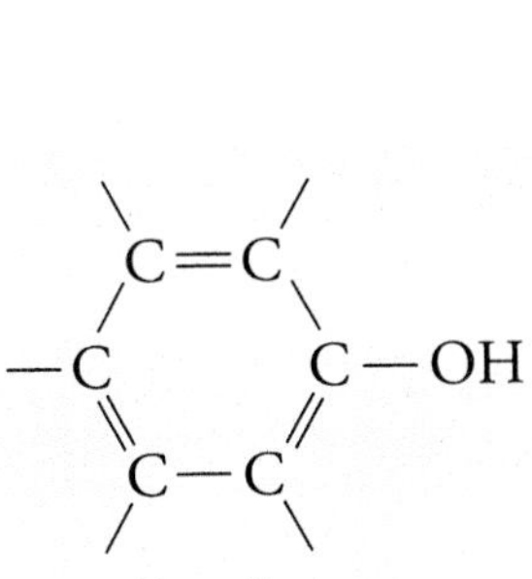

The reason for this acidity is illustrated in Figure 12.12 on page 360. How readily an acid donates a hydrogen ion is a function of how well the acid is able to accommodate the resulting negative charge it gains after donating the hydrogen ion. After phenol donates the hydrogen ion, it becomes a negatively charged phenoxide ion. The negative charge of the phenoxide ion, however, is not restricted to the oxygen atom. Recall that the electrons of the benzene ring are able to migrate around the ring. In a similar manner, the electrons responsible for the negative charge of the phenoxide ion are also able to migrate around the ring, as shown in Figure 12.12. Just as it is easy for

Phenolic group

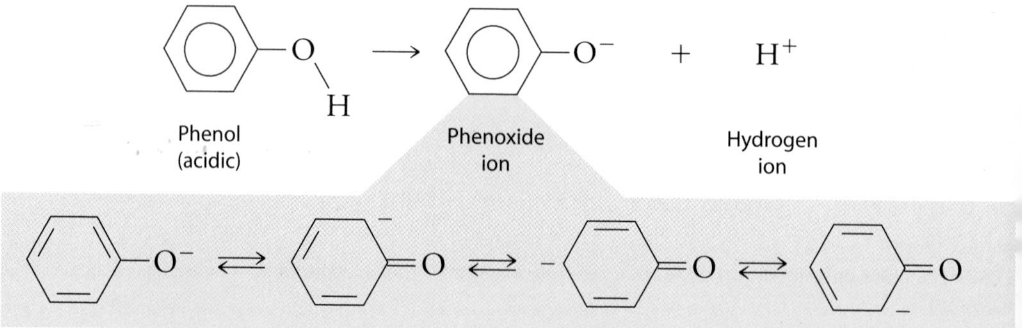

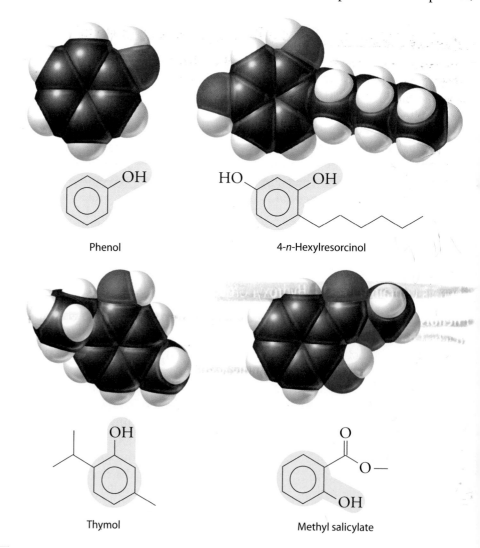

Figure 12.12
The negative charge of the phenoxide ion is able to migrate to select positions on the benzene ring. This mobility helps to accommodate the negative charge, which is why the phenolic group readily donates a hydrogen ion.

several people to hold a hot potato by quickly passing it around, it is easy for the phenoxide ion to hold the negative charge because the charge gets passed around. Because the negative charge of the ion is so nicely accommodated, the phenolic group is more acidic than it would be otherwise.

The simplest phenol, shown in Figure 12.13, is called phenol. In 1867, Joseph Lister (1827–1912) discovered the antiseptic value of phenol,

Phenol

4-*n*-Hexylresorcinol

Thymol

Methyl salicylate

Figure 12.13
Every phenol contains a phenolic group (highlighted in blue).

which, when applied to surgical instruments and incisions, greatly increased surgery survival rates. Phenol was the first purposefully used antibacterial solution, or *antiseptic*. Phenol damages healthy tissue, however, and so a number of milder phenols have since been introduced. The phenol 4-*n*-hexylresorcinol, for example, is commonly used in throat lozenges and mouthwashes. This compound has even greater antiseptic properties than phenol, and yet it does not damage tissue. Listerine brand mouthwash (named after Joseph Lister) contains the antiseptic phenols thymol and methyl salicylate.

Concept Check ✓

Why are alcohols less acidic than phenols?

Was this your answer? An alcohol does not contain a benzene ring adjacent to the hydroxyl group. If the alcohol were to donate the hydroxyl hydrogen, the result would be a negative charge on the oxygen. Without an adjacent benzene ring, this negative charge has nowhere to go. As a result, an alcohol behaves only as a very weak acid, much the way water does.

The Oxygen of an Ether Group Is Bonded to Two Carbon Atoms

Ethers are organic compounds structurally related to alcohols. The oxygen atom in an ether group, however, is bonded not to a carbon and a hydrogen but rather to two carbons. As we see in Figure 12.14, ethanol and dimethyl ether have the same chemical formula, C_2H_6O, but their physical properties are vastly different. Whereas ethanol is a liquid at room temperature (boiling point 78°C) and mixes quite well with water, dimethyl ether is a gas at room temperature (boiling point −25°C) and is much less soluble in water.

$$-\overset{|}{\underset{|}{C}}-O-\overset{|}{\underset{|}{C}}-$$

Ether group

Ethanol: Soluble in water, boiling point 78°C

Dimethyl ether: Insoluble in water, boiling point −25°C

Figure 12.14
The oxygen in an alcohol such as ethanol is bonded to one carbon atom and one hydrogen atom. The oxygen in an ether such as dimethyl ether is bonded to two carbon atoms. Because of this difference, alcohols and ethers of similar molecular mass have vastly different physical properties.

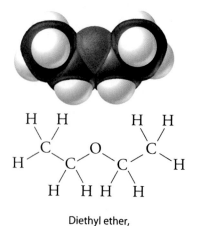

Diethyl ether,
boiling point 35°C

Figure 12.15
Diethyl ether is the systematic name
for the "ether" historically used as an
anesthetic.

Ethers are not very soluble in water because, without the hydroxyl group, they are unable to form strong hydrogen bonds with water (Section 7.1). Furthermore, without the polar hydroxyl group, the molecular attractions among ether molecules are relatively weak. As a result, it does not take much energy to separate ether molecules from one another. This is why ethers have relatively low boiling points and evaporate so readily.

Diethyl ether, shown in Figure 12.15, was one of the first anesthetics. The anesthetic properties of this compound were discovered in the early 1800s and revolutionized the practice of surgery. Because of its high volatility at room temperature, inhaled diethyl ether rapidly enters the bloodstream. Because this ether has low solubility in water and high volatility, it quickly leaves the bloodstream once introduced. Because of these physical properties, a surgical patient can be brought in and out of anesthesia (a state of unconsciousness) simply by regulating the gases breathed. Modern-day gaseous anesthetics have fewer side effects than diethyl ether but work on the same principle.

Amines Form Alkaline Solutions

Amines are organic compounds that contain the amine group—a nitrogen atom bonded to one, two, or three saturated carbons. Amines are typically less soluble in water than are alcohols because the nitrogen–hydrogen bond is not quite as polar as the oxygen–hydrogen bond. The lower polarity of amines also means their boiling points are typically somewhat lower than those of alcohols of similar formula mass. Table 12.3 lists three simple amines.

Amine group

Table 12.3

Three Simple Amines

Structure	Name	Melting Point (°C)	Boiling Point (°C)
	Ethylamine	−81	17
	Diethylamine	−50	55
	Triethylamine	−7	89

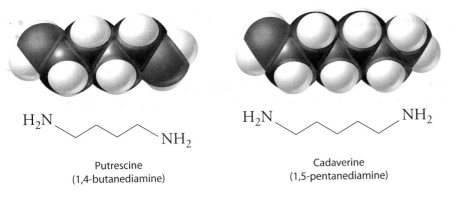

Putrescine
(1,4-butanediamine)

Cadaverine
(1,5-pentanediamine)

One of the most notable physical properties of many low-formula-mass amines is their offensive odor. Figure 12.16 shows two appropriately named amines, putrescine and cadaverine, responsible for the odor of decaying flesh.

Amines are typically alkaline because the nitrogen atom readily accepts a hydrogen ion from water, as Figure 12.17 illustrates.

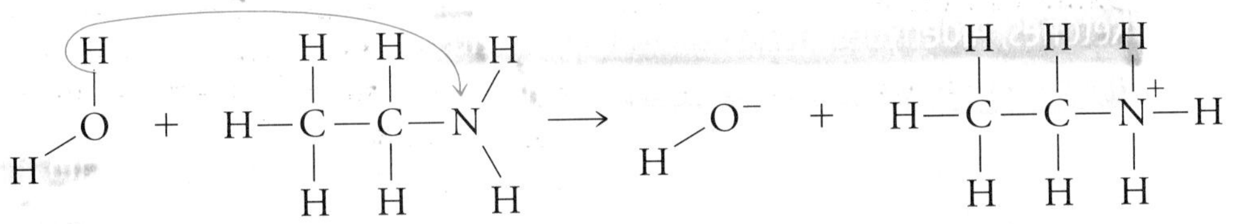

| Water (acid) | Ethylamine (base) | Hydroxide ion | Ethylammonium ion |

Figure 12.17
Ethylamine acts as a base and accepts a hydrogen ion from water to become the ethylammonium ion. This reaction generates a hydroxide ion, which increases the pH of the solution.

A group of naturally occurring complex molecules that are alkaline because they contain nitrogen atoms are often called *alkaloids*. Because many alkaloids have medicinal value, there is great interest in isolating these compounds from plants or marine organisms containing them. As shown in Figure 12.18, an alkaloid reacts with an acid to form a salt that is usually quite soluble in water. This is in contrast to the nonionized form of the alkaloid, known as a *free base* and typically insoluble in water.

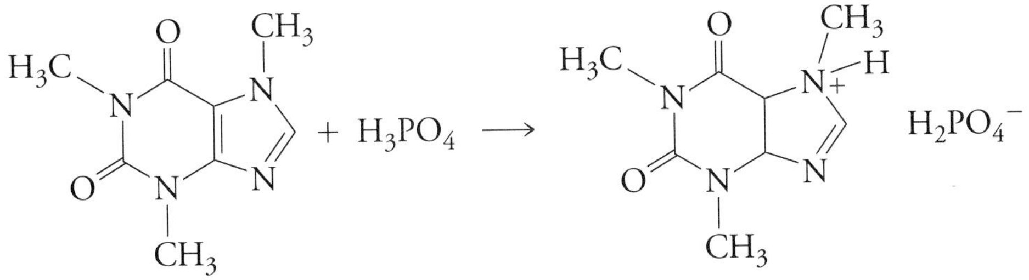

Caffeine, free-base form
(water-insoluble)

Phosphoric acid

Caffeine–phosphoric acid salt
(water-soluble)

$+ H_3PO_4 \longrightarrow$

$H_2PO_4^-$

Figure 12.18
All alkaloids are bases that react with acids to form salts. An example is the alkaloid caffeine, shown here reacting with phosphoric acid.

Figure 12.19
Tannins are responsible for the brown stains in coffee mugs or on a coffee drinker's teeth. Because tannins are acidic, they can be readily removed with an alkaline cleanser. Use a little laundry bleach on the mug, and brush your teeth with baking soda.

Most alkaloids exist in nature not in their free-base form but rather as the salt of naturally occurring acids known as *tannins*, a group of phenol-based organic acids that have complex structures. The alkaloid salts of these acids are usually much more soluble in hot water than in cold water. The caffeine in coffee and tea exists in the form of the tannin salt, which is why coffee and tea are more effectively brewed in hot water. As Figure 12.19 relates, tannins are also responsible for the stains caused by these beverages.

Concept Check ✓

Why do most caffeinated soft drinks also contain phosphoric acid?

Was this your answer? The phosphoric acid, as shown in Figure 12.18, reacts with the caffeine to form the caffeine phosphoric acid salt, which is much more soluble in cold water than the naturally occurring tannin salt.

Ketones, Aldehydes, Amides, Carboxylic Acids, and Esters All Contain a Carbonyl Group

Ketones, aldehydes, amides, carboxylic acids, and esters all contain a **carbonyl group**, which consists of a carbon atom double-bonded to an oxygen atom.

A **ketone** is a carbonyl-containing organic molecule in which the carbonyl carbon is bonded to two carbon atoms. A familiar example of a ketone is *acetone*, which is often used in fingernail polish remover and is shown in Figure 12.20a. In an **aldehyde**, the carbonyl carbon is bonded either to one carbon atom and one hydrogen atom, as in Figure 12.20b, or, in the special case of formaldehyde, to two hydrogen atoms.

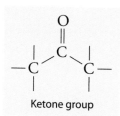

Ketone group

Aldehyde group

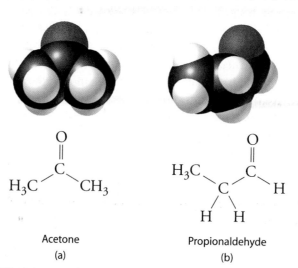

Acetone
(a)

Propionaldehyde
(b)

Figure 12.20
(a) When the carbon of a carbonyl group is bonded to two carbon atoms, the result is a ketone. An example is acetone. (b) When the carbon of a carbonyl group is bonded to at least one hydrogen atom, the result is an aldehyde. An example is propionaldehyde.

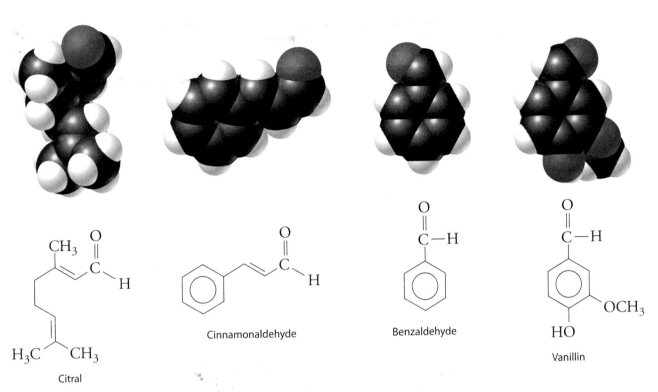

Figure 12.21
Aldehydes are responsible for many familiar fragrances.

Many aldehydes are particularly fragrant. A number of flowers, for example, owe their pleasant odor to the presence of simple aldehydes. The smells of lemons, cinnamon, and almonds are due to the aldehydes citral, cinnamaldehyde, and benzaldehyde, respectively. The structures of these three aldehydes are shown in Figure 12.21. The aldehyde vanillin, introduced at the beginning of this chapter, is the key flavoring molecule derived from the vanilla orchid. You may have noticed that vanilla beans and vanilla extract are fairly expensive. Imitation vanilla flavoring is less expensive because it is merely a solution of the compound vanillin, which is economically synthesized from the waste chemicals of the wood pulp industry. Imitation vanilla does not taste the same as natural vanilla extract, however, because in addition to vanillin many other flavorful molecules contribute to the complex taste of natural vanilla. Many books made in the days before "acid-free" paper smell of vanilla because of the vanillin formed and released as the paper ages, a process that is accelerated by the acids the paper contains.

An **amide** is a carbonyl-containing organic molecule in which the carbonyl carbon is bonded to a nitrogen atom. The active ingredient of most mosquito repellents is an amide whose chemical name is *N,N*-diethyl-*m*-toluamide but is commercially known as DEET, shown in Figure 12.22. This compound is actually not an insecticide. Rather, it causes certain insects, especially mosquitoes, to lose their sense of direction, which effectively protects DEET wearers from being bitten.

Amide group

N,N-Diethyl-*m*-toluamide
(DEET)

Figure 12.22
N,N-diethyl-*m*-toluamide is an example of an amide. Amides contain the amide group, shown highlighted in blue.

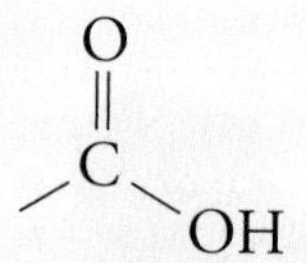

O
‖
C
OH

Carboxyl group

A **carboxylic acid** is a carbonyl-containing organic molecule in which the carbonyl carbon is bonded to a hydroxyl group. As its name implies, this functional group is able to donate hydrogen ions, and as a result organic molecules containing it are acidic. An example is acetic acid, $C_2H_4O_2$, the main ingredient of vinegar. You may recall that this organic compound was used as an example of a weak acid back in Chapter 10.

As with phenols, the acidity of a carboxylic acid results in part from the ability of the functional group to accommodate the negative charge of the ion that forms after the hydrogen ion has been donated. As shown in Figure 12.23, a carboxylic acid transforms to a carboxylate ion as it loses the hydrogen ion. The negative charge of the carboxylate ion is able to pass back and forth between the two oxygens. This spreading out helps to accommodate the negative charge.

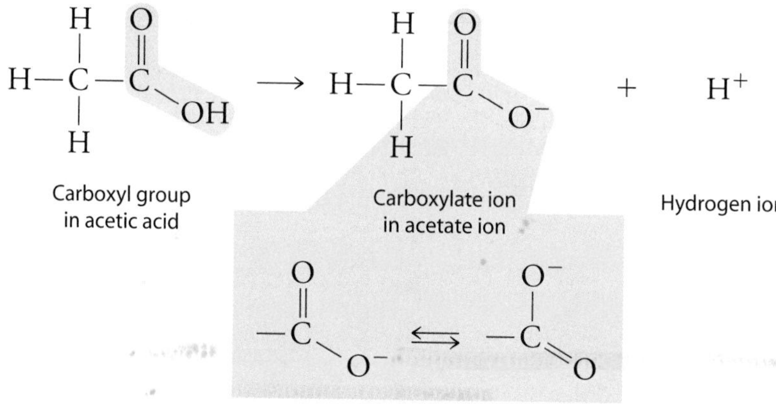

Figure 12.23
The negative charge of the carboxylate ion is able to pass back and forth between the two oxygen atoms of the carboxyl group.

An interesting example of an organic compound that contains both a carboxylic acid and a phenol is salicylic acid, found in the bark of the willow tree and illustrated in Figure 12.24a. At one time brewed for its antipyretic (fever-reducing) effect, salicylic acid is an important analgesic (painkiller), but it causes nausea and stomach upset because of its relatively high acidity, a result of the presence of two acidic functional groups. In 1899, Friederich Bayer and Company, in Germany, introduced a chemically modified version of this compound in which the phenolic group was transformed to an ester functional group. Because both the carboxyl group and the phenolic group contribute to the high acidity of salicylic acid, getting rid of the phenolic group reduced the acidity of the molecule considerably. The result was the less acidic and more tolerable acetylsalicylic acid, the chemical name for aspirin, shown in Figure 12.24b.

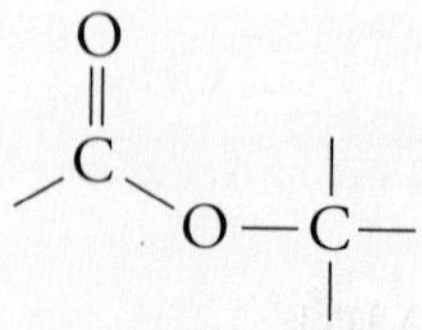

An **ester** is an organic molecule similar to a carboxylic acid except that in the ester the hydroxyl hydrogen is replaced by a carbon. Unlike carboxylic acids, esters are not acidic because they lack the hydrogen of the hydroxyl group. Like aldehydes, many simple esters have notable fragrances and are used as flavorings. Some familiar ones are listed in Table 12.4 on page 368.

O
‖
C
O—C—

Ester group

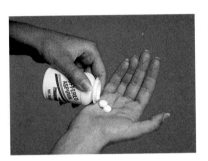

(a) Salicylic acid

(b) Aspirin (acetylsalicylic acid)

Figure 12.24
(a) Salicylic acid, found in the bark of the willow tree, is an example of a molecule containing both a carboxyl group and a phenolic group. (b) Aspirin, acetylsalicylic acid, is less acidic than salicylic acid because it no longer contains the acidic phenolic group, which has been converted to an ester.

Concept Check ✓

Identify all the functional groups in these four molecules (ignore the sulfur group in penicillin G):

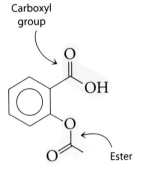

Acetaldehyde

Penicillin G

Testosterone

Morphine

Was this your answer? Acetaldehyde: aldehyde; penicillin G: amide (two amide groups), carboxylic acid; testosterone: alcohol and ketone; morphine: alcohol, phenol, ether, and amine.

Table 12.4

Some Esters and Their Flavors

Structure	Name	Flavor
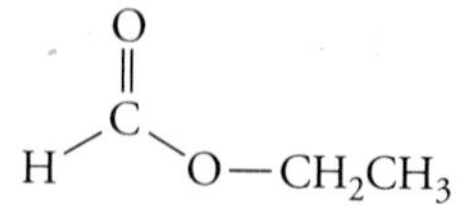	Ethyl formate	Rum
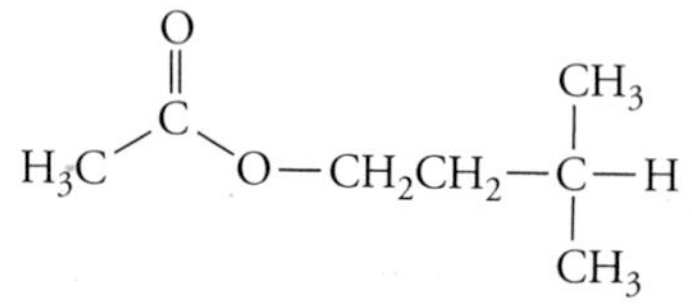	Isopentyl acetate	Banana
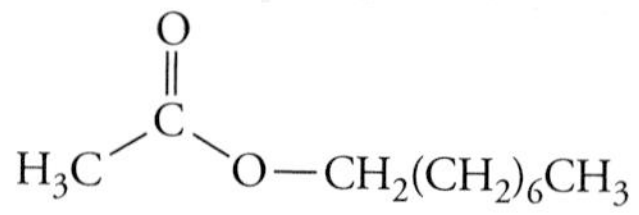	Octyl acetate	Orange
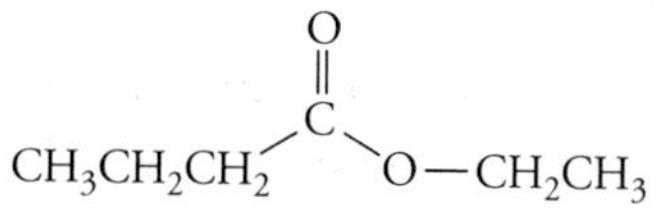	Ethyl butyrate	Pineapple
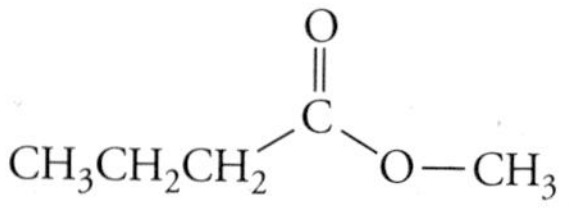	Methyl butyrate	Apple
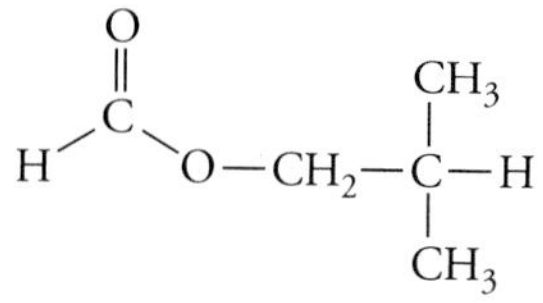	Isobutyl formate	Raspberry
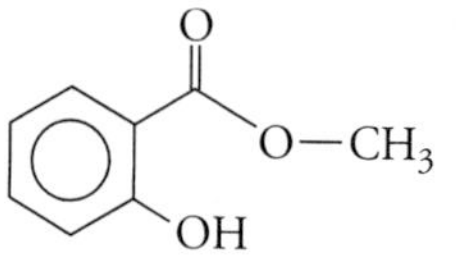	Methyl salicylate	Wintergreen

12.4 Organic Molecules Can Link To Form Polymers

Polymers are exceedingly long molecules that consist of repeating molecular units called **monomers**, as Figure 12.25 illustrates. Monomers have relatively simple structures consisting of anywhere from 4 to 100 atoms per molecule. When chained together, they can form polymers consisting of hundreds of thousands of atoms per molecule. These large molecules are still too small to be seen with the unaided eye. They are, however, giants in the world of the submicroscopic—if a typical polymer molecule were as thick as a kite string, it would be 1 kilometer long.

Many of the molecules that make up living organisms are polymers, including DNA, proteins, the cellulose of plants, and the complex carbohydrates of starchy foods. We leave a discussion of these important biological molecules to Chapter 13. For now, we focus on the human-made polymers,

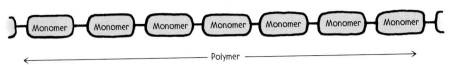

Figure 12.25
A polymer is a long molecule consisting of many smaller monomer molecules linked together.

also known as synthetic polymers, that make up the class of materials commonly known as plastics.

We begin by exploring the two major types of synthetic polymers used today—*addition polymers* and *condensation polymers*. This provides a good background for the discussion of plastics in Chapter 18.

As shown in Table 12.5 on pages 370 and 371, addition and condensation polymers have a wide variety of uses. Solely the product of human design, these polymers pervade modern living. In the United States, for example, synthetic polymers have surpassed steel as the most widely used material.

Addition Polymers Result from the Joining Together of Monomers

Addition polymers form simply by the joining together of monomer units. For this to happen, each monomer must contain at least one double bond. As shown in Figure 12.26, polymerization occurs when two of the electrons from each double bond split away from each other to form new covalent bonds with neighboring monomer molecules. During this process, no atoms are lost, meaning that the total mass of the polymer is equal to the sum of the masses of all the monomers.

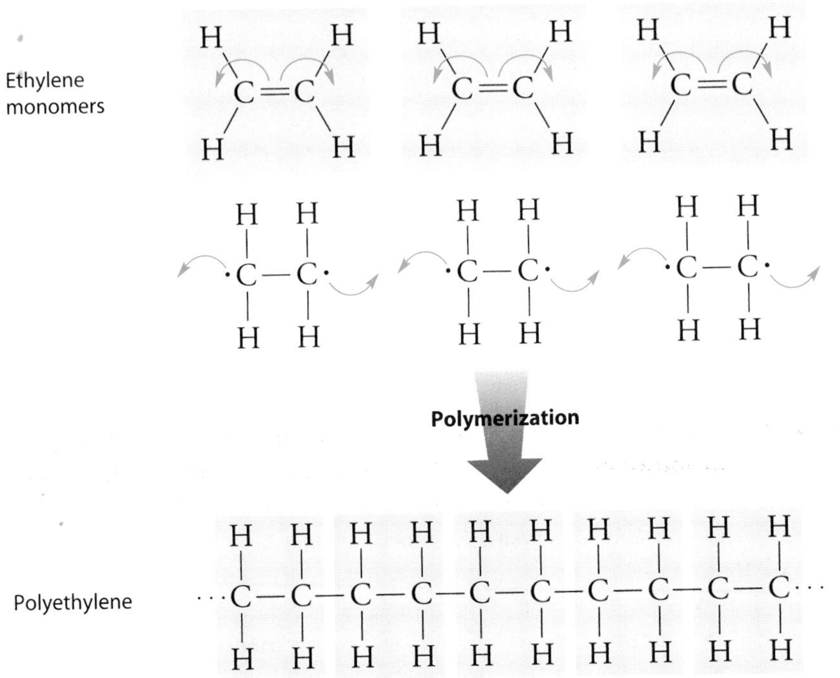

Ethylene monomers

Polymerization

Polyethylene

Figure 12.26
The addition polymer polyethylene is formed as electrons from the double bonds of ethylene monomer molecules split away and become unpaired valence electrons. Each unpaired electron then joins with an unpaired electron of a neighboring carbon atom to form a new covalent bond that links two monomer units together.

Table 12.5

Addition and Condensation Polymers

Addition Polymers	Repeating Unit	Common Uses	Recycling Code
Polyethylene (PE)	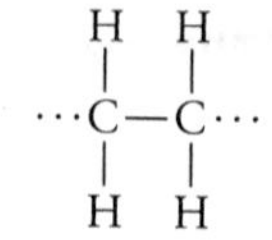 $\cdots\overset{\displaystyle H}{\underset{\displaystyle H}{C}}-\overset{\displaystyle H}{\underset{\displaystyle H}{C}}\cdots$	Plastic bags, bottles	2 HDPE 4 LDPE
Polypropylene (PP)	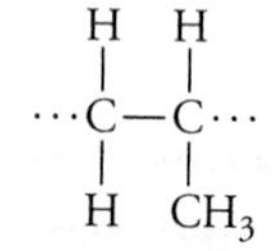 $\cdots\overset{\displaystyle H}{\underset{\displaystyle H}{C}}-\overset{\displaystyle H}{\underset{\displaystyle CH_3}{C}}\cdots$	Indoor–outdoor carpets	5 PP
Polystyrene (PS)	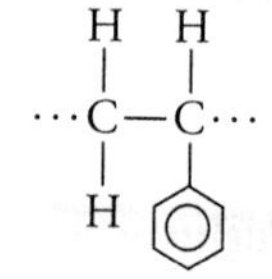 $\cdots\overset{\displaystyle H}{\underset{\displaystyle H}{C}}-\overset{\displaystyle H}{\underset{\displaystyle \bigcirc}{C}}\cdots$	Plastic utensils, insulation	6 PS
Polyvinyl chloride (PVC)	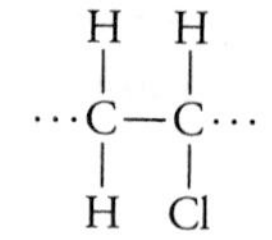 $\cdots\overset{\displaystyle H}{\underset{\displaystyle H}{C}}-\overset{\displaystyle H}{\underset{\displaystyle Cl}{C}}\cdots$	Shower curtains, tubing	3 V
Polyvinylidene chloride (Saran)	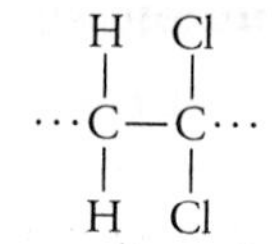 $\cdots\overset{\displaystyle H}{\underset{\displaystyle H}{C}}-\overset{\displaystyle Cl}{\underset{\displaystyle Cl}{C}}\cdots$	Plastic wrap	—
Polytetrafluoroethylene (Teflon)	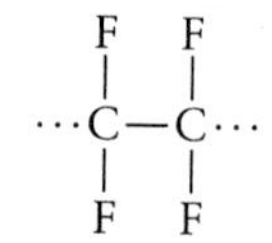 $\cdots\overset{\displaystyle F}{\underset{\displaystyle F}{C}}-\overset{\displaystyle F}{\underset{\displaystyle F}{C}}\cdots$	Nonstick coating	—
Polyacrylonitrile (Orlon)	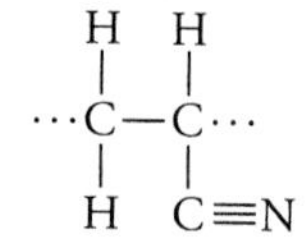 $\cdots\overset{\displaystyle H}{\underset{\displaystyle H}{C}}-\overset{\displaystyle H}{\underset{\displaystyle C\equiv N}{C}}\cdots$	Yarn, paints	—
Polymethyl methacrylate (Lucite, Plexiglas)	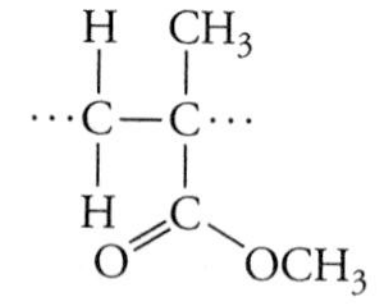 $\cdots\overset{\displaystyle H}{\underset{\displaystyle H}{C}}-\overset{\displaystyle CH_3}{\underset{\displaystyle \underset{O}{\overset{\parallel}{C}}-OCH_3}{C}}\cdots$	Windows, bowling balls	—
Polyvinyl acetate (PVA)	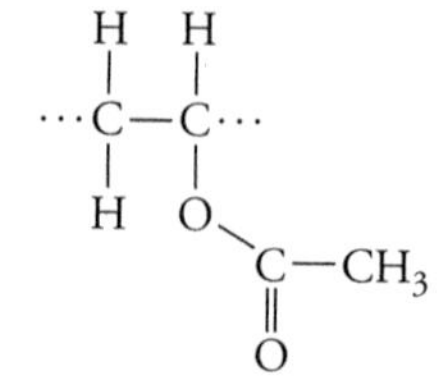 $\cdots\overset{\displaystyle H}{\underset{\displaystyle H}{C}}-\overset{\displaystyle H}{\underset{\displaystyle \underset{\underset{O}{\parallel}}{O}-\overset{}{C}-CH_3}{C}}\cdots$	Adhesives, chewing gum	—

(continued)

Table 12.5 *(continued)*

Addition and Condensation Polymers

Condensation Polymers

Nylon	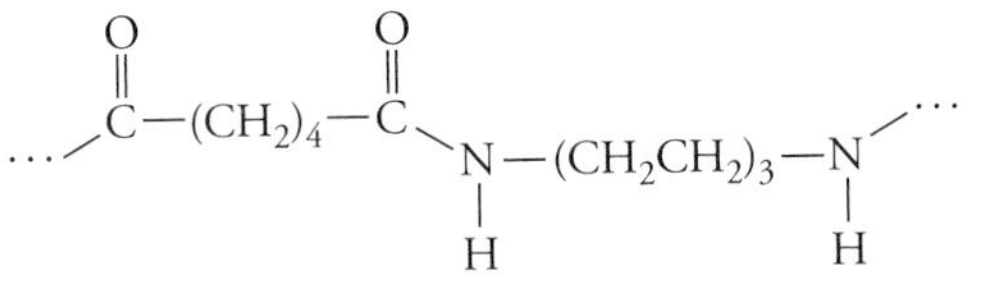	Carpeting, clothing	—
Polyethylene terephthalate (Dacron, Mylar)	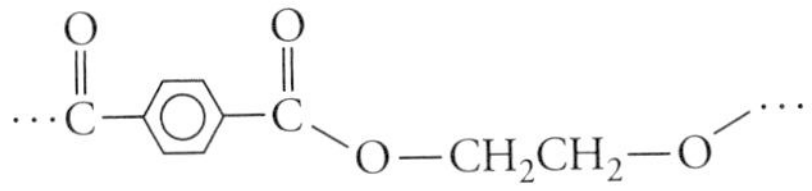	Clothing, plastic bottles	PET
Melamine–formaldehyde resin (Melmac, Formica)	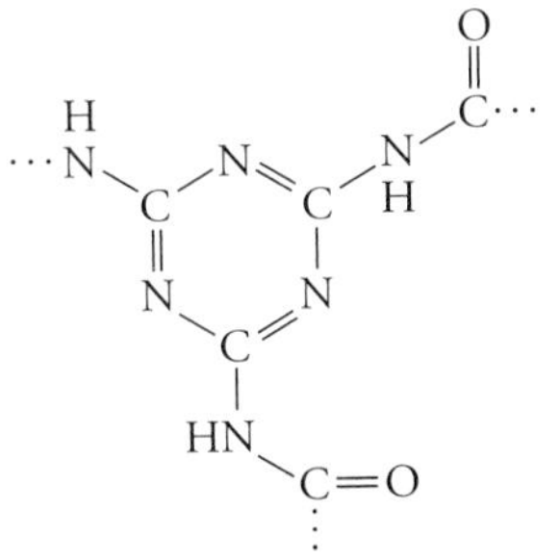	Dishes, countertops	—

Nearly 12 million tons of polyethylene is produced annually in the United States; that's about 90 pounds per U.S. citizen. The monomer from which it is synthesized, ethylene, is an unsaturated hydrocarbon produced in large quantities from petroleum.

Two principal forms of polyethylene are produced by using different catalysts and reaction conditions. High-density polyethylene (HDPE), shown schematically in Figure 12.27a, consists of long strands of straight-chain molecules packed closely together. The tight alignment of neighboring strands makes HDPE a relatively rigid, tough plastic useful for such things as bottles and milk jugs. Low-density polyethylene (LDPE), shown in Figure 12.27b, is made of strands of highly branched chains, an architecture that prevents the strands from packing closely together. This makes LDPE more bendable than HDPE and gives it a lower melting point. While HDPE holds its shape in boiling water, LDPE deforms. It is most useful for such items as plastic bags, photographic film, and electrical-wire insulation.

(a) Molecular strands of HDPE   (b) Molecular strands of LDPE

Figure 12.27
(a) The polyethylene strands of HDPE are able to pack closely together, much like strands of uncooked spaghetti. (b) The polyethylene strands of LDPE are branched, which prevents the strands from packing well.

Figure 12.28
Propylene monomers polymerize to form polypropylene.

Propylene monomers

Polymerization

Polypropylene

Other addition polymers are created by using different monomers. The only requirement is that the monomer must contain a double bond. The monomer propylene, for example, yields polypropylene, as shown in Figure 12.28. Polypropylene is a tough plastic material useful for pipes, hard-shell suitcases, and appliance parts. Fibers of polypropylene are used for upholstery, indoor–outdoor carpets, and even thermal underwear.

Figure 12.29 shows that using styrene as the monomer yields polystyrene. Transparent plastic cups are made of polystyrene, as are thousands of other household items. Blowing gas into liquid polystyrene generates Styrofoam, widely used for coffee cups, packing material, and insulation.

Styrene monomers

Polymerization

Polystyrene

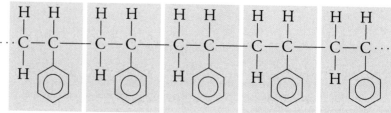

Figure 12.29
Styrene monomers polymerize to form polystyrene.

Figure 12.30
PVC is tough and easily molded, which is why it is used to fabricate many household items.

Polyvinyl chloride (PVC)

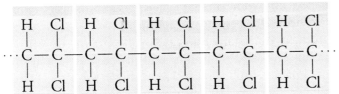

Another important addition polymer is polyvinylchloride (PVC), which is tough and easily molded. Floor tiles, shower curtains, and pipes are most often made of PVC, shown in Figure 12.30.

The addition polymer polyvinylidene chloride (tradename Saran), shown in Figure 12.31, is used as plastic wrap for food. The large chlorine atoms in this polymer help it stick to surfaces such as glass by dipole–induced dipole attractions, as we saw in Section 7.1.

Polyvinylidene chloride (Saran)

Figure 12.31
The large chlorine atoms in polyvinylidene chloride make this addition polymer sticky.

Figure 12.32
The fluorine atoms in polytetrafluoroethylene tend not to experience molecular attractions, which is why this addition polymer is used as a nonstick coating and lubricant.

Polytetra-
fluoroethylene
(Teflon)

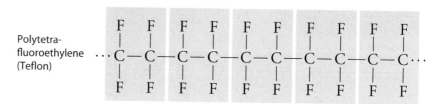

The addition polymer polytetrafluoroethylene, shown in Figure 12.32, is what you know as Teflon. In contrast to the chlorine-containing Saran, fluorine-containing Teflon has a nonstick surface because the fluorine atoms tend not to experience any molecular attractions. Also, carbon–fluorine bonds are unusually strong, which means Teflon can be heated to high temperatures before decomposing. These properties make Teflon an ideal coating for cooking surfaces. It is also relatively inert, which is why many corrosive chemicals are shipped or stored in Teflon containers.

Concept Check ✓

What do all monomers of addition polymers have in common?

Was this your answer? A double covalent bond between two carbon atoms.

Condensation Polymers Form with the Loss of Small Molecules

A **condensation polymer** is one formed when the joining of monomer units is accompanied by the loss of a small molecule, such as water or hydrochloric acid. Any monomer capable of becoming part of a condensation polymer must have a functional group on each end. When two such monomers come together to form a condensation polymer, one functional group of the first monomer links up with one functional group of the other monomer. The result is a two-monomer unit that has two terminal functional groups, one from each of the two original monomers. Each of these terminal functional groups in the two-monomer unit is now free to link up with one of the functional groups of a third monomer, and then a fourth, and so on. In this way a polymer chain is built. Figure 12.33 shows this process for the condensation polymer called nylon, created in 1937 by DuPont chemist Wallace

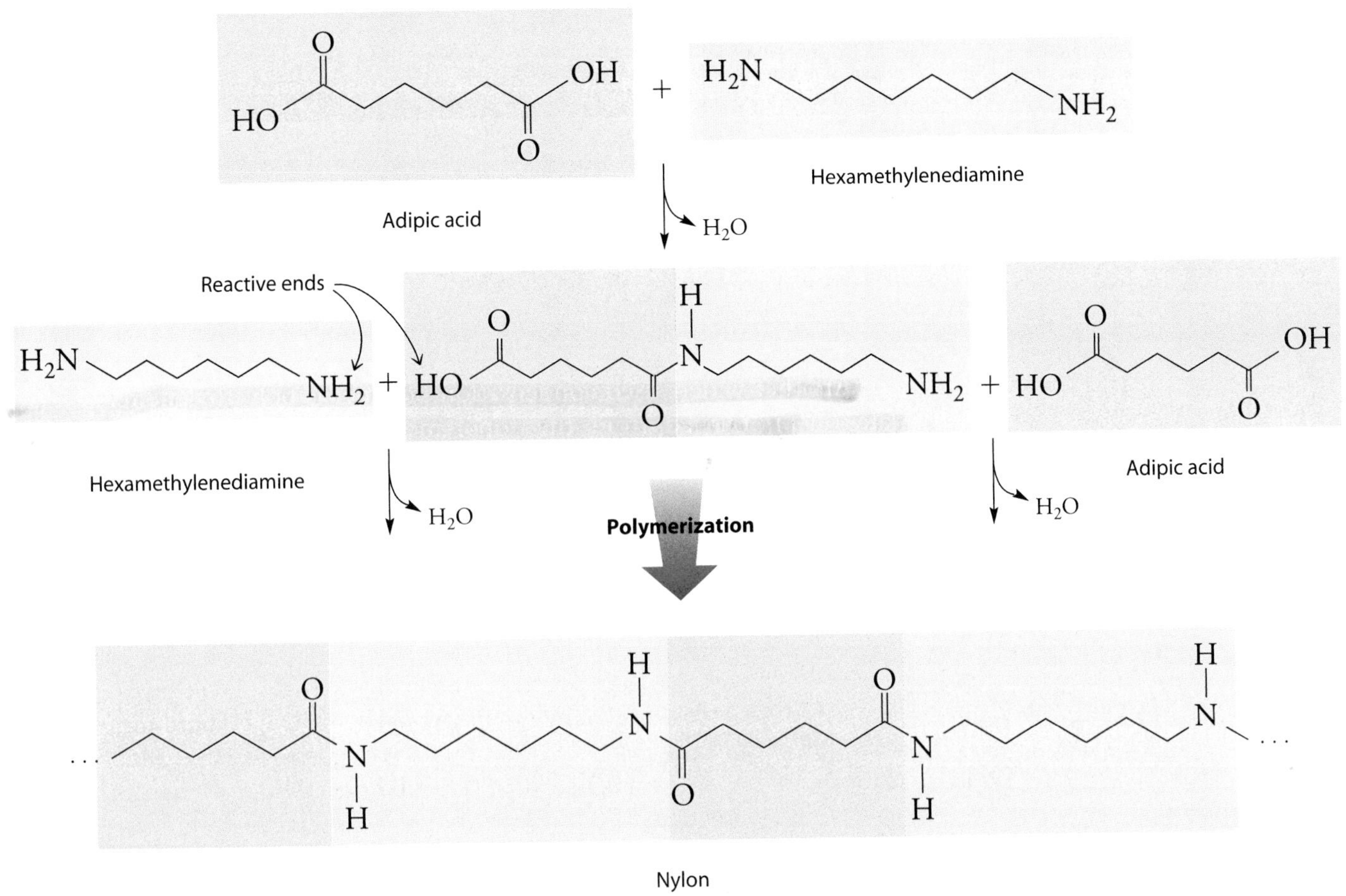

Adipic acid

Hexamethylenediamine

Reactive ends

Hexamethylenediamine

Adipic acid

Polymerization

Nylon

Carothers (1896–1937). This polymer is composed of two different monomers, as shown in Figure 12.33, which classifies it as a *copolymer*. One monomer is adipic acid, which contains two reactive end groups, both carboxyl groups. The second monomer is hexamethylenediamine, in which two amine groups are the reactive end groups. One end of an adipic acid molecule and one end of a hexamethylamine molecule can be made to react with each other, splitting off a water molecule in the process. After two monomers have joined, reactive ends still remain for further reactions, which leads to a growing polymer chain. Aside from its use in hosiery, nylon also finds great use in the manufacture of ropes, parachutes, clothing, and carpets.

Figure 12.33
Adipic acid and hexamethylenediamine polymerize to form the condensation copolymer nylon.

Concept Check ✔

The structure of 6-aminohexanoic acid is

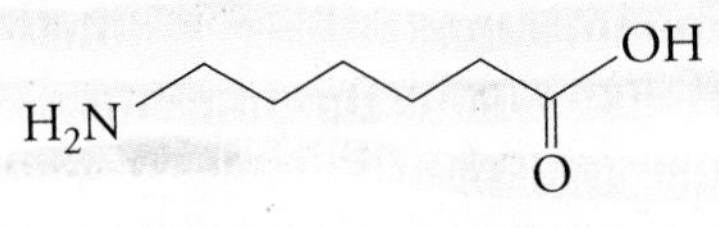

Is this compound a suitable monomer for forming a condensation polymer? If so, what is the structure of the polymer formed, and what small molecule is split off during the condensation?

Was this your answer? Yes, because the molecule has two reactive ends. You know both ends are reactive because they are the ends shown in Figure 12.33. The only difference here is that both types of reactive ends are on the same molecule. Monomers of 6-aminohexanoic acid combine by splitting off water molecules to form the polymer known as nylon-6:

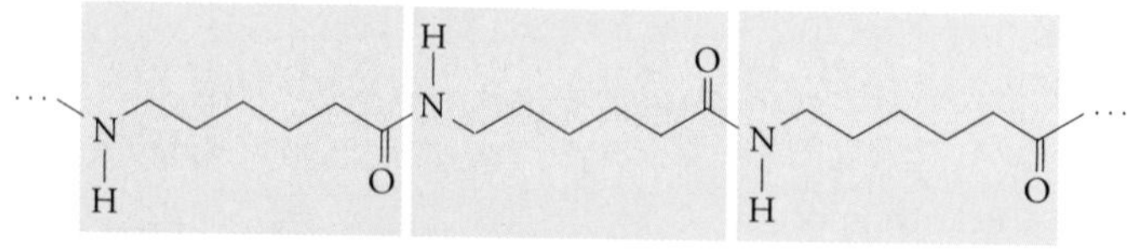

Another widely used condensation polymer is polyethylene terephthalate (PET), formed from the copolymerization of ethylene glycol and terephthalic acid, as shown in Figure 12.34. Plastic soda bottles are made from this polymer. Also, PET fibers are sold as Dacron polyester, used in clothing and stuffing for pillows and sleeping bags. Thin films of PET are called Mylar and can be coated with metal particles to make magnetic recording tape or those metallic-looking balloons you see for sale at most grocery store check-out counters.

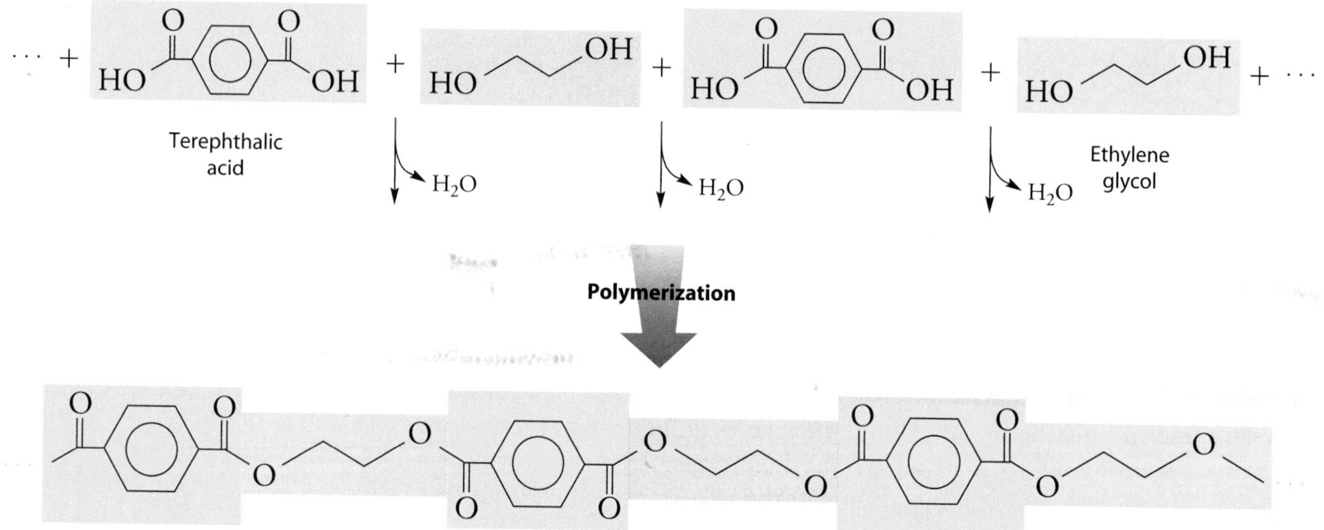

Polyethylene terephthalate (PET)

Figure 12.34
Terephthalic acid and ethylene glycol polymerize to form the condensation copolymer polyethylene terephthalate.

Monomers that contain three reactive functional groups can also form polymer chains. These chains become interlocked in a rigid three-dimensional network that lends considerable strength and durability to the polymer. Once formed, these condensation polymers cannot be remelted or reshaped, which makes them hard-set, or *thermoset*, polymers. A good example is the thermoset polymer shown in Figure 12.35, formed from the reaction of formaldehyde with melamine. Hard plastic dishes (Melmac) and countertops (Formica) are made of this material. A similar polymer,

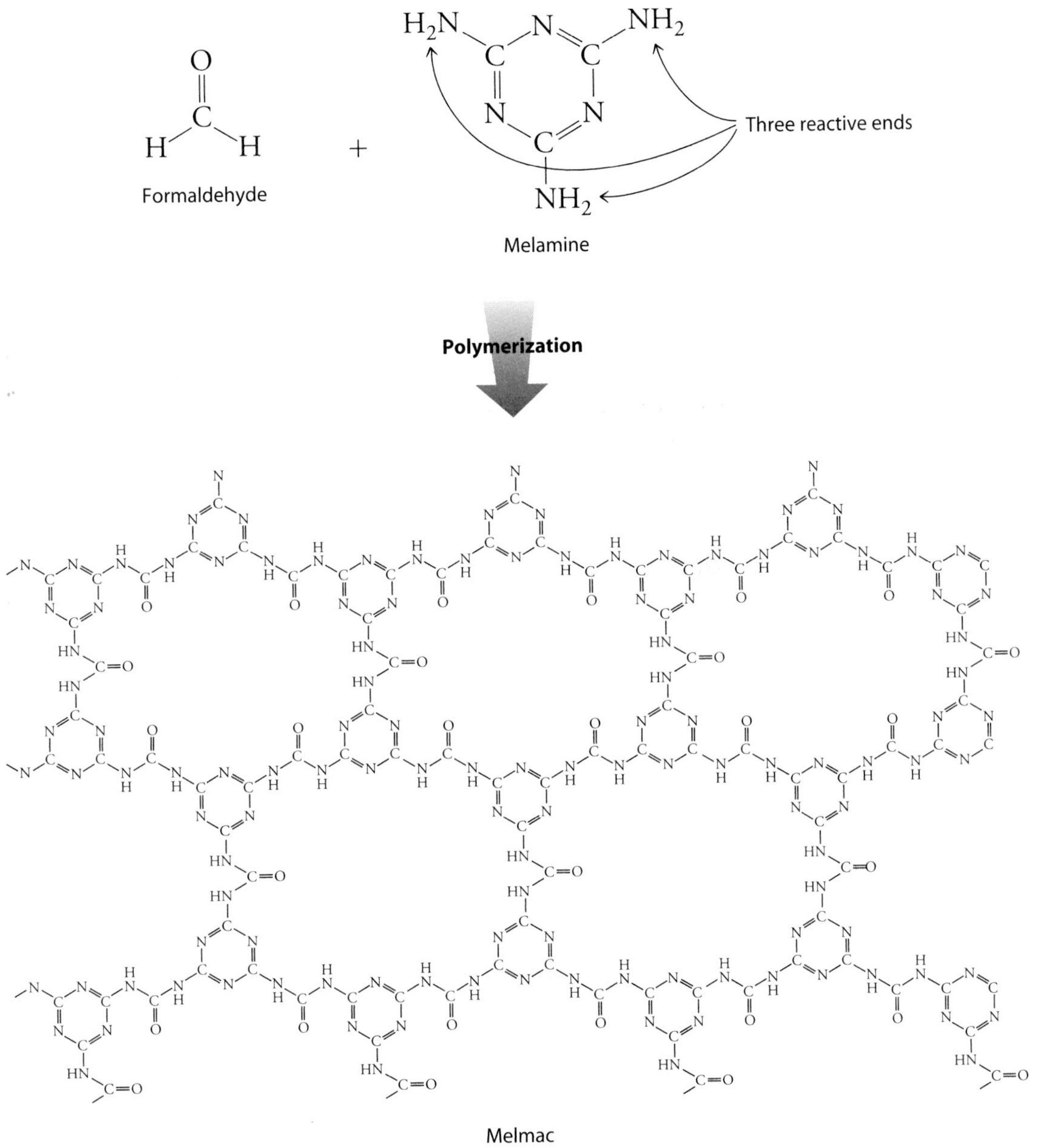

Formaldehyde   +   Melamine

Three reactive ends

Polymerization

Melmac

Figure 12.35
The three reactive groups of melamine allow it to polymerize with formaldehyde to form a three-dimensional network.

Bakelite, made from formaldehyde and phenol, is used to bind plywood and particle board. Bakelite was synthesized in the early 1900s, and it was the first widely used polymer.

The synthetic-polymers industry has grown remarkably over the past 50 years. Annual production of polymers in the United States alone has grown from 3 billion pounds in 1950 to 100 billion pounds in 2000. Today, it is a challenge to find any consumer item that does *not* contain a plastic of one sort or another. Try this yourself.

In the future, watch for new kinds of polymers having a wide range of remarkable properties. One interesting application is shown in Figure

Hands-On Chemistry: Racing Water Drops

The chemical composition of a polymer has a significant effect on its macroscopic properties. To see this for yourself, place a drop of water on a new plastic sandwich bag, and then tilt the bag vertically so that the drop races off. Observe the behavior of the water carefully. Now race a drop of water off a freshly pulled strip of plastic food wrap. How does the behavior of the drop on the wrap compare with the behavior of the drop on the sandwich bag?

Most brands of sandwich bags are made of polyethylene terephthalate, and most brands of food wrap are made of polyvinylidene chloride. Look carefully at the chemical composition of these polymers, shown in Table 12.5. Which contains larger atoms? Which might be involved in stronger dipole–induced dipole interactions with water? Need help with these questions? Refer back to Sections 6.7 and 7.1.

12.36. We already have polymers that conduct electricity, others that emit light, others that replace body parts, and still others that are stronger but much lighter than steel. Imagine synthetic polymers that mimic photosynthesis by transforming solar energy to chemical energy or efficiently separate fresh water from the oceans. These are not dreams. They are realities chemists have already demonstrated in the laboratory. Polymers hold a clear promise for the future.

The plastics industry is but one outgrowth of our knowledge of organic chemistry. As we explore in the next chapter, our understanding of life itself is based on our understanding of the properties of carbohydrates, fats, proteins, and nucleic acids, all of which are polymers containing the functional groups introduced in this chapter.

Figure 12.36
Flexible and flat video displays can now be fabricated from polymers.

Key Terms and Matching Definitions

_____ addition polymer
_____ alcohol
_____ aldehyde
_____ amide
_____ amine
_____ aromatic compound
_____ carbonyl group
_____ carboxylic acid
_____ condensation polymer
_____ conformation
_____ ester
_____ ether
_____ functional group
_____ heteroatom
_____ hydrocarbon
_____ ketone
_____ monomer
_____ organic chemistry
_____ phenol
_____ polymer
_____ saturated hydrocarbon
_____ structural isomers
_____ unsaturated hydrocarbon

1. The study of carbon-containing compounds.
2. A chemical compound containing only carbon and hydrogen atoms.
3. Molecules that have the same molecular formula but different chemical structures.
4. One of the possible spatial orientations of a molecule.
5. A hydrocarbon containing no multiple covalent bonds, with each carbon atom bonded to four other atoms.
6. A hydrocarbon containing at least one multiple covalent bond.
7. Any organic molecule containing a benzene ring.
8. Any atom other than carbon or hydrogen in an organic molecule.
9. A specific combination of atoms that behave as a unit in an organic molecule.
10. An organic molecule that contains a hydroxyl group bonded to a saturated carbon.
11. An organic molecule in which a hydroxyl group is bonded to a benzene ring.
12. An organic molecule containing an oxygen atom bonded to two carbon atoms.

13. An organic molecule containing a nitrogen atom bonded to one or more saturated carbon atoms.
14. A carbon atom double-bonded to an oxygen atom, found in ketones, aldehydes, amides, carboxylic acids, and esters.
15. An organic molecule containing a carbonyl group the carbon of which is bonded to two carbon atoms.
16. An organic molecule containing a carbonyl group the carbon of which is bonded either to one carbon atom and one hydrogen atom or to two hydrogen atoms.
17. An organic molecule containing a carbonyl group the carbon of which is bonded to a nitrogen atom.
18. An organic molecule containing a carbonyl group the carbon of which is bonded to a hydroxyl group.
19. An organic molecule containing a carbonyl group the carbon of which is bonded to one carbon atom and one oxygen atom bonded to another carbon atom.
20. A long organic molecule made of many repeating units.
21. The small molecular unit from which a polymer is formed.
22. A polymer formed by the joining together of monomer units with no atoms lost as the polymer forms.
23. A polymer formed by the joining together of monomer units accompanied by the loss of a small molecule, such as water.

Review Questions

Hydrocarbons Contain Only Carbon and Hydrogen

1. What are some examples of hydrocarbons?
2. What are some uses of hydrocarbons?
3. How do two structural isomers differ from each other?
4. How are two structural isomers similar to each other?
5. What physical property of hydrocarbons is used in fractional distillation?
6. What types of hydrocarbons are more abundant in higher-octane gasoline?

7. To how many atoms is a saturated carbon atom bonded?

Unsaturated Hydrocarbons Contain Multiple Bonds

8. What is the difference between a saturated hydrocarbon and an unsaturated hydrocarbon?

9. How many multiple bonds must a hydrocarbon have in order to be classified as unsaturated?

10. Aromatic compounds contain what kind of ring?

Organic Molecules Are Classified by Functional Group

11. What is a heteroatom?

12. Why do heteroatoms make such a difference in the physical and chemical properties of an organic molecule?

13. Which molecule should have the higher boiling point and why:

$$CH_3CH_2CH_2CH_3$$
$$CH_3CH_2CH_2CH_2-OH$$

14. Why are low-formula-mass alcohols soluble in water?

15. What distinguishes an alcohol from a phenol?

16. What distinguishes an alcohol from an ether?

17. Why do ethers typically have lower boiling points than alcohols?

18. Which heteroatom is characteristic of an amine?

19. Do amines tend to be acidic, neutral, or basic?

20. Are alkaloids found in nature?

21. What are some examples of alkaloids?

22. Which elements make up the carbonyl group?

23. How are ketones and aldehydes related to each other? How are they different from each other?

24. What is one commercially useful property of aldehydes?

25. How are amides and carboxylic acids related to each other? How are they different from each other?

26. From what naturally occurring compound is aspirin prepared?

27. Identify each molecule as hydrocarbon, alcohol, or carboxylic acid:

$$CH_3CH_2CH_2CH_3$$
$$CH_3CH_2CH_2CH_2-OH$$

Organic Molecules Can Link To Form Polymers

28. What happens to the double bond of a monomer participating in the formation of an addition polymer?

29. What is released in the formation of a condensation polymer?

30. Why is plastic food wrap a stickier plastic than polyethylene?

31. What is a copolymer?

Hands-On Chemistry Insights

Twisting Jellybeans

What you should discover in this activity is that the carbon–carbon double bond greatly restricts the number of possible conformations for an organic molecule. While *n*-butane, for instance, can twist like a snake, 2-butene is restricted to one of two possible conformations. (Check back to Figure 12.7 for the structures of these two molecules.) In one conformation, the two end carbons are on the same side of the double bond—this is called the *cis* conformation. In the second conformation, the two end carbons are on opposite sides of the double bond—the *trans* conformation:

cis-2-Butene   *trans*-2-Butene

Because the double bond cannot rotate, the *cis* and *trans* conformations are not interconvertible. They therefore represent two different molecules (structural isomers), each having its own unique set of properties. The melting point of *cis*-2-butene, for example, is −139°C, while that of *trans*-2-butene is a warmer −106°C.

Racing Drops

You may need to play around with the drops for a while in order to see the differing affinities that the bag and wrap have for water. One way to do this is to tape the polymers side by side stretched out on a sturdy piece of cardboard. Tilt the cardboard to various angles, testing for the speed with which water drops roll down the incline on the two surfaces. Ultimately, you should find that the drops roll more slowly on the wrap (polyvinylidene chloride) than on the bag (polyethylene terephthalate). The source of this greater "stickiness" in the wrap is the fairly large chlorine atoms of the polyvinylidene chloride. Recall from Section 7.1 that the larger the atom, the greater its potential for forming induced dipole molecular interactions.

The greater stickiness of the wrap is also apparent when you try to glide one sheet of wrap over another.

Exercises

1. Which contains more hydrogen atoms: a five-carbon saturated hydrocarbon molecule or a five-carbon unsaturated hydrocarbon molecule?

2. Why does the melting point of hydrocarbons increase as the number of carbon atoms per molecule increases?

3. Draw all the structural isomers for hydrocarbons having the molecular formula C_4H_{10}.

4. Draw all the structural isomers for hydrocarbons having the molecular formula C_6H_{14}.

5. How many structural isomers are shown here:

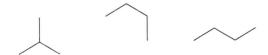

6. Which two of these four structures are of the same structural isomer:

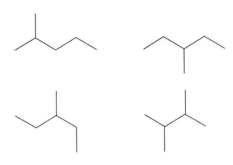

7. The temperatures in a fractionating tower at an oil refinery are important, but so are the pressures. Where might the pressure in a fractionating tower be greatest, at the bottom or at the top? Defend your answer.

8. Heteroatoms make a difference in the physical and chemical properties of an organic molecule because
   a. they add extra mass to the hydrocarbon structure.
   b. each heteroatom has its own characteristic chemistry.
   c. they can enhance the polarity of the organic molecule.
   d. all of the above.

9. Why might a high-formula-mass alcohol be insoluble in water?

10. What is the percent volume of water in 80-proof vodka?

11. How does ingested methanol lead to the damaging of a person's eyes?

12. One of the skin-irritating components of poison oak is tetrahydrourushiol:

OH
OH

The long, nonpolar hydrocarbon tail embeds itself in a person's oily skin, where the molecule initiates an allergic response. Scratching the itch spreads tetrahydrourushiol molecules over a greater surface area, causing the zone of irritation to grow. Is this compound an alcohol or a phenol? Defend your answer.

13. The phosphoric acid salt of caffeine has the structure

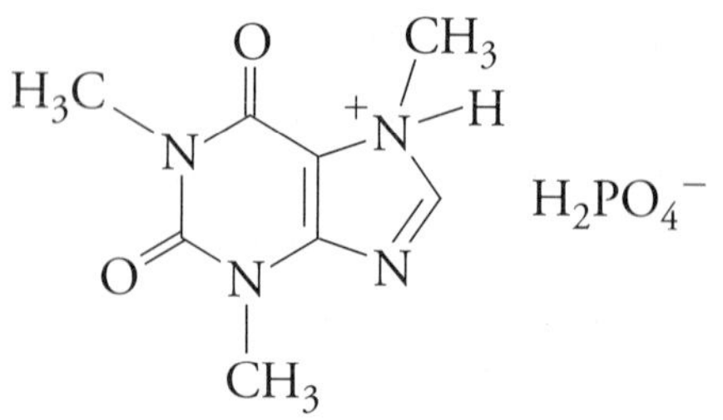

Caffeine–phosphoric acid salt

This molecule behaves as an acid in that it can donate a hydrogen ion, created from the hydrogen atom bonded to the positively charged nitrogen atom. What are all the products formed when 1 mole of this salt reacts with 1 mole of sodium hydroxide, NaOH, a strong base?

14. The solvent diethyl ether can be mixed with water but only by shaking the two liquids together. After the shaking is stopped, the liquids separate into two layers, much like oil and vinegar. The free-base form of the alkaloid caffeine is readily soluble in diethyl ether but not in water. Suggest what might happen to the caffeine of a caffeinated beverage if the beverage was first made alkaline with sodium hydroxide and then shaken with some diethyl ether.

15. Alkaloid salts are not very soluble in the organic solvent diethyl ether. What might happen to the free-base form of caffeine dissolved in diethyl ether if gaseous hydrogen chloride, HCl, were bubbled into the solution?

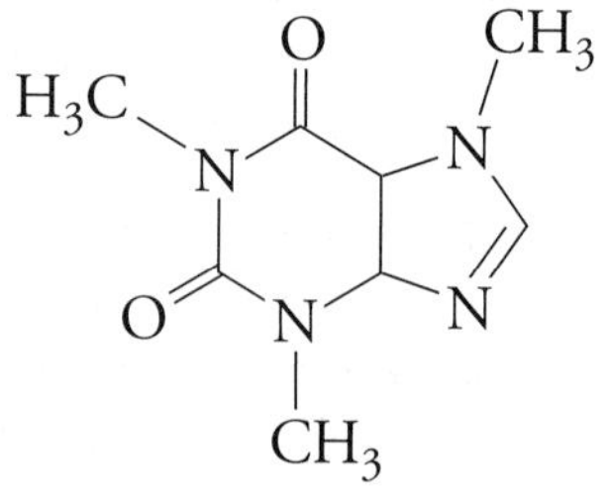

Caffeine
(free base)

16. Draw all the structural isomers for amines having the molecular formula C_3H_9N.

17. Explain why caprylic acid, $CH_3(CH_2)_6COOH$, dissolves in a 5 percent aqueous solution of sodium hydroxide but caprylaldehyde, $CH_3(CH_2)_6CHO$, does not.

18. In water, does the molecule

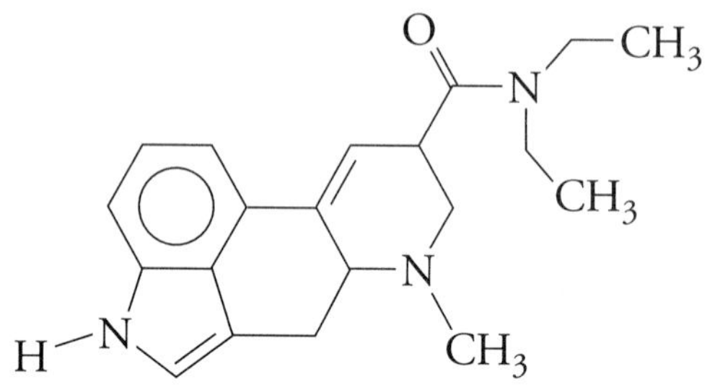

Lysergic acid diethylamide

act as an acid, a base, neither, or both?

19. If you saw the label phenylephrine · HCl on a decongestant, would you worry that consuming it would expose you to the strong acid hydrochloric acid? Explain.

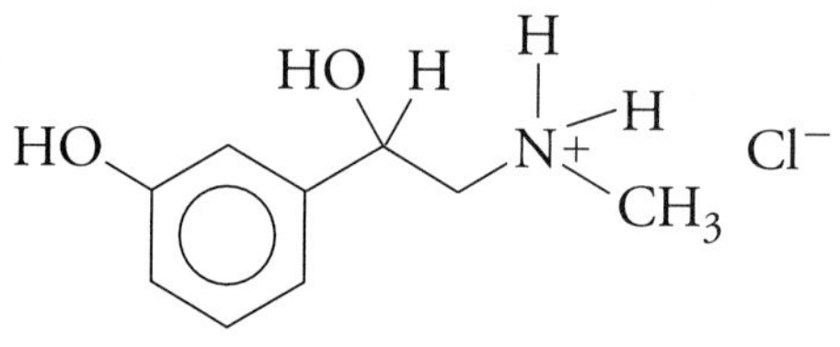

Phenylephrine

20. Suggest an explanation for why aspirin has a sour taste.

21. An amino acid is an organic molecule that contains both an amine group and a carboxyl group. At neutral pH, which structure is most likely:

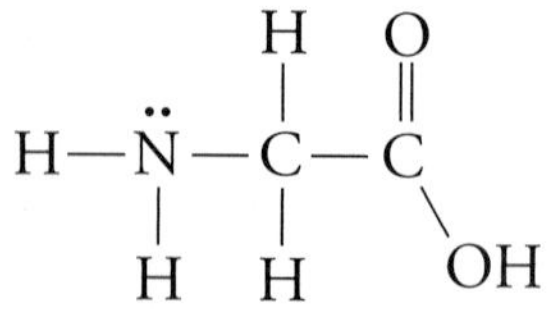

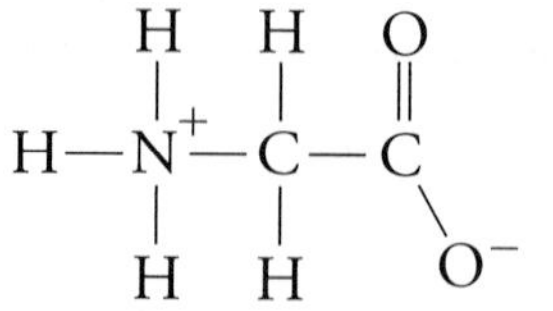

Explain your answer.

22. An amino acid is an organic molecule that contains both an amine group and a carboxyl group. At an acidic pH, which structure is most likely:

(a)

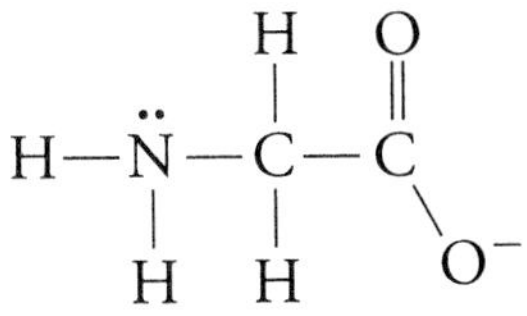

(b)

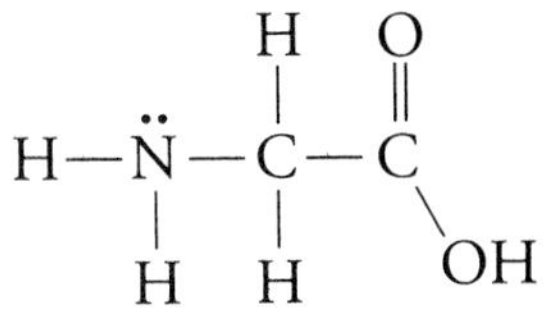

(c)

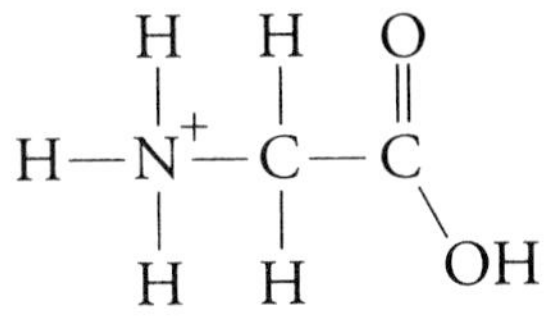

Explain your answer.

23. Identify the following functional groups in this organic molecule—amide, ester, ketone, ether, alcohol, aldehyde, amine:

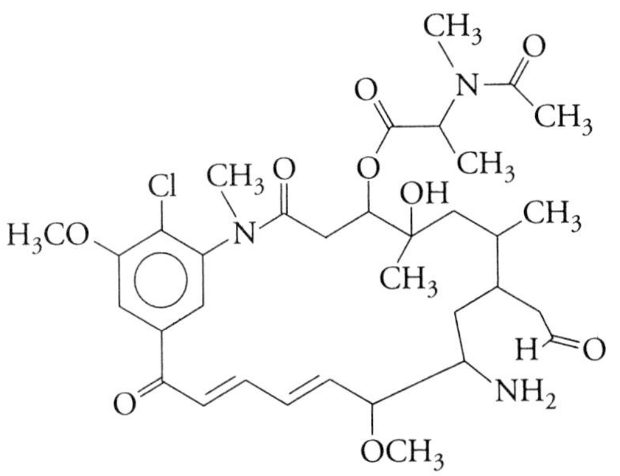

24. Would you expect polypropylene to be denser or less dense than low-density polyethylene? Why?

25. Many polymers emit toxic fumes when burning. Which polymer in Table 12.5 produces hydrogen cyanide, HCN? Which two produce toxic hydrogen chloride, HCl, gas?

26. One solution to the problem of our overflowing landfills is to burn plastic objects instead of burying them. What would be some of the advantages and disadvantages of this practice?

27. Which would you expect to be more viscous, a polymer made of long molecular strands or one made of short molecular stands? Why?

28. Hydrocarbons release a lot of energy when ignited. Where does this energy come from?

29. What type of polymer would be best to use in the manufacture of stain-resistant carpets?

30. As noted in the Concept Check on page 375, the compound 6-aminohexanoic acid is used to make the condensation polymer nylon-6. Polymerization is not always successful, however, because of a competing side reaction. What is this side reaction? Would polymerization be more likely in a dilute solution of this monomer or in a concentrated solution? Why?

Suggested Reading and Web Sites

P. W. Atkins, *Molecules*. New York: W. H. Freeman, 1987.
> An enchanting account of some of the more important organic molecules of nature as well as those produced by chemists. Written for the general public, the dialogue is warm, intriguing, and accompanied by spectacular photographs.

http://www.icco.org/
> The home page of the International Cocoa Organization. Through this site, you can find answers to many of the questions you may have regarding the chemistry of chocolate and its path from the cocoa tree to your mouth.

http://www.chevron.com/explore/index.html
> Web address for the Learning Zone of the Chevron Corporation, where you can find information about crude oil and the refining process.

Appendix A
Scientific Notation Is Used to Express Large and Small Numbers

In science, we often encounter very large and very small numbers. Written in standard decimal notation, these numbers can be cumbersome. There are, for example, about 33,460,000,000,000,000,000,000 water molecules in a thimbleful of water, each having a mass of about 0.00000000000000000000002991 gram. To represent such numbers, scientists often use a mathematical shorthand called **scientific notation**. Written in this notation, the number of molecules in a thimbleful of water is 3.346×10^{22}, and the mass of a single molecule is 2.991×10^{-23} gram.

To understand how this shorthand notation works, consider the large number 50,000,000. Mathematically this number is equal to 5 multiplied by $10 \times 10 \times 10 \times 10 \times 10 \times 10 \times 10$ (check this out on your calculator!). We can abbreviate this chain of numbers by writing all the 10s in exponential form, which gives us the scientific notation 5×10^7. (Note that 10^7 is the same as $10 \times 10 \times 10 \times 10 \times 10 \times 10 \times 10$. Table A.1 shows the exponential form of some other large and small numbers.) Likewise, the small number 0.0005 is mathematically equal to 5 divided $10 \times 10 \times 10 \times 10$, which is $5/10^4$. Because dividing by a number is exactly equivalent to multiplying by the reciprocal of that number, $5/10^4$ can be written in the form 5×10^{-4}, and so in scientific notation 0.0005 becomes 5×10^{-4} (note the negative exponent).

All scientific notation is written in the general form

$$C \times 10^n$$

where C, called the *coefficient*, is a number between 1 and 10 and n is the *exponent*. A positive exponent indicates a number greater than 1, and a negative exponent indicates a number between 1 and 0 (*not* a number less than 0).

Table A.1

Decimal and Exponential Notations

$$
\begin{aligned}
1{,}000{,}000 &= 10 \times 10 \times 10 \times 10 \times 10 \times 10 = 10^6 \\
100{,}000 &= 10 \times 10 \times 10 \times 10 \times 10 = 10^5 \\
10{,}000 &= 10 \times 10 \times 10 \times 10 = 10^4 \\
1000 &= 10 \times 10 \times 10 = 10^3 \\
100 &= 10 \times 10 = 10^2 \\
10 &= 10 = 10^1 \\
1 &= 1 = 10^0 \\
0.1 &= 1/10 = 10^{-1} \\
0.01 &= 1/(10 \times 10) = 10^{-2} \\
0.001 &= 1/(10 \times 10 \times 10) = 10^{-3} \\
0.0001 &= 1/(10 \times 10 \times 10 \times 10) = 10^{-4} \\
0.00001 &= 1/(10 \times 10 \times 10 \times 10 \times 10) = 10^{-5} \\
0.000001 &= 1/(10 \times 10 \times 10 \times 10 \times 10 \times 10) = 10^{-6}
\end{aligned}
$$

Numbers less than 0 are indicated by putting a negative sign *before the coefficient* (not in the exponent):

	Decimal notation	**Scientific notation**
Large positive number (greater than 1)	6,000,000,000	6×10^9
Small positive number (between 0 and 1)	0.0006	6×10^{-4}
Large negative number (less than -1)	$-6{,}000{,}000{,}000$	-6×10^9
Small negative number (between -1 and 0)	-0.0006	-6×10^{-4}

Table A.2 shows scientific notation used to express some of the physical data often used in science.

Table A.2

Number of molecules in thimbleful of water	3.346×10^{22}
Mass of water molecule	2.991×10^{-23} gram
Average radius of hydrogen atom	5×10^{-11} meter
Proton mass	1.6726×10^{-27} kilogram
Neutron mass	1.6749×10^{-27} kilogram
Electron mass	9.1094×10^{-31} kilogram
Electron charge	1.602×10^{-19} coulomb
Avogadro's number	6.022×10^{23} particles
Atomic mass unit	1.661×10^{-24} gram

To change a decimal number that is greater than $+1$ or less than -1 to scientific notation, you shift the decimal point to the left until you arrive at a number between 1 and 10. For decimal numbers between $+1$

and -1, you move the decimal point to the right until you arrive at a number between 1 and 10. This number is the coefficient part of the notation. The exponent part is simply the number of places you moved the decimal point. For example, to convert the decimal number 45,000 to scientific notation, move the decimal point four places to the left to get a number between 1 and 10:

$$45{,}000 = 4.5 \times 10^4$$
4 3 2 1

The number 0.00045, on the other hand, is converted to scientific notation by moving the decimal point four places to the right to arrive at a number between 1 and 10:

$$0.00045 = 4.5 \times 10^{-4}$$
1 2 3 4

Note that because you moved the decimal point to the right in this case, you must put a minus sign on the exponent.

Your Turn

Express the following exponentials as decimal numbers:

a. 10^{-7} b. 10^8 c. 8.8×10^5

Express the following decimal numbers in scientific notation:

d. 740,000   e. -0.00354 f. 15

Were these your answers?   a. 0.0000001   b. 100,000,000   c. 880,000   d. 7.4×10^5
e. -3.54×10^{-3} f. 1.5×10^1

Appendix B
Significant Figures Are Used to Show Which Digits Have Experimental Meaning

Two kinds of numbers are used in science—those that are *counted or defined* and those that are *measured*. There is a great difference between a counted or defined number and a measured number. The exact value of a counted or defined number can be stated, but the exact value of a measured number can never be stated.

You can count the number of chairs in your classroom, the number of fingers on your hand, or the number of quarters in your pocket with absolute certainty. Thus counted numbers are not subject to error (unless, of course, you count wrong).

Defined numbers are about exact relationships and are defined as being true. The defined number of centimeters in a meter, the defined number of seconds in an hour, and the defined number of sides on a square are examples. Thus defined numbers also are not subject to error (unless you forget a definition).

Every measured number, however, no matter how carefully measured, has some degree of uncertainty. This uncertainty (or margin of error) in a measurement can be illustrated by the two metersticks shown in Figure B.1. Both sticks are being used to measure the length of a table. Assuming that the zero end of each meterstick has been carefully and accurately positioned at the left end of the table, how long is the table?

The upper meterstick has a scale marked off in centimeter intervals. Using this scale, you can say with certainty that the length is between 51 and 52 centimeters. You can say further that it is closer to 51 centimeters than to 52 centimeters; you can even estimate it to be 51.2 centimeters.

The scale on the lower meterstick has more subdivisions—and therefore greater precision—because it is marked off in millimeters. With this scale, you can say that the length is definitely between 51.2 and 51.3 centimeters, and you can estimate it to be 51.25 centimeters.

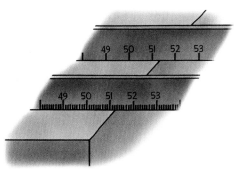

Figure B.1

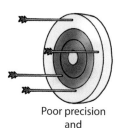

Good precision
but
poor accuracy

Poor precision
and
poor accuracy

Good precision
and
good accuracy

Figure B.2
Archery as a model for understanding the difference between precision and accuracy. *Precision* means close agreement in a group of measured numbers; *accuracy* means a measured value that is very close to the true value of what is being measured. If you measure the same thing several times and get numbers that are close to one another but all far from the true value (perhaps because your measuring device is not working properly), your measurements are *precise* but not *accurate*.

Note how both readings contain some digits that are *known*, and one digit (the last one) that is *estimated*. Note also that the uncertainty in the reading from the lower meterstick is less than the uncertainty in the reading from the upper meterstick. The lower meterstick can give a reading to the hundredths place, but the upper one can give a reading only to the tenths place. The lower one is more *precise* than the top one. So, in any measured number, the digits tell us the *magnitude* of the measurement and the location of the decimal point tells us the *precision* of the measurement. (Figure B.2 illustrates the distinction between *precision* and *accuracy*.)

Significant figures are the digits in any measurement that are known with certainty plus one final digit that is estimated and hence uncertain. These are the digits that reflect the precision of the instrument used to generate the number. They are the digits that have experimental meaning. The measurement 51.2 centimeters made with the upper meterstick in Figure B.1, for example, has three significant figures, and the measurement 51.25 centimeters made with the lower meterstick has four significant figures. The rightmost digit is always an estimated digit, and only one estimated digit is ever recorded for a measurement. It would be incorrect to report 51.253 centimeters as the length measured with the lower meterstick. This five-significant-figure value has two estimated digits (the final 5 and 3) and is incorrect because it indicates a *precision* greater than the meterstick can obtain.

Here are some standard rules for writing and using significant figures.

Rule 1 In numbers that do not contain zeros, all the digits are significant:

4.1327	five significant figures
5.14	three significant figures
369	three significant figures

Rule 2 All zeros between significant digits are significant:

8.052	four significant figures
7059	four significant figures
306	three significant figures

Rule 3 Zeros to the left of the first nonzero digit serve only to fix the position of the decimal point and are not significant:

0.0068	two significant figures
0.0427	three significant figures
0.0003506	four significant figures

Rule 4 In a number that contains digits to the right of the decimal point, zeros to the right of the last nonzero digit are significant:

53.0	three significant figures
53.00	four significant figures
0.00200	three significant figures
0.70050	five significant figures

Rule 5   In a number that has no decimal point and that ends in one or more zeros, the zeros that end the number are not significant:

3600	two significant figures
290	two significant figures
5,000,000	one significant figure
10	one significant figure
6050	three significant figures

Rule 6   When a number is expressed in scientific notation, all digits in the coefficient are taken to be significant:

4.6×10^{-5}	two significant figures
4.60×10^{-5}	three significant figures
4.600×10^{-5}	four significant figures
2×10^{-5}	one significant figure
3.0×10^{-5}	two significant figures
4.00×10^{-5}	three significant figures

Your Turn

How many significant figures in:

a. 43,384
b. 43,084
c. 0.004308
d. 43,084.0
e. 43,000
f. 4.30×10^{4}

Were these your answers? a. 5 b. 5 c. 4 d. 6 e. 2 f. 3

In addition to the rules cited above, there is another full set of rules to be followed for significant figures when two or more measured numbers are subtracted, added, divided, or multiplied. These rules are summarized in the appendix of the *Conceptual Chemistry Laboratory Manual.*

Appendix C
Solutions to Odd-Numbered Exercises and Problems

Chapter 1

1. The Exercises are designed to allow you to work with the concepts you learned by reading the chapter and answering the Review Questions. If you have not already learned the concepts, you will have a most difficult time with the Exercises, which are the types of questions often found on exams. To benefit most from the Exercises, either write out your answers or, better yet, explain your answers to a friend.

3. Biology is based on the principles of chemistry applied to living organisms, and chemistry is based on the principles of physics applied to atoms and molecules. Physics is the study of the fundamental rules of nature, which more often than not are simple in design and readily described by mathematical formulas. Thus biology is based on both chemistry *and* physics and so can be considered the most complex science of the three.

5. A good scientist must change his or her mind whenever experimental results disprove a previously held belief. Holding on to hypotheses and theories that are either not testable or have been shown to be wrong is contrary to the spirit of science.

7. A hypothesis is a testable assumption often used to explain an observed phenomenon. A theory is a single comprehensive idea that can be used to explain a broad range of phenomena.

9. This is not unusual at all. As discussed in the answer to Exercise 3, there is much overlap among the sciences. Whereas Baker is interested in how the chemical produced by the sea butterfly may be used for some human purpose, McClintock is interested in how the sea butterfly uses this chemical for self-defense. Here we see two different approaches to the same phenomenon. Studying the system together allows these researchers both to pool their research resources and to learn from each other.

11. If all the material came from the soil, you would expect a large hole to develop in the dirt around the plant. Also, if the plant were grown in a pot, the mass of the soil in the pot should be greater when the plant is young than when the plant is older.

13. The volume of the car and its average density change.

15. Yes, an object can have mass without having weight. This can occur deep in space, where a floating object (which has mass) is "weightless." In order to have weight, however, the object must have mass. So an object cannot have weight without having mass.

17. The mass of a 6-kilogram object is 6 kilograms on the moon, on the Earth, and anyplace else! Mass is always independent of gravity.

19. Yes, a 2-kilogram iron brick has twice the mass of a 1-kilogram block of wood. Volume, however, is a different story. Because the density of iron is much greater than the density of wood, the 1-kilogram wood block occupies more volume than the 2-kilogram iron brick.

21. Yes, your body will possess energy after you die, in the form of chemical potential energy. If you are cremated, however, the amount of this chemical potential energy is reduced substantially.

23. Glass contracts when cooled and expands when warmed. Therefore you should fill the inner glass with cold water while running hot water over the outer glass.

25. The swimming pool has much more total energy. To understand this difference in the amounts of energy in the two bodies of water, consider what your electric utility bill would be after heating them to their respective temperatures.

27. At 25°C, there is a certain amount of energy possessed by each submicroscopic particle of a material. If the attractions between particles are not very strong, the energy each particle has may allow the particles to separate from one another and exist in the gaseous phase. If the attractions are strong, the energy may not be enough to overcome these attractions and keep the particles far away from one another, and so they may be held together in the solid phase. You can assume, therefore, that the attractions among the submicroscopic particles of a material that is a solid at 25°C are stronger than the particle-to-particle attractions in a material that is a gas at this temperature.

29. The different spacings between particles in the left box tell you two phases are present. The very regular stacking of particles on the left indicates a solid, and so this is probably a solid/liquid combination. Taking heat away causes the liquid to freeze so that only solid is present, and that is represented in the middle box—note the regular stacking of particles. Adding heat causes the solid to melt so that only liquid is present, represented in the right box. If these particles represent water molecules, the box on the left represents ice melting, which occurs at 0°C.

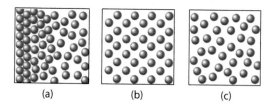

(a)   (b)   (c)

31. Density is the ratio of a material's mass to its volume. Because the mass stays the same but the volume decreases, the density of the gas increases.

33. Box a represents the highest density because it has the greatest number of particles packed in the given volume. Because the particles in this

box are packed close together but randomly oriented, this box represents a liquid. Box c represents the gaseous phase, which occurs at higher temperatures. This box therefore represents the highest temperature. For most materials, the solid phase is denser than the liquid phase. For the material represented here, however, the liquid phase (box a) is denser than the solid phase (box b). As we explore further in Chapter 8, this is exactly the case for water— the solid phase (ice) is less dense than the liquid phase (liquid water).

Problems

1. Multiply by the conversion factor to arrive at the answer:

$$130 \text{ lb} \times \frac{1 \text{ kg}}{2.205 \text{ lb}} = 59 \text{ kg}$$

3. Multiply by the conversion factor to arrive at the answer:

$$230{,}000 \text{ cal} \times \frac{1 \text{ J}}{0.239 \text{ cal}} = 960{,}000 \text{ J}$$

5. Divide the mass by the volume it displaces to arrive at the density:

$$\text{density} = \frac{\text{mass}}{\text{volume}} = \frac{52.3 \text{ g}}{4.16 \text{ mL}} = 12.6 \text{ g/mL}$$

From Table 1.3, you see that this value is substantially less than the density of pure gold, which is 19.3 g/mL. This evidence indicates that the piece is far from pure.

Chapter 2

1. That this process is reversible suggests a physical change. As you sleep in a reclined position, pressure is taken off the discs in your spinal column, and the reduced pressure allows the discs to expand so that you are significantly taller in the morning. Astronauts returning from extended space visits may be up to 2 inches taller than they were at launch time.

3. In the left box, each particle is made up of one atom of one kind and one atom of another kind, but in the right box, each particle is made up of two identical atoms. This difference tells

you that the particles split apart during the transformation and came together in different combinations, which means a chemical change.

5. The change from A to B represents a physical change because no new types of molecules are formed. The collection of blue/yellow molecules on the bottom of B represents these molecules in either the liquid or the solid phase after having been in the gaseous phase in A. This phase change means there must have been a decrease in temperature. At this lower temperature, the yellow molecules are still in the gaseous phase, which means that they have a lower boiling point than the blue/yellow molecules.

7. The oldest known are the ones that have atomic symbols that don't match their modern atomic names. Examples include iron, Fe; gold, Au; and copper, Cu.

9. A percentage is converted to a fraction by dividing by 100. To find 50 percent of something, for example, you multiply that something by 50/100 = 0.50. Thus 0.0001 percent is equal to the fraction 0.000001, which when multiplied by 1×10^{24} equals 1×10^{18}. This is certainly a lot of impurity molecules in your glass of water. The number of water molecules, however, far exceeds this number (see Exercise 10), and so these impurity molecules are not a problem. As an analogy, consider that there were about 12 billion pennies minted in 1990. This is certainly a lot of pennies, but they are nonetheless relatively rare in general circulation because the total number of pennies in circulation is far greater—on the order of 300 billion.

11. Study the answer to Exercise 9 to make a strong case that this sample of water is ultra-ultrapure!

13. Salt (sodium chloride), compound because made of two elements bonded together. Stainless steel, mixture because made of elements (iron and carbon) not bonded together. Tap water, mixture of dihydrogen oxide plus impurities. Sugar, compound made of one substance—sucrose. Vanilla extract, mixture of water, alcohol, and flavor molecules. Butter, mixture of fat, water, and milk solids. Maple syrup, mixture of water and maple sugar. Aluminum, element. Ice, compound (H_2O) in pure form, mixture when made from impure tap water. Milk, mixture of water and milk solids. Cherry-flavored cough drops, mixture of sugar and flavoring.

15. Elemental material, C; compound, B; mixture, A. There are three types of molecules shown: one made of two large atoms, one made of two small atoms, and one made of one large atom and one small atom.

17. The atoms in a compound are chemically bonded together and do not come apart during a physical change. The components of a mixture, however, can be separated from one another by physical means.

19. Taking advantage of differences in chemical properties means you have to make the components of the mixture undergo chemical change. During chemical change, at least one component changes its identity. Thus, you may have separated the component, but now it is something else, which means you need to make it undergo a second chemical change to convert it back to what it was. This can be an energy-intensive and time-intensive process that is much less efficient than a separation based on differences in physical properties.

21. Based on its location in the periodic table, you know that gallium, Ga, is more metallic than germanium, Ge. This means that gallium should be a better conductor of electricity. Gallium chips should therefore operate faster than germanium chips. (Gallium has a low melting point of 30°C, which makes its use in the manufacture of computer chips impractical. Mixtures of gallium and arsenic, however, have found great use in the manufacture of ultrafast, though relatively expensive, computer chips.)

23. Helium is placed at the far right of the periodic table, in group 18, because it has physical and chemical properties similar to those of the other elements of group 18.

25. Calcium is readily absorbed by the body for the building of bones. Because calcium and strontium are in the same group of the periodic table, they have similar physical and chemical properties. The body therefore has a hard time distinguishing between the two, and strontium is absorbed just as though it were calcium.

27. The iron can be separated based on a difference in physical properties. The iron particles are attracted to a magnet, but the pieces of cereal are not. Try this with your next box of iron-fortified cereal.

Chapter 3

1. The cat leaves a trail of molecules across the yard. These molecules leave the ground and mix with the air, where they enter the dog's nose, activating the sense of smell.

3. The atoms in the baby are just as old as those in the elderly person—all appreciably older than the solar system.

5. You are a part of every person around you in the sense that you are composed of atoms that at one time were part of not only every person around you but also every person who ever lived on the Earth!

7. Lavoisier *observed* that tin gained mass as it decomposed into a gray powder and *asked* how that could happen. He *hypothesized* that the tin gained mass because it absorbed something from the air. He then *predicted* that if he could keep track of air volume as this reaction took place, he would find a change in air volume. He *tested* his prediction by heating a piece of tin floating on a wood block enclosed by a glass container. After observing that the volume of air surrounding the tin decreased by 20 percent, Lavoisier *theorized* that 20 percent of the air is made of a gaseous compound that reacts with tin.

9. Oxygen and hydrogen react in an 8:1 ratio by mass to form water. Thus, 1 gram of hydrogen always reacts with only 8 grams of oxygen (no more and no less). If the amount of oxygen available were 10 grams, only 8 grams of this 10 grams would react with 1 gram of hydrogen—2 grams of oxygen would be left over. When they react, the 1 gram of hydrogen and 8 grams of oxygen form a combined mass of 9 grams of water.

11. Both were right. Proust saw oxygen and hydrogen react in an 8:1 ratio by *mass*, and Gay-Lussac saw them react in a 1:2 ratio by *volume*.

13. Iron metal consists only of iron atoms, Fe. Rust is a compound of iron and oxygen (iron oxide, Fe_2O_3). So a sample of iron weighs more after it rusts because it has gained the mass of oxygen atoms. Be sure to recognize that the parts of the sample that have rusted are no longer iron. Rather, those parts are now iron oxide.

15. Avogadro correctly assumed that equal volumes of oxygen gas and water vapor contain equal numbers of particles. To account for the fact that the volume of oxygen weighs more than the volume of water vapor, Avogadro hypothesized that each particle of oxygen gas consists of two oxygen atoms bound together into a single unit that we know today as an oxygen molecule, O_2. With two oxygen atoms per particle, a volume of oxygen gas is heavier than an equal volume of water vapor, which has only one oxygen atom per particle (along with two lightweight hydrogen atoms).

17. For the first reaction, the box on the far right should show the same thing as the box adjacent to it—ten HCl molecules. Each box contains 36.5 grams of HCl. For the second reaction, there is insufficient hydrogen to react with all the chlorine. Thus only 36.5 grams of hydrogen chloride forms. The half-size box on the far right should show the five unreacted Cl_2 molecules. Their mass is 35.5 grams.

19. Throughout the development of modern chemistry, there were numerous instances where investigators clung tightly to the ideas of the past. One example presented in this chapter was the reluctance of Dalton and other early chemists to accept Avogadro's hypothesis of the diatomic nature of oxygen and hydrogen. There are many other examples that the text didn't have the time to go into. Boyle, for example, held on to Artistotle's notion that there was only one form of matter and that this "one form" took on different "qualities" to make up the materials around us. Priestley refused to believe Lavoisier's explanation that his new gas was a new element absorbed by materials as they burned. Instead, Priestley used the ideas of his predecessors in stating that the "new air" he had generated was a form of air that lacked an "essence" that materials *release* as they burn. Fire burned brighter in his air because it rapidly absorbed this essence as the essence was released by the burning material.

21. The youngest was Gay-Lussac, who in 1808 at the age of 30 showed that gases react in definite volume ratios. More significantly, you should recognize that most of these investigators were in their 30s at the time of their noted scientific contribution (average age about 37). Thus it is in science that a person's greatest contributions typically are made when she or he is young and not yet fully established in a field. Fresh ideas come from fresh minds.

23. If the particles had a greater charge, they would be bent more because the deflecting force is directly proportional to the charge. (If the particles were more massive, they would be bent less by the magnetic force—obeying the law of inertia.)

25. The neon sign is a fancy cathode ray tube, which means that the ray of light is the result of the flow of electrons through the tube. A magnet held up to these flowing electrons alters their path, which shows up as a distortion of the light ray.

27. The one on the far right, where the nucleus is not visible.

29. The resulting nucleus would be that of arsenic, which is poisonous!

31. The iron atom is electrically neutral when it has 26 electrons to balance its 26 protons.

33. Carbon-13 atoms have more mass than carbon-12 atoms. Because of this, a given mass of carbon-13 contains fewer atoms than the same mass of carbon-12. Look at it this way—golf balls have more mass than Ping-Pong balls. So, which contains more balls: 1 kilogram of golf balls or 1 kilogram of Ping-Pong balls? Because Ping-Pong balls are so much lighter, you need many more of them to get 1 kilogram.

Problems

1. Eight grams of oxygen will react with only 1 gram of hydrogen to produce $8 + 1 = 9$ grams of water. Because only 1 gram of the hydrogen reacts, there is $8 - 1 = 7$ grams of hydrogen left over.

3.

	Mass (amu)	Fraction of Abundance
Mass of Li-6	6.0151	$\times$ 0.0742 = 0.446
Mass of Li-7	7.0160	$\times$ 0.9258 = 6.495
		6.941 amu

Chapter 4

1. Any radioactive sample is always a little warmer than its surroundings because the radiating alpha or beta particles impart heat energy to the atoms. (Interestingly enough, the heat energy of the Earth originates from the radioactive decay of the Earth's core and surrounding material.)

3. Alpha and beta rays are deflected in opposite directions in a magnetic field because they are oppositely charged—alpha positive and beta negative. Gamma rays have no electric charge and are therefore undeflected.

5. Alpha radiation decreases the atomic number of the emitting element by 2 and the mass number by 4. Beta radiation increases the atomic number by 1 and does not affect the mass number. Gamma radiation does not affect either atomic number or mass number. So alpha radiation results in the greatest change both in atomic number and in mass number.

7. Only gamma rays are able to penetrate the metal hull of an airplane. Flight crews are required to limit their flying time so as to minimize the potential harm caused by the significant amounts of radiation present at high altitudes. Recall from the text that merely two round-trip flights from New York to California expose each human in the plane to about as much radiation as a chest X ray.

9. Alpha particles are much bigger than beta particles, which makes alphas less able to pass through the "pores" of materials. The smaller beta particles are therefore more effective in penetrating materials.

11. To decay to one-sixteenth the original amount will take four half-lives, which in this case equals 120 years.

13. When radium (atomic number 88) emits an alpha particle, its atomic number decreases by 2, and so the resulting nucleus is radon (atomic number 86). The alpha decay causes the mass number of the radium to decrease by 4. Because the radium here is the isotope radium-226, the radon isotope must have mass number 222, which means its atomic mass is 222 atomic mass units.

15. An element can decay to one that has a higher atomic number by emitting an electron (beta particle). When this happens, a neutron becomes a proton and the atomic number increases by 1.

17. The Earth's natural energy that heats the water in the hot spring is the energy of radioactive decay, which keeps the Earth's interior molten. Radioactivity heats the water but doesn't make the water radioactive. The warmth of hot springs is one of the nicer effects of radioactive decay. You and your friend will most likely encounter more radioactivity from the granite outcroppings of the foothills than you would

encounter near a nuclear power plant. Furthermore, at high altitude you'll both be exposed to increased cosmic radiation. However, these radiations are not appreciably different from the radiation you would encounter in the "safest" of situations. The probability of dying from something or other is 100 percent, and so in the meantime you and your friend should enjoy life!

19. Although there is significantly more radioactivity in a nuclear power plant than in a coal-fired plant, the absence of shielding in the coal plant results in more radioactivity in the environment around the coal plant. All nuclear plants are shielded; coal plants are not.

21. Radioactive decay rates are statistical averages of large numbers of decaying atoms. Because of the relatively short half-life of carbon-14, only trace amounts would be left after 50,000 years—too little to be statistically meaningful.

23. At 3:00 P.M., there will be 1/8 gram left. At 6:00 P.M., 1/64 gram left. At 10:00 P.M., 1/1024 gram left.

25. A neutron makes a better "bullet" for penetrating atomic nuclei because it has no electric charge and is therefore not deflected from its path by electrical interactions, nor is it electrically repelled by the nuclei.

27. Plutonium has a short half-life (24,360 years) relative to the age of the Earth (about 4 billion years), and so any plutonium initially in the Earth's crust has long since decayed. The same is true for any heavier elements that have even shorter half-lives and might have been the elements that decayed to plutonium. Trace amounts of plutonium can occur naturally in uranium-238 deposits, however, as a result of neutron capture. The neutron capture changes uranium-238 to uranium-239, which then beta decays to neptunium-239. The neptunium-239 then beta decays to plutonium-239. (There are elements in the Earth's crust with half-lives shorter than plutonium's, but these are the products of uranium decay and fall between uranium and lead in the periodic table.)

29. Because fissionable plutonium-239 is formed as the uranium-238 absorbs neutrons from the fissioning uranium-235.

31. To predict the energy release of a nuclear reaction, the physicist needs to know the difference between the average mass per nucleon for the beginning nucleus and the average mass per nucleon for the products formed in the reaction (either fission or fusion). This mass difference (called the *mass defect*) can be found from the curve of Figure 4.31 or from a table of nuclear masses. The physicist then multiplies this mass difference by the speed of light squared to determine the energy released—$E = mc^2$.

33. If a uranium nucleus split into three equal-size segments, each segment would be smaller than if the nucleus split into only two segments. The smaller segments would have lower atomic numbers, more toward iron on the graph of Figure 4.30. The resulting mass per nucleon would be less, which means more mass was converted to energy and so more energy was released.

35. Such speculation could fill volumes. The energy and material abundance that are the expected outcome of a fusion age will likely prompt several fundamental changes. Obvious changes would occur in the fields of economics and commerce, which would be geared to relative abundance rather than scarcity. Our present price system, which is geared to and in many ways dependent on scarcity, often malfunctions in an environment of abundance. Hence we see instances where scarcity is created to keep the economic system functioning. Change at the international level will likely include worldwide economic reform, and change at the personal level might mean a re-evaluation of the idea that scarcity ought to be the basis of value. A fusion age will likely see changes that will touch every facet of our way of life.

Chapter 5

1. Atoms are smaller than the wavelengths of visible light and hence not *visible* in the true sense of the word. We can, however, measure the surface topography of a collection of atoms by scanning an electric current back and forth across the surface. A computer can then assemble the data from such scanning into an image that reveals how the atoms are arranged on the surface. It would be more appropriate to say that with the scanning tunneling microscope we *feel* atoms rather than *see* them.

3. Many objects or systems can be described just as well by a physical model as by a conceptual

model. In general, a physical model is used to replicate an object or system on a different scale. A conceptual model is used to represent abstract ideas or to demonstrate how a system behaves. Of the examples given in the exercise, the following are best described by a physical model: brain, solar system, stranger, gold coin, car engine, and virus. The following are best described by a conceptual model: mind, birth of universe, best friend (whose complex behavior you have some understanding of), dollar bill (which represents wealth but is really only a piece of paper), spread of a sexually transmitted disease.

5. The one electron can be boosted to many energy levels and can therefore make many combinations of transitions to lower levels. Each transition is of a specific energy and accompanied by the emission of a photon of a specific frequency. Thus the variety of spectral lines.

7. In accordance with the law of conservation of energy, the combined energies must equal the energy of the single transition. (Thus the sum of the frequencies of the light emitted during the two-step transition equals the frequency of the light emitted during the one-step transition.)

9. Blue light has a higher frequency than red light. Therefore the blue light comes from the larger energy transition.

11. An electron not restricted to particular energy levels would release light continuously as it spiraled closer in toward the nucleus. A broad spectrum of colors would be observed rather than distinct lines.

13. It takes *no time at all* for the transition to occur; it is instantaneous. The electron is *never* found between two orbitals.

15. Because of the electron's wave nature, it would be better to say that the electron exists in both lobes at the same time.

17. Electrons ordinarily fill lower orbitals before entering higher ones. The electron configuration for carbon shown on the right, $1s^2 2s^1 2p^3$, shows that one of the $2s$ electrons has been boosted to a (higher-energy) $2p$ orbital. This configuration therefore represents the greater amount of energy.

19. Lowest energy $1s^2 2s^2 2p^5$, highest energy $1s^0 2s^2 2p^5 3s^2$.

21.

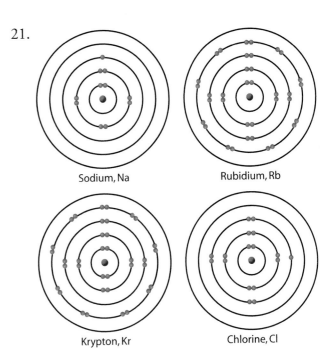

Sodium, Na   Rubidium, Rb

Krypton, Kr   Chlorine, Cl

23. An orbital is just a region of space in which an electron of a given energy resides. This region of space exists with or without the electron. The same logic applies to a shell, which is just a collection of orbitals of similar energy levels. The space defined by the shell exists whether or not an electron is to be found there.

25. Neon's outermost occupied shell is filled to capacity with electrons. Any additional electrons would have to occupy the next shell out, which has an effective nuclear charge of zero.

27. An electron in the outermost occupied shell of sodium experiences the greatest effective nuclear charge. The strength of the electric force diminishes with increasing distance, and the outermost sodium electron is closer to the nucleus than are the outermost electrons of the other atoms discussed in the Exercise.

29. Pb < Sn < As < P.

31. Potassium has one electron in its outermost occupied shell, which is the fourth shell. The effective nuclear charge felt by the electron in this shell is relatively weak (+1), and so this electron is readily lost. If the atom were to lose a second electron, that electron would need to come from the next shell inward (the third shell), where the effective nuclear charge is much stronger (+9). Thus, it is very difficult to pull a second electron away from the potassium atom because this electron is being held so

tightly by this much greater effective nuclear charge.

33. Note that each shell has been divided into a series of finer shells known as *subshells*. Each subshell contains only one type of orbital. In the seventh shell, for instance, working in order of increasing energy levels, the first (innermost) subshell, indicated by the digit 2 in the rightmost stack of numbers in the drawing, is for the 2 electrons of the $7s$ orbital. The second subshell of the seventh shell is for the 14 electrons of the seven $5f$ orbitals, the third subshell is for the 10 electrons of the five $6d$ orbitals, and the fourth subshell is for the 6 electrons of the three $7p$ orbitals. Gallium is larger than zinc because gallium has an electron in each of the three subshells of the fourth shell, whereas zinc has an electron only in each of the first two inner subshells of the fourth shell. What you see here is a refinement of the model presented in Section 5.7. Don't worry about fully understanding this refinement, however. Rather, it is more important that you understand that all conceptual models are subject to refinement. We choose whatever level of refinement best suits our needs in a given situation.

Chapter 6

1. This is an example of a chemical change involving the formation of ions, which are different from the neutral atoms from which the ions are made.

3. The nuclear charge experienced by an electron in sodium's third shell is not strong enough to hold this many electrons. As was discussed in Chapter 5, this is because there are 10 inner-shell electrons shielding any third-shell electron from the $+11$ nucleus. The effective nuclear charge in the third shell is therefore about $+1$, which means that the shell is able to hold only one electron.

5. Ba_3N_2.

7. There is no more room available in its outermost occupied shell.

9. The hydrogen atom has only one electron to share.

11. There is a gradual change. You can determine which type of bond is likely by noting relative positions in the periodic table. If the elements forming a bond are close together in the peri-

odic table and toward the upper right of the table, the bond is more covalent. If the elements are on opposite sides of the periodic table, the bond is more ionic. For elements between these two extremes, the bonding tends to be a blend, referred to as a *polar covalent* bond.

13. When bonded to an atom that has low electronegativity, such as any group 1 element, the nonmetal atom pulls the bonding electrons so close to itself that an ion is formed.

15. The chemical formula for phosphine is PH_3, which is similar to the formula for ammonia, NH_3. Note how phosphorus is directly below nitrogen in the periodic table.

17. $:\ddot{C}l:^{1-}$ Ca^{2+} $:\ddot{C}l:^{1-}$

19.
$$\begin{matrix} & H & \\ :\ddot{O}: & \ddot{O}: \\ & H & \end{matrix}$$

21. There are four substituents and no nonbonding pairs around the central atom. Therefore the shape of this molecule is the same as the geometry: tetrahedral.

23. The source of an atom's electronegativity is the positive charge of the nucleus. More specifically, it is the effective nuclear charge experienced in the shell the bonding electrons are occupying.

25. The least symmetrical molecule: $O=C=S$.

27. N–N $<$ N–O $<$ N–F $<$ H–F.

29. Water is a polar molecule because the dipoles in the H_2O molecule do not cancel. Polar molecules tend to stick to one another, which gives rise to relatively high boiling points. Methane is a nonpolar molecule because of its symmetry, which results in no net dipole in the molecule and a relatively low boiling point. The boiling points of water and methane are influenced only a little by molecular mass but a great deal by the intermolecular attractions in each liquid.

31. The greater the polarity of the molecules of a liquid, the higher the boiling point of the liquid. (a) The compound with the two chlorines on the same side of the molecule is more polar and thus has the higher boiling point. (b) The SCO molecule, with a carbon atom flanked by a sulfur atom and an oxygen atom, is less symmetrical, which means that the dipoles in it do not cancel as well as they do in the symmetrical carbon dioxide molecule, CO_2. The SCO therefore has the higher boiling point. (c) The chlo-

rine atoms have a relatively strong electronegativity that pulls electrons away from the carbon. In the $COCl_2$ molecule, this tug by the chlorine atoms is counteracted by a relatively strong tug by the oxygen atom, which tends to decrease the polarity of this molecule. The hydrogens of the $C_2H_2Cl_2$ molecule have an electronegativity that is less than that of carbon, and so they assist the chlorine atoms in allowing electrons to be yanked toward one side, which means this molecule is more polar than $COCl_2$. The $C_2H_2Cl_2$ therefore has the higher boiling point.

Chapter 7

1. Ion–dipole attractions are stronger because the magnitude of the electric charge associated with an ion is much greater than the magnitude of the charge associated with a dipole.

3. It sticks to itself by way of induced dipole–induced dipole attractions between molecules.

5. The boiling points go up because of an increase in the number of molecule-to-molecule interactions. The boiling point of a substance refers to a pure sample of that substance. The boiling point of 1-pentanol (the third molecule in the list) is relatively high because 1-pentanol molecules are very strongly attracted to one another (by induced dipole–induced dipole, dipole–dipole, and dipole–induced dipole attractions). Solubility refers to how well a substance interacts with a second substance—in this case, water. Water is much less attracted to 1-pentanol molecules because most of a 1-pentanol molecule is nonpolar (the only polar portion is the –OH group). For this reason, 1-pentanol is not very soluble in water. Put yourself in the position of a water molecule and ask yourself how strongly you are attracted to a methanol molecule (the first molecule in the list) compared to how strongly you are attracted to a pentanol molecule.

7. Nitrogen atoms are bigger than helium atoms, and so nitrogen molecules should be more soluble in water because greater dipole–induced dipole attractions.

9. The helium is less soluble in body fluids, and so less of it dissolves at a given pressure. Upon decompression, there is less helium to "bubble out" and cause potential harm.

11. One way is to add more sugar and see if it dissolves. If it does, the solution was not saturated.

Alternatively, cool the solution a couple of degrees and see if any sugar precipitates out. If any does, the solution was saturated. Because sugar forms supersaturated solutions so easily, however, neither of these methods is foolproof.

13. The sodium nitrate solution is more concentrated (80 grams/milliliter versus only about 28 grams/milliliter for the solution).

15. Assuming concentration is given as mass (or moles) of solute in a given volume of solution, the concentration decreases with increasing temperature because you have the same mass of solute as before but dissolved in a larger volume of solvent.

17. For a given substance, molecule polarity has a far greater influence on boiling point than does molecule mass. Recall that boiling involves separating the molecules of a liquid from one another. (The more polar the molecules, the more "sticky" they are and hence the higher boiling point.) The extra neutron in deuterium does not affect the chemical bonding in the D_2O molecule, which means that D_2O has the same chemical structure as H_2O. With the same chemical structure, these two molecules have about equal polarity, making their boiling points very close: 100°C for H_2O and 101°C for D_2O. The extra mass of the deuterium has only a small affect on boiling point.

19. Although oxygen gas, O_2, has poor solubility in water, there are many examples of gases that have good solubility in water. From the concepts discussed in Chapter 6, you should be able to deduce that hydrogen chloride is a somewhat polar molecule. This gaseous material therefore has good solubility in water by virtue of the dipole–dipole attractions between HCl and H_2O molecules.

21. Motor oil is much thicker (more viscous) than gasoline. This difference suggests that molecules of motor oil are more strongly attracted to one another than are molecules of gasoline. A material consisting of molecules of structure A would have greater induced dipole–induced dipole interactions than a material consisting of molecules of structure B. Motor oil molecules therefore are best represented by structure A, and gasoline molecules are best represented by structure B.

23. The arrangement of atoms in a molecule makes all the difference as to physical and chemical

properties. Ethanol contains the −OH group, which is polar. This polarity is what allows the ethanol to dissolve in water. The oxygen of dimethyl ether is bonded to two carbon atoms. The difference in electronegativity between oxygen and carbon is not as great as the difference in electronegativity between oxygen and hydrogen. The polarity of the C−O bond is therefore less than that of the O−H bond. As a consequence, dimethyl ether is significantly less polar than ethanol and not readily soluble in water.

25. In order for you to smell something, the molecules of that something must evaporate and reach your nose. If the new perfume doesn't evaporate, it will not have an odor.

27. These bubbles are gases that were dissolved in the cold water and are now coming out of solution. Because the solubility of gases in water decreases with increasing temperature, a pot of warm water has more bubbles than a pot of cold water.

29. Most home water softeners work by replacing the calcium and magnesium ions of the tap water with sodium ions. The softened water therefore contains increased levels of sodium ions.

Problems

1. Multiply concentration by volume:
   $(0.5 \text{ g/L})(5 \text{ L}) = 2.5 \text{ g}$.

3. $\dfrac{1 \text{ mole}}{1 \text{ L}} = 1 \text{ M}$

   $\dfrac{2 \text{ moles}}{0.5 \text{ L}} = 4 \text{ moles / L} = 4 \text{ M}$

Chapter 8

1. As discussed in Chapter 6, both hydrogen fluoride, HF, and ammonia, NH_3, are polar molecules. Thus the molecule-to-molecule attractions in either liquid are relatively strong, which translates to relatively high boiling points.

3. As the ice melts, the water level does not change. For insight as to why this is so, think about the answer to Exercise 4.

5. It is important to keep the pipes from freezing because the water in them expands more than the pipe material does, and the expanded volume can fracture the pipes.

7. Any portion of the added heat that goes to the ice increases the vibrations in the H_2O molecules making up the ice. The increased vibrations cause more hydrogen bonds to be broken. Because hydrogen bonds are largely responsible for holding ice crystals together, the increased vibrations mean less ice can form.

9. Graph d.

11. Just as the presence of a solute affects the rate at which ice crystals form, so does it affect the rate at which ice microcyrstals form. As you should recall, it is the formation of microcrystals in fresh water that results in fresh water's expansion as it cools to below 4°C. Without the formation of microcrystals, ocean water continues to contract all the way to its freezing temperature. Ocean water is therefore most dense *just before* it freezes, which makes its freezing behavior most different from that of fresh water. To see for yourself, place a cupful of salt water next to a cupful of fresh water in your kitchen freezer.

13. As it cools to 4°C, the oxygen-rich surface water sinks to the bottom of the lake. This is of benefit to the aquatic organisms living at the bottom. Concurrently, the nutrient-rich deeper water is pushed to the surface. This is of benefit to the aquatic organisms living near the surface.

15. Nutrients are concentrated mostly at lower depths in any body of water. Because tropical surface water never sinks, there is no circulation in the water, with the result that nutrients stay on or near the ocean floor and the water is clear to a considerable depth.

17. The mercury–mercury cohesive forces must be stronger than the mercury–glass adhesive forces.

19. At colder temperatures, water molecules are moving more slowly, which makes it relatively easy for them to cohere to one another, increasing the surface tension. A tablespoon of vegetable oil poured into a pot of cold water typically stays together as a single blob (because the water molecules are so attracted to one another). At higher temperatures, water molecules are moving faster, which makes it more difficult for them to cohere to one another, decreasing the surface tension. A tablespoon of vegetable oil poured into a pot of hot water is more inclined to disperse throughout the water, which is of great benefit when someone is cooking spaghetti.

21. Water is not strongly attracted to the wax surface, which is nonpolar. To minimize surface area, the water on the wax surface tends to form a sphere. Sitting on a solid surface, however, the sphere is squashed down into a bead by the force of gravity.

23. When a wet finger is held to the wind, evaporation is greatest on the windy side, which feels cool. The cool side of your finger is windward.

25. A bottle wrapped in a wet cloth cools as the liquid evaporates from the cloth. As evaporation progresses, the average temperature of the water left behind in the cloth can easily drop to below the temperature of the water originally used to wet the cloth. So to cool a bottle of beer, soda, or whatever at a picnic, wet a piece of cloth in a bucket of cool water and wrap the wet cloth around the bottle. As evaporation progresses, the temperature of the water in the cloth drops and cools the bottle to a temperature below that of the water in the bucket.

27. A high temperature and the resulting heat energy given to the food are responsible for cooking. If the water boils at a low temperature (presumably under reduced pressure), there is not enough heat energy to cook the food.

29. The instructor removed most of the air from the flask (which is only partially filled with water). Removing the air caused the air pressure above the water surface to be extremely low. At such low pressure, the small amount of heat that travels from your hand to the water is enough to cause the water to boil. Remember, the boiling point of any liquid decreases as atmospheric pressure decreases.

31. The lid traps heat inside the pot, which shortens the amount of time it takes to bring all the water to its boiling point. The lid also increases the pressure exerted on the water, which raises the boiling point. The hotter water cooks food in a shorter time.

33. You want your radiator liquid to absorb heat from the engine so that the engine doesn't melt. A liquid that has a high specific heat capacity will be more effective at absorbing this heat. Engine efficiency increases with increasing temperature, however, and so keeping the engine too cool is not desirable. Commerically sold radiator liquids are formulated to have a specific heat capacity that helps your engine run at an optimal temperature.

35. The climate of Bermuda, like that of all other islands, is moderated by the high specific heat capacity of water. The climate is moderated by the large amounts of energy given off and absorbed by water for small changes in temperature. When the air is cooler than the water, the water warms the air; when the air is warmer than the water, the water cools the air.

37. Much of the heat from the oven is consumed in changing the phase of the water from liquid to gaseous. As long as any of the water remains in the liquid phase, the temperature of the oven will not rise much higher than the boiling point of the water—100°C.

39. This heat is radiated outward to the environment. In order to melt the ice, the heat would have to be reflected back into the ice.

Problems

1. Heat into water = specific heat capacity × mass × temperature change

   heat into water = $(4.184 \text{ J/g} \cdot \text{C}°)(100 \text{ g})(+7 \text{ C}°)$
   $= 2928.8 \text{ J}$

   which to the proper number of significant figures is 3000 J.

3.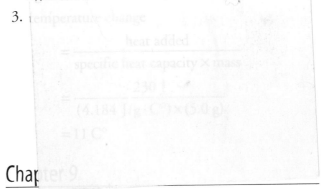

temperature change
$$= \frac{\text{heat added}}{\text{specific heat capacity} \times \text{mass}}$$
$$= \frac{230 \text{ J}}{(4.184 \text{ J/g} \cdot \text{C}°) \times (5.0 \text{ g})}$$
$$= 11 \text{ C}°$$

Chapter 9

1. The coefficients needed to balance this equation are 8, 1, 8.

3. a. 4, 3, 2   b. 3, 1, 2   c. 1, 2, 1, 2   d. 1, 2, 1, 2 (Remember that, by convention, a coefficient of 1s is not shown in the balanced equation.)

5. H_2O, 18 atomic mass units; C_3H_6, 42 atomic mass units; C_3H_8O, 60 atomic mass units.

7. They have about the same number of atoms. Consider that the mass of NH_3 represents 1 mole of NH_3, which means 6.02×10^{23} NH_3 molecules. Because there are four atoms per molecule, there are $4(6.02 \times 10^{23}) = 24.08 \times 10^{23}$ atoms in the 17.031 grams.

The mass of HCl represents 2 moles of HCl, which means $2(6.02 \times 10^{23})$ molecules. Because there are only two atoms per molecule in this case, you have $2(2)(6.02 \times 10^{23}) = 24.08 \times 10^{23}$ atoms in the 72.922 grams.

9. There is 1 mole of N_2 in 28 grams of N_2, 1 mole of O_2 in 32 grams of O_2; 2 moles of CH_4 in 32 grams of CH_4, and 1 mole of F_2 in 38 grams of F_2. Therefore the answer is c.

11. They assumed incorrectly that one hydrogen atom bonds to one oxygen atom to form water, which would mean that the chemical formula was HO. We know today, however, that two hydrogen molecules (not atoms) react with one oxygen molecule to form water. By a count of molecules—which translates to a count of atoms—the hydrogen and oxygen react in a 2:1 ratio and the formula for water is H_2O. By mass, hydrogen and oxygen still always react in a 1:8 ratio. Because two hydrogen atoms are needed for every one oxygen atom, however, this ratio is better expressed as 0.5 gram of hydrogen to 4 grams of oxygen. Comparing one hydrogen atom to one oxygen atom thus shows us that oxygen is actually 16 times more massive than hydrogen.

13. A single oxygen atom has the very small mass of 16 atomic mass units.

15. Because 1 atomic mass unit equals 1.661×10^{-24} gram, 16 atomic mass units must equal $(16)(1.661 \times 10^{-24}$ gram$) = 26.576 \times 10^{-24}$ gram $= 2.6576 \times 10^{-23}$ gram.

17. No, because this mass is less than that of a single oxygen atom.

19. The water molecules have the greater mass, just as a bunch of golf balls have more mass than the same number of Ping-Pong balls. The water molecules have about nine times more mass because each H_2O molecule ($16 + 1 + 1 = 18$ amu) is about nine times more massive than each H_2 molecule ($1 + 1 = 2$ amu): 18 amu/2 amu $= 9$. The big numbers don't change anything: 1.204×10^{24} molecules of water have a greater mass than 1.204×10^{24} molecules of molecular hydrogen.

21. Chemical reactions, including the biological ones responsible for the spoilage of food, slow down with decreasing temperature. The refrigerator therefore merely delays spoilage.

23. In pure oxygen, there is a greater concentration of one of the reactants (oxygen) for the chemical reaction (combustion). The greater the concentration of reactants, the higher the rate of the reaction.

25. The bubbling is the result of a reaction between the Alka-Seltzer tablet and the water. In the alcohol–water mix, there is a lower proportion of water molecules, which leads to a lower rate of reaction. In terms of molecular collisions, with fewer water molecules around, the probability of collisions between Alka-Seltzer and water molecules is less in the alcohol–water mix.

27. The final result of this reaction is the transformation of three oxygen molecules, O_2, to two ozone molecules, O_3. Although there is no net consumption or production of nitrogen monoxide, NO, nitrogen dioxide, NO_2, or atomic oxygen, O, only the nitrogen monoxide appears to be required for this reaction to begin. Therefore the nitrogen monoxide is best described as the catalyst.

29. Putting more ozone into the atmosphere to replace what's been destroyed is like throwing more fish into a pool of sharks to replace those the sharks have eaten. The solution to the ozone problem is to remove the CFCs that destroy the ozone. Unfortunately, CFCs degrade only slowly, and the ones up there now will remain there for many years to come. Our best bet is to stop producing CFCs and hope we haven't already caused too much damage.

31. $N_2H_4 \longrightarrow 2H_2 + N_2$

Energy absorbed as bonds break	Energy released as bonds form
N–N = 159 kJ	H–H = 436 kJ
N–H = 389 kJ	H–H = 436 kJ
N–H = 389 kJ	
N–H = 389 kJ	
N–H = 389 kJ	N≡N = 946 kJ
Total = +1715 kJ absorbed	Total = −1818 kJ released

$$\text{net energy of reaction} = +1715 \text{ kJ} + (-1818 \text{ kJ})$$
$$= -103 \text{ kJ (negative net energy means exothermic reaction)}$$

$$2 H_2O_2 \longrightarrow O_2 + 2 H_2O$$

Energy absorbed as bonds break	Energy released as bonds form
O–O = 138 kJ	
H–O = 464 kJ	O=O = 498 kJ
H–O = 464 kJ	H–O = 464 kJ
O–O = 138 kJ	H–O = 464 kJ
H–O = 464 kJ	O–H = 464 kJ
H–O = 464 kJ	O–H = 464 kJ
Total = +2132 kJ absorbed	Total = −2354 kJ released

$$
\begin{aligned}
\text{net energy of reaction} &= +2132 \text{ kJ} + (-2354 \text{ kJ}) \\
&= -222 \text{ kJ (negative net} \\
&\quad \text{energy means exother-} \\
&\quad \text{mic reaction)}
\end{aligned}
$$

33. The reactions in a disposable battery are exothermic, evidenced by the fact that the battery is producing energy used to operate some device. The reactions taking place as a rechargeable battery is recharged are endothermic, evidenced by the fact that you need to connect the recharger to an external supply of electricity. (Both the disposable battery and the recharging one get warm because of the heat generated as electricity passes through them.)

Problems

1. $(0.250 \text{ g})\left(\dfrac{1 \text{ mole}}{180 \text{ g}}\right)\left(\dfrac{6.02 \times 10^{23} \text{ molecules}}{1 \text{ mole}}\right)$

$= 8.36 \times 10^{20}$ molecules

3. The chemical equation tells you that 1 mole of 2-propanol yields 1 mole of propene and 1 mole of water. From the chemical formula C_3H_8O, you know that the molar mass of 2-propanol is 60 grams/mole, and so 6.0 grams is 0.10 mole of 2-propanol. Therefore this mass of 2-propanol yields 0.10 mole of propene and 0.10 mole of water. The masses of the two products are therefore

C_3H_6 (42 g/mole)(0.10 mole) = 4.2 g
H_2O (18 g/mole)(0.10 mole) = 1.8 g

5. The molar mass of sulfur dioxide is 64.058 grams/mole, and so 64.058 grams is 1 mole of SO_2. According to the balanced equation, 1 mole of SO_2 reacts with 1 mole of CaO. Because 1 mole of CaO has a mass of 56.079 grams, this is the amount of CaO that reacts with 64.058 grams of SO_2. The balanced equation tells you that 1 mole of $CaSO_3$ forms, which is 120.137 grams.

Chapter 10

1. Potassium carbonate in the ashes acts as a base and reacts with skin oils to produce a slippery solution of soap.

3. The base accepted one or more hydrogen ions, H^+, and thus gained positive charge. In order to accept H^+ ions, the base had to give up some other positive ions. The base thus formed the positive ions of the salt. The acid donated one or more hydrogen ions and thus lost positive charge. Once the acid lost all its H^+ ions, what remained was only negative ions. The acid thus formed the negative ions of the salt.

5. In the first reaction, the H_3O^+ transforms to a water molecule. This means the H_3O^+ loses a hydrogen ion, which is donated to the Cl^-. The H_3O^+ therefore is behaving as an acid, and the Cl^- is behaving as a base. In the reverse direction, the H_2O gains a hydrogen ion (behaving as a base) to become H_3O^+. It gets this hydrogen ion from the HCl, which in donating is behaving as an acid. You should be able to make similar arguments to arrive at the following answers:
   a. acid, base, base, acid.
   b. acid, base, acid, base.
   c. acid, base, acid, base.

7. When the sodium hydroxide, NaOH, accepts a hydrogen ion from water, the products formed are water and sodium hydroxide! In solution this sodium hydroxide is dissolved as individual sodium ions and hydroxide ions.

9. That the value of K_w is so small tells you that the extent to which water ionizes is also quite small.

11. a. As more hydronium and hydroxide ions form as the temperature increases, the concentration of these ions increases. This means that

the product of their concentrations, which is K_w, also increases. Thus, K_w is constant only so long as the temperature is constant. Interestingly, K_w is 1.0×10^{-14} only at 24°C. At 40°C, K_w is 2.92×10^{-14}.

b. pH is a measure of hydronium ion concentration. The greater the hydronium ion concentration, the lower the pH. According to the information given in this Exercise, the hydronium ion concentration increases (albeit only slightly as water warms ups). Thus, pure water that is hot has a slightly lower pH than pure water that is cold.

c. As water warms up, the hydronium ion concentration increases, but so does the hydroxide ion concentration—and by the same amount. Thus, the pH decreases and yet the solution remains neutral because the hydronium ion and hydroxide ion concentrations are still equal. At 40°C, for example, the hydronium ion and hydroxide ion concentrations in pure water are both 1.71×10^{-7} mole per liter (the square root of K_w). The pH of this solution is the negative of the logarithm of this number, which is 6.77. This is why most pH meters need to be adjusted for the temperature of the solution being measured. Except for here in this Exercise, which probes your powers of analytical thinking, this textbook ignores the slight role that temperature plays in pH. Unless noted otherwise, please continue to assume that K_w always has the value 1.0×10^{-14}—in other words, assume that the solution being measured is at 24°C.

13. $pH = -\log [H_3O^+] = -\log 1 = -0 = 0$

This an acidic solution. Yes, pH can be equal to zero!

15. Because pH is defined as the *negative* of the logarithm, you have

$$pH = -\log [H_3O^+] = -3$$
$$\log [H_3O^+] = 3$$
$$[H_3O^+] = 10^3 \, M = 1000 \, M$$

The solution would be impossible to prepare because only so much acid can dissolve in water before the solution is saturated. The highest concentration possible for hydrochloric acid, for example, is 12 M. Beyond this concentration,

any HCl, which is a gas, added to the water simply bubbles back out into the atmosphere.

17. As pure water is added to an acidic solution, the concentration of hydronium ions (and of anything else dissolved in the solution) drops as the solution becomes more dilute, that is, less concentrated. Because $[H_3O^+]$ decreases, the pH increases.

19. If the chalk is made of calcium carbonate, $CaCO_3$, it is made of the active ingredient in many antacids. Calcium carbonate is a base that neutralizes an acid. Be careful, though, never to take too much calcium carbonate because the stomach is designed to always be somewhat acidic.

21. Limestone (also known as calcium carbonate) is a base. Thus any slight amounts of it dissolved in lake water neutralize some of the acid rain that enters the lake. Granite is not basic, and so there is no such neutralizing possible for acid rain falling into granite-lined lakes.

23. The warmer the ocean, the lower the solubility of any dissolved gases, such as carbon dioxide, CO_2. Thus less CO_2 would be absorbed in a warmer ocean, meaning that more of this gas would remain in the atmosphere to perpetuate global warming.

25. The hydrogen chloride, which behaves as an acid, reacts with the ammonia, which behaves as a base, to form ammonium chloride. The concentration of ammonium chloride increases, and the concentration of ammonia decreases.

27. When the active buffering components are all neutralized.

Problems

1. The concentration of hydroxide ions must be 1×10^{-4} mole per liter because $[H_3O^+][OH^-] = 1 \times 10^{-14}$ mole per liter.

3. The pH of this solution is 4, and the solution is acidic.

5. Doubling the volume of solution means that the hydronium ion concentration is cut in half. The hydronium ion concentration after dilution is therefore 0.05 M. The pH is

$$pH = -\log [H_3O^+]$$
$$= -\log 0.05$$
$$= -(-1.3) = 1.3$$

Chapter 11

1. The atom that loses an electron and thus becomes positively charged (the red one) is the one that is oxidized.

3. An oxidizing agent causes other materials to lose electrons. It does so by its tendency to gain electrons. Atoms with high electronegativity tend to have a strong attraction for electrons and therefore behave as strong oxidizing agents. Conversely, a reducing agent causes other materials to gain electrons. It does so by its tendency to lose electrons. Atoms with high electronegativity therefore have little tendency to behave as reducing agents.

5. Fluorine should be the stronger oxidizing agent because it has the greater effective nuclear charge.

7. The electrons flow from the nail to the copper ions.

9. The anode is where oxidation takes place and where free-roaming electrons are generated. The negative sign at a battery anode indicates that this electrode is the source of negatively charged electrons. They run from the anode, through an external circuit, to the cathode, which carries a positive charge to which the electrons are attracted. (When a battery is being recharged, energy is used to force electrons in the opposite direction. In other words, during recharging, electrons move from the positive electrode to the negative electrode—a place where they would not ever go without the input of energy. Electrons are thus gained at the negative electrode, which is now classified as the cathode because the cathode is where reduction—the gain of electrons—occurs. Look carefully at Figure 11.10b to see how this is so.)

11. According to the chemical formula for iron hydroxide, there are two hydroxide groups for every one iron ion. Each hydroxide group has a single negative charge. This means that the iron ion must carry a double positive charge, which is no different from the free Fe^{2+} ion from which the $Fe(OH)_2$ is formed. This reaction is merely the coming together of oppositely charged ions.

13. The Cu^{2+} ion is reduced as it gains electrons to form copper metal, Cu. The magnesium metal,

Mg, is oxidized as it loses electrons to form the Mg^{2+} ion.

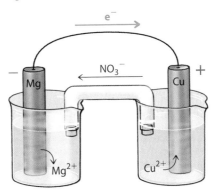

15. How much power a battery can deliver is a function of the number of ions in contact with the electrodes—the more ions, the greater the power. If the lead electrodes are completely submerged both before and after the water is added, diluting the ionic solution in the battery decreases the number of ions in contact with the electrodes and thus decreases the power of the battery. This effect is only temporary, however, because more ions are soon generated as the battery is recharged by the car's generator. If the water level inside the battery is so low that the lead electrodes are not completely submerged, adding water increases the amount of electrode surface area in contact with the solution. This counterbalances the weakening effect of diluting the ionic solution.

17. Aluminum oxide is insoluble in water and thus forms a protective coating that prevents continued oxidation of the aluminum.

19. Combustion reactions are generally exothermic because they involve the transfer of electrons to oxygen, which of all atoms in the periodic table has one of the greatest tendencies for gaining electrons.

21. In water, the oxygen is chemically bound to hydrogen atoms. That chemically bound —O— is completely different from molecular oxygen, O_2, which is what is required for combustion. Another way to phrase your answer would be to say that the oxygen in water is already "reduced" in the sense that it has gained electrons from the hydrogen atoms to which it is attached. Being already reduced, this oxygen atom no longer has a great attraction for additional electrons.

23. This is very bad news. The iron atoms will lose electrons to the copper atoms, which, being very poor reducing agents, will pass those electrons on to oxygen molecules in the air in contact with the pipe surface, much as is indicated in Figure 11.17.

25. This water is in the gaseous phase and merely floats away from the fire.

Chapter 12

1. A 5-carbon saturated hydrocarbon contains 12 hydrogen atoms. A 5-carbon unsaturated hydrocarbon contains 10 or fewer hydrogen atoms.

3.

5. There are only two structural isomers drawn. The one in the middle and the one on the right are two conformations of the same isomer.

7. The pressure is greatest at the bottom because the temperature is highest here, and the high temperature means the greatest number of vaporized molecules present to cause the high pressure.

9. If the bulk of the alcohol molecule is a nonpolar hydrocarbon chain, the alcohol may be insoluble in water.

11. Ingesting methanol is indirectly harmful to eyes because in the body it is metabolized to formaldehyde, a chemical most toxic to living tissue. In addition, methanol, just like ethanol, has inherent toxicity and is thus also directly harmful.

13. $+ H_2O + Na^+H_2PO_4^-$

Caffeine
(free base)

15. The HCl would react with the free base to form the hydrochloric acid salt of caffeine, which is soluble in water but insoluble in diethyl ether. With no water available to dissolve this material, it would precipitate out of the diethyl ether as a solid that could be collected by filtration.

17. The caprylic acid reacts with the sodium hydroxide to form a water-soluble salt, which dissolves in the water. The aldehyde is not acidic so does not form a water-soluble salt.

19. No! This label indicates that the decongestant contains the hydrogen chloride salt of phenylephrine, *not* acidic hydrogen chloride. This organic salt is as different from hydrogen chloride as is sodium chloride (table salt), which could go by the name "hydrogen chloride salt of sodium." Think of it this way: Assume you have a cousin named George. You may be George's cousin, but in no way are you George. In a similar fashion, the hydrogen chloride salt of phenylephrine is made using hydrogen chloride, but it is in no way hydrogen chloride. A chemical substance is different from the elements or compounds from which it is made.

21. At acidic pH values, the nitrogen atom accepts hydrogen ions from solution and so carries a positive charge as shown in the amine part of structure b. The carboxylic acid, however, remains unchanged and so appears as it does in the carboxylic acid part of structure a. At alkaline pH values, the carboxylic acid part of the molecule loses its hydrogen ion as it reacts with hydroxide ions in solution. As a result, this part of the molecule carries a negative charge as shown in structure b. Because the solution is basic, the nitrogen atom cannot pick up any hydrogen ions and so remains as shown in the amine part of structure a. At neutral pH, both the concentration of hydronium ions and the concentration of hydroxide ions are quite low. This situation allows the acidic carboxylic acid part of the molecule and the basic amine part of the molecule to react *with each other* to form structure b.

23. 1. ether   2. amide   3. ester   4. amide
    5. alcohol   6. aldehyde   7. amine   8. ether
    9. ketone

25. The combustion of polyacrylonitrile produces hydrogen cyanide. The combustion of polyvinyl chloride and polyvinylidene chloride produces hydrogen chloride gas.

27. The polymer made of long strands is likely to be more viscous because of the tendency of longer strands to get tangled.

29. A fluorine-containing polymer, such as Teflon.

Chapter 13

1. A carbohydrate is made from water and carbon dioxide, but in no way does it "contain" these two materials. Recall from Chapter 2 that any chemical compound produced in a reaction is different from the reactants used to make it.

3. Both cellulose and starch are polymers of glucose. They differ in how the glucose units are linked together. In cellulose, the linking results in linear polymers that align with one another, giving rise to a tough material useful for structural purposes in plants. In starch, the linking permits the formation of alpha helices, with periodic branching along the polymer chain.

5. Lipids are nonpolar molecules containing no polar functional groups. They are made primarily of nonpolar hydrocarbons and therefore do not dissolve in water because they cannot compete with the strong attraction water molecules have for one another.

7. A fat molecule is a triglyceride. So if a product contains no triglycerides, perhaps there is some legitimacy to saying it is "free of fat molecules." When fat (triglyceride) molecules consumed in food are digested, however, they are broken down to fatty acids and glycerol molecules. This "fat-free" product therefore would still offer your body the same type of molecules that fat-containing food does, which means the same number of calories.

9. Your customer's hair is fine because each strand is thin. Because each strand is thin, there is less mass per strand. Less mass per strand means each strand is made of fewer amino acids, which means fewer cysteine amino acids and disulfide cross-linkings. Adding concentrated or even regular-strength reducing agent might cause his hair to fall apart completely. Yikes! You should dilute your reducing agent prior to application. You might even skip the reducing step altogether and move right to the oxidizing step in which disulfide bonds are formed.

11. Ser–Leu–Ser–Leu–Cys

13. At a: dipole–dipole attractions (hydrogen bonding). At b: disulfide bonds. At c: induced dipole–induced dipole attractions (hydrophobic attractions). The primary structure is the sequence of amino acids. The secondary structure is the three alpha-helix regions (the coils) and the one pleated-sheet region (the zig-zags). The tertiary structure is the overall shape of the polypeptide chain. No quaternary structure is observed because this polypeptide is not associated with an adjacent polypeptide.

15. Cytosine without its amine group is uracil. If uracil were present as a normal component of DNA, this "authentic" uracil would not be distinguishable from any uracil generated by cytosine deamination. The methyl group on thymine is apparently the "label" that tells repair enzymes to leave it alone, thereby preventing loss of genetic information.

17. The sequence ATG in DNA give rise to the codon UAC on mRNA, which codes for the amino acid tyrosine.

19. Asp–Pro–Ala

21. The hydroxyl group on the ribose sugar provides a conformation for the mRNA polymer that doesn't bind well with DNA.

23. Water readily passes through the body. Excess quantities of the water-soluble vitamins are therefore readily excreted. Water-insoluble vitamins, by contrast, tend to build up in nonpolar fatty tissue, where they can remain for extended periods of time.

25. You should tell her that her body needs and will absorb only a certain amount of vitamin C each day. If she loads up with an excessive amount only once a week, her body has no way of storing any excess. Instead, the excess is excreted, leaving her potentially low on this vitamin for days at a time.

27. Sucrose is a disaccharide and must be broken down to its two saccharide units—only one of which is glucose—before it can be used by the body.

29. These polyunsaturated fatty acids came from the vegetarian diet eaten by the cows from which the beef fat came.

31. Every muscle in your body is a storage site of amino acids for yourself (as well as for any organisms that might end up eating you). In times of starvation, your body will access this "stockpile" of amino acids, resulting in a decrease in your muscle mass.

Chapter 14

1. It is the vast diversity of organic chemicals that permits the manufacture of the many types of medicines needed to match the many types of illnesses humans are susceptible to.

3. Whether a drug is isolated from nature or synthesized in the laboratory makes no difference as to "how good it may be for you." There are a multitude of natural products that are harmful, just as there are many synthetic drugs that are harmful. The effectiveness of a drug depends on its chemical structure, not on the source of the drug.

5. Typically, cancer chemotherapeutics kill not *all* cancer cells but rather only a high percentage of them. The remaining cancer cells are finished off by the immune system. The earlier the cancer is caught, the fewer the number of cancer cells present in the body, which makes it easier for the chemotherapy and the immune system to work together. With later-stage cancer, the number of cancer cells left over after chemotherapy might be too much for the immune system to handle. Also, most cancer chemotherapy agents used today work by killing cancer cells that are dividing. Young tumors have a greater percentage of dividing cells than do older tumors. Thus, young tumors are quicker to succumb to chemotherapy.

7. They work well together because of the synergistic effect. An invading virus is slowed down by the protease inhibitors and also by the antiviral nucleosides. Combining these agents creates an effect that is greater than the effect of either agent given independently.

9. Of the 6 billion humans on the planet, 3 billion are woman. The percentage of women using birth control pills is therefore (60 million/ 3 billion) × 100 = 2 percent. Birth control pills therefore have probably had only a minor impact on the worldwide growth of the human population.

11. Many stimulant drugs work by blocking the re-uptake of excitatory neurotransmitters. Stuck in the synaptic cleft, these neurotransmitters are decomposed by enzymes. By the time re-uptake is no longer blocked by a stimulant, there are few neurotransmitters left to be reabsorbed by the presynaptic neuron, which by this point is also deprived of neurotransmitters. With a lack of neurotransmitters, there is little communication between adjacent neurons, and this has the effect of making the drug user depressed.

13. Gardeners must exercise extreme care when using solutions of nicotine because nicotine is extremely poisonous to humans.

15. The effective dose of MDA is many times greater than the effective dose of LSD. In other words, MDA is taken by the milligram but LSD is taken by the microgram. Because so much MDA is taken, negative side effects are more likely.

The mechanisms of drug withdrawal are quite complex, however. Consider the following: A coffee drinker gets a headache when he or she stops drinking coffee. The headache is a result of a side effect of caffeine. This stimulant component of coffee causes blood vessels to dilate. Over time, the coffee drinker's body becomes accustomed to this dilation and counteracts it by applying a force that causes the dilated blood vessels to constrict. When coffee is no longer consumed, the body doesn't know to stop counteracting the dilation. Blood vessels therefore become overly constricted, and that gives rise to a headache, which prompts the coffee drinker to drink more coffee.

Likewise, with repeated use of MDA, the body develops a tolerance to its side effects. When a person stops using MDA, the body is still working hard to tolerate the drug. Thus, it is the body's own counteraction to the drug that drives the MDA user to continue using it—a vicious cycle driven by some very real chemistry.

17. The advantage is that the person doesn't run the risk of being sent to jail for smoking marijuana. The disadvantage is that if the person is already nauseated, she or he may not be able to hold the Marinol down long enough for the antinausea effect to occur. Recall from this chapter that one of the quickest routes of drug administration is inhalation.

19. The effect would be devastating! The addict's dopamine levels are already extremely low. To be "uplifted" requires more dopamine or, more specifically, more dopamine to be activating dopamine receptor sites. Recall from page 472 that chlorpromazine blocks dopamine from reaching its receptor site by binding to the site. This is a useful mechanism for individuals who have excess dopamine in their synaptic clefts. However, for a cocaine addict, who already has *low* levels of dopamine, this is a recipe for severe depression.

21. Replace the $-CH_3$ group with a group having a $-C-C-N-$ sequence. With this sequence, there is a nitrogen atom two carbons away from the single-bonded oxygen of the ester (see Figure 14.43). This change gives either procaine or a compound very similar to procaine, and the anesthetic properties of these compounds are greater than those of benzocaine. Of course, once the structure is modified, it is no longer benzocaine but some other chemical.

23. Endorphins likely came first, and then humans discovered how opium contains compounds that mimic the effect of endorphins. Thus, "opioids have endorphin activity" is the more appropriate statement. Why this is so is something you should be sure to discuss with your instructor.

25. The plaque deposits can break off and become lodged in narrow arteries, where they prevent the flow of oxygen-rich and nutrient-rich blood to cells.

Chapter 15

1. This oxygen is not gaseous O_2 but rather oxygen atoms bound to the cellulose structure of the plants.

3. *Tyrannosaurus rex* was at the top of its food chain (a quaternary consumer), which means its population was limited because of the small food supply available at this level.

5. As it decomposes, the humus releases carbon dioxide, which reacts with moisture in the soil to form carbonic acid.

7. If the open spaces are too large, the soil will not retain water very well. Instead, the water will leach out, taking many plant nutrients with it.

9. Clay is a very compact material containing few open spaces. Because water cannot penetrate clay very well, nutrients are not washed away.

11. In alkaline soil, the ammonium ion, NH_4^+, behaves as a weak acid—it loses a hydrogen ion and thereby becomes ammonia, NH_3. Although ammonia is soluble in water, it is a gas at ambient temperatures and is thus readily lost to the atmosphere.

13. The organic bulk of compost, even though it is chemically inert, provides many open spaces to the soil, and these open spaces are where water and atmospheric oxygen become available to plant roots.

15. Synthetic fertilizers provide no organic bulk to the soil. Without an adequate supply of organic bulk, soil becomes chalky and loses its capacity to hold water, with the result that leaching becomes more significant. The synthetic fertilizers are quickly leached away, which means that greater quantities of them must be applied to compensate for this leaching effect.

17. Sawdust is mostly ground-up cellulose, which, as you learned in Chapter 13, is made of only carbon, oxygen, and hydrogen. The sawdust should therefore have the lowest rating of 0.2–0–0.2. Fish meal is a good source of protein, and proteins are high in nitrogen. The most likely rating for the fish meal therefore is 5–3–3. As discussed in Section 10.1, wood ashes are a source of the alkaline material potassium carbonate, K_2CO_3, and so the most likely rating for the ashes is 0–1.5–8.

19. The plant cannot distinguish between the two ions. An ammonium ion is an ammonium ion

no matter where it is from! The main difference for the plant would be that the compost would provide the added benefit of organic bulk.

21. Here, it is all just a matter of semantics. The word *organic* in the phrase *organic farming* refers to an environmentally friendly method of farming. When a pesticide is classified as "organic," the likely meaning is that the pesticide is made of organic molecules, which, as discussed in Chapter 12, are molecules built by the linking together of carbon atoms.

23. One of the most precious resources of a nation is its topsoil because from this topsoil comes the food to feed the nation. One important reason the U.S. government is paying farmers not to farm and thereby allow native grasslands to remain untouched is to conserve topsoil. At present, food supplies are more than adequate, and so there is an argument to be made that these conservation efforts are prudent. For the millions of starving people in the world, the problem is not an inadequate food supply but rather an inadequate distribution infrastructure for the food.

25. The advances in genetic engineering allow us to modify plants to improve their nutritional qualities and make them more resistant to pest infiltration.

27. Some plants are fairly tolerant of salty soil. The gene or genes that allow for this greater tolerance might be inserted into other plants that normally have a low tolerance for salty soil.

Chapter 16

1. People need fresh water to survive and prosper. Thus it's only natural that communities developed around areas where fresh water was easy to obtain, which means alongside rivers, lakes, and streams. Only with newer technologies has it become feasible for humans to settle in places where aboveground fresh water is not so abundant. In these regions—such as where Denver, Colorado, is now located—the majority of drinking water is obtained from deep wells that tap into groundwater.

3. The ultimate sink for nearly all rainfall on the Earth is the oceans.

5. Most groundwater exists in aquifers, which are underground regions through which water flows relatively slowly. If groundwater removal is stopped, the flow of water through the aquifer will slowly recharge the aquifer. If subsidence has occurred, the underground soil is much more compact than it was originally, which means it is not likely to hold as much water as it once did. If water removal is stopped, therefore, the land may rise some because of the recharging effect, but probably not back to its original level.

7. Groundwater moves only slowly, which means that any pollutants added to it are not flushed away for quite some time. Furthermore, there is no way to clean polluted groundwater while it is in the ground. Our only choice would be to purify the water after we extract it from the ground.

9. A big advantage to using chlorine is that it provides protection from pathogens for several days after treatment. A drawback is that the residual chlorine can adversely affect the taste of the water. Ozone, O_3, is very effective at killing pathogens. However, soon after it is bubbled through the water, it decomposes to oxygen, O_2. Thus, ozone does not remain in the water for as long as chlorine does to provide long-lasting protection. If the ozonated water is consumed fairly soon, however, this may not be a problem. Futhermore, because the ozone decomposes, ozonated water tends to taste better than water treated with chlorine.

11. Reverse osmosis can be used to get fresh water from any solution. The only prerequisite is that the solute particles be larger than the water molecules. When this is the case, only water molecules pass through the semipermeable membrane from the solution side to the fresh-water side.

13. Our mouths are pretty good at discerning the taste of residual components in drinking water—so much so that many of us are willing to pay the 1000 percent markup that water bottlers charge for their products, which are only a fraction of a percentage purer than municipal water. Because the purity of municipal water and the purity of bottled water are comparable, flushing a toilet with municipal water is about as wasteful as flushing it with bottled water. At the wastewater treatment

facility, human waste is extracted from the water and typically ends up in a solid-waste disposal site. So why not use a composting toilet and send our wastes directly to farmlands rather than to disposal sites? If you simply must have a water-flush toilet, let it be a low-flush model or one that uses "gray water" from an upstairs bathtub. Your sketch for such a system should look something like this:

15. When a red blood cell is placed in fresh water, the concentration of water inside the cell is lower than the concentration of water outside the cell. As a result, water migrates into the cell (moving from a region of high water concentration to a region of low water concentration). When enough water has collected in the cell, the cell bursts.

It's important to note that when we speak of osmosis and reverse osmosis, we are referring to the concentration *of water*. This is quite unlike discussions in earlier chapters, where we talked about the concentrations of *solutes* dissolved in water. For the record, the concentration of pure water can be obtained from its density, which is 1.00 gram per milliliter. This mass of water equals 0.0556 mole, and 1.00 milliliter equals 0.00100 liter. Thus, the concentration of pure water is 0.0556 mole/0.00100 liter = 55.6 moles/liter = 55.6 *M*.

17. As the water freezes, dissolved salts are excluded from the ice crystals that form. Seawater can therefore be desalinated by cooling it to form crystals, which can then be melted to produce fresh water. Before the seawater is completely frozen, however, the mixture of crystals and liquid water needs to be "rinsed" with fresh water to remove the salts. Otherwise, the salts collect in tiny pockets in the ice. Unfortunately, the amount of fresh water required to rinse the freezing seawater is comparable to the amount of fresh water obtained by this process, making the process relatively inefficient.

19. Phosphates are a nutrient for many plants and microorganisms. In the past, the phosphates from used laundry detergents often made their way into rivers, lakes, and ponds. The phosphate-rich water supported such rampant growth of plants and microorganisms that the natural supply of dissolved oxygen was choked off—a process known as eutrophication.

21. The decomposition is primarily anaerobic because very little oxygen makes it from our mouths to our intestines, where food decomposition takes place. As a consequence, gases that come out the other end are frequently of the odoriferous sort.

23. At the wastewater treatment facility, human waste is extracted from the water and typically ends up in a solid-waste disposal site. So why not use a composting toilet, which allows you to stop wasting water, and send wastes directly to farmlands?

25. To date, advanced integrated pond systems are best suited to small communities that have access to large areas of undeveloped land and lots of sunshine. Even if conditions are right for a particular community, however, still to be overcome is the social inertia almost always associated with doing something different.

Chapter 17

1. The molecules of the gases that make up the atmosphere are held down by the force of gravity.

3. The air pressure exerted on the outside of your eardrums is decreasing more quickly than is the air pressure exerted on the inside of your eardrums. FYI, commercial airplanes maintain a cabin pressure equal to the pressure one experiences at about 2400 meters (8000 feet) up a mountain.

5. Oxygen molecules are more massive and hence heavier than nitrogen molecules. An oxygen molecule therefore requires more kinetic energy to travel to the same altitude as a nitrogen molecule. This is one of the reasons the ratio of nitrogen molecules to oxygen molecules increases (slightly) with increasing altitude.

7. Coal is a fossil fuel, which means it formed from decomposed organic matter. The sulfur in organic matter is primarily in the form of the amino acids cysteine and methionine. Plants obtain the sulfur to make these amino acids from atmospheric sulfur oxides that originated from volcano eruptions and the burning of fossil fuels. Thus, there is no original source of sulfur on the Earth. Rather, like all other elements, the sulfur that is already here recycles through various pathways. Sulfur does have an ultimate origin, however—the nuclear fusion occurring in our sun and all other stars.

9. The airborne sulfur dioxide reacts with oxygen and water to form sulfuric acid, which is carried to the ground by rainwater.

11. Atmospheric nitrogen reacts with atmospheric oxygen under conditions of extreme heat, such as occurs in an automobile engine or in the air surrounding a lightning bolt. The balanced equation for this reaction is $N_2 + O_2 \longrightarrow 2\ NO$.

13. Photosynthesis produces oxygen, O_2, which migrates from the Earth's surface to high up in the stratosphere, where it is converted by the energy of ultraviolet light to ozone, O_3. Plants and all other organisms living on the planet's surface benefit from this stratospheric ozone because of its ability to shade the planet's surface from ultraviolet light coming from the sun.

15. As discussed on pages 558 and 559, ozone is a fairly reactive molecule. Close to the Earth's surface, it decomposes as it reacts with various materials, such as plants and airborne hydrocarbons. Thus, the ozone from automobiles doesn't last long enough to make it to distant locations, such as the stratospheric skies over the South Pole.

17. The coating of whitewash keeps visible light out of the greenhouse so that the temperature inside the greenhouse does not get too high.

19. The greenhouse effect works because of the atmosphere's ability to trap terrestrial radiation. If the atmosphere were less able to trap terrestrial radiation, the greenhouse effect would be weaker and global temperatures would drop.

Problems

1. You would need to know the total number of molecules in 1 liter of air. You would divide the number of CFC molecules by that total number and then multiply the quotient by 100 to get the percentage of CFC molecules.

3. $(1.250\ \text{g/L})(1\ \text{mole}/28\ \text{g}) = 0.04\ \text{mole}$

Chapter 18

1. Both paper and cooked spaghetti consist of many overlapping and intertwined strands.

3. In a given length of time, industrial hemp produces much more cellulose fiber per acre than do trees. Hemp plants also contain a much lower proportion of lignins, which means that the cellulose fibers can be extracted from the hemp without the use of harsh chemicals. A disadvantage to using hemp for making paper is that the paper industry is well established at using trees. The short-term costs of outfitting new machinery and other infrastructure would therefore be great. Also, there would be political inertia to overcome because the hemp plant is a close relative of the marijuana plant. Industrial hemp, however, contains insignificant amounts of THC, the active ingredient in marijuana. Furthermore, any cross-breeding between industrial hemp and marijuana would result in a plant that contains smaller amounts of THC and hence would not be so desirable to the illicit drug community.

5. As with any other scientific endeavor, chance played an important role in the development of polymers. In all cases, however, there was a scientist with an open and innovative mind ready to recognize and take advantage of a chance observation. Charles Goodyear accidently tipped sulfur into heated natural rubber to invent vulcanized rubber. Christian Schobein inadvertantly wiped up a nitric acid spill with a cotton rag to create nitrocellulose. Jaque Brandenberger thought of cellophane as he observed stains on tablecloths. Also, as was discussed in Chapter 1, Teflon was first observed when Roy Plunkett sawed open a gas-storage tank looking for contents that had "disappeared."

7. Celluloid and cellophane are both derived from cellulose. The difference between the two molecules is that in celluloid every hydroxyl group of celluose has been replaced by a nitrate group. Cellophane has the same chemical composition as cellulose but has been transformed to a film by chemical and mechanical processing.

9. They are made of nitrocellulose, which is the highly combustible material used to make guncotton.

11. Collodion, Parkesine, celluloid, viscose yarn, cellophane, PVC, nylon, teflon.

13. Definitely not! Metal halides are by no means restricted to group 1 metals. In fact, most metals are able to form halides. Iron chloride, $FeCl_3$, and copper chloride, $CuCl_2$, are examples. Figure 18.19 shows only the most common forms of metal compounds. In nature, iron is most commonly found as an oxide, and copper is most commonly found as a sulfide.

15. One process that exploits differences in physical properties takes place in the blast furnace when, because of its greater density, molten iron sinks beneath slag. Another is flotation, a technique that takes advantage of the fact that metal sulfides are relatively nonpolar and therefore attracted to oil. One process that exploits differences in chemical properties is the electrolysis of a metal, such as impure copper. Another is the reduction of a purified metal ore, such as iron ore, using carbon as the reducing agent and the high temperatures found in a blast furnace.

17. The problem is not whether or not we have the metal atoms on this planet—we do! The problem is in the expense of collecting those metal atoms. This expense would be too great if the metal atoms were evenly distributed throughout the planet. We are fortunate, therefore, that there are geological formations where metal ores have been concentrated by natural processes. Bear in mind that it is only the metal atoms that we can extract from the ground that we are able to recycle. If we don't recycle these metal atoms, then down the road we'll have substantial shortages of new metal ores from which to feed our ever-growing appetite for metal-based consumer goods and building materials.

19. Glass is not fragile when it is molten.

21. Ceramics are made by heating clay to high temperatures. Clay is made up of microcapsules of aluminum oxides and silicon oxides surrounded by water. The heating melts the silicon oxides, and the molten material then surrounds all remaining microcapsules. When the clay cools, the silicon oxides solidify, holding the microcapsules together, much like a hardened glue.

23. Any composite is weakest along any direction in which fibers do not run. Plywood is made by gluing together thin layers of wood such that the grain in one layer runs perpendicular to the grain in the layers above and below. This arrangement provides great strength in two directions. Lay a sheet of plywood flat on the ground, however, and there is no grain that runs in the vertical direction—in other words, in the direction of the sheet's thickness. Plywood is therefore relatively weak in this direction, which is why the first step when an old sheet of plywood deteriorates is the "unstacking" of the once-bound thin layers.

Chapter 19

1. One of the reasons a gas turbine is more efficient at generating electricity is that it provides a more direct method of getting the turbine to rotate. In a steam turbine, fuel is burned to heat water to steam, and it is the steam that cases the turbine to rotate. While the water is being heated, some energy is invariably lost as heat that escapes to the surroundings. In a gas turbine, the hot products of combustion are used to turn the turbine.

3. Fossil fuels are made from plants that lived millions of years ago. These plants got their energy from the sun through photosynthesis. Burning fossil fuels is therefore an indirect way of using solar energy.

5. In order to produce carbon dioxide, there must be carbon. The lower the percentage of carbon in a fuel, the less carbon dioxide in the exhaust when that fuel is burned. Coal is almost nothing but carbon, and so the percentage of carbon is extremely high, close to 100 percent. This means burning coal produces much carbon dioxide. The carbon percentage is also high in petroleum-based fuels. Octane, to take just one example, has eight carbons for every 18 hydrogens, meaning the percentage of carbon by mass is about 84 percent. In the molecules that make up natural gas, on the other hand, there is a

lower percentage of carbon. Methane, for example, has one carbon for every four hydrogens, meaning the mass percentage of carbon is a relatively low 75 percent.

7. If the control substance loses neutron-absorbing power with increasing temperature, then as the reactor gets warmer, there is a proportionate increase in the number of neutrons available to initiate further fission reactions. These are the neutrons that the control substance does not absorb because of the higher temperature. This condition can lead to a runaway reaction. Then once the reactor hits a critical temperature, fission reactions escalate to the point of meltdown. Today's reactors have control substances that become *better* neutron absorbers with increasing temperature, a design that gives the units an effective passive safety mechanism.

9. The 1973 OPEC oil embargo was a boon to the nuclear power industry. The embargo was instrumental in alerting people to the foolishness of depending on one source of energy and prompted the building of many nuclear power plants. Interestingly, there have been no new nuclear facilities constructed in the United States since that time.

11. The fuel supply for nuclear fusion—hydrogen isotopes from the ocean—is orders of magnitude greater than all other sources of energy combined. A nuclear fusion reactor will produce no air pollutants and fewer radioactive products than present-day fission reactors.

13. Although dams produce virtually no chemical pollutants, they do radically alter ecosystems, to the detriment of many species, including the humans displaced from their homes by the rising waters that come behind a dam.

15. The moon energy available to us here on the Earth is the energy of the tides, which result from the gravitational pull between the Earth and the moon. Interestingly, the energy from the Earth–moon system that goes into creating the tides results in a slowing down of the Earth's rotation. Back during the time of the dinosaurs, a day was only about 19 hours long. In the far, far future, a day will be on the order of 46 hours long. At that time, the Earth's spin rate will exactly match the rate at which the moon orbits the Earth. The result will be that, to future Earthlings, the moon will always appear in the same location in the sky.

17. If your pool has a nonsolar heating unit, such as a gas burner, a nonsolar pool cover helps keep the pool warm by reducing the amount of evaporation that takes place.

19. Pass the drinking water through the hot zone of a solar collector. If contained within pressurized pipes, the water would become superheated, and pathogens would be quickly destroyed. A less expensive use of solar energy for producing drinking water would be to build a solar distillation apparatus like the one shown in Figure 16.11.

21. Natural gas, A; wind, B; nuclear fusion, A; hydroelectric, B; coal, A.

23. The electrons do not travel to the negatively charged silicon on their own. They are forced to move in this direction by an external energy source. For a photovoltaic cell, this energy source is sunlight, which literally knocks electrons in the proper direction.

25. The electricity generated during the inflow or outflow of the tides may be used to produce hydrogen from the electrolysis of water. This hydrogen could be stored and used to generate electricity through a fuel cell during times when the tide is reversing its direction.

Problems

1. First calculate the cost of running the 100-watt bulb for 1 hour, understanding that 100 watts is the same as 0.1 kilowatt:

$$0.1 \, kW \times 1 \, h = 0.1 \, kWh$$

$$0.1 \, kWh \times \frac{15 \, cents}{1 \, kWh} = 1.5 \, cents$$

Then calclucate the cost of running the 20-watt bulb for 1 hour, understanding that 20 watts is the same as 0.02 kilowatt:

$$0.02 \, kW \times 1 \, h = 0.02 \, kWh$$

$$0.02 \, kWh \times \frac{15 \, cents}{1 \, kWh} = 0.3 \, cents$$

The savings each hour is therefore 1.5 cents − 0.3 cents = 1.2 cents. This may not seem like much, but if 50 million households changed just one bulb from a 100-watt incandescent to a 20-watt fluorescent, the total annual savings on electric bills would be on the order of 1.2 billion dollars!

Glossary

absolute zero The lowest possible temperature any substance can have; the temperature at which the atoms of a substance have no kinetic energy: 0 K = −273.15°C = −459.7°F.

acid A substance that donates hydrogen ions.

acidic solution A solution in which the hydronium ion concentration is higher than the hydroxide ion concentration.

actinide Any seventh-period inner transition metal.

activation energy The minimum energy required in order for a chemical reaction to proceed.

addition polymer A polymer formed by the joining together of monomer units with no atoms lost as the polymer forms.

adhesive force An attractive force between molecules of two different substances.

aerobic bacteria Bacteria able to decompose organic matter only in the presence of oxygen.

aerosol A moisture-coated microscopic airborne particle up to 0.01 millimeter in diameter that is a site for many atmospheric chemical reactions.

agriculture The organized use of resources for the production of food.

alchemy A medieval endeavor concerned with turning other metals to gold.

alcohol An organic molecule that contain a hydroxyl group bonded to a saturated carbon.

aldehyde An organic molecule containing a carbonyl group the carbon of which is bonded either to one carbon atom and one hydrogen atom or to two hydrogen atoms.

alkali metal Any group 1 element.

alkaline-earth metal Any group 2 element.

alloy A mixture of two or more metallic elements.

alpha particle A helium atom nucleus, which consists of two neutrons and two protons and is ejected by certain radioactive elements.

amide An organic molecule containing a carbonyl group the carbon of which is bonded to a nitrogen atom.

amine An organic molecule containing a nitrogen atom bonded to one or more saturated carbon atoms.

amino acid The monomers of polypeptides, each monomer consisting of an amine group and a carboxylic acid group bonded to the same carbon atom.

amphoteric A description of a substance that can behave as either an acid or a base.

anabolism Chemical reactions that synthesize biomolecules in the body.

anaerobic bacteria Bacteria able to decompose organic matter in the absence of oxygen.

analgesic A drug that enhances the ability to tolerate pain without abolishing nerve sensations.

anesthetic A drug that prevents neurons from transmitting sensations to the central nervous system.

anode The electrode where oxidation occurs.

applied research Research dedicated to the development of useful products and processes.

aquifer A soil layer in which groundwater may flow.

aromatic compound Any organic molecule containing a benzene ring.

atmospheric pressure The pressure exerted on any object immersed in the atmosphere.

atomic mass The mass of an element's atoms listed in the periodic table as an average value based on the relative abundance of the element's isotopes.

atomic nucleus The dense, positively charged center of every atom.

atomic number A count of the number of protons in the atomic nucleus.

atomic orbital A region of space in which an electron in an atom has a 90 percent chance of being located.

atomic spectrum The pattern of frequencies of electromagnetic radiation emitted by the atoms of an element, considered to be an element's "fingerprint."

atomic symbol An abbreviation for an element or atom.

Avogadro's number The number of particles—6.02×10^{23}—contained in 1 mole of anything.

base A substance that accepts hydrogen ions.

basic research Research dedicated to the discovery of the fundamental workings of nature.

basic solution A solution in which the hydroxide ion concentration is higher than the hydronium ion concentration.

beta particle An electron ejected from an atomic nucleus during the radioactive decay of certain nuclei.

bioaccumulation The process whereby a toxic chemical that enters a food chain at a low trophic level becomes more concentrated in organism higher up the chain.

biochemical oxygen demand A measure of the amount of oxygen consumed by aerobic bacteria in water.

biomass A general term for plant material.

boiling Evaporation in which bubbles form beneath the liquid surface.

bond energy The amount of energy either absorbed as a chemical bond breaks or released as a bond forms.

buffer solution A solution that resists large changes in pH, made from either a weak acid and one of its salts or a weak base and one of its salts.

capillary action The rising of liquid into a small vertical space due to the interplay of cohesive and adhesive forces.

carbohydrate A biomolecule that contains only carbon, hydrogen, and oxygen atoms and is produced by plants through photosynthesis.

carbon-14 dating The process of estimating the age of once-living material by measuring the amount of a radioactive isotope of carbon present in the material.

carbonyl group A carbon atom double-bonded to an oxygen atom, found in ketones, aldehydes, amides, carboxylic acids, and esters.

carboxylic acid An organic molecule containing a carbonyl group the carbon of which is bonded to a hydroxyl group.

catabolism Chemical reactions that break down biomolecules in the body.

catalyst Any substance that increases the rate of a chemical reaction without itself being consumed by the reaction.

cathode ray tube A device that emits a beam of electrons.

cathode The electrode where reduction occurs.

central nervous system The network of neurons in the brain and spinal cord.

chain reaction A self-sustaining reaction in which the products of one fission event stimulate further events.

chemical change During this kind of change, atoms in a substance are rearranged to give a new substance having a new chemical identity.

chemical equation A representation of a chemical reaction.

chemical formula A notation used to indicate the composition of a compound, consisting of the atomic symbols for the different elements of the compound and numerical subscripts indicating the ratio in which the atoms combine.

chemical property A type of property that characterizes the ability of a substance to change its chemical identity.

chemical reaction Synonymous with chemical change.

chemistry The study of matter and the transformations it can undergo.

chemotherapy The use of drugs to destroy pathogens without destroying the animal host.

chromosome An elongated bundle of DNA and protein that appear in a cell's nucleus just prior to cellular division.

coal A solid consisting of a tightly bound three-dimensional network of hydrocarbon chains and rings.

coefficient A number used in a chemical equation to indicate either the number of atoms/molecules or the number of moles of a reactant or product.

cohesive force An attractive force between two identical molecules.

combinatorial chemistry The production of a large number of compounds in order to increase the chances of finding a new drug having medicinal value.

combustion An exothermic oxidation–reduction reaction between a nonmetallic material and molecular oxygen.

composite Any thermoset medium strengthened by the incorporation of fibers.

compost Fertilizer formed by the decay of organic matter.

compound A material in which atoms of different elements are bonded to one another.

concentration A quantitative measure of the amount of solute in a solution.

conceptual model A representation of an object on a different scale.

condensation A transformation from a gas to a liquid.

condensation polymer A polymer formed by the joining together of monomer units accompanied by the loss of a small molecule, such as water.

conformation One of the possible spatial orientations of a molecule.

consumer An organism that takes in the matter and energy of other organisms.

control test A test performed by scientists to increase the conclusiveness of an experimental test.

corrosion The deterioration of a metal, typically caused by atmospheric oxygen.

covalent bond A chemical bond in which atoms are held together by their mutual attraction for two or more electrons they share.

covalent compound An element or chemical compound in which atoms are held together by covalent bonds.

critical mass The minimum mass of fissionable material needed in a reactor or nuclear bomb that will sustain a chain reaction.

decomposer An organism in the soil that transforms once-living matter to nutrients.

density The ratio of an object's mass to its volume.

deoxyribonucleic acid A nucleic acid containing a deoxygenated ribose sugar, having a double helical structure, and carrying the genetic code in the nucleotide sequence.

dipole A separation of charge that occurs in a chemical bond because of differences in the electronegativities of the bonded atoms.

dissolving The process of mixing a solute in a solvent.

effective nuclear charge The amount of energy required to remove an electron from an atom.

electrochemistry The branch of chemistry concerned with the relationship between electrical energy and chemical change.

electrode Any material that conducts electrons into or out of a medium in which electrochemical reactions are occurring.

electrolysis The use of electrical energy to produce chemical change.

electromagnetic spectrum The complete range of waves, from radio waves to gamma rays.

electron configuration The arrangement of electrons in the orbitals of an atom.

electron An extremely small, negatively charged subatomic particle found outside the atomic nucleus.

electron-dot structure A shorthand notation of the shell model of the atom in which valence electrons are shown around an atomic symbol.

electronegativity The ability of an atom to attract a bonding pair of electrons to itself when bonded to another atom.

element A fundamental material consisting of only one type of atom.

elemental formula A notation that uses the atomic symbol and (sometimes) a numerical subscript to denote how atoms are bonded in an element.

endothermic A term that describes a chemical reaction in which there is a net absorption of energy.

energy The capacity to do work.

energy-level diagram Drawing used to arrange atomic orbitals in order of energy levels.

enzyme A protein that catalyzes biochemical reactions.

ester An organic molecule containing a carbonyl group the carbon of which is bonded to one carbon atom and one oxygen atom bonded to another carbon atom.

ether An organic molecule containing an oxygen atom bonded to two carbons atoms.

eutrophication The process whereby inorganic wastes in water fertilize algae and plants growing in the water and the resulting overgrowth reduces the dissolved oxygen concentration of the water.

evaporation A transformation from a liquid to a gas.

exothermic A term that describes a chemical reaction in which there is a net release of energy.

fat A biomolecule that packs a lot of energy per gram and consists of a glycerol unit attached to three fatty acid molecules.

formula mass The sum of the atomic masses of the elements in a chemical compound.

freezing A transformation from a liquid to a solid.

functional group A specific combination of atoms that behave as a unit in an organic molecule.

gamma ray High-energy radiation emitted by the nuclei of radioactive atoms.

gas Matter that has neither a definite volume nor a definite shape, always filling any space available to it.

gene cloning The technique of incorporating a gene from one organism into the DNA of another organism.

gene A nucleotide sequence in the DNA strand in a chromosome that leads a cell to manufacture a particular polypeptide.

glycogen A glucose polymer stored in animal tissue and also known as animal starch.

greenhouse effect The process by which visible light from the sun is absorbed by the Earth, which then emits infrared energy that cannot escape and so warms the atmosphere.

group A vertical column in the periodic table, also known as a family of elements.

half reaction One portion of an oxidation–reduction reaction, represented by an equation showing electrons as either reactants or products.

half-life The time required for half the atoms in a sample of a radioactive isotope to decay.

halogen Any "salt-forming" element.

heat of condensation The energy released by a substance as it transforms from gas to liquid phase.

heat of freezing The heat energy released by a substance as it transforms from liquid to solid phase.

heat of melting The heat energy absorbed by a substance as it transforms from solid to liquid phase.

heat of vaporization The heat energy absorbed by a substance as it transforms from liquid to gas.

heat The energy that flows from one object to another because of a temperature difference between the two.

heteroatom Any atom other than carbon or hydrogen in an organic molecule.

heterogeneous mixture A mixture in which the various components can be seen as individual substances.

homogeneous mixture A mixture in which the components are so finely mixed that the composition is the same throughout.

humus The organic matter of topsoil.

hydrocarbon A chemical compound containing only carbon and hydrogen atoms.

hydrogen bond A strong dipole–dipole attraction between a slightly positive hydrogen atom on one molecule and a pair of nonbonding electrons on another molecule.

hydrologic cycle The natural circulation of water throughout our planet.

hydronium ion A water molecule after accepting a hydrogen ion.

hydroxide ion A water molecule after losing a hydrogen ion.

impure The state of a material that is a mixture of more than one element or compound.

induced dipole A dipole temporarily created in an otherwise nonpolar molecule, induced by a neighboring charge.

industrial smog Visible airborne pollution, containing large amounts of particulates and sulfur dioxide and produced largely from the combustion of coal and oil.

inner transition metal Any element in the two subgroups of the transition metals.

inner-shell shielding The nuclear charge experienced by outer-shell electrons, diminished by the shielding effect of inner-shell electrons.

insoluble Not capable of dissolving to any appreciable extent in a given solution.

integrated crop management A whole-farm strategy that involves managing crops in ways that suit local soil, climatic, and economic conditions.

integrated pest management A pest-control strategy that emphasizes prevention, planning, and the use of a variety of pest-control resources.

involuntary neuron A neuron not under conscious control.

ion An electrically charged particle created when an atom either loses or gains one or more electrons.

ionic bond A chemical bond in which an attractive electric force holds ions of opposite charge together.

ionic compound Any chemical compound containing ions.

ionization energy The amount of energy required to remove an electron from an atom.

isotope Atoms of the same element whose nuclei contain the same number of protons but different numbers of neutrons.

ketone An organic molecule containing a carbonyl group the carbon of which is bonded to two carbon atoms.

kilowatt-hour The amount of energy consumed in 1 hour at a rate of 1 kilowatt.

kinetic energy Energy due to motion.

lanthanide Any sixth-period inner transition metal.

law of definite proportions A law stating that elements combine in definite mass ratios to form compounds.

law of mass conservation A law stating that matter is neither created nor destroyed in a chemical reaction.

leachate A solution formed by water that has percolated through a solid-waste disposal site and picked up water-soluble substances.

lipid A broad class of biomolecules that are not soluble in water.

liquid Matter that has a definite volume but no definite shape, assuming the shape of its container.

lock-and-key model A model that explains how drugs interact with receptor sites.

mass number The number of nucleons (protons and neutrons) in the atomic nucleus. Used primarily to identify isotopes.

mass The quantitative measure of how much matter an object contains.

matter Anything that occupies space.

melting A transformation from a solid to a liquid.

meniscus The curving of the surface of a liquid at the interface between the liquid surface and its container.

metabolism The general term describing all chemical reactions in the body.

metal An element that is shiny, opaque, and able to conduct electricity and heat.

metallic bond A chemical bond in which the metal ions in a piece of solid metal are held together by their attraction to a "fluid" of electrons in the metal.

metalloid An element that exhibits some properties of metals and some properties of nonmetals.

microirrigation A method of delivering water directly to plant roots.

mineral Inorganic chemicals that play a wide variety of roles in the body.

mixed fertilizer A fertilizer that contains more than one nutrient.

mixture A combination of two or more substances in which each substance retains its properties.

molar mass The mass of 1 mole of a substance.

molarity A unit of concentration equal to the number of moles of a solute per liter of solution.

mole 6.02×10^{23} of anything.

molecule A group of atoms held tightly together by covalent bonds.

monomer The small molecular unit from which a polymer is formed.

motor neuron A peripheral neuron that transmits electrical signals from the central nervous system to muscles.

natural gas A mixture of methane plus small amounts of ethane and propane.

neuron A specialized cell capable of receiving and sending electrical impulses.

neurotransmitter re-uptake A mechanism whereby a presynaptic neuron absorbs neurotransmitters from the synaptic cleft for reuse.

neurotransmitter An organic compound capable of activating receptor sites on proteins embedded in the membrane of a neuron.

neutral solution A solution in which the hydronium ion concentration is equal to the hydroxide ion concentration.

neutralization A reaction in which an acid and base combine to form a salt.

neutron An electrically neutral subatomic particle of the atomic nucleus.

nitrogen fixation A chemical reaction that converts atmospheric nitrogen to some form of nitrogen usable by plants.

noble gas Any unreactive element.

nonbonding pair Two paired valence electrons that don't participate in a chemical bond and yet influence the shape of the molecule.

nonmetal An element located toward the upper right of the periodic table and is neither a metal nor a metalloid.

nonpoint source A pollution source in which the pollutants originate at different locations.

nonpolar bond A chemical bond having no dipole.

nuclear fission The splitting of a heavy nucleus into two lighter nuclei, accompanied by the release of much energy.

nuclear fusion The joining together of light nuclei to form a heavier nucleus, accompanied by the release of much energy.

nucleic acid A long polymeric chain of nucleotide monomers.

nucleon Any subatomic particle found in the atomic nucleus. Another name for either proton or neutron.

nucleotide A nucleic acid monomer consisting of three parts: a nitrogenous base, a ribose sugar, and an ionic phosphate group.

ore A geologic deposit containing relatively high concentrations of one or more metal-containing compounds.

organic chemistry The study of carbon-containing compounds.

organic farming Farming without the use of pesticides or synthetic fertilizers.

osmosis The net flow of water across a semipermeable membrane from a region where the water concentration is higher to a region where the water concentration is lower.

oxidation–reduction reaction A reaction involving the transfer of electrons from one reactant to another.

oxidation The process whereby a reactant loses one or more electrons.

particulate A large airborne particle.

period A horizontal row in the periodic table.

periodic table A chart in which all known elements are organized by physical and chemical properties.

periodic trend The gradual change of any property in the elements across a period.

peripheral nervous system The network of neurons that carry signals to and from the central nervous system.

petroleum A liquid mixture of loosely held hydrocarbon molecules containing not more than 30 carbon atoms each.

pH A measure of the acidity of a solution, equal to the negative of the base-10 logarithm of the hydronium ion concentration.

phenol An organic molecule in which a hydroxyl group is bonded to a benzene ring.

pheromone An organic molecule secreted by insects to communicate with one another.

photochemical smog Airborne pollution consisting of pollutants that participate in chemical reactions induced by sunlight.

photoelectric effect The ability of light to knock electrons out of atoms.

photon Another term for a single quantum of light, a name chosen to emphasize the particulate nature of light.

physical change A change in which a substance changes its physical properties without changing its chemical identity.

physical dependence A dependence characterized by the need to continue taking a drug to avoid withdrawal symptoms.

physical model A representation of a system that helps us predict how the system behaves.

physical property Any physical attribute of a substance, such as color, density, or hardness.

point source A specific, well-defined location where pollutants enter a body of water.

polar bond A chemical bond having a dipole.

polymer A long organic molecule made of many repeating units.

potential energy Stored energy.

power The rate at which energy is expended.

precipitate A solute that has come out of solution.

principal quantum number n An integer that specifies the quantized energy level of an atomic orbital.

probability cloud The pattern of electron positions plotted over time to show the likelihood of an electron being at a given position at a given time.

producer An organism at the bottom of a trophic structure.

product A new material formed in a chemical reaction, appearing after the arrow in a chemical equation.

protein A polymer of amino acids, also known as a polypeptide.

proton A positively charged subatomic particle of the atomic nucleus.

psychoactive Said of a drug that affects the mind or behavior.

psychological dependence A deep-rooted craving for a drug.

pure The state of a material that consists of a single element or compound.

quantum hypothesis The idea that light energy is contained in discrete packets called quanta.

quantum A small, discrete packet of light energy.

rad A unit for measuring radiation dosage, equal to 0.01 joule of radiant energy absorbed per kilogram of tissue.

radioactivity The tendency of some elements, such as uranium, to emit radiation as a result of changes in the atomic nucleus.

reactant A starting material in a chemical reaction, appearing before the arrow in a chemical equation.

reaction rate A measure of how quickly the concentration of products in a chemical reaction increases or the concentration of reactants decreases.

recombinant DNA A hybrid DNA composed of DNA strands from different organisms.

reduction The process whereby a reactant gains one or more electrons.

rem A unit for measuring radiation dosage, obtained by multiplying the number of rads by a factor that allows for the different health effects of different types of radiation.

replication The process by which DNA strands are duplicated.

reverse osmosis A technique for purifying water by forcing it through a semipermeable membrane.

ribonucleic acid A nucleic acid containing a fully oxygenated ribose sugar.

saccharide Another term for carbohydrate. The prefixes *mono-*, *di-*, and *poly-* are used before this term to indicate the length of the carbohydrate.

salinization The process whereby irrigated land becomes more salty.

salt An ionic compound formed from the reaction between an acid and a base.

saturated hydrocarbon A hydrocarbon containing no multiple covalent bonds, with each carbon atom bonded to four other atoms.

saturated solution A solution containing the maximum amount of solute that will dissolve.

scientific hypothesis A testable assumption often used to explain an observed phenomenon.

scientific law Any scientific hypothesis that has been tested over and over again and has not been contradicted. Also known as a scientific principle.

semipermeable membrane A membrane that allows water molecules to pass through its submicroscopic pores but not solute molecules.

sensory neuron A peripheral neuron that transmits electrical signals from the senses to the central nervous system.

soil horizon A layer of soil.

solid Matter that has a definite volume and a definite shape.

solubility The ability of a solute to dissolve in a given solvent.

soluble Capable of dissolving to an appreciable extent in a given solvent.

solute Any component in a solution that is not the solvent.

solution A homogeneous mixture in which all components are in the same phase.

solvent The component in a solution present in the largest amount.

specific heat capacity The quantity of heat required to change the temperature of 1 gram of a substance by 1 Celsius degree.

spectroscope A device that uses a prism or diffraction grating to separate light into its color components.

steel Iron strengthened by small percentages of carbon.

straight fertilizer A fertilizer that contains only one nutrient.

stratosphere The atmospheric layer above the troposphere containing the ozone layer.

strong nuclear force The force of interaction between all nucleons, effective only at very, very, very close distances.

structural isomers Molecules that have the same molecular formula but different chemical structures.

sublimation The process of a material transforming from a solid to a gas.

submicroscopic The realm of atoms and molecules, where objects are smaller than can be detected by optical microscopes.

substituent An atom or nonbonding pair of electrons surrounding a central atom.

superconductor Any material having zero electrical resistance.

surface tension The elastic tendency found at the surface of a liquid.

suspension A homogeneous mixture in which the various components are in different phases.

synaptic cleft A narrow gap across which neurotransmitters pass either from one neuron to the next or from a neuron to a muscle or gland.

synergistic effect One drug enhancing the effect of another.

temperature How warm or cold an object is relative to some standard. Also, a measure of the average kinetic energy per molecule of a substance, measured in degrees Celsius, degrees Fahrenheit, or kelvins.

theory A comprehensive idea that can be used to explain a broad range of phenomena.

thermometer An instrument used to measure temperature.

thermonuclear fusion Nuclear fusion produced by high temperature.

transcription The process whereby the genetic information of DNA is used to specify the nucleotide sequence of a complementary single strand of messenger RNA.

transgenic organism An organism that contains one or more genes from another species.

transition metal Any element of groups 3 through 12.

translation The process of bringing amino acids together according to the codon sequence on mRNA.

transmutation The conversion of an atomic nucleus of one element to an atomic nucleus of another element through a loss or gain of protons.

trophic structure The pattern of feeding relationships in a community of organisms.

troposphere The atmospheric layer closest to the Earth's surface, containing 90 percent of the atmosphere's mass and essentially all water vapor and clouds.

unsaturated hydrocarbon A hydrocarbon containing at least one multiple covalent bond.

unsaturated solution A solution that will dissolve additional solute if it is added.

valence electron An electron that is located in the outermost occupied shell in an atom and can participate in chemical bonding.

valence shell The outermost occupied shell of an atom.

valence-shell electron-pair repulsion A model that explains molecular geometries in terms of electron pairs striving to be as far apart from one another as possible.

vitamin Organic chemicals that assist in various biochemical reactions in the body and can be obtained only from food.

volume The quantity of space an object occupies.

voluntary neuron A neuron the body can control consciously.

water table The upper boundary of a soil's zone of saturation, which is the area where every space between soil particles is filled with water.

watt A unit for measuring power, equal to 1 joule of energy expended per second.

wave frequency A measure of how rapidly a wave oscillates. The higher this value, the greater the amount of energy in the wave.

wavelength The distance between two crests of a wave.

weight The gravitational force of attraction between two bodies (where one body is usually the Earth).

Photo Credits

Chapter 1
Chapter Opener: John Beatty/Stone; 1.1(a) Lennard Lessin/ Peter Arnold, Inc., (b) Ray Nelson/Phototake, (c) David Parker/Photo Researchers; (d) Ray Nelson/Phototake; (e) Malin Space Science Systems; 1.2 PhotoDisc; 1.4 Todd Gipstein/Corbis; 1.6 (left) University of Alabama, (right) Jim McClintock; 1.7 (a, b) Jim Mastro; 1.11 "Re-enactment of the Invention of DuPont Teflon® fluoropolymer in April, 1938." Roy Plunkett is shown at right. Photo courtesy of DuPont; 1.12 Lisa Jeffers-Fabro; 1.13 John Suchocki; 1.14 National Bureau of Standards/SKA Photofiles; 1.16 (left, middle, right) Rachel Epstein/SKA; 1.18 John Suchocki; 1.19 Eric Schrempp/ Photo Researchers; 1.20 Rachel Epstein/SKA; 1.26 (left, middle, right) Sharon Hopwood; 1.30 Jim Goodwin/Photo Researchers; p. 29 Tracy Suchocki. **Concept Check:** p. 15 NASA. **Hands-On Chemistry**: p. 14: Rachel Epstein/SKA; p. 17 (top, bottom) : Rachel Epstein/SKA; p. 25 Tom Pantages.

Chapter 2
Chapter Opener: (main photo) Astrid & Hanns-Friedler Michler/ Photo Resarchers; (margin photos) top: Charles D. Winters/Photo Researchers; second from top: Phillip Hayson/Photo Researchers; third & fourth from top: Tom Pantages; 2.1 (left) Fundamental Photographs, (center) Definitive Stock; 2.2 (a) PhotoDisc; 2.3 (left, middle, right) Tom Pantages; 2.5 John Suchocki; 2.6 Stephen R. Swinburne/Stock, Boston; 2.7 Sharon Hopwood; 2.8 Sharon Hopwood; 2.11 (left, middle) Rachel Epstein/SKA, (right) Tony Freeman/PhotoEdit; 2.13 (left, middle, right) Tom Pantages; 2.14 Stone; 2.15 John Suchocki; 2.16 Runk, Scoenberger/Grant Heilman; 2.18 (a) Tom Pantages, (b) Dave Bartruff/Stock, Boston; 2.19 Georg Gerster/Photo Researchers; 2.21 (a) (left) Kevin Adams/ Nature Photography, (middle) Stone, (right) PhotoDisc, (b) (left) Science Source/Photo Researchers, (middle, right) PhotoDisc; 2.22 Brian Yarvin/Photo Researchers; 2.24 (top: left & second from left) PhotoDisc, (top: third from left) Peter Arnold, Inc., (right) PhotoDisc, (bottom: left) Fundamental Photographs, (bottom: second from left) Photo Researchers, (bottom: third from left) PhotoDisc, (bottom: right) Fundamental Photographs; 2.25 Mark Martin/Photo Researchers; 2.29 Rachel Epstein/SKA. **Concept Check**: p. 44 John Suchocki. **Hands-On Chemistry:** pp.41, 48, 53 Tom Pantages.

Chapter 3
Chapter Opener: FPG, (overlay) John Suchocki; p. 70 The Granger Collection; p. 72 Science Photo Library/Photo Researchers; p. 76 (top) Culver Pictures, (bottom) Science Photo Library/Photo Researchers; pp. 77, 78, 79 Science Photo Library/Photo Researchers; 3.11 The Granger Collection; 3.12 (a) Rachel Epstein/SKA, (b) Richard Megna/Fundamental Photographs; p. 83 Culver Pictures;

p. 84 Courtesy of the Archives, California Institute of Technology; p. 86 Science Photo Library/Photo Researchers; 3.19 John Suchocki. **Hands-On Chemistry:** pp. 72, 73, 84 Tom Pantages.

Chapter 4
Chapter Opener: Comstock; 4.1 Eric Schrempp/Photo Researchers; 4.3 (a, b) Science Photo Library/Photo Researchers; 4.6 International Atomic Energy Agency; 4.8 Larry Mulvehill/Photo Researchers; 4.9 Richard Megna/Fundamental Photographs; 4.11 Chris Priest/ Photo Researchers; 4.18 Rich Frishman/Stone; 4.20 NASA/Photo Researchers; 4.27 Comstock; 4.32 Plasma Physics Laboratory, Princeton University; 4.33 Lawrence Livermore National Laboratory **Hands-On Chemistry:** pp. 105, 113 Rachel Epstein/SKA.

Chapter 5
Chapter Opener: John Suchocki; 5.3 (a) Volker Steger/Peter Arnold, Inc., (b) IBM/Peter Arnold, Inc., (c) Alamaden Research Center, IBM Research Division; 5.4 (a) Tom Pantages, (b) Rachel Epstein/SKA; 5.6 (a) Phototake, (b) John Suchocki; 5.7 (a, b) John Suchocki; 5.8 (flame tests) Tom Pantages, (spectra) Alan J. Jircitano; 5.9 Science Photo Library/Photo Researchers; 5.15 (a) John Suchocki, (b) David Scharf/Peter Arnold, Inc.; 5.16 (a, b, c) John Suchocki; 5.20 John Suchocki; 5.27 Material used by permission of DuPont Central Research and Development; p. 166 (left column) John Suchocki, (right column: top, bottom) Ed Elliott, (right column: middle) Wide World. **Hands-On Chemistry:** pp. 139, 147 Tom Pantages; p. 151 Rachel Epstein/SKA.

Chapter 6
Chapter Opener: Charles M. Falco/Photo Researchers; 6.3 Science Photo Library/Photo Researchers; 6.8 (a) Rachel Epstein/SKA, (b) F. Hache/Photo Researchers; 6.9 John Suchocki; 6.10 (top) M. Claye/Photo Researchers, (bottom) E. R. Degginger/Photo Researchers; 6.11 Dee Breger/Photo Researchers; 6.16 (a, b) Rachel Epstein/SKA; 6.17 Vaughan Fleming/Photo Researchers; 6.25 David Taylor/Photo Researchers; 6.29 Natalie Fobes/Stone, p. 199 (molecular models) Tom Pantages. **Hands-On Chemistry:** pp. 179, 188 Tom Pantages.

Chapter 7
Chapter Opener: Dr. & T.S. Schrichte/Photo Resource Hawaii; 7.6 Rachel Epstein/SKA; 7.9 (a, b) Tom Pantages; 7.10 Rachel Epstein/SKA; 7.13 (a) Fred Ward/Black Star; (b) Rachel Epstein/ SKA, (c) Image Works; 7.19 Leonard Lessin/Peter Arnold, Inc.; 7.20 John Suchocki; 7.24 Gordon Baer; 7.26 Sheila Terry/Photo Researchers. **Hands-On Chemistry:** pp. 208, 214, 219 (margin: middle, bottom) Tom Pantages; (margin: top) Rachel Epstein/SKA.

Chapter 8
Chapter Opener: Kirk Weddle; 8.1 John Suchocki; 8.3 (a, b) Tom Pantages; 8.4 Nuridsany et Perennou/Photo Researchers; 8.5 (and inset) Wm. R. Sallaz/Duomo; 8.13 (and inset) Rachel Epstein/SKA; 8.15 (a) NASA, (b) Diane Hirsch/Fundamental Photographs; 8.17 (a, b) Tom Panages; 8.18 Sinclair Stammers/Photo Researchers; 8.23 Leonard Lessin/Peter Arnold, Inc.; 8.24 (a) J & P Wegner/Animals, Animals, (b) Pat Crowe/Animals, Animals; 8.26 Charles Cook; 8.27 NASA/Photo Researchers; 8.29 Charles D. Winters/Photo Researchers; 8.31 Galen Rowell/Mountain Light; 8.33 Richard Megna/Fundamental Photographs; 8.39 Okonewski/The Image Works; 8.40 John Suchocki; 8.41 Michael Dick/Animals, Animals. **Hands-On Chemistry:** pp. 234, 255 Tom Pantages.

Chapter 9
Chapter Opener: Michael Fewings; 9.4 (left, middle, right) Tom Pantages 9.13 Wide World; 9.15 Rachel Epstein/SKA; 9.16 Photo Researchers; 9.17 (top) E. R. Degginger/Photo Researchers, (bottom) Jon Lemker/Earth Scenes; 9.19 NASA/SKA Photofiles; 9.21 Rachel Epstein/SKA; **Hands-On Chemistry:** p.289 Rachel Epstein/SKA.

Chapter 10
Chapter Opener: David Harris; 10.1 (a) M.P. Gadomski/Photo Researchers, (b, c, d) Rachel Epstein/SKA; 10.2 (a) S. Grant/PhotoEdit, (b, c, d) Rachel Epstein/SKA; 10.5 Rachel Epstein/SKA; 10.9 (a, b, c) Tom Pantages; 10.13 (a, b) Tom Pantages; 10.14 (a) (left & right) M. Bleier/Peter Arnold, Inc., (b) Will McIntyre/Photo Researchers; 10.16 Tom Pantages; 10.23 Rachel Epstein/SKA.

Chapter 11
Chapter Opener: John-Peter Lahall/Photo Researchers; 11.1 Tom Pantages; 11.3 John Suchocki; 11.4 (left) John Suchocki; 11.9 Lennard Lesson/Peter Arnold, Inc.; 11.12 Xcellis Fuel Cell Engines, Inc.; 11.13 C. Liu, et al., "Single-Walled Carbon Nanotubes at Room Temperature," *Science*, Nov. 5, 1999: 1127-1129; 11.14 John Suchocki; 11.16 Frank Siteman/Stock, Boston; 11.18 Rachel Epstein/SKA; 11.19 Chevron Shipping Co. LLC. **Hands-On Chemistry:** pp. 328, 339 Tom Pantages.

Chapter 12
Chapter Opener: John Suchocki; 12.5 Rachel Epstein/SKA; 12.10 Rachel Epstein/SKA; 12.12 (a) Bob Gibbons/Photo Researchers, (b) Peter Arnold, Inc.; 12.30 John Suchocki; 12.31 Rachel Epstein/SKA; 12.32 Rachel Epstein/SKA; 12.36 Cambridge Display Technologies. **Hands-On Chemistry:** p. 355 Tom Pantages; p. 378 Rachel Epstein/SKA.

Chapter 13
Chapter Opener: John Suchocki; 13.1 (a) John Suchocki, (b) J.C. Munoz/Peter Arnold, Inc.; 13.2 Mark Chappel/Animals, Animals; 13.3 Rachel Epstein/SKA; 13.4 Lennard Lesson/Peter Arnold, Inc.; 13.5 (a) Rachel Epstein/SKA, (b) Fred Whitehead/ Animals, Animals;13.6 (left) Wally Eberhart/Visuals Unlimited, (right) Manfred Kage/Peter Arnold, Inc.; 13.7 (a) David Leah/Allsport, (b) Cabisco/Visuals Unlimited; 13.9 (left) Fritz Prenzil/Animals, Animals, (right) Science Photo Library/Photo Researers; 13.10 (left) Scott Camazine/Photo Researchers, (right) M. Abbey /Visuals Unlimited; 13.12 Johnny Johnson/Animals, Animals; 13.13 (a, b) Rachel Epstein/SKA ; 13.18 (clockwise from left) David Scharf/Peter Arnold,

Inc., Gray Mortimore/Allsport, Science Photo Library/Photo Researchers, Blair Seitz/Photo Resarchers, Rachel Epstein/SKA, Science Photo Library/Photo Researchers, John Suchocki; 13.19 Stan Fleger/Visuals Unlimited; 13.28 (left) Cabisco/Visuals Unlimited, (right) Science Photo Library/Photo Researchers; 13.29 A. Lesk/Photo Researchers; 13.32 (a) A. Barrington Brown/Photo Researchers, (b) Corbis, (c) Science Photo Library/Photo Researchers; 13.37 Simon Frazer/Photo Researchers;13.44 Lennard Lesson/Peter Arnold, Inc; 13.46 (a, inset, b) John Suchocki. **Hands-On Chemistry:** pp. 391, 428 Tom Panages.

Chapter 14
Chapter Opener: Dr. J.Burgess/Photo Researchers; 14.3 Kurt Hostettmann; 14.4 (left) David Nunuk/Photo Researchers, (right) Tom & Pat Leeson/Photo Researchers; 14.5 (b) Upjohn; 14.8 Sim/Visuals Unlimited; 14.12 (a) NIBSC/Photo Researchers; 14.14 (left, middle, right) Michael Abbey/Photo Researchers; 14.16 ScottCamazine/Photo Researchers;131) 14.28 Alan D. Carey/Photo Researchers; 14.30 (clockwise from left) Inga Spence/Visuals Unlimited, Adam Jones/Photo Researchers; Tim Hazael/Stone, Matt Meadows/Peter Arnold, Inc., Cristina Pedrazzini/Photo Researchers; 14.33 E. R. Degginger/Earth Scenes; 14.34 Science Photo Library/Photo Researchers; 14.35 Labat/Jerrican/Photo Researchers. **Hands-On Chemistry:** p. 455 Tom Pantages.

Chapter 15
Chapter Opener: Monsanto Company; 15.2 Will Trayer/Visuals Unlimited; 15.3 Norm Thomas/Photo Researchers; 15.5 (a, c) Nigel Cattlin/Photo Researchers, (b) SKA Photofiles; 15.7 K. W. Fink/Photo Researchers; 15.12 Rachel Epstein/SKA; 15.14 (clockwise from left) Norm Thomas/Photo Researchers, G. S. Grant/Photo Researchers, Nigel Cattlin/Photo Researchers, G. Ochocki/ Photo Researchers, Robert Calentine/Visuals Unlimited; 15.16 Wide World; 15.19 Nigel Cattlin/Photo Researchers; 15.24 T. McCabe/Visuals Unlimited; 15.25 Wide World; 15.26 USGS; 15.27 University of New Mexico; 15.28 (left) Grant Heilman; (right) Cavagnaro/Visuals Unlimited; 15.29 Arthur Hill/Visuals Unlimited; 15.30 (left, right) Rachel Epstein/SKA; 15.31 Joe Munroe/Photo Researchers; 15.32 A. C. Smith III/Grant Heilman; 15.33 Marjorie A. Hoy; 15.34 (left) T. H. Martin/Photo Researchers, (right) W. J. Weber/Visuals Unlimited; 15.36 C.S. Prakashi; p. 516 Wide World; **Hands-On Chemistry:** p. 496 Rachel Epstein/SKA; p. 504 Tom Pantages.

Chapter 16
Chapter Opener: John Serrao/Visuals Unlimited; 16.3 Bachmann/Photo Researchers; 16.7 NEPCCO; 16.8 SunRay Tecnologies, Inc.; 16.10 Saline Water Conversion Corporation, Saudi Arabia; 6.11 SolAgua; 16.14 Ray Pfortner/Peter Arnold, Inc.; 16.15 (a) Will McIntyre/Photo Researchers, (b) Rachel Epstein/SKA; 16.16 Rachel Epstein/SKA; 16.20 Doug Sokell/Visuals Unlimited; 16.21 Courtesy of the City and County of Honolulu; 16.24 City of St. Helena, California; 16.25 EcoGam; **Concept Check:** p. 538 (left) W. A. Banaszewski/Visuals Unlimited, (right) Jim Zipp/Photo Researchers. **Hands-On Chemistry:** p. 526 Rachel Epstein/SKA; p. 534 Tom Pantages.

Chapter 17
Chapter Opener:NASA/Photo Researchers; 17.3 NASA; 17.5 NOAA; 17.6 (top, bottom) PPC Industries; 17.9 Rachel Epstein/SKA 17.10 Astrid & Hans-Frieder Michler/Photo Researchers;

17.11 Englehard Corporation; 17.12 Wide World; 17.16 JPL; 17.17 NASA; 17.22 (a) Michael Sewell/Peter Arnold, Inc., (b) U. S. Army Cold Regions Lab 17.22b trapped air bubbles A.J. Gow/ U.S.Army Cold Regions Lab; 17.24 (left) Tony Buxton/Photo Researchers, (right) B & C Alexander/Photo Researchers. **Hands-On Chemistry:** p. 553 Tom Pantages.

Chapter 18

Chapter Opener: (main photo) Phillip Hayson/Photo Researchers, (margin, top) Argonne National Laboratories, (margin, bottom) Volker Steger/Photo Researchers; 18.1 Leonard Lessin/Peter Arnold, Inc; 18.2 Tom Hollyman/Photo Researchers; 18.3 Rachel Epstein/SKA; 18.4 Peter Arnold, Inc.; 18.5 Paolo Koch/Photo Researchers; 18.8 (a) John Suchocki, (b) Tom Pantages; 18.9 Bettmann/Corbis; 18.10 Greenwood Communications AB; 18.11 Leonard Lessin/PAeter Arnold, Inc.; 18.12 AtoFina Chemicals, Inc.; 18.13 Post Street Archives; 18.15 Jeff Daly/Stock, Boston; 18.16 Francois Gohier/Photo Researchers;18.21 Phelps Dodge Corporation; 18.23 Dawson Jones/Stock, Boston; 18.25 Phelps Dodge Corporation; 18.26 Ron Reid/Photo Researchers; 18.27 Alcoa Aluminum; 18.28 (top) Myron Taplin/Stone, (middle) Courtesy of the Corning Incorporated Department of Archives and Records Management, Corning, NY; (bottom) Brooks/Brown/Photo Researchers; 18.29 John Elk/Stone; 18.30 Greg Pease/Stone; 18.31 Rachel Epstein/SKA; 18.32 Chuck O'Rear/Corbis; 18.33 Chuck O'Rear/Corbis; 18.34 (left) John Suchocki, (second from left) Rachel Epstein/SKA, (third from left) D.Brookstein/Albany International Research Co., (right) Jeffry Myers/FPG; 18.35 NASA; 18.36 NASA. **Hands-On Chemistry:** p. 602 Rachel Epstein/SKA.

Chapter 19

Chapter Opener: Phototake; 19.3 (left) SKA Photofiles, (middle) Stephen Frish/Stock, Boston, (right) Tom Pantages; 19.4 (a) Robert Sassen, Texas A & M University, (b) GEOMAR; 19.5 Lawrence Thornton/Archive; 19.6 Tom Pantages; 19.8 Jim Caldwell/FPG; 19.9 Nikolay Zurek/FPG; 19.10 John Suchocki; 19.13 Photo Researchers; 19.14 ©AFP/Corbis; 19.16 National Institute for Fusion Science; 19.18 Christopher Liu/China Stock; 19.20 National Energy Lab, Hawaii; 19.22 Ken Ross/FPG; 19.23 Philip Jon Bailey/Stock, Boston; 19.24 Future Energy Resources Corp., Norcross, GA; 19.25 Bruce Wellman/Stock, Boston; 19.26 Westinghouse Electric; 19.27 Peter Menzel/Stock, Boston; 19.29 E. J. West/FPG; 19.33 Spirit LakeSchool District; 19.32 (left) Mat Meadows/Peter Arnold, Inc., (right) Alex Bartel/Photo Researchers; 19.37 Martin Bond/Photo Researchers; 19.38 Nathan Lewis, p. 642 John Suchocki. **Hands-On Chemistry:** p.631 Rachel Epstein/SKA.

Index

References beyond page 383 require accessing Chapters 13–19 from the CD at the back of this book.

Useful Conversion Factors

Length

SI unit: meter (m)

$1\ km = 0.621\ 37\ mi$

$1\ mi = 5280\ ft$

$\quad = 1.6093\ km$

$1\ m = 1.0936\ yd$

$1\ in. = 2.54\ cm\ (exactly)$

$1\ cm = 0.393\ 70\ in.$

$1\ Å = 10^{-10}\ m$

$1\ nm = 10^{-9}\ m$

Mass

SI unit: kilogram (kg)

$1\ kg = 10^3\ g = 2.2046\ lb$

$1\ oz = 28.345\ g$

$1\ lb = 16\ oz = 453.6\ g$

$1\ amu = 1.661 \times 10^{-24}\ g$

Temperature

SI unit: Kelvin (K)

$0\ K = -273.15°C$

$\quad = -459.67°F$

$K = °C + 273.15$

$°C = \frac{5}{9}(°F - 32)$

$°F = \frac{9}{5}(°C) + 32$

Energy

SI unit: Joule (J)

$1\ J = 0.239\ 01\ cal$

$1\ kJ = 0.239\ kcal$

$1\ cal = 4.184\ J$

Pressure

SI unit: Pascal (Pa)

$1\ atm = 101,325\ Pa$

$\quad = 760\ mm\ Hg\ (torr)$

$\quad = 29.9\ in.\ Hg$

$\quad = 14.696\ lb/in.^2$

Volume

SI unit: cubic meter (m³)

$1\ L = 10^{-3}\ m^3$

$\quad = 1\ dm^3$

$\quad = 10^3\ cm^3$

$\quad = 1.057\ qt$

$1\ gal = 4\ qt$

$\quad = 3.7854\ L$

$1\ mL = 0.0339\ fl\ oz$

$1\ cm^3 = 1\ mL$

$\quad = 10^{-6}\ m^3$

$1\ in.^3 = 16.4\ cm^3$

Fundamental Constants

Avogadro's number $= 6.02 \times 10^{23} = 1$ mole

Mass of electron, $m_e = 9.109\ 390 \times 10^{-31}$ kg

$\quad = 1/1836$ of mass of H

Mass of neutron, $m_n = 1.674\ 929 \times 10^{-27}$ kg

$\quad \approx$ mass of H

Mass of proton, $m_p = 1.672\ 623 \times 10^{-27}$ kg

$\quad \approx$ mass of H

Planck's constant, $h = 6.626 \times 10^{-34}$ J $\cdot$ s

Speed of light, $c = 3.00 \times 10^8$ m/s